# *Higher*
# MATHEMATICS
## *for OCR GCSE*

## Tony Banks and David Alcorn

Causeway
Press

Pearson Education Limited
Edinburgh Gate
Harlow
Essex
CM20 2JE
England

978-1-4058-3145-6

Second impression 2007

**Exam questions**
Past exam questions, provided by the *Oxford Cambridge and RSA Examinations*, are denoted by the letters OCR. The answers to all questions are entirely the responsibility of the authors/publisher and have neither been provided nor approved by OCR.

Every effort has been made to locate the copyright owners of material used in this book. Any omissions brought to the notice of the publisher are regretted and will be credited in subsequent printings.

**Page design**
Billy Johnson

**Reader**
Barbara Alcorn

**Artwork**
David Alcorn

**Cover design**
Raven Design

Typesetting by Billy Johnson, San Francisco, California, USA

Printed and bound by Scotprint, Haddington, Scotland

# *preface*

*Higher Mathematics for OCR GCSE* has been written to meet the requirements of the
National Curriculum Key Stage 4 Programme of Study and provides full coverage of the new
**OCR Specifications for the Higher Tier of entry**.

The book is suitable for students preparing for assessment at the Mathematics Higher Tier of entry on
either a 1-year or 2-year course or as a revision text.

In preparing the text, full account has been made of the requirements for students to be able to use and
apply mathematics in written examination papers and be able to solve problems both with and without a
calculator. Some chapters include ideas for investigational, practical and statistical tasks and give the
student the opportunity to improve and practice their skills of using and applying mathematics.

The planning of topics within chapters and sections has been designed to provide efficient coverage of
the specifications. Depending on how the book is to be used you can best decide on the order in which
chapters are studied.

Chapters  1 -  9     Number
Chapters 10 - 22     Algebra
Chapters 23 - 34     Shape, Space and Measures
Chapters 35 - 40     Handling Data

Each chapter consists of fully worked examples with explanatory notes and commentary; carefully
graded questions, a summary of what you need to know and a review exercise.
The review exercises provide the opportunity to consolidate topics introduced within the chapter and
consist of exam-style questions, which reflect how the work is assessed, plus lots of past examination
questions (marked OCR).

Further opportunities to consolidate skills acquired over a number of chapters are provided with
section reviews, which have been organised into two parts for non-calculator and calculator practice.

As final preparation for the exams a further compilation of exam and exam-style questions,
organised for non-calculator paper and calculator paper practice, has been included.

> The book has been designed so that it can be used in conjunction with the companion book
> *Higher Mathematics for OCR GCSE - Student Support Book*
> *Without Answers: ISBN 1-405835-04-4*
> *With Answers: ISBN 1-405835-05-2*

# contents

**CHAPTER 1  Whole Numbers**

| | |
|---|---|
| Place value | 1 |
| Reading and writing numbers | 1 |
| Non-calculator methods for addition and subtraction | 1 |
| Non-calculator methods for multiplication and division | 2 |
| Order of operations in a calculation | 4 |
| Negative numbers | 5 |
| Adding and subtracting negative numbers | 5 |
| Multiplying and dividing negative numbers | 5 |
| What you need to know | 6 |

**CHAPTER 2  Decimals and Fractions**

| | |
|---|---|
| Decimals | 8 |
| Non-calculator methods for addition and subtraction of decimals | 8 |
| Non-calculator method for multiplying decimals | 8 |
| Non-calculator method for dividing decimals | 8 |
| Numerical calculations with a calculator | 11 |
| Fractions | 11 |
| Equivalent fractions | 11 |
| Simplifying fractions | 12 |
| Types of fractions | 12 |
| Finding fractions of quantities | 12 |
| Adding and subtracting fractions | 13 |
| Multiplying fractions | 15 |
| Dividing fractions | 16 |
| Problems involving fractions | 17 |
| Fractions on a calculator | 17 |
| Fractions and decimals | 17 |
| Recurring decimals | 18 |
| What you need to know | 18 |

**CHAPTER 3  Approximation and Estimation**

| | |
|---|---|
| Approximation | 20 |
| Rounding to the nearest 10, 100, 1000 | 20 |
| Rounding in real-life problems | 21 |
| Rounding using decimal places | 22 |
| Rounding using significant figures | 23 |
| Choosing a suitable degree of accuracy | 24 |
| Estimation | 25 |
| Accuracy in measurement | 26 |
| Calculations involving bounds | 28 |
| What you need to know | 29 |

# CHAPTER 4 — Percentages and Money

| | |
|---|---|
| The meaning of a percentage | 31 |
| Changing percentages to decimals and fractions | 31 |
| Changing decimals and fractions to percentages | 31 |
| Expressing one quantity as a percentage of another | 32 |
| Finding a percentage of a quantity | 33 |
| Percentage change | 33 |
| Percentage increase and decrease | 34 |
| Reverse percentage problems | 36 |
| Wages | 37 |
| Income tax | 37 |
| Spending | 38 |
| Best buys | 39 |
| Household bills | 39 |
| VAT | 40 |
| Savings | 41 |
| Simple Interest and Compound Interest | 41 |
| What you need to know | 42 |

# CHAPTER 5 — Working with Number

| | |
|---|---|
| Multiples | 45 |
| Factors | 45 |
| Common factors | 45 |
| Prime numbers | 45 |
| Powers | 46 |
| Prime factors | 46 |
| Products of prime factors | 46 |
| Least common multiples | 46 |
| Highest common factors | 47 |
| Square numbers | 48 |
| Cube numbers | 48 |
| Using a calculator | 48 |
| Reciprocals | 48 |
| Square roots | 48 |
| Cube roots | 48 |
| Multiplying and dividing numbers with powers | 49 |
| Rules of indices | 50 |
| Negative powers and reciprocals | 50 |
| Powers and roots | 52 |
| Harder fractional powers | 52 |
| What you need to know | 54 |

# CHAPTER 6 — Standard Index Form

| | |
|---|---|
| Large numbers and your calculator | 56 |
| Small numbers and your calculator | 57 |
| Standard form | 58 |
| Using large and small numbers with a calculator | 59 |
| Solving problems involving large and small numbers | 59 |
| Standard form calculations without a calculator | 61 |
| What you need to know | 62 |

## CHAPTER 7  Ratio and Proportion

| | |
|---|---|
| Ratio | 63 |
| Equivalent ratios | 63 |
| Simplifying ratios | 63 |
| Sharing in a given ratio | 64 |
| Proportion | 66 |
| Direct proportion and inverse proportion | 66 |
| What you need to know | 68 |

## CHAPTER 8  Speed and Other Compound Measures

| | |
|---|---|
| Speed | 69 |
| Other compound measures | 72 |
| Density | 72 |
| Population density | 72 |
| What you need to know | 73 |

## CHAPTER 9  Extending the Number System

| | |
|---|---|
| Rational numbers | 75 |
| Changing recurring decimals to fractions | 75 |
| Irrational numbers | 77 |
| Surds | 78 |
| Manipulating and simplifying surds | 78 |
| Rationalising denominators of fractions | 79 |
| What you need to know | 80 |

## SR  Section Review - Number

| | |
|---|---|
| Non-calculator Paper | 81 |
| Calculator Paper | 84 |

## CHAPTER 10  Introduction to Algebra

| | |
|---|---|
| Algebra | 87 |
| Expressions and terms | 88 |
| Simplifying expressions | 88 |
| Multiplying and dividing algebraic expressions with powers | 89 |
| Brackets | 91 |
| Factorising | 92 |
| What you need to know | 93 |

## CHAPTER 11  Solving Equations

| | |
|---|---|
| Solving equations | 95 |
| Solving equations by working backwards | 96 |
| The balance method | 97 |
| Equations with brackets | 99 |
| Equations with letters on both sides | 99 |
| Equations with fractions | 100 |
| Using equations to solve problems | 101 |
| What you need to know | 103 |

## CHAPTER 12 Formulae

| | |
|---|---|
| Substitution | 105 |
| Writing expressions and formulae | 105 |
| Using formulae | 107 |
| Substitution into formulae with powers and roots | 109 |
| Writing and using formulae | 109 |
| Rearranging formulae | 110 |
| Solve problems by rearranging formulae | 111 |
| What you need to know | 112 |

## CHAPTER 13 Sequences

| | |
|---|---|
| Continuing a sequence | 114 |
| Using rules | 115 |
| Number sequences | 117 |
| Sequences of numbers from shape patterns | 119 |
| Special sequences of numbers | 119 |
| What you need to know | 121 |

## CHAPTER 14 Straight Line Graphs

| | |
|---|---|
| Coordinates | 123 |
| Linear functions | 123 |
| Drawing a graph of a linear function | 123 |
| Gradient and intercept | 126 |
| Drawing graphs of other linear equations | 129 |
| Using graphs to solve linear equations | 130 |
| Perpendicular lines | 131 |
| Rearranging equations | 132 |
| What you need to know | 134 |

## CHAPTER 15 Using Graphs

| | |
|---|---|
| Real-life situations | 136 |
| Distance-time graphs | 138 |
| Speed-time graphs | 141 |
| What you need to know | 143 |

## CHAPTER 16 Inequalities

| | |
|---|---|
| Inequalities | 146 |
| Number lines | 146 |
| Solving inequalities | 148 |
| Multiplying (or dividing) an inequality by a negative number | 149 |
| Double inequalities | 149 |
| Inequalities involving integers | 150 |
| Graphs of inequalities | 150 |
| Regions | 151 |
| Inequalities involving sloping lines | 152 |
| What you need to know | 153 |

## CHAPTER 17 — Further Graphs

| | |
|---|---|
| Quadratic functions | 155 |
| Drawing a graph of a quadratic function | 155 |
| Using graphs to solve quadratic equations | 156 |
| Cubic graphs | 158 |
| The graph of the reciprocal function | 159 |
| The graph of the exponential function | 159 |
| The graph of a circle | 160 |
| Sketching graphs | 161 |
| What you need to know | 162 |

## CHAPTER 18 — Direct and Inverse Proportion

| | |
|---|---|
| Direct proportion | 164 |
| Inverse proportion | 166 |
| Other forms of proportion | 168 |
| Proportion and graphs | 170 |
| What you need to know | 172 |

## CHAPTER 19 — Quadratic Equations

| | |
|---|---|
| Brackets | 173 |
| More brackets | 173 |
| Factorising | 174 |
| Factorising quadratic expressions | 174 |
| Further factorising | 177 |
| Solving quadratic equations | 178 |
| Using the quadratic formula | 179 |
| Completing the square | 181 |
| Rearranging quadratics | 181 |
| Solving quadratic equations by completing the square | 183 |
| Problems solved using quadratic equations | 184 |
| What you need to know | 186 |

## CHAPTER 20 — Simultaneous Equations

| | |
|---|---|
| Using graphs to solve simultaneous equations | 188 |
| Simultaneous equations with no solution | 190 |
| Using the elimination method to solve simultaneous equations | 191 |
| Further use of the elimination method | 192 |
| Using the substitution method to solve simultaneous equations | 194 |
| Solving problems using simultaneous equations | 194 |
| Simultaneous equations in which one equation is linear and one is quadratic | 196 |
| Using the method of substitution | 196 |
| What you need to know | 198 |

## CHAPTER 21 — Algebraic Methods

| | |
|---|---|
| Simplifying expressions | 200 |
| Identities | 200 |
| Algebraic fractions | 202 |
| Simplifying algebraic fractions | 202 |
| Arithmetic of algebraic fractions | 203 |
| Solving equations involving algebraic fractions | 204 |
| Iteration | 206 |
| Trial and improvement | 207 |
| What you need to know | 208 |

## CHAPTER 22 — Transforming Graphs

| | |
|---|---|
| Translating a graph | 210 |
| Stretching a graph | 211 |
| Function notation | 213 |
| Reflecting a graph | 214 |
| Using graphs to find relationships | 217 |
| Linear functions | 217 |
| Non-linear functions | 218 |
| What you need to know | 220 |

## SR — Section Review - Algebra

| | |
|---|---|
| Non-calculator Paper | 222 |
| Calculator Paper | 225 |

## CHAPTER 23 — Angles and 2-D Shapes

| | |
|---|---|
| Types and names of angles | 228 |
| Angle properties | 228 |
| Lines | 228 |
| Perpendicular lines | 228 |
| Parallel lines | 228 |
| Parallel lines and angles | 228 |
| Naming angles | 229 |
| Triangles | 230 |
| Types of triangle | 230 |
| Special triangles | 230 |
| Exterior angle of a triangle | 230 |
| Quadrilaterals | 232 |
| Special quadrilaterals | 232 |
| Polygons | 234 |
| Interior and exterior angles of a polygon | 234 |
| Sum of the interior angles of a polygon | 234 |
| Sum of the exterior angles of a polygon | 234 |
| Regular polygons | 236 |
| Exterior angles of a regular polygon | 236 |
| Tessellations | 237 |
| Symmetry | 238 |
| Lines of symmetry | 238 |
| Rotational symmetry | 238 |
| What you need to know | 240 |

## CHAPTER 24 — Circle Properties

| | |
|---|---|
| Circles | 243 |
| Circle properties | 244 |
| Tangents | 247 |
| Alternate segment theorem | 248 |
| Geometrical proofs | 250 |
| What you need to know | 251 |

## CHAPTER 25  Perimeters and Areas

| | |
|---|---|
| Perimeter | 254 |
| Area | 254 |
| Area formulae | 254 |
| Circles | 256 |
| The Greek letter $\pi$ | 256 |
| Circumference of a circle | 256 |
| Area of a circle | 257 |
| Compound shapes | 259 |
| Segments and sectors | 260 |
| Lengths of arcs and areas of sectors | 260 |
| What you need to know | 262 |

## CHAPTER 26  Maps, Loci and Constructions

| | |
|---|---|
| Maps | 264 |
| Compass points | 264 |
| Three-figure bearings | 264 |
| Back bearings | 264 |
| Scale drawing | 265 |
| Locus | 266 |
| Accurate constructions | 268 |
| Perpendicular bisector of a line | 268 |
| Bisector of an angle | 268 |
| More constructions | 271 |
| Perpendicular from a point to a line | 271 |
| Perpendicular from a point on a line | 271 |
| What you need to know | 273 |

## CHAPTER 27  Transformations

| | |
|---|---|
| Reflection | 275 |
| Rotation | 276 |
| Translation | 278 |
| Enlargement | 279 |
| Using a centre of enlargement | 279 |
| Using a scale factor which is a fraction | 280 |
| Enlargement with a negative scale factor | 281 |
| Describing transformations | 282 |
| To find a line of reflection | 283 |
| To find the centre and angle of rotation | 283 |
| To find the centre and scale factor of an enlargement | 283 |
| Combinations of transformations | 286 |
| What you need to know | 288 |

## CHAPTER 28  Pythagoras' Theorem

| | |
|---|---|
| Checking the Theorem of Pythagoras | 291 |
| Finding the hypotenuse | 292 |
| Finding one of the shorter sides | 293 |
| Problems involving the use of Pythagoras' Theorem | 294 |
| Solving problems in three dimensions | 296 |
| What you need to know | 297 |

## CHAPTER 29   Trigonometry

| | |
|---|---|
| The sine ratio | 300 |
| Finding the length of the opposite side | 301 |
| Finding an angle | 302 |
| Finding the hypotenuse | 303 |
| The cosine and tangent ratios | 304 |
| How to select and use the correct ratio | 304 |
| Angles of elevation and depression | 307 |
| Bearings | 308 |
| Solving problems in three-dimensions | 310 |
| The angle between a line and a plane | 310 |
| What you need to know | 312 |

## CHAPTER 30   3-D Shapes

| | |
|---|---|
| 3-D shapes (or solids) | 314 |
| Making and drawing 3-D shapes | 314 |
| Naming parts of a 3-D shape | 314 |
| Symmetry in three-dimensions | 315 |
| Planes of symmetry | 315 |
| Axes of symmetry | 315 |
| Plans and elevations | 316 |
| Surface area of a cuboid | 317 |
| Volume | 317 |
| Volume of a cuboid | 317 |
| Prisms | 318 |
| Volume of a prism | 319 |
| Volume of a cylinder | 319 |
| Surface area of a cylinder | 320 |
| Cones | 322 |
| Pyramids | 322 |
| Spheres | 322 |
| What you need to know | 325 |

## CHAPTER 31   Understanding and Using Measures

| | |
|---|---|
| Units of measurement | 328 |
| Metric units | 328 |
| Changing from one metric unit to another | 328 |
| Changing units - areas and volumes | 328 |
| Estimating with sensible units using suitable degrees of accuracy | 329 |
| Imperial units | 330 |
| Metric and imperial conversions | 331 |
| Discrete and continuous measures | 332 |
| Calculations involving continuous measures | 333 |
| Dimensions and formulae | 335 |
| What you need to know | 337 |

## CHAPTER 32   Congruent Triangles and Similar Figures

| | |
|---|---|
| Congruent shapes | 339 |
| Congruent triangles | 339 |
| Similar figures | 342 |
| Similar triangles | 344 |
| Showing that two triangles are similar | 346 |
| Lengths, areas and volumes of similar figures | 348 |
| Scale factors for length, area and volume | 348 |
| What you need to know | 351 |

# CHAPTER 33 Vectors

| | |
|---|---|
| Vectors and scalars | 353 |
| Vector notation | 353 |
| Equal vectors | 354 |
| Multiplying a vector by a scalar | 354 |
| Vectors in opposite directions | 355 |
| Vector addition | 356 |
| Vector diagrams | 356 |
| Vectors and geometry | 358 |
| What you need to know | 361 |

# CHAPTER 34 Further Trigonometry

| | |
|---|---|
| Trigonometric functions and their graphs | 363 |
| Sines, cosines and tangents of angles between $0°$ and $360°$ | 364 |
| Finding angles | 366 |
| Another look at the graphs of trigonometric functions | 367 |
| Triangles which are not right-angled | 368 |
| The Sine Rule | 369 |
| Finding sides | 369 |
| Finding angles | 370 |
| The ambiguous case | 371 |
| Deriving the Cosine Rule | 372 |
| The Cosine Rule | 373 |
| Finding sides | 373 |
| Finding angles | 374 |
| Area of a triangle | 375 |
| Solving problems involving triangles | 377 |
| What you need to know | 379 |

# SR Section Review - Shape, Space and Measures

| | |
|---|---|
| Non-calculator Paper | 382 |
| Calculator Paper | 385 |

# CHAPTER 35 Collection and Organisation of Data

| | |
|---|---|
| Primary and secondary data | 388 |
| Data | 388 |
| Collection of data | 389 |
| Databases | 390 |
| Questionnaires | 392 |
| Hypothesis | 392 |
| Two-way tables | 393 |
| Sampling | 395 |
| Sampling methods | 395 |
| What you need to know | 397 |

# CHAPTER 36 Averages and Range

| | |
|---|---|
| Types of average | 399 |
| Range | 399 |
| Frequency distributions | 400 |
| Calculating averages from diagrams | 401 |
| Grouped frequency distributions | 402 |
| Comparing distributions | 403 |
| Which is the best average to use? | 405 |
| What you need to know | 406 |

## CHAPTER 37   Presentation of Data 1

| | |
|---|---|
| Bar charts | 408 |
| Pie charts | 408 |
| Stem and leaf diagrams | 410 |
| Scatter graphs | 412 |
| Correlation | 412 |
| Line of best fit | 414 |
| What you need to know | 415 |

## CHAPTER 38   Presentation of Data 2

| | |
|---|---|
| Time series | 418 |
| Seasonal variation | 418 |
| Moving averages | 419 |
| Moving average graphs | 420 |
| Frequency diagrams | 421 |
| Histogram with equal class intervals | 421 |
| Frequency polygons | 422 |
| Histograms with unequal class intervals | 424 |
| What you need to know | 428 |

## CHAPTER 39   Cumulative Frequency

| | |
|---|---|
| Cumulative frequency tables | 430 |
| Cumulative frequency graphs | 430 |
| Using a cumulative frequency graph | 431 |
| Another look at cumulative frequency graphs | 432 |
| Comparing distributions | 435 |
| Box plots | 437 |
| What you need to know | 440 |

## CHAPTER 40   Probability

| | |
|---|---|
| What is probability? | 442 |
| Probability and the probability scale | 442 |
| Calculating probabilities using equally likely outcomes | 443 |
| Estimating probabilities using relative frequency | 445 |
| Mutually exclusive events | 447 |
| The probability of an event not happening | 447 |
| Combining two events | 449 |
| Independent events | 452 |
| Using tree diagrams to work out probabilities | 452 |
| Conditional probability | 456 |
| What you need to know | 459 |

## SR   Section Review - Handling Data

| | |
|---|---|
| Non-calculator Paper | 462 |
| Calculator Paper | 465 |

## EP   Exam Practice

| | |
|---|---|
| Non-calculator Paper | 468 |
| Calculator Paper | 472 |
| **Answers** | 476 |
| **Index** | 528 |

# Whole Numbers ●●●●●●●●●

The numbers   0,   1,   2,   3,   4,   5,   …   can be used to count objects.
Such numbers are called **whole numbers**.
Whole numbers that end in 0, 2, 4, 6 or 8 are called **even** numbers.
Whole numbers that end in 1, 3, 5, 7 or 9 are called **odd** numbers.

## Place value

Our number system is made up of the digits 0, 1, 2, 3, 4, 5, 6, 7, 8 and 9.
The position a digit has in a number is called its **place value**.
In the number 5384 the digit 8 is worth 80, but in the number 4853 the digit 8 is worth 800.

## Reading and writing numbers

$543 = 5 \times 100 + 4 \times 10 + 3 \times 1$
The number 543 is written or read as,   "five hundred and forty-three."

For numbers bigger than one thousand:
- split the number into groups of three digits, starting from the units,
- combine the numbers of *millions* and *thousands* with the number less than 1000.

$4567205 = 4\ 567\ 205$ is written and read as,
"four *million* five hundred and sixty-seven *thousand* two hundred and five."

## Non-calculator methods for addition and subtraction

### Addition

Write the numbers in tidy columns according to place value.
Add together the numbers of units, tens, hundreds, etc.
If any of these answers are 10 or more, something is carried to the next column.

> **EXAMPLE**
>
> Work out   $4567 + 835$.
>
> $$\begin{array}{r} 4\,5\,6\,7 \\ +\ \ \ 8\,3\,5 \\ \hline 5\,4\,0\,2 \\ \hline {\scriptstyle 1\ \ 1\ \ 1} \end{array}$$
>
> $7 + 5 = 12$          which is 2 carry 1.
> $6 + 3 + \text{carried } 1 = 10$,   which is 0 carry 1.
> $5 + 8 + \text{carried } 1 = 14$,   which is 4 carry 1.
> $4 + \text{carried } 1 = 5$.

### Subtraction

Write the numbers in columns according to place value.
Then, in turn, subtract the numbers of units, tens, hundreds, etc.
If the subtraction in a column cannot be done because the number being subtracted is greater, borrow 10 from the next column.

> Addition is the opposite (inverse) operation to subtraction.
> If          $a - b = c$,
> then     $c + b = a$.

> **EXAMPLE**
>
> Work out   $7238 - 642$.
>
> $$\begin{array}{r} {\scriptstyle 6\ \ 11\ 1} \\ \cancel{7}\,\cancel{2}\,3\,8 \\ -\ \ 6\,4\,2 \\ \hline 6\,5\,9\,6 \end{array}$$
>
> Units: $8 - 2 = 6$
> Tens: $3 - 4$ cannot be done, so, borrow 10 from the 2 in the next column.
> Now   $10 + 3 - 4 = 9$.
> Hundreds: $1 - 6$ cannot be done, so, borrow 10 from the 7 in the next column.
> Now   $10 + 1 - 6 = 5$.
> Thousands: $6 - 0 = 6$.
>
> You can use addition to check your subtraction.   *Does   $6596 + 642 = 7238$?*

Do not use a calculator for this exercise.

**1**   Write the following numbers in figures.
(a)   five hundred and forty-six
(b)   seventy thousand two hundred and nine
(c)   one million two hundred thousand and fifty-two

**2**   Write the following numbers in words.
(a)   23590        (b)   6049        (c)   93145670        (d)   9080004

**3**   Which digit has the greater value,   the 7 in 745   or   the 9 in 892?

**4**   Write these numbers in ascending order (smallest to largest).
3842,   5814,   3874,   3801,   4765

**5**   Write these numbers in descending order (largest to smallest).
9434,   9646,   9951,   9653,   9648

**6**   By using each of the digits   5,   1,   6   and   2   make:
(a)   the largest four-digit **even** number,
(b)   the smallest four-digit **odd** number.
In each case explain your method.

**7**   Work these out in your head.
(a)   15 + 12        (b)   19 + 16        (c)   26 + 48        (d)   29 + 41        (e)   13 + 99
(f)   26 − 9          (g)   87 − 38        (h)   204 − 99      (i)   1000 − 425    (j)   1003 − 999

**8**   Work these out by writing the numbers in columns.
(a)   324 + 628        (b)   1273 + 729      (c)   3495 + 8708      (d)   431 + 865 + 245
(e)   407 − 249        (f)   2345 − 1876    (g)   8045 − 1777      (h)   10 000 − 6723

**9**   Marcus drove 1754 miles on his holiday.
His milometer reading was 38 956 at the start.
What was his milometer reading at the end?

**10**   What is the total weight of these packages?

**11**   The last four attendances at a football stadium were:
21 004,   19 750,   18 009,   22 267.
What is the total attendance?

**12**   A batsman has scored 69 runs. How many more runs must he score to get a century?

**13**   A car park has spaces for 345 cars. On Tuesday 256 spaces are used.
How many spaces are not used?

**14**   (a)   Ricky buys a bunch of spring onions.
He pays with 50p.
How much change is he given?
(b)   Liz buys a cucumber and a lettuce.
She pays with £1.
How much change is she given?

Salad Specials

| | |
|---|---|
| Cucumber | 39p each |
| Lettuce | 55p each |
| Spring onions | 33p a bunch |

**15**   The table shows the milometer readings for three cars at the start and end of a year.

|       | Car A | Car B | Car C |
|-------|-------|-------|-------|
| Start | 2501  | 55667 | 48050 |
| End   | 10980 | 67310 | 61909 |

Which car has done the most miles in the year?

## Non-calculator methods for multiplication and division

### Short multiplication

**Short multiplication** is when the multiplying number is less than 10, e.g.  $165 \times 7$.
Multiply the units, tens, hundreds, etc. in turn.

```
  1 6 5
×     7
─────────
  1 1 5 5
  1 4 3
```

Units: $7 \times 5 = 35$,                                   which is 5 carry 3.
Tens: $7 \times 6 = 42 +$ carried $3 = 45$,   which is 5 carry 4.
Hundreds: $7 \times 1 = 7 +$ carried $4 = 11$,   which is 1 carry 1.
There are no more digits to be multiplied by 7, the carried 1 becomes 1 thousand.

### Long multiplication

**Long multiplication** is used when the multiplying number is greater than 10, e.g.  $24 \times 17$.

Work out  $24 \times 17$.

```
        2 4
      × 1 7
    ─────────
      1 6 8   ←24 ×  7 = 168
    + 2 4 0   ←24 × 10 = 240
    ─────────
      4 0 8
```

A standard non-calculator method for doing long multiplication multiplies the number by:

● the units figure, then

● the tens figure, then

● the hundreds figure, and so on.

All these answers are added together.

### Short division

The process of dividing a number by a number less than 10 is called **short division**.
Short division relies on knowledge of the Multiplication Tables.
What is  $32 \div 8$,   $42 \div 7$,   $72 \div 9$,   $54 \div 6$?

Work out  $882 \div 7$.

```
7)8 ¹8 ⁴2
  1 2 6
```

Starting from the left:
   $8 \div 7 = 1$ remainder 1,   which is 1 carry 1.
   $18 \div 7 = 2$ remainder 4,   which is 2 carry 4.
   $42 \div 7 = 6$, with no remainder.
   So,   $882 \div 7 = 126$.

You can check your division by multiplying.
*Does   $126 \times 7 = 882$?*

Multiplication is the opposite (inverse) operation to division.
If      $a \div b = c$,
then   $c \times b = a$.

### Long division

**Long division** works in exactly the same way as short division, except that all the working out is written down.

Work out  $952 \div 7$.

```
    1 3 6
7)9 5 2
  7
  ───
  2 5
  2 1
  ───
    4 2
    4 2
    ───
      0
```

$9 \div 7 = 1$ and a remainder.
What is the remainder?
$1 \times 7 = 7$   (write below the 9).
$9 - 7 = 2$   (which is the remainder).
Bring down the next figure (5) to make 25.
Repeat the above process.
$25 \div 7 = 3$ and a remainder.
$3 \times 7 = 21$,   $25 - 21 = 4$ (remainder).
Bring down the next figure (2) to make 42
and repeat the process.
$42 \div 7 = 6$, but there is no remainder.
$6 \times 7 = 42$,   $42 - 42 = 0$ (remainder).
There are no more figures to be brought down and there is no remainder.
So,   $952 \div 7 = 136$.

**Long division process:**
➤ ÷ (obtain biggest answer possible)
× } calculates
− } the remainder
Bring down the next figure
Repeat process until there are no more figures to be brought down.

Do not use a calculator for this exercise.

**1** Work out. (a) 183 × 3     (b) 36 × 7     (c) 264 × 8     (d) 3179 × 5

**2** Work out these divisions. Use multiplication to check your answers.
(a) 85 ÷ 5     (b) 816 ÷ 6     (c) 824 ÷ 4     (d) 9882 ÷ 9     (e) 80 560 ÷ 4

**3** When John uses a store card he gets 4 points for every pound he spends. He spends £18.
How many points does he get?

**4** A caretaker puts out 7 rows of chairs. There are 13 chairs in each row.
How many more chairs are needed for 120 chairs to be put out?

**5** Sanjay is paid £7 per hour. One week he is paid £238.
How many hours did he work that week?

**6** Work out. (a) 537 × 40     (b) 260 × 50     (c) 412 × 80     (d) 239 × 90

**7**

Tickets: £19     Programmes: £3

On the first night of the show, 70 tickets and 40 programmes are sold.
How much money is paid in total for the tickets and programmes?

**8** There are 400 metres in one lap of a running track. How many metres are there in 25 laps?

**9** A secretary buys one dozen boxes of staples. There are 5000 staples in each box.
How many staples does she buy?

**10** Work out. (a) 7590 ÷ 30     (b) 7110 ÷ 90     (c) 21 480 ÷ 40     (d) 7560 ÷ 60

**11** The total cost of a New Year's Eve party for 80 people is £2800.
What is the cost for each person?

**12** A computer can print 50 000 characters per minute.
How many minutes would it take to print one million characters?

**13** Work out. (a) 76 × 32     (b) 234 × 57     (c) 537 × 103     (d) 693 × 875

**14** What is the total cost of 14 desks and 23 cabinets?

Office Supplies

Desk     £126
Cabinet  £149

**15** The organisers of a concert sell 1624 tickets at £27 each.
How much money is collected from the sale of tickets?

**16** Work out. (a) 473 ÷ 11     (b) 7560 ÷ 15     (c) 9430 ÷ 23     (d) 20 928 ÷ 32

**17** John collects £17 each from his friends to buy tickets for a football match.
He collects a total of £391. How many tickets does he buy?

**18** Work these out and state the remainder each time.
(a) 410 ÷ 25     (b) 607 ÷ 24     (c) 800 ÷ 45     (d) 525 ÷ 37

**19** A pint of milk costs 35 pence. How many pints of milk can be bought for £5?
How much change will there be?

**20** Tins of beans are packed in boxes of 24. A supplier has 1000 tins of beans.
(a) How many full boxes is this?     (b) How many tins are left over?

## Order of operations in a calculation

*What is* $4 + 3 \times 5$? It is not sensible to have two possible answers.
It has been agreed that calculations are done obeying certain rules:

| | |
|---|---|
| **First** | Brackets and Division line |
| **Second** | Divide and Multiply |
| **Third** | Addition and Subtraction |

### EXAMPLES

**1** $4 + 3 \times 5$      $= 4 + 15$      $= 19$

**2** $10 \div 2 + 3$      $= 5 + 3$      $= 8$

**3** $10 \div (2 + 3)$      $= 10 \div 5$      $= 2$

**4** $(5 + 6) \times 3 + 4$      $= 11 \times 3 + 4$      $= 33 + 4$      $= 37$

**5** $\dfrac{12}{11 - 8} - 3$      $= \dfrac{12}{3} - 3$      $= 4 - 3$      $= 1$

This is the same as $12 \div (11 - 8) - 3$.

### Exercise **1.3**      Do not use a calculator for this exercise.

**1** Work out the value of $17 - 3 \times (6 - 1)$.

**2** Work these out.
   (a) $7 + 6 \times 5$        (b) $7 - (6 - 2)$        (c) $24 \div 6 + 5$
   (d) $7 \times 6 + 8 \times 2$     (e) $10 \div 5 + 8 \div 2$     (f) $(5 - 2) \times 7 + 9$
   (g) $60 \div (5 + 7)$       (h) $60 \div 5 + 7$        (i) $4 \times 3 + 2$
   (j) $4 \times (3 + 2)$        (k) $12 \times (20 - 2) \div 9$    (l) $36 \div (5 + 4)$
   (m) $4 \times 12 \div 8 - 6$     (n) $\dfrac{15}{18 - 3} + 4$       (o) $\dfrac{22 - 4}{9} + 12 \div 3$

**3** Use brackets and the signs $+$, $-$, $\times$ and $\div$ to complete these sums.
   (a) $7 \quad 2 \times 3 = 15$      (b) $3 + 5 \quad 2 = 4$      (c) $(4 \quad 1) \times 7 \quad 2 = 25$

**4** Using all the numbers 6, 3, 2 and 1 in this order, brackets and the signs $+$, $-$, $\times$ and $\div$,
make all the numbers from 1 to 10.
       $6 - 3 \times 2 + 1 = 1$,      $6 - 3 - 2 + 1 = 2$,     and so on.

**5** Claire is 16 cm taller than Rachel. Their heights add up to 312 cm.
How tall is Rachel?

**6** A box, which contains 48 matches, has a total weight of 207 g.
If each match weighs 4 g, what is the weight of the empty box?

**7** The admission charges to a zoo are £7 for a child and £12 for an adult.
Zoe is organising a trip to the zoo for a group of people and worked out that the total cost
would be £336.
She collected £84 from the adults in the group.
   (a) How many children are in the group?
   (b) What is the total number of people in the group?

## Negative numbers

The number line can be extended to include **negative whole numbers**.

As you move from left to right along the number line the numbers become bigger.

As you move from right to left along the number line the numbers become smaller.

Negative whole numbers, zero and positive whole numbers are called **integers**.
$-5$ can be read as "minus five" or "negative five".
A number written without a sign before it is assumed to be positive. $+5$ has the same value as 5.
Many problems in mathematics involve calculations with negative numbers.

## Adding and subtracting negative numbers

### EXAMPLES

**1** Work out $2 + (-6)$.

$+ -$ can be replaced with $-$.
Start at 2 and move 6 to the left.
$2 + (-6) = 2 - 6 = -4$

**2** Work out $-2 - (-8)$.

$- -$ can be replaced with $+$.
Start at $-2$ and move 8 to the right.
$-2 - (-8) = -2 + 8 = 6$

To add or subtract negative numbers:
Replace double signs with the single sign.

> $+ +$ can be replaced by $+$
> $- -$ can be replaced by $+$
> $+ -$ can be replaced by $-$
> $- +$ can be replaced by $-$

## Multiplying and dividing negative numbers

### EXAMPLES

**1** Work out $(-4) \times (-8)$.

Signs: $- \times - = +$
Numbers: $4 \times 8 = 32$
So, $(-4) \times (-8) = 32$.

**2** Work out $(+8) \div (-2)$.

Signs: $+ \div - = -$
Numbers: $8 \div 2 = 4$
So, $(+8) \div (-2) = -4$.

Use these rules for multiplying and dividing negative numbers:

| When multiplying: | When dividing: |
|---|---|
| $+ \times + = +$ | $+ \div + = +$ |
| $- \times - = +$ | $- \div - = +$ |
| $+ \times - = -$ | $+ \div - = -$ |
| $- \times + = -$ | $- \div + = -$ |

**Work logically:**
Work out the sign first. Then work out the numbers.

## Exercise 1.4

Do not use a calculator for this exercise.

**1** List these temperatures from coldest to hottest. $23°C$, $-28°C$, $-3°C$, $19°C$, $-13°C$.

**2** List these numbers from lowest to highest. $31$, $-78$, $51$, $-39$, $-16$, $-9$, $11$.

**3** At midnight, the temperature in York is $3°C$ below freezing and in Bath the temperature is $2°C$ above freezing.
What is the difference in temperature between York and Bath?

**4** Adrian is 5 kg heavier than Tim. Matt is 3 kg lighter than Tim.
What is the difference in weight between Matt and Adrian?

**5** Work out.
(a)  $-3 + (+5)$
(b)  $5 + (-4)$
(c)  $-2 + (-7)$
(d)  $-1 + (+9)$
(e)  $7 + (-3)$
(f)  $15 + (-20)$
(g)  $-11 + (+4)$
(h)  $11 + (-4)$
(i)  $8 + (-7)$
(j)  $-8 + (-7)$
(k)  $3 + (+3) + (-9)$
(l)  $-7 + (-5) + 6$

**6** Work out.
(a)  $8 - (-5)$
(b)  $-4 - (-10)$
(c)  $10 - (+3)$
(d)  $6 - (-1)$
(e)  $-5 - (-10)$
(f)  $-4 - (+8)$
(g)  $-7 - (-6)$
(h)  $7 - (-6)$
(i)  $-2 - (+9)$
(j)  $2 - (-9)$
(k)  $5 - (+5) + 9$
(l)  $-10 - (-6) + 4$

**7** Work out.
(a)  $10 + 5 - 8 + 6 - 7$
(b)  $12 + 8 - 15 + 7 - 20$
(c)  $30 - 20 + 12 - 50$
(d)  $6 + 12 - 14 - 4$
(e)  $37 - 23 - 24 - 25$
(f)  $12 + 13 + 14 - 20$

**8** Work out.
(a)  $5 + (-4) - (-3) + 2 - (-1)$
(b)  $5 - 4 + (-3) - (-2) + (-1)$
(c)  $10 - (-11) + (-12) + 13 - (-14)$
(d)  $-7 - (-7) + 6 + (-3) + (-9)$
(e)  $12 + 8 - (-8) + 9 - (-1)$
(f)  $15 - (-5) + 5 - (-10) + (-20)$
(g)  $-5 + (-5) + (-5) + (-5) - (-5)$
(h)  $5 - (-5) - (-5) - (-5) - (-5)$

**9** What is the difference in temperature between
(a)  Edinburgh and Rome,
(b)  Edinburgh and New York,
(c)  Moscow and New York,
(d)  Moscow and Cairo?

| Edinburgh | $-7°C$ |
| Moscow | $-22°C$ |
| New York | $-17°C$ |
| Rome | $3°C$ |
| Cairo | $15°C$ |

**10** The temperature inside an igloo is $-5°C$. The temperature outside the igloo is $17°C$ cooler.
What is the temperature outside the igloo?

**11** Work out.
(a)  $(-7) \times (+5)$
(b)  $(-7) \times (-5)$
(c)  $8 \times (-3)$
(d)  $(-5) \times 9$
(e)  $(-8) \times (-8)$
(f)  $(-7) \times 6$
(g)  $8 \times (-10)$
(h)  $(-4) \times (-8)$
(i)  $(+5) \times (-2) \times (+2)$
(j)  $(+4) \times (-3) \times (-5)$
(k)  $(-3) \times (-2) \times (-5)$
(l)  $(-5) \times (+3) \times (-4)$
(m)  $(-5) \times (+3) \times (+4)$
(n)  $(-5) \times (-4) \times (-5)$
(o)  $(-3) \times (+7) \times (+9)$

**12** Work out.
(a)  $(-8) \div (+2)$
(b)  $(-8) \div (-2)$
(c)  $(+20) \div (+4)$
(d)  $(+20) \div (-4)$
(e)  $(-20) \div (+4)$
(f)  $(-20) \div (-4)$
(g)  $(+18) \div (+3)$
(h)  $(-18) \div (+3)$
(i)  $(-24) \div (-6)$
(j)  $(+24) \div (-3)$
(k)  $(-30) \div (-5)$
(l)  $(-30) \div (+6)$
(m)  $\dfrac{(-3) \times (+8)}{(-6)}$
(n)  $\dfrac{(-6) \times (-8)}{(+3) \times (-4)}$
(o)  $\dfrac{(-2) \times (-3) \times (+4)}{(+3) \times (-8)}$

## What you need to know

- You should be able to read and write numbers expressed in figures and words.
- Be able to recognise the place value of each digit in a number.
- Know the Multiplication Tables up to $10 \times 10$.
- Use non-calculator methods for addition, subtraction, multiplication and division.
- Know the order of operations in a calculation.
- Add $(+)$, subtract $(-)$, multiply $(\times)$ and divide $(\div)$ with negative numbers.

Do not use a calculator for this exercise.

**1** By using each of the digits 4, 8, 7 and 5, write the smallest 4-digit **odd** number you can.

**2** Gaby stated: **"The sum of three consecutive numbers is always an odd number."**
By means of an example, show that this statement is not true.

**3** In a cricket match, England's two scores were 326 runs and 397 runs.
Australia's two scores were 425 runs and 292 runs.
Which team had the higher total score?
How many more runs did they score than the other team? OCR

**4** The table below shows the distances, in miles, between some cities.

| | | | |
|---|---|---|---|
| Leeds | | | |
| 74 | Nottingham | | |
| 36 | 44 | Sheffield | |
| 24 | 87 | 60 | York |

A driver makes a trip from York to Leeds then to Nottingham and finally back to York.
How far did he travel? OCR

**5** A plank of wood is 396 cm in length. The plank is cut into two pieces.
One piece is 28 cm longer than the other. How long is the shorter piece of wood?

**6** (a) Work out the values of $(1 + 3) \times 5 + 5$
(b) Add brackets ( ) to make each statement correct.
You may use more than one pair of brackets in each statement.
(i) $1 + 3 \times 5 + 5 = 40$  (ii) $1 + 3 \times 5 + 5 = 31$

**7** The calculation shown is correct.
Use this to calculate $18\,468 \div 270$

$$684 \times 27 = 18\,468$$

OCR

**8** Work out. (a) $-7 - (-11) + (-5)$  (b) $(-8) \times (-5)$  (c) $\dfrac{(-1) \times (-5) \times (+6)}{(-3)}$

**9** A theatre has 48 rows of seats. Each row has 31 seats.
Work out the number of seats in the theatre. OCR

**10** Sylvia has collected £1632 to provide Christmas meals for retired people. Each meal costs £12.
How many meals can she provide?

**11** A group of 43 people pay £379 each to go on a skiing holiday.
What is the total cost of the holiday?

**12** A computer can process 2000 forms in 1 hour.
How many hours will it take to process 15 million forms?

**13** At midday on 1st February the temperature in Moscow was $-2°C$.
London was $3°C$ warmer than Moscow. Oslo was $8°C$ colder than London.
What was the temperature in Oslo at midday on 1st February? OCR

**14** Temperatures in degrees Centigrade (°C) can be changed to temperatures in
degrees Fahrenheit (°F) by using this rule:
Use the rule to change $-10°C$ to °F.  **Multiply by 9, divide by 5 and then add 32**

**15** A multichoice test has 20 questions. For each question the mark given is:

**+2 for a correct answer, −1 for a wrong answer, 0 if the question is not attempted**

Tim attempts all the questions and gets 10 correct.
Naomi attempts 13 questions and gets 8 correct.
Who scores the better mark? Explain your answer.

# Decimals and Fractions

Numbers and quantities are not always whole numbers.
The number system you met in Chapter 1 can be extended to include **decimal numbers** and **fractions**.

## Decimals

A **decimal point** is used to separate the whole number part from the decimal part of the number.

$$73.26$$ This number is read as seventy-three point two six.

whole number, 73    decimal part, 2 tenths + 6 hundredths (which is the same as 26 hundredths)

Many measurements are recorded using decimals, including money, time, distance, weight, volume, etc.
The metric and imperial measures you need to know are given in Chapter 31.

## Non-calculator methods for addition and subtraction of decimals

Write the numbers in tidy columns according to place value.
This is easily done by keeping the decimal points in a vertical column.
Start the addition or subtraction from the right, just as you did for whole numbers.
Use the same methods for carrying and borrowing as well.

### EXAMPLE

Work out   $17.1 - 8.72$.

$$
\begin{array}{r}
1\,7.\overset{6}{\cancel{1}}\overset{10}{\cancel{1}}\overset{1}{0} \\
- \phantom{1}8.7\,2 \\
\hline
8.3\,8
\end{array}
$$

*Check the answer by addition.*

**Useful tip:**
Writing 17.1 as 17.10 can make the working easier.
This does not change the value of 17.1.

## Exercise 2.1          Do not use a calculator for this exercise.

**1** On these scales what numbers are shown by the arrows?

(a)

(b)

**2** Write these decimals in ascending order.   3.567,   3.657,   3.576,   3.675,   3.652

**3** Kevin is 0.15 m shorter than Sally.   Sally is 1.7 m tall.   How tall is Kevin?

**4** Work these out in your head.
(a)  $2.5 + 8.4$        (b)  $0.7 + 0.95$        (c)  $0.36 + 0.54$        (d)  $6.47 + 4.53$
(e)  $2.7 - 1.5$        (f)  $1.3 - 0.7$        (g)  $0.4 - 0.16$        (h)  $15.3 - 6.4$

**5** Work out.
(a)  $6.54 + 0.27 + 0.03$        (b)  $10 - 4.78$        (c)  $9.57 - 4.567$
(d)  $2.22 + 0.78$        (e)  $9.13 - 7.89$        (f)  $5.564 + 0.017 + 10.2$

**6** Add these amounts of money:   31p,   £0.25,   27p,   £2.49.
What is the change from £5?

**7** Fred cuts three pieces of wood of length   0.95 m,   1.67 m   and   2.5 m
from a plank 10 m long.
How much wood is left?

## Non-calculator method for multiplying decimals

1. Ignore the decimal points and multiply the numbers using long multiplication.
2. Count the total number of decimal places in the numbers being multiplied together.
3. Place the decimal point so that the answer has the same total number of decimal places.

The result of multiplying two numbers is called the **product**.

### EXAMPLES

**1** Work out $0.2 \times 0.4$.

$$\begin{array}{r} 0.2 \\ \times\, 0.4 \\ \hline 0.0\,8 \end{array}$$

0.2 has 1 decimal place.
0.4 has 1 decimal place.
The answer has 2 decimal places.

$4 \times 2 = 8$
The answer must have 2 decimal places.
Noughts are used in the answer to locate the decimal point and to preserve place value.

**2** Work out $4.25 \times 0.18$.

$$\begin{array}{r} 4.2\,5 \\ \times\, 0.1\,8 \\ \hline 3\,4\,0\,0 \quad \leftarrow 425 \times 8 \\ 4\,2\,5\,0 \quad \leftarrow 425 \times 10 \\ \hline 0.7\,6\,5\,0 \end{array}$$

The answer must have 4 decimal places because 4.25 has 2 and 0.18 has 2.

$4.25 \times 0.18 = 0.7650$    This can be written as 0.765 which has the same value as 0.7650.

## Non-calculator method for dividing decimals

1. Multiply the dividing number by a power of 10 (10, 100, 1000, …) so that it becomes a whole number.
2. Multiply the number to be divided by the same number.
3. If necessary the answer will have a decimal point in the same place.

The result of dividing one number by another is called the **quotient**.

### EXAMPLES

**1** Work out $4 \div 0.8$.

Multiply both numbers by 10.
$40 \div 8 = 5$

**2** Work out $2 \div 0.25$.

Multiply both numbers by 100.
$200 \div 25 = 8$

**3** Work out $9 \div 4$.

$$\begin{array}{r} 4\overline{)9.0^{1}0^{2}} \\ \hline 2.2\,5 \end{array}$$

Noughts are added until the division is finished. Adding noughts does not change the value of the number. 9 has the same value as 9.00.
Continue dividing until either there is no remainder or the required accuracy is obtained.

Do not use a calculator for this exercise.

**1** A biro costs 25 pence.  (a)  How much will 10 cost?  (b)  How much will 100 cost?

**2** (a)  100 calculators cost £795. How much does one cost?
  (b)  1000 pencils cost £120. How much does one cost?
  (c)  10 litres of petrol cost £8.69. How would the cost of 1 litre be advertised?

**3** Write down pairs of calculations which give the same answer.
  12.3 × 1000   12.3 ÷ 100   12.3 × 0.1   12.3 ÷ 0.01   12.3 × 10   12.3 ÷ 0.1
  12.3 × 100   12.3 × 0.001   12.3 ÷ 0.001   12.3 ÷ 10   12.3 ÷ 1000   12.3 × 0.01

**4** A puzzle costs £1.90. How much will 4 puzzles cost?

**5** (a)  I buy 5 kites which cost £2.99 each. What is the total cost?
  (b)  How much change will I get from £20?

**6** Work these out in your head.
  (a)  1.7 × 5    (b)  2.6 × 0.5    (c)  0.6 × 0.8    (d)  0.3 × 0.2
  (e)  6 ÷ 0.4    (f)  10 ÷ 2.5    (g)  6 ÷ 0.12    (h)  12 ÷ 0.5

**7** A cup of coffee costs £1.15. How much will I have to pay for 9 cups?

**8** A pack of 7 tubes of oil paint costs £9.45. How much does each tube of oil paint cost?

**9** Calculate these products.
  (a)  0.25 × 0.3    (b)  2.5 × 3.5    (c)  8.7 × 1.9    (d)  4.1 × 0.25
  (e)  0.9 × 4.32    (f)  13.4 × 0.7    (g)  0.06 × 0.72    (h)  0.35 × 0.08

**10** Work out the cost of these vegetables.
  (a)  0.6 kg of carrots at 35p per kilogram.
  (b)  4.6 kg of potatoes at 40p per kilogram.
  (c)  1.2 kg of cabbage at 65p per kilogram.

**11** Work out.
  (a)  8 ÷ 5    (b)  10.5 ÷ 6    (c)  9 ÷ 8    (d)  2.46 ÷ 0.2
  (e)  0.146 ÷ 0.05    (f)  100.1 ÷ 0.07    (g)  0.05 ÷ 0.004    (h)  0.3 ÷ 0.008

**12** (a)  Multiply each of these numbers by 0.6.  (i)  5   (ii)  2.5   (iii)  0.4
  (b)  What do you notice about the original numbers and each of your answers?

**13** (a)  Divide each of these numbers by 0.6.   (i)  6   (ii)  3.6   (iii)  0.18
  (b)  What do you notice about the original numbers and each of your answers?

**14** What is the cost of each of 4.5 metres of linen at £13.50 per metre?

**15** (a)  Work out the cost for each of these portions of cheese.
      (i)  0.7 kg of Stilton.
      (ii)  1.6 kg of Cheddar.
      (iii)  0.8 kg of Sage Derby.
      (iv)  0.45 kg of Cotherstone.
  (b)  Corrine buys:
      0.25 kg of Stilton and 1.4 kg of Cheddar.
      She pays with a £10 note.
      How much change will she get?

*Select*
**CHEESES**
Price per kilogram

| Cheddar | £4.80 |
| Cotherstone | £6.20 |
| Sage Derby | £4.50 |
| Stilton | £7.60 |

**16** 8 bandages cost £14. How much does each bandage cost?

**17** A steel bar is 12.73 metres long.
  How many pieces, each 0.19 metres long, can be cut from it?

**18** A jug holds 1.035 litres. A small glass holds 0.023 litres.
  How many of the small glasses would be required to fill the jug?

## Numerical calculations with a calculator

### EXAMPLE

Calculate the value of $\dfrac{326.4}{(5 - 3.3)} - 500$

This is the same as $326.4 \div (5 - 3.3) - 500$.
So, the division line is the same as brackets.

To do the calculation enter the following sequence into your calculator.

$\boxed{3}$ $\boxed{2}$ $\boxed{6}$ $\boxed{.}$ $\boxed{4}$ $\boxed{\div}$ $\boxed{(}$ $\boxed{5}$ $\boxed{-}$ $\boxed{3}$ $\boxed{.}$ $\boxed{3}$ $\boxed{)}$ $\boxed{-}$

$\boxed{5}$ $\boxed{0}$ $\boxed{0}$ $\boxed{=}$      (The answer is $-308$)

### Exercise 2.3          Use a calculator in this exercise.

**1**  (a)  Calculate the value of $\dfrac{2.76 + 3.2}{1.25}$

  (b)  Write down the sequence of key presses that you made to work out (a).

**2**  (a)  Calculate $\dfrac{43.7}{22.5 \times 0.92}$

  (b)  Write down the sequence of key presses that you made to work out (a).

**3**  (a)  Work out $\dfrac{5.76 \times 3.6}{6.4 - 4.7}$

  (b)  Write down a sequence of calculator keys that could be used to answer (a).

**4**  Jill used the following key sequences to answer the questions below.

  **A**  $\boxed{5}$ $\boxed{.}$ $\boxed{4}$ $\boxed{2}$ $\boxed{\div}$ $\boxed{2}$ $\boxed{.}$ $\boxed{3}$ $\boxed{=}$ $\boxed{+}$ $\boxed{5}$ $\boxed{.}$ $\boxed{7}$ $\boxed{5}$ $\boxed{=}$

  **B**  $\boxed{5}$ $\boxed{.}$ $\boxed{4}$ $\boxed{2}$ $\boxed{+}$ $\boxed{5}$ $\boxed{.}$ $\boxed{7}$ $\boxed{5}$ $\boxed{=}$ $\boxed{\div}$ $\boxed{2}$ $\boxed{.}$ $\boxed{3}$ $\boxed{=}$

  **C**  $\boxed{5}$ $\boxed{.}$ $\boxed{4}$ $\boxed{2}$ $\boxed{+}$ $\boxed{(}$ $\boxed{5}$ $\boxed{.}$ $\boxed{7}$ $\boxed{5}$ $\boxed{\div}$ $\boxed{2}$ $\boxed{.}$ $\boxed{3}$ $\boxed{)}$ $\boxed{=}$

  **D**  $\boxed{5}$ $\boxed{.}$ $\boxed{4}$ $\boxed{2}$ $\boxed{\div}$ $\boxed{(}$ $\boxed{2}$ $\boxed{.}$ $\boxed{3}$ $\boxed{+}$ $\boxed{5}$ $\boxed{.}$ $\boxed{7}$ $\boxed{5}$ $\boxed{)}$ $\boxed{=}$

  (a)  $5.42 + \dfrac{5.75}{2.3}$    (b)  $\dfrac{5.42 + 5.75}{2.3}$    (c)  $\dfrac{5.42}{2.3 + 5.75}$    (d)  $\dfrac{5.42}{2.3} + 5.75$

  Which key sequences can be used to answer the questions correctly?

**5**  Calculate the following. Write down the full calculator display.

  (a)  $\dfrac{4.326 \times 0.923}{5.623 \times 9.123}$    (b)  $\dfrac{4.326 + 0.923}{5.623 + 9.123}$    (c)  $\dfrac{5.19 \times 37.2}{16.7 + 0.78}$    (d)  $\dfrac{5.2 \times 2.5 + 6.3}{10.34 - 4.7}$

  (e)  $300 - \dfrac{5.7 \times 8.3}{4.6 - 6.7}$    (f)  $19.3 \div (5.7 - 2.3 \div 0.4)$    (g)  $(5 - (5.6 - 4.1) \times 2.3) \div (6.9 + 3.1)$

### Fractions

$\frac{3}{8}$ is a **fraction**.

In a fraction:   the top number is called the **numerator**,
        the bottom number is called the **denominator**.

$\frac{3}{8}$ of this rectangle is shaded.

### Equivalent fractions

Fractions which are equal are called **equivalent fractions**.

Each of the fractions $\frac{1}{4}$, $\frac{3}{12}$, $\frac{6}{24}$,
is the same fraction written in different ways.

These fractions are all equivalent to $\frac{1}{4}$.

**To write an equivalent fraction:**
Multiply the numerator and
denominator by the **same** number.

For example.   $\dfrac{1}{4} = \dfrac{1 \times 3}{4 \times 3} = \dfrac{3}{12}$

## Simplifying fractions

Fractions can be **simplified** if both the numerator and denominator can be divided by the **same number**.

To write a fraction in its **simplest form** divide both the numerator and denominator by the largest number that divides into them both.

This is sometimes called **cancelling** a fraction.

**Remember:**
Multiplication and division are inverse (opposite) operations.
Equivalent fractions can also be made by dividing the numerator and denominator of a fraction by the same number.

### EXAMPLE

Write the fraction $\frac{25}{30}$ in its simplest form.

The largest number that divides into both the numerator and denominator of $\frac{25}{30}$ is 5.

$\frac{25}{30} = \frac{25 \div 5}{30 \div 5} = \frac{5}{6}$        $\frac{25}{30} = \frac{5}{6}$ in its simplest form.

## Types of fractions

Numbers like $2\frac{1}{2}$ and $1\frac{1}{4}$ are called **mixed numbers** because they are a mixture of whole numbers and fractions.
Mixed numbers can be written as **improper** or '**top heavy**' fractions.
These are fractions where the numerator is larger than the denominator.

### EXAMPLES

**1**  Write  $3\frac{4}{7}$  as an improper fraction.

$3\frac{4}{7} = \frac{(3 \times 7) + 4}{7} = \frac{21 + 4}{7} = \frac{25}{7}$

**2**  Write  $\frac{32}{5}$  as a mixed number.

$32 \div 5 = 6$   remainder 2.

$\frac{32}{5} = 6\frac{2}{5}$

## Finding fractions of quantities

### EXAMPLES

**1**  Find  $\frac{2}{5}$ of £65.

Divide £65 into 5 equal parts.
    £65 ÷ 5 = £13.
Each of these parts is $\frac{1}{5}$ of £65.

Two of these parts is $\frac{2}{5}$ of £65.

So,  $\frac{2}{5}$ of £65 = 2 × £13 = £26.

**2**  A coat costing £138 is reduced by $\frac{1}{3}$.
What is the reduced price of the coat?

Find  $\frac{1}{3}$ of £138.

$\frac{1}{3}$ of £138 = £138 ÷ 3 = £46

So, reduced price = £138 − £46 = £92

## Exercise 2.4

Do this exercise without using a calculator.

**1**  Write three equivalent fractions for the shaded part of this rectangle.
What is the simplest form of the fraction for the shaded part?

**2**  Write these fractions in order, smallest first.  $\frac{2}{3}$    $\frac{3}{5}$    $\frac{7}{10}$    $\frac{8}{15}$

**3** Which of these fractions is the largest? $\frac{4}{5}$ $\frac{13}{20}$ $\frac{7}{10}$ $\frac{3}{4}$

**4** Write these fractions in their simplest form. (a) $\frac{12}{15}$ (b) $\frac{18}{27}$ (c) $\frac{50}{75}$ (d) $\frac{16}{40}$

**5** Change these fractions to mixed numbers: (a) $\frac{3}{2}$ (b) $\frac{17}{8}$ (c) $\frac{15}{4}$ (d) $\frac{23}{5}$

**6** Change these numbers to improper fractions: (a) $2\frac{7}{10}$ (b) $1\frac{3}{5}$ (c) $5\frac{5}{6}$

**7** Write 42 as a fraction of 70. Give your answer in its simplest form.

**8** A box of 50 chocolates includes 30 soft-centred chocolates.
What fraction of the chocolates are soft-centred?

**9** Calculate:
(a) $\frac{1}{4}$ of 12 (b) $\frac{1}{5}$ of 20 (c) $\frac{1}{10}$ of 30 (d) $\frac{1}{6}$ of 48 (e) $\frac{2}{5}$ of 20

(f) $\frac{3}{10}$ of 30 (g) $\frac{2}{7}$ of 42 (h) $\frac{5}{9}$ of 36 (i) $\frac{5}{6}$ of 48 (j) $\frac{3}{8}$ of 32

**10** Richard has 30 marbles. He gives $\frac{1}{5}$ of them away.
(a) How many marbles does he give away?
(b) How many marbles has he got left?

**11** Alfie collects £12.50 for charity. He gives $\frac{3}{5}$ of it to Oxfam.
How much does he give to other charities?

**12** In a sale all prices are reduced by $\frac{3}{10}$.
What is the sale price of a microwave which was originally priced at £212?

**13** A publisher offers a discount of $\frac{3}{20}$ for orders of more than 100 books.
How much would a shop pay for an order of 250 books costing £15 each?

**14** Lauren and Amelia share a bar of chocolate. The chocolate bar has 24 squares.
Lauren eats $\frac{3}{8}$ of the bar. Amelia eats $\frac{5}{12}$ of the bar.
(a) How many squares has Lauren eaten?
(b) How many squares has Amelia eaten?
(c) What fraction of the bar is left?

## Adding and subtracting fractions

Calculate $1\frac{3}{4} + \frac{5}{6}$

Change mixed numbers to improper ('top heavy') fractions. $1\frac{3}{4} = \frac{7}{4}$

The calculation then becomes $\frac{7}{4} + \frac{5}{6}$

Find the smallest number into which both 4 and 6 will divide.
4 divides into: 4, 8, 12, 16, ...
6 divides into: 6, 12, 18, ...
So, 12 is the smallest.

Change the original fractions to equivalent fractions using the smallest number as the new denominator. $\frac{7}{4} = \frac{21}{12}$ and $\frac{5}{6} = \frac{10}{12}$

Add the new numerators.
Keep the new denominator the same. $\frac{21}{12} + \frac{10}{12} = \frac{21 + 10}{12} = \frac{31}{12}$

Write the answer in its simplest form. $\frac{31}{12} = 2\frac{7}{12}$

Fractions must have the **same denominator** before addition (or subtraction) can take place.

*What happens when you use a denominator that is **not** the smallest?*

**Decimals and Fractions**

**1** Work out $\frac{5}{8} - \frac{7}{12}$.

24 is the smallest number into which both 8 and 12 divide.

$\frac{5}{8} = \frac{5 \times 3}{8 \times 3} = \frac{15}{24}$ and $\frac{7}{12} = \frac{7 \times 2}{12 \times 2} = \frac{14}{24}$

$\frac{5}{8} - \frac{7}{12} = \frac{15}{24} - \frac{14}{24} = \frac{1}{24}$

**2** Calculate $3\frac{3}{10} - 1\frac{5}{6}$.

$3\frac{3}{10} = \frac{33}{10}$ and $1\frac{5}{6} = \frac{11}{6}$

$\frac{33}{10} = \frac{99}{30}$ and $\frac{11}{6} = \frac{55}{30}$

$3\frac{3}{10} - 1\frac{5}{6} = \frac{99}{30} - \frac{55}{30} = \frac{44}{30}$

$\frac{44}{30} = \frac{22}{15} = 1\frac{7}{15}$

**Remember:**
- Add the numerators only.
- When the answer is an improper fraction change it into a mixed number.

## Exercise 2.5

Do not use a calculator in this exercise.

**1** Work out:
   (a) $\frac{1}{4} + \frac{1}{8}$   (b) $\frac{1}{3} + \frac{1}{4}$   (c) $\frac{1}{2} + \frac{1}{5}$   (d) $\frac{1}{3} + \frac{1}{5}$   (e) $\frac{1}{2} + \frac{1}{7}$

**2** Work out:
   (a) $\frac{1}{4} - \frac{1}{8}$   (b) $\frac{1}{3} - \frac{1}{4}$   (c) $\frac{1}{2} - \frac{1}{5}$   (d) $\frac{1}{3} - \frac{1}{5}$   (e) $\frac{1}{2} - \frac{1}{7}$

**3** Work out:
   (a) $\frac{1}{2} + \frac{3}{4}$   (b) $\frac{2}{3} + \frac{5}{6}$   (c) $\frac{3}{4} + \frac{4}{5}$   (d) $\frac{5}{7} + \frac{2}{3}$   (e) $\frac{3}{8} + \frac{5}{6}$

**4** Calculate:
   (a) $\frac{5}{8} - \frac{1}{2}$   (b) $\frac{13}{15} - \frac{1}{3}$   (c) $\frac{5}{6} - \frac{5}{24}$   (d) $\frac{7}{15} - \frac{2}{5}$   (e) $\frac{3}{4} - \frac{5}{12}$

**5** Calculate:
   (a) $2\frac{3}{4} + 1\frac{1}{2}$   (b) $1\frac{1}{2} + 2\frac{1}{3}$   (c) $1\frac{3}{4} + 2\frac{5}{8}$   (d) $2\frac{1}{4} + 3\frac{3}{5}$   (e) $4\frac{3}{5} + 1\frac{5}{6}$

**6** Calculate:
   (a) $2\frac{1}{2} - 1\frac{2}{5}$   (b) $1\frac{2}{3} - 1\frac{1}{4}$   (c) $3\frac{3}{4} - 2\frac{3}{8}$   (d) $5\frac{2}{5} - 2\frac{1}{10}$   (e) $4\frac{5}{12} - 2\frac{1}{6}$

**7** Colin buys a bag of flour.   He uses $\frac{1}{3}$ to bake a cake and $\frac{2}{5}$ to make a loaf.
   What fraction of the bag of flour is left?

**8** Edward, Marc, Dee and Lin share an apple pie.   Edward has $\frac{1}{3}$, Marc has $\frac{1}{5}$ and Dee has $\frac{1}{4}$.
   How much is left for Lin?

**9** Both Lee and Mary have a packet of the same sweets.
   Mary eats $\frac{1}{3}$ of her packet.   Lee eats $\frac{3}{4}$ of his packet.
   (a)   Find the difference between the fraction Mary eats and the fraction Lee eats.

   Lee gives his remaining sweets to Mary.
   (b)   What fraction of a packet does Mary now have?

**10** Jon, Billy and Cathy are the only candidates in a school election.
   Jon got $\frac{7}{20}$ of the votes.   Billy got $\frac{2}{5}$ of the votes.
   (a)   What fraction of the votes did Cathy get?
   (b)   Which candidate won the election?

## Multiplying fractions

Calculate $\frac{3}{8} \times \frac{1}{9}$

Simplify, where possible, by cancelling. $\frac{\cancel{3}^{1}}{8} \times \frac{1}{\cancel{9}_{3}}$

Multiply the numerators.
Multiply the denominators. $\frac{1 \times 1}{8 \times 3} = \frac{1}{24}$

Write the answer in its simplest form. $\frac{3}{8} \times \frac{1}{9} = \frac{1}{24}$

**To simplify:**
Divide a numerator **and** a denominator by the **same number.**

In this case:
3 and 9 can be divided by 3.
$3 \div 3 = 1$ and $9 \div 3 = 3$.

### EXAMPLES

**1** Work out $\frac{3}{8} \times 12$

**Note:**
$12 = \frac{12}{1}$

$\frac{3}{8} \times \frac{12}{1}$

Simplify by cancelling.

$= \frac{3}{\cancel{8}_{2}} \times \frac{\cancel{12}^{3}}{1}$

Multiply out.

$= \frac{3 \times 3}{2 \times 1} = \frac{9}{2}$

$= 4\frac{1}{2}$

**2** Calculate $1\frac{1}{2} \times 1\frac{3}{5}$

Change mixed numbers to improper fractions.

$1\frac{1}{2} \times 1\frac{3}{5} = \frac{3}{2} \times \frac{8}{5}$

Simplify by cancelling.

$= \frac{3}{\cancel{2}_{1}} \times \frac{\cancel{8}^{4}}{5}$

Multiply out.

$= \frac{3 \times 4}{1 \times 5} = \frac{12}{5} = 2\frac{2}{5}$

### Exercise **2.6**

Do not use a calculator in this exercise.

**1** Work out. Give your answers as mixed numbers.
   (a) $\frac{1}{2} \times 7$
   (b) $\frac{3}{5} \times 3$
   (c) $\frac{5}{8} \times 10$
   (d) $\frac{3}{4} \times 12$
   (e) $\frac{7}{10} \times 15$

**2** Work out:
   (a) $\frac{1}{4} \times \frac{1}{5}$
   (b) $\frac{3}{5} \times \frac{1}{6}$
   (c) $\frac{1}{2} \times \frac{3}{4}$
   (d) $\frac{1}{10} \times \frac{5}{8}$
   (e) $\frac{3}{10} \times \frac{1}{6}$

**3** Work out:   **Hint** - Change mixed numbers to improper fractions first.
   (a) $1\frac{1}{2} \times 5$
   (b) $1\frac{1}{4} \times 6$
   (c) $1\frac{1}{5} \times 4$
   (d) $3\frac{2}{3} \times 2$
   (e) $2\frac{2}{5} \times 3$
   (f) $4\frac{1}{2} \times \frac{1}{2}$
   (g) $3\frac{3}{4} \times \frac{1}{5}$
   (h) $2\frac{2}{5} \times \frac{1}{3}$
   (i) $2\frac{2}{3} \times \frac{1}{4}$
   (j) $4\frac{3}{8} \times \frac{1}{7}$

**4** Calculate:
   (a) $\frac{2}{3} \times \frac{3}{4}$
   (b) $\frac{3}{4} \times \frac{2}{5}$
   (c) $\frac{2}{5} \times \frac{5}{6}$
   (d) $\frac{2}{5} \times \frac{5}{7}$
   (e) $\frac{3}{10} \times \frac{5}{6}$

**5** Calculate:
   (a) $1\frac{1}{2} \times \frac{3}{4}$
   (b) $1\frac{1}{2} \times 1\frac{1}{3}$
   (c) $2\frac{1}{4} \times 1\frac{2}{3}$
   (d) $2\frac{3}{4} \times 1\frac{2}{5}$
   (e) $1\frac{1}{2} \times 3\frac{1}{4}$
   (f) $1\frac{3}{5} \times 1\frac{1}{6}$
   (g) $6\frac{3}{10} \times 2\frac{2}{9}$
   (h) $3\frac{3}{4} \times 3\frac{3}{5}$
   (i) $1\frac{1}{4} \times 2\frac{4}{25}$
   (j) $2\frac{5}{8} \times 3\frac{1}{3}$

**6** Kylie has $\frac{2}{3}$ of a litre of orange.   She drinks $\frac{2}{5}$ of the orange.
   (a)   What fraction of a litre does she drink?
   (b)   What fraction of a litre is left?

**7** Tony eats $\frac{1}{5}$ of a bag of sweets.
   He shares the remaining sweets equally among Bob, Jo and David.
   (a)   What fraction of the bag of sweets does Bob get?
   (b)   What is the smallest possible number of sweets in the bag?

## Dividing fractions

The method normally used when one fraction is divided by another is to change the division to a multiplication. The fractions can then be multiplied in the usual way.

Calculate $\quad 2\frac{2}{15} \div 1\frac{3}{5}$

Change mixed numbers to improper ('top heavy') fractions. $\quad 2\frac{2}{15} = \frac{32}{15} \quad$ and $\quad 1\frac{3}{5} = \frac{8}{5}$

Change the division to a multiplication. $\quad \frac{32}{15} \div \frac{8}{5} = \frac{32}{15} \times \frac{5}{8}$

Simplify, where possible, by cancelling. $\quad \dfrac{\overset{4}{\cancel{32}}}{\underset{3}{\cancel{15}}} \times \dfrac{\overset{1}{\cancel{5}}}{\underset{1}{\cancel{8}}}$

Multiply the numerators.
Multiply the denominators. $\quad \dfrac{4 \times 1}{3 \times 1} = \dfrac{4}{3}$

Write the answer in its simplest form. $\quad \frac{4}{3} = 1\frac{1}{3}$

---

### EXAMPLES

**1** Work out $\frac{2}{3} \div 5$.

$\frac{2}{3} \div 5$

$= \frac{2}{3} \times \frac{1}{5}$

$= \frac{2}{15}$

> Divide by 5 is the same as multiply by $\frac{1}{5}$.

**2** Calculate $1\frac{3}{5} \div \frac{4}{9}$.

$1\frac{3}{5} \div \frac{4}{9} = \frac{8}{5} \div \frac{4}{9}$

$= \frac{8}{5} \times \frac{9}{4}$

$= \dfrac{\overset{2}{\cancel{8}}}{5} \times \dfrac{9}{\underset{1}{\cancel{4}}}$

$= \frac{18}{5} = 3\frac{3}{5}$

> Divide by $\frac{4}{9}$ is the same as multiply by $\frac{9}{4}$.

---

### Exercise 2.7

Do not use a calculator in this exercise.

**1** Work out. Give your answers in their simplest form.

(a) $\frac{1}{2} \div 5$ 　　(b) $\frac{3}{4} \div 2$ 　　(c) $\frac{2}{3} \div 2$ 　　(d) $\frac{2}{5} \div 4$ 　　(e) $\frac{6}{7} \div 3$

**2** Work out: **Hint** - Change mixed numbers to improper fractions first.

(a) $1\frac{1}{2} \div 2$ 　　(b) $1\frac{2}{3} \div 5$ 　　(c) $1\frac{5}{7} \div 3$ 　　(d) $3\frac{1}{9} \div 7$ 　　(e) $2\frac{2}{3} \div 4$

**3** Calculate:

(a) $\frac{1}{2} \div \frac{1}{4}$ 　　(b) $\frac{1}{5} \div \frac{1}{2}$ 　　(c) $\frac{7}{8} \div \frac{1}{3}$ 　　(d) $\frac{2}{3} \div \frac{1}{5}$ 　　(e) $\frac{3}{4} \div \frac{1}{8}$

**4** Calculate:

(a) $\frac{2}{3} \div \frac{4}{5}$ 　　(b) $\frac{3}{8} \div \frac{2}{3}$ 　　(c) $\frac{3}{5} \div \frac{3}{4}$ 　　(d) $\frac{2}{5} \div \frac{3}{10}$ 　　(e) $\frac{3}{8} \div \frac{9}{16}$

(f) $\frac{7}{12} \div \frac{7}{18}$ 　　(g) $\frac{4}{9} \div \frac{2}{3}$ 　　(h) $\frac{7}{10} \div \frac{3}{5}$ 　　(i) $\frac{9}{20} \div \frac{3}{10}$ 　　(j) $\frac{21}{25} \div \frac{7}{15}$

**5** Calculate:

(a) $1\frac{3}{4} \div \frac{1}{8}$ 　　(b) $1\frac{1}{2} \div \frac{3}{10}$ 　　(c) $1\frac{3}{5} \div \frac{4}{5}$ 　　(d) $2\frac{1}{10} \div \frac{7}{20}$ 　　(e) $3\frac{3}{4} \div \frac{5}{8}$

(f) $1\frac{1}{4} \div 1\frac{9}{16}$ 　　(g) $3\frac{1}{5} \div 2\frac{2}{15}$ 　　(h) $2\frac{1}{4} \div 1\frac{4}{5}$ 　　(i) $2\frac{1}{7} \div 1\frac{7}{8}$ 　　(j) $1\frac{2}{5} \div 1\frac{2}{3}$

**6** Neil uses $\frac{1}{2}$ of a block of paté to make 5 sandwiches.
What fraction of the block of paté does he put on each sandwich?

**7** Lauren uses $\frac{2}{3}$ of a bag of flour to make 6 muffins.
What fraction of the bag of flour is used for each muffin?

**8** A shelf is $40\frac{3}{4}$ cm long. How many books of width $1\frac{3}{4}$ cm can stand on the shelf?

## Problems involving fractions

### Exercise 2.8

Do not use a calculator in this exercise.

**1** Ben spends $\frac{5}{8}$ of his pocket money. He has £1.20 left.
How much pocket money did Ben get?

**2** A cyclist travels from A to B in two stages. Stage 1 is 28 km which is $\frac{2}{7}$ of the total journey.
How long is stage 2?

**3** Robert pays £9.60 for a CD in the sale.
How much did he save?

> **Music Sale** - $\frac{1}{4}$ off all CDs

**4** Sara's hourly wage is increased by $\frac{1}{10}$. Her new hourly wage is £6.60.
What was her original hourly wage?

**5** A young tree is $\frac{3}{8}$ taller in August than it was in May. In August it is 132 centimetres tall.
How tall was it in May?

## Fractions on a calculator

Fraction calculations can be done quickly using the fraction button on a calculator.

On most calculators the fraction button looks like this … $\boxed{a^b/_c}$

### EXAMPLE

Use a calculator to work out $4\frac{3}{5} \div 2\frac{1}{4}$.

This can be calculated with this calculator sequence.

$$\boxed{4}\ \boxed{a^b/_c}\ \boxed{3}\ \boxed{a^b/_c}\ \boxed{5}\ \boxed{\div}\ \boxed{2}\ \boxed{a^b/_c}\ \boxed{1}\ \boxed{a^b/_c}\ \boxed{4}\ \boxed{=}$$

This gives the answer $2\frac{2}{45}$.

*Use a calculator to check your answers to some of the questions in Exercises 2.4 to 2.8.*

## Fractions and decimals

All fractions can be written as decimals and vice versa.

### Changing decimals to fractions

#### EXAMPLES

Change the following decimals to fractions in their simplest form.

**1** 0.02 $\quad 0.02 = \frac{2}{100} = \frac{2 \div 2}{100 \div 2} = \frac{1}{50}$

**2** 0.36 $\quad 0.36 = \frac{36}{100} = \frac{36 \div 4}{100 \div 4} = \frac{9}{25}$

### Changing fractions to decimals

#### EXAMPLES

Change the following fractions to decimals.

**1** $\frac{1}{5} = 1 \div 5 = 0.2$

**2** $\frac{11}{20} = 11 \div 20 = 0.55$

> **Remember:**
> $11 \div 20 = 11.00 \div 20$
>
> $$\begin{array}{r} 0.5\,5 \\ 20\overline{)1\,1.0^{11}\,0^{10}} \end{array}$$

Some decimals have recurring digits. These are shown by:

> a single dot above a single recurring digit,
> a dot above the first and last digit of a set of recurring digits.

For example:    $\frac{1}{3}$ = 0.3333333... = $0.\dot{3}$

$\frac{123}{999}$ = 0.123123123... = $0.\dot{1}2\dot{3}$

## Exercise 2.9

Do not use a calculator for questions 1 to 3.

**1** Change the following decimals to fractions in their simplest form.
(a)  0.12       (b)  0.6       (c)  0.32       (d)  0.175       (e)  0.45       (f)  0.65
(g)  0.22       (h)  0.202     (i)  0.28       (j)  0.555       (k)  0.625       (l)  0.84

**2** Change the following fractions to decimals.
(a)  $\frac{1}{4}$       (b)  $\frac{1}{10}$       (c)  $\frac{2}{5}$       (d)  $\frac{3}{4}$       (e)  $\frac{7}{10}$       (f)  $\frac{4}{5}$

**3** Change the following fractions to decimals.
(a)  $\frac{3}{20}$       (b)  $\frac{4}{25}$       (c)  $\frac{7}{100}$       (d)  $\frac{19}{20}$       (e)  $\frac{9}{25}$       (f)  $\frac{106}{200}$

**4** Change these fractions to decimals.
(a)  $\frac{1}{8}$       (b)  $\frac{5}{8}$       (c)  $\frac{9}{40}$       (d)  $\frac{29}{40}$

**5** Write these decimals using dots to represent recurring digits.
(a)  0.77777...       (b)  0.11111...       (c)  0.363636...       (d)  0.828282...
(e)  0.135135...      (f)  0.216216...      (g)  0.166666...       (h)  0.285714285714...

**6** Write each of these fractions as recurring decimals, using dots to represent recurring digits.
(a)  $\frac{8}{9}$       (b)  $\frac{4}{9}$       (c)  $\frac{17}{33}$       (d)  $\frac{8}{11}$       (e)  $\frac{1}{7}$
(f)  $\frac{6}{7}$       (g)  $\frac{1}{30}$       (h)  $\frac{7}{15}$       (i)  $\frac{5}{6}$       (j)  $\frac{17}{22}$

## What you need to know

- **Without using a calculator** you should be able to add, subtract, multiply and divide decimals.
- Carry out a variety of calculations involving decimals.
- Know that:   when a number is **multiplied** by a number between 0 and 1
  the result will be **smaller** than the original number,
  when a number is **divided** by a number between 0 and 1
  the result will be **larger** than the original number.
- The top number of a fraction is called the **numerator**,
  the bottom number is called the **denominator**.
- $2\frac{1}{2}$ is an example of a **mixed number**. It is a mixture of whole numbers and fractions.
- $\frac{5}{2}$ is an **improper** (or '**top heavy**') fraction.
- Fractions must have the **same denominator** before **adding** or **subtracting**.
- Mixed numbers must be changed to **improper fractions** before **multiplying** or **dividing**.
- All fractions can be written as decimals.
  Some decimals have **recurring digits**. These are shown by:
  a single dot above a single recurring digit, e.g.  $\frac{2}{3}$ = 0.6666... = $0.\dot{6}$
  a dot above the first and last digit of a set of recurring digits, e.g.  $\frac{5}{11}$ = 0.454545... = $0.\dot{4}\dot{5}$

**1**  (a)  Write 0.45 as a fraction. Give your answer in its simplest form.
   (b)  Write as a decimal.  (i)  $\frac{7}{25}$          (ii)  $\frac{5}{9}$

**2**  Work out.
   (a)  $2.94 + 9.47$       (b)  $10 - 5.67$       (c)  $8 \div 0.4$       (d)  $0.2 \times 0.4$

**3**  An examination in French is marked out of 80.
   (a)  Jean scored $\frac{4}{5}$ of the marks.  How many marks did she score?
   (b)  Pete scored 35 marks. What fraction of the total did he score?

**4**  36 girls and 24 boys applied to go on a rock climbing course.
   $\frac{2}{3}$ of the girls and $\frac{3}{4}$ of the boys went on the course.
   What fraction of the 60 students who applied went on the course?
   Write the fraction in its simplest form.

**5**  (a)  Change $\frac{3}{8}$ into a decimal.
   (b)  Use your answer to part (a) to write $\frac{3}{80}$ as a decimal.          OCR

**6**  Work out.  (a)  $\frac{1}{4} + \frac{2}{3}$       (b)  $\frac{2}{5} - \frac{1}{8}$       (c)  $\frac{3}{5} \times \frac{5}{7}$       (d)  $\frac{5}{8} \div \frac{3}{4}$

**7**  At Wendy's party $\frac{1}{3}$ of the children have blue eyes and $\frac{2}{5}$ have brown eyes.
   What fraction of the children do not have blue or brown eyes?

**8**  Given that  $275 \times 41 = 11\,275$,  work out the value of:
   (a)  $275 \times 0.0041$          (b)  $112.75 \div 4.1$

**9**  A group of students went to a fast food restaurant.
   (a)  $\frac{2}{5}$ of them bought a beef burger  and  $\frac{1}{3}$ of them bought a chicken burger.
       The rest of them just bought drinks.
       What fraction of the group bought food?
   (b)  $\frac{3}{4}$ of those who bought a beef burger also bought chips.
       What faction of the whole group bought beef burgers and chips?
       Give your answer as a fraction in its simplest form.          OCR

**10**  Work out the following.  (a)  $\frac{2}{3} + \frac{4}{5}$       (b)  $2\frac{2}{5} \times \frac{5}{6}$          OCR

**11**  The price of a coat is reduced by $\frac{2}{5}$ to £48.  What was the original price of the coat?

**12**  Sonya uses her calculator to work out  $\dfrac{2.34 + 1.76}{3.22} + 1.85$
   Sonya presses keys as follows.

   $\boxed{2}\ \boxed{.}\ \boxed{3}\ \boxed{4}\ \boxed{+}\ \boxed{1}\ \boxed{.}\ \boxed{7}\ \boxed{6}\ \boxed{\div}\ \boxed{3}\ \boxed{.}\ \boxed{2}\ \boxed{2}\ \boxed{+}\ \boxed{1}\ \boxed{.}\ \boxed{8}\ \boxed{5}\ \boxed{=}$

   (a)  Explain clearly what is wrong with Sonya's method.
   (b)  Calculate the correct answer.

**13**  On average, a car travels 100 km on fuel costing £8.80.
   (a)  Calculate the cost of fuel for a journey of 720 km.
   (b)  The fuel for another journey cost £28.60.
       Calculate the length of this journey.          OCR

**14**  Work out  (a)  $\dfrac{197.6}{2.4 + 7.1}$,       (b)  $\dfrac{4.3 \times 3.5}{4.3 - 3.5}$.
   Write down your full calculator display.

**15**  Is the value of  $\dfrac{a + c}{b + d}$  always between the fractions  $\dfrac{a}{b}$  and  $\dfrac{c}{d}$ ?
   Explain your answer.

# 3 Approximation and Estimation

## Approximation

In real-life it is not always necessary to use exact numbers. A number can be **rounded** to an **approximate** number. Numbers are rounded according to how accurately we wish to give details. For example, the distance to the Sun can be given as 93 million miles.

*Can you think of other situations where approximations might be used?*

## Rounding to the nearest 10, 100, 1000

If there were 7487 people at a football match a newspaper report could say,
*"7000 at the football match."*

The number 7487 can be approximated as 7490, 7500 or 7000 depending on the degree of accuracy required.

    7487 rounded to the nearest 10 is 7490.
    7487 rounded to the nearest 100 is 7500.
    7487 rounded to the nearest 1000 is 7000.

It is a convention to round a number which is in the middle to the higher number.
75 to the nearest 10 is 80.
450 to the nearest 100 is 500.
8500 to the nearest 1000 is 9000.

### EXAMPLE

A lifeguard says, "There are 120 people in the pool today."
This figure is correct to the nearest 10.
What is the smallest and largest possible number of people in the pool?

The smallest whole number that rounds to 120 is 115.
The largest whole number that rounds to 120 is 124.
So, the smallest possible number of people is 115 and the largest possible number of people is 124.

## Exercise 3.1

**1** Write each of these numbers to the nearest 10.   (a)  47      (b)  53      (c)  65

**2** Round the number 7475
    (a)  to the nearest 10,      (b)  to the nearest 100,      (c)  to the nearest 1000.

**3** (a)  Rearrange the cards:  5  4  6  3  to make the smallest possible number.
    (b)  Round your number to the nearest 100.

**4** Write down a number each time which fits these roundings.
    (a)  It is 750 to the nearest 10 but 700 to the nearest 100.
    (b)  It is 750 to the nearest 10 but 800 to the nearest 100.
    (c)  It is 8500 to the nearest 100 but 8000 to the nearest 1000.
    (d)  It is 8500 to the nearest 100 but 9000 to the nearest 1000.

**5** Write down these figures to appropriate degrees of accuracy.
    (a)  The class raised £49.67 for charity.
    (b)  The population of a town is 24 055.
    (c)  The land area of the country is 309 123 km².
    (d)  The distance to London is 189 km.

**6** 64 537 people signed a petition. A newspaper report stated: '65 000 people sign petition'
To what degree of accuracy is the number given in the newspaper report?

**7** Pete says, "I had 40 birthday cards." The number is correct to the nearest 10.
(a) What is the smallest possible number of cards Pete had?
(b) What is the largest possible number of cards Pete had?

**8** The number of people at a concert is 2000 to the nearest 100.
(a) What is the smallest possible number of people at the concert?
(b) What is the largest possible number of people at the concert?

**9** **"43 000 spectators watch thrilling Test Match."**
The number reported in the newspaper was correct to the nearest thousand.
What is the smallest possible number of spectators?

**10** Carl has 140 postcards in his collection. The number is given to the nearest ten.
What is the smallest and greatest number of postcards Carl could have in his collection?

**11** "You require 2700 tiles to tile your swimming pool." This figure is correct to the nearest 100.
What is the greatest number of tiles needed?

## Rounding in real-life problems

In a real-life problem a rounding must be used which gives a sensible answer.

### EXAMPLES

**1** A Year group in a school are going to Alton Towers.
There are 242 students and teachers going.
Each coach can carry 55 passengers. How many coaches should be ordered?
$242 \div 55 = 4.4$     This should be rounded up to 5.
4 coaches can only carry 220 passengers  $(4 \times 55 = 220)$.

**2** Filing cabinets are to be placed along a wall. The available space is 460 cm.
Each cabinet is 80 cm wide. How many can be fitted in?
$460 \div 80 = 5.75$     This should be rounded down to 5.
Although the answer is nearly 6 the 6th cabinet would not fit in.

### Exercise **3.2**     Do not use a calculator for this exercise.

**1** 49 students are waiting to go to the Sports Stadium.
A minibus can take 15 passengers at a time. How many trips are required?

**2** A classroom wall is 700 cm long.
How many tables, each 120 cm long, could be fitted along the wall?

**3** There are 210 students in a year group. They each need an exercise book.
The exercise books are sold in packs of 25. How many packs should be ordered?

**4** Car parking spaces should be 2.5 m wide.
How many can be fitted into a car park which is 61 m wide?

**5** How many 30p stamps can be bought for £5?

**6** Kim needs 26 candles. The candles are sold in packs of 4. How many packs must she buy?

**7** A sweet manufacturer puts 17 sweets in a bag.
How many bags can be made up if there are 500 sweets?

## Rounding using decimal places

What is the cost of 1.75 metres of material costing £3.99 a metre?

$1.75 \times 3.99 = 6.9825$

The cost of the material is £6.9825 or 698.25p.
As you can only pay in pence, a sensible answer is £6.98,
correct to two decimal places (nearest penny).
This means that there are only two decimal places after the
decimal point.

> Often it is not necessary to use an exact answer. Sometimes it is impossible, or impractical, to use the exact answer.

## To round a number to a given number of decimal places

When rounding a number to one, two or more decimal places:

1. Write the number using one more decimal place than asked for.

2. Look at the last decimal place and
   - if the figure is 5 or more round up,
   - if the figure is less than 5 round down.

3. When answering a problem remember to include any units and state the degree of approximation used.

### EXAMPLES

**1** Write 2.76435 to
    (a) 2 decimal places,       (b) 1 decimal place.

    (a) Look at the third decimal place. **4**
        This is less than 5, so, round down.
        Answer 2.76

    (b) Look at the second decimal place. **6**
        This is 5 or more, so, round up.
        Answer 2.8

**2** Write 7.104 to 2 decimal places.
$7.104 = 7.10$ to 2 d.p.
The zero is written down because it shows the
accuracy used, 2 decimal places.

> **Notation:**
> Often decimal place is shortened to d.p.

**3** $5.98 = 6.0$ to 1 d.p.
Notice that the next tenth after 5.9 is 6.0.

## Exercise 3.3

**1** Write the number 3.9617 correct to
    (a) 3 decimal places,    (b) 2 decimal places,    (c) 1 decimal place.

**2** Write the number 567.654 correct to
    (a) 2 decimal places,    (b) 1 decimal place,    (c) the nearest whole number.

**3** The display on a calculator shows the result of $34 \div 7$.

$$\boxed{4.857142857}$$

What is the result correct to two decimal places?

**4** 68.847 kg

The scales show Gary's weight.
Write Gary's weight correct to one decimal place.

**5** Copy and complete this table.

| Number | 2.367 | 0.964 | 0.965 | 15.2806 | 0.056 | 4.991 | 4.996 |
|--------|-------|-------|-------|---------|-------|-------|-------|
| d.p.   | 1     | 2     | 2     | 3       | 2     | 2     | 2     |
| Answer | 2.4   |       |       |         |       |       |       |

**6** Carry out these calculations giving the answers correct to
    (a)  1 d.p.      (b)  2 d.p.      (c)  3 d.p.

    (i)   $6.12 \times 7.54$      (ii)  $89.1 \times 0.67$      (iii)  $90.53 \times 6.29$
    (iv)  $98.6 \div 5.78$      (v)  $67.2 \div 101.45$

**7** In each of these short problems decide upon the most suitable accuracy for the answer.
Then calculate the answer.
Give a reason for your degree of accuracy.
    (a)    One gallon is 4.54596... litres.
         How many litres is 9 gallons?
    (b)    What is the cost of 0.454 kg of cheese at £5.21 per kilogram?
    (c)    The total length of 7 equal sticks, lying end to end, is 250 cm.
         How long is each stick?
    (d)    A packet of 6 bandages costs £7.99.
         How much does one bandage cost?
    (e)    Petrol costs 91.4 pence a litre. I buy 15.6 litres.
         How much will I have to pay?

## Rounding using significant figures

Consider the calculation   $600.02 \times 7500.97 = 4500732.0194$
To 1 d.p. it is 4500732.0,   to 2 d.p. it is 4500732.02.
The answers to either 1 or 2 d.p. are very close to the actual answer and are almost as long.
There is little advantage in using either of these two roundings.
The point of a rounding is that it is a more convenient number to use.

Another kind of rounding uses **significant figures**.
The **most** significant figure in a number is the figure which has the greatest place value.

Consider the number 237.
The figure 2 has the greatest place value. It is worth 200.
So, 2 is the most significant figure.

In the number 0.00328, the figure 3 has the greatest place value.
So, 3 is the most significant figure.

> Noughts which are used to locate the decimal point and preserve the place value of other figures are not significant.

## To round a number to a given number of significant figures

When rounding a number to one, two or more significant figures:
1. Start from the most significant figure and count the required number of figures.
2. Look at the next figure to the right of this and
   - if the figure is 5 or more round up,
   - if the figure is less than 5 round down.
3. Add noughts, as necessary, to locate the decimal point and preserve the place value.
4. When answering a problem remember to include any units and state the degree of approximation used.

**1** Write 4 500 732.0194 to 2 significant figures.

The figure after the first 2 significant figures **45** is 0.
This is less than 5, so, round down, leaving 45 unchanged.
Add noughts to 45 to locate the decimal point and
preserve place value.
So, 4 500 732.0194 = 4 500 000 to 2 sig. fig.

**Notation:**
Often significant figure
is shortened to sig. fig.

**2** Write 0.000364907 to 1 significant figure.

The figure after the first significant figure 3 is 6.
This is 5 or more, so, round up, 3 becomes 4.
So, 0.000364907 = 0.0004 to 1 sig. fig.

Notice that the noughts before the 4 locate the decimal point and preserve place value.

## Choosing a suitable degree of accuracy

In some calculations it would be wrong to use the complete answer from the calculator.
The result of a calculation involving measurement should not be given to a greater degree of accuracy
than the measurements used in the calculation.

**EXAMPLE**

What is the area of a rectangle measuring 4.6 cm by 7.2 cm?

**Note:**
To find the area of a rectangle:
multiply length by breadth.

$4.6 \times 7.2 = 33.12$
Since the measurements used in the calculation (4.6 cm and 7.2 cm) are given to 2 significant figures
the answer should be as well.
$33 \text{ cm}^2$ is a more suitable answer.

## Exercise **3.4**

**1** Write these numbers correct to one significant figure.
    (a) 17      (b) 523      (c) 350      (d) 1900      (e) 24.6
    (f) 0.083   (g) 0.086   (h) 0.00948   (i) 0.0095

**2** Copy and complete this table.

| Number | 456 000 | 454 000 | 7 981 234 | 7 981 234 | 1290 | 19 602 |
|---|---|---|---|---|---|---|
| sig. fig. | 2 | 2 | 3 | 2 | 2 | 1 |
| Answer | 460 000 | | | | | |

**3** Copy and complete this table.

| Number | 0.000567 | 0.093748 | 0.093748 | 0.093748 | 0.010245 | 0.02994 |
|---|---|---|---|---|---|---|
| sig. fig. | 2 | 2 | 3 | 4 | 2 | 2 |
| Answer | | | | | | |

**4** This display shows the result of 3400 ÷ 7.
What is the result correct to two significant figures?

485.7142857

**5** Carry out these calculations giving the answers correct to
  (a)   1 sig. fig.        (b)   2 sig. fig.        (c)   3 sig. fig.

   (i)   672 × 123          (ii)   6.72 × 12.3          (iii)   78.2 × 12.8
   (iv)  7.19 ÷ 987.5       (v)   124 ÷ 65300

**6** A rectangular field measures 18.6 m by 25.4 m.
   Calculate the area of the field, giving your answer to a suitable degree of accuracy.

**7** In each of these short problems decide upon the most suitable accuracy for the answer.
   Then work out the answer, remembering to state the units.
   Give a reason for your degree of accuracy.
   (a)   The area of a rectangle measuring 13.2 cm by 11.9 cm.
   (b)   The area of a football pitch measuring 99 m by 62 m.
   (c)   The total length of 13 tables placed end to end measures 16 m.
         How long is each table?
   (d)   The area of carpet needed to cover a rectangular floor measuring 3.65 m by 4.35 m.

## Estimation

It is always a good idea to find an **estimate** for any calculation.
An estimate is used to check that the answer to the actual calculation is of the right magnitude (size).
If the answer is very different to the estimate then a mistake has possibly been made.

Estimation is done by approximating every number in the calculation to one significant figure.
The calculation is then done using the approximated values.

### EXAMPLES

**1** Estimate   421 × 48.

  Round 421 to one significant figure: 400
  Round 48 to one significant figure: 50
  400 × 50 = 20 000

*Use long multiplication to calculate 421 × 48.*
*Comment on your answer.*

**2** Use estimation to show that   $\frac{78.5 \times 0.51}{18.7}$   is close to 2.

  Approximating:        78.5 = 80  to 1 sig. fig.
                        0.51 = 0.5 to 1 sig. fig.
                        18.7 = 20  to 1 sig. fig.

  $\frac{80 \times 0.5}{20} = \frac{40}{20} = 2$ (estimate)

**Remember:**
When you are asked to estimate, write each number in the calculation to one significant figure.

  Using a calculator   $\frac{78.5 \times 0.51}{18.7} = \frac{40.035}{18.7} = 2.140909...$

  Is 2.140909 reasonably close to 2?   Yes.

## Exercise 3.5

**1** John estimated   43 × 47   to be about 2000. Explain how he did it.

**2** Make estimates to these calculations by using approximations to one significant figure.
   (a)   (i)   39 × 21          (ii)   115 × 18          (iii)   797 × 53          (iv)   913 × 59
   (b)   (i)   76 ÷ 18          (ii)   597 ÷ 29          (iii)   889 ÷ 61          (iv)   3897 ÷ 82

**3** Lilly ordered 39 prints of her holiday photographs. Each print cost 52 pence.
   Use suitable approximations to **estimate** the total cost of the prints. Show your working.

**4**  (a)  When estimating the answer to  $29 \times 48$  the approximations 30 and 50 are used.
How can you tell that the estimation must be bigger than the actual answer?

(b)  When estimating the answer to  $182 \div 13$  the approximations 200 and 10 are used.
Will the estimate be bigger or smaller than the actual answer? Explain your answer.

**5**  Bernard plans to buy a conservatory costing £8328 and furniture costing £984.

(a)  By using approximations, estimate the total amount Bernard plans to spend.

(b)  Find the actual cost.

**6**  Kath uses her calculator to work out the value of  $396 \times 0.470$.
The answer she gets is 18.612.
Use approximations to show that her answer is wrong.

**7**  (a)  Calculate  $\dfrac{49.7 + 10.6}{9.69 \times 3.04}$

(b)  Do not use your calculator in this part of the question.
By using approximations show that your answer to (a) is about right.

**8**  Find estimates to these calculations by using approximations to 1 significant figure.
Then carry out the calculations with the original figures.
Compare your estimate to the actual answer.

(a)  $\dfrac{7.9 \times 3.9}{4.8}$   (b)  $\dfrac{400 \times 0.29}{6.2}$   (c)  $\dfrac{81.7 \times 4.9}{1.9 \times 10.3}$   (d)  $\dfrac{4.12 \times 49.7}{0.096}$

**9**  (a)  Calculate  $\dfrac{78.9}{0.037 \times 5.2}$

(b)  Show how you can use approximations to check your answer is about right.

**10**  Niamh calculates  $5\,967\,000 \div 0.029$.  She gets an answer of  $2\,057\,586\,207$.
Use approximations to check whether Niamh's answer is of the right magnitude.

## Accuracy in measurement

No measurement is ever exact.
Measures which can lie within a range of possible values are called **continuous measures**.
The value of a continuous measure depends on the accuracy of whatever is making the measurement.

Jane is 160 cm tall to the nearest 10 cm.
What are the limits between which her actual height lies?

Height is a continuous measure.
When rounding to the nearest 10 cm:
The minimum value that rounds to 160 cm is 155 cm.
155 cm is the minimum height that Jane can be.

The maximum value that rounds to 160 cm is $164.\dot{9}$ cm.
$164.\dot{9}$ cm is the maximum height that Jane can be.
For ease the value $164.\dot{9}$ cm is normally called 165 cm.

So, Jane's actual height is any height from 155 cm to 165 cm.
This can be written as the inequality:
155 cm $\leqslant$ Jane's height $<$ 165 cm

155 cm is the **lower bound** of Jane's height.
165 cm is the **upper bound** of Jane's height.

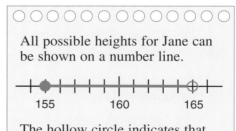

All possible heights for Jane can be shown on a number line.

The hollow circle indicates that 165 is **not** included

If a **continuous measure**, $c$, is recorded to the nearest $x$, then:

**Lower bound** $= c - \frac{1}{2}x$     **Upper bound** $= c + \frac{1}{2}x$

The **limits** of the possible values of $c$
can be written as  $c \pm \frac{1}{2}x$

**EXAMPLES**

① The length of a pencil is 17 cm to the nearest centimetre.
What are the limits between which the actual length of the pencil lies?

When rounding to the nearest centimetre:   The smallest value that rounds to 17 cm is 16.5 cm.
                                          The largest value that rounds to 17 cm is 17.4$\dot{9}$ cm.
So, the actual length of the pencil lies between 16.5 cm and 17.5 cm.
                        16.5 cm ≤ length of pencil < 17.5 cm

② A concrete block weighs 1.8 kg, correct to the nearest tenth of a kilogram.
What is the minimum possible weight of the concrete block?
                Minimum weight = 1.8 kg − 0.05 kg = 1.75 kg

③ The length of this page is 26 cm to the nearest centimetre.
What are the upper and lower bounds of the true length of this page?
                Upper bound = 26 + 0.5 = 26.5 cm      Lower bound = 26 − 0.5 = 25.5 cm

## Exercise **3.6**

① A girl's height is 168 cm, correct to the nearest centimetre.
What is the minimum possible height of the girl?

② The height of a building is 9 m, correct to the nearest metre.
Copy and complete the inequality:   …… ≤ height of building < ……

③ A brick weighs 840 g, correct to the nearest 10 g.
What is the minimum and maximum possible weight of the brick?

④ An athlete completed a race in 11.6 seconds, correct to the nearest tenth of a second.
What is the minimum possible time the athlete could have taken?

⑤ A pane of glass weighs 9.4 kg, correct to one decimal place.
What is the minimum possible weight of the pane of glass?

⑥ The length of a table is 2.7 m, correct to the nearest tenth of a metre.
Write down the least and greatest possible length of the table.

⑦ A glass contains 24 ml of milk, correct to the nearest millilitre.
Find the minimum possible number of millilitres in four glasses.

⑧ Loaves of bread each weigh 0.8 kg, correct to the nearest 100 g.
Write down the minimum and maximum possible weight of ten loaves of bread.

⑨ At birth a baby is 39 cm in length, correct to the nearest centimetre,
and has a mass of 3.4 kg, correct to one decimal place.
(a)   What is the lower bound of the baby's length?
(b)   What is the upper bound of the baby's mass?

⑩ A tea bag weighs 3.2 g, correct to the nearest tenth of a gram.
What is the lower bound of the weight of 60 tea bags?

⑪ Duncan drives to work and back 5 days a week.
The journey to work is 8.6 km, correct to one decimal place.
What is the lower bound of the distance Duncan drives to and from work each week?

⑫ A book weighs 0.53 kg, correct to 2 decimal places.
(a)   What are the limits between which the true weight of the book lies?
(b)   What is the upper bound of the weight of 10 copies of the book?

## Calculations involving bounds

| Calculation involving … | For upper bound calculate … | For lower bound calculate … |
| --- | --- | --- |
| Adding measures | Upper bound + Upper bound | Lower bound + Lower bound |
| Multiplying measures | Upper bound × Upper bound | Lower bound × Lower bound |
| Subtracting measures | Upper bound − Lower bound | Lower bound − Upper bound |
| Dividing measures | Upper bound ÷ Lower bound | Lower bound ÷ Upper bound |

### EXAMPLE

Two strips of wood have lengths of 124 cm and 159 cm, to the nearest centimetre.
(a)  What is the lower bound of the total length of the strips of wood?
(b)  What is the upper bound of the difference between the lengths of the strips of wood?

Shorter strip
Lower bound = 124 cm − 0.5 cm = 123.5 cm
Upper bound = 124 cm + 0.5 cm = 124.5 cm

Longer strip
Lower bound = 159 cm − 0.5 cm = 158.5 cm
Upper bound = 159 cm + 0.5 cm = 159.5 cm

(a)  To find the lower bound of the total length use the lower bounds of both strip lengths.
Lower bound of the total length = 123.5 + 158.5 = 282 cm.

(b)  The upper bound of the difference in lengths is found from:
Upper bound of the longer strip − lower bound of the shorter strip = 159.5 − 123.5 = 36 cm

### Exercise 3.7

**1**  Fiona measures a corridor as being 126 paces in length.
The length of her pace is 90 cm, to the nearest 10 cm.
What is the difference between the maximum and minimum possible lengths of the corridor?

**2**  The distance between $A$ and $B$ is 12.2 km to the nearest 100 m.
The distance between $B$ and $C$ is 14.34 km to the nearest 10 m.
Trevor walks from $A$ to $B$ and then from $B$ to $C$.
Calculate the upper and lower bounds of the total distance that Trevor walks.

**3**  A bag of potatoes weighs 5.0 kg to the nearest 100 g.
(a)  Find the upper bound of the weight of 100 bags of potatoes.

1.5 kg of potatoes to the nearest 100 g are taken from a bag.
(b)  What is the lower bound of the weight of potatoes left in the bag?

**4**  Books are packed into boxes for delivery.
The total weight of a box should **not exceed** 30 kg.
A book weighs 2.7 kg, to the nearest 0.1 kg.
What is the maximum number of books that can be packed in a box?

**5**  Petra buys 24 litres of petrol at 89 pence per litre.
The amount of petrol and the price of petrol are both given correct to 2 significant figures.
Find the difference between the minimum and maximum amount that Petra could have spent on petrol.

**6**  $m = 7.4$,  correct to two significant figures.
$n = 3.68$, correct to three significant figures.
(a)  (i)   What is the upper bound of $m$?     (ii)  What is the lower bound of $n$?
(b)  Calculate the lower and upper bounds of  $m - n$.
(c)  Calculate the least possible value of $mn$.
(d)  Calculate the greatest possible value of  $\frac{m}{n}$.

- A number can be rounded to an **approximate** number.
- How to approximate using **decimal places**.
    1. Write the number using one more decimal place than asked for.
    2. Look at the last decimal place and
        - if the figure is 5 or more round up,    • if the figure is less than 5 round down.
- How to approximate using **significant figures**.
    1. Start from the most significant figure and count the required number of figures.
    2. Look at the next figure to the right of this and
        - if the figure is 5 or more round up,    • if the figure is less than 5 round down.
    3. Add noughts, as necessary, to locate the decimal point and preserve the place value.
- When answering a problem, include any units and state the degree of approximation used.
- You should be able to choose a suitable degree of accuracy.
- Be able to use approximations to estimate that the actual answer to a calculation is of the right magnitude.
- Be able to recognise limitations on the accuracy of data and measurements.

    A **discrete measure** can only take a particular value and a **continuous measure** lies within a range of possible values which depends upon the degree of accuracy of the measurement.

> If a **continuous measure**, $c$, is recorded to the nearest $x$, then:
> **Lower bound** $= c - \frac{1}{2}x$     **Upper bound** $= c + \frac{1}{2}x$

## Review Exercise 3

Do not use a calculator for questions 1 to 16.

**1**       "2 million listen to the Cup Final on the radio."
The number is given to the nearest million. What is the smallest possible number of listeners?

**2**  Write 102.349:    (a)   correct to one decimal place,      (b)   correct to two decimal places.    OCR

**3**  The display shows the result of   $179 \div 7$.
What is the result correct to one significant figure?

$$\boxed{25.57142857}$$

**4**  Find **estimates** to these calculations by using approximations to one significant figure.
(a)   $86.5 \times 1.9$          (b)   $2016 \div 49.8$

**5**  (a)   Work out   $75.6 \div 27$.
(b)   What approximate calculation could you do to check the answer to part (a)?    OCR

**6**  Aimee uses her calculator to multiply   18.7 by 0.96.   Her answer is 19.752.
Without finding the exact value of   $18.7 \times 0.96$,   explain why her answer must be wrong.

**7**  A theatre has 792 seats. A pantomime is going to be performed 29 times.
All the tickets are sold. Each ticket costs £10.
(a)   Do an approximate calculation to estimate how much money has been taken.
(b)   Is your estimate more or less than the actual amount of money taken?
Explain your answer.    OCR

**8**  Pat needs 136 crackers for a Christmas party. The crackers are only sold in packs of 12.
How many packs must Pat buy?

**9**  The number of people at a beach party is 90, to the nearest 10.
What is the smallest and largest possible number of people at the party?

**10**  The number of visitors to a local museum was reported as 2600, to the nearest hundred.
(a)   What is the smallest possible number of visitors?
(b)   What is the largest possible number of visitors?

**11** A party of 42 people went on a theatre trip to London.
The total cost of the trip, including transport, was £2017.
**Estimate** the cost per person.

OCR

**12** **Estimate** the answer to this calculation. $\dfrac{39.8 \times 4.9}{20.3}$
You must show all the approximations you use.

OCR

**13** (a) Round 8640 to one significant figure.
(b) A school buys 62 textbooks costing £10.25 each.
    (i) Write down a calculation you could do in your head to **estimate** the total cost of the textbooks.
    (ii) Is your estimate of the total cost bigger or smaller than the actual cost?
        Explain how you know.

OCR

**14** Jo has to calculate $\dfrac{481 + 97}{32}$. She calculates the answer to be 180.625.

By rounding each number to one significant figure estimate whether her answer is of the right order of magnitude. Show your working.

**15** What is the smallest possible length of a piece of string which measures 25 cm to the nearest centimetre?

**16** A bus is 18 m in length, correct to the nearest metre.
(a) What is the minimum possible length of the bus?
(b) Copy and complete this inequality: …… ⩽ length of bus < ……

**17** (a) Estimate the value of $S = \dfrac{738 \times 19}{593 + 392}$. Do not use your calculator.

    Show all your approximations and working.
(b) Now use your calculator to work out the value of S.
    (i) Write down all the figures in your calculator display.
    (ii) Write your answer correct to 3 significant figures.

OCR

**18** A book on dieting states that one pancake contains 155 Calories, correct to the nearest Calorie.
Write down the greatest and least number of Calories that one pancake could contain.

OCR

**19** The floor of a lounge is a rectangle which measures 5.23 m by 3.62 m.
The floor is to be carpeted.
(a) Calculate the area of carpet needed.
    Give your answer to an appropriate degree of accuracy.
(b) Explain why you chose this degree of accuracy.

**20** A lorry weighs 1800 kg, correct to the nearest 100 kg.
What are the lower and upper bounds of the weight of the lorry?

**21**

| **p = 600, correct to the nearest 100** | **q = 50, correct to the nearest 10** |
|---|---|

(a) (i) What is the lower bound of p?      (ii) What is the upper bound of q?
(b) Calculate (i) the upper bound of p + q,      (ii) the lower bound of pq.
(c) Calculate the least possible value of $\dfrac{p}{q}$.

**22** Graham has a plank of wood of length 610 cm, correct to the nearest 10 cm.
He uses a cutting machine to cut the plank into pieces, without any wastage.
Each piece of wood is of length 15 cm, correct to the nearest half centimetre.
Find the maximum number of pieces of wood that Graham can be certain of getting.

OCR

**23** Pond A has a surface area of 150 m², to an accuracy of 2 significant figures.
Pond B has a surface area of 90 m², to an accuracy of 2 significant figures.
What is the lower bound of the difference between the surface areas of Ponds A and B?

# Percentages and Money

## The meaning of a percentage

'Per cent' means 'out of 100'.
The symbol for per cent is %.
A percentage can be written as a fraction with denominator 100.

> 10% means 10 out of 100.
> 10% can be written as $\frac{10}{100}$.
> 10% is read as '10 per cent'.

## Changing percentages to decimals and fractions

> To change a percentage to a decimal or a fraction: **divide by 100**

### EXAMPLES

**1** Write 38% as a fraction in its simplest form.

38% means '38 out of 100'.

This can be written as $\frac{38}{100}$.

$\frac{38}{100} = \frac{38 \div 2}{100 \div 2} = \frac{19}{50}$

$38\% = \frac{19}{50}$

> **Remember:**
> To write a fraction in its **simplest form** divide both the numerator and denominator of the fraction by the **largest** number that divides into them both.
>
> **To change a fraction to a decimal:**
> divide the numerator by the denominator.

**2** Write 42.5% as a decimal.

$42.5\% = \frac{42.5}{100} = 42.5 \div 100 = 0.425$

## Changing decimals and fractions to percentages

> To change a decimal or a fraction to a percentage: **multiply by 100**

### EXAMPLES

**1** Change 0.3 to a percentage.

$0.3 \times 100 = 30$
So, 0.3 as a percentage is 30%.

**2** Change $\frac{11}{25}$ to a percentage.

$\frac{11}{25} \times 100 = 11 \times 100 \div 25$
$\qquad\qquad = 1100 \div 25 = 44\%$

**3** Ben scored 17 out of 20 in a Maths test and 21 out of 25 in a History test.
Which is Ben's better mark?

Change each mark to a percentage.

Maths: $\frac{17}{20}$  $\quad \frac{17}{20} \times 100 = 17 \times 100 \div 20 = 85\%$

History: $\frac{21}{25}$  $\quad \frac{21}{25} \times 100 = 21 \times 100 \div 25 = 84\%$

So, Ben's better mark was his Maths mark of 85%.

> Fractions can be compared by first writing them as percentages.

## Expressing one quantity as a percentage of another

This involves writing a fraction and then changing it to a percentage.
The units of any quantities in the numerator and denominator of the fraction must be the same.

### EXAMPLES

**1** Express 30p as a percentage of £2.

$$\frac{30p}{£2} = \frac{30p}{200p} = \frac{30}{200}$$

$$\frac{30}{200} = \frac{30 \div 2}{200 \div 2} = \frac{15}{100} = 15\%$$

This means that 30p is 15% of £2.

**2** A newspaper contains 48 pages, 6 of which are Sports pages.
What percentage of the pages are Sports pages?

6 out of 48 pages are Sports pages.

$$\frac{6}{48} = 6 \div 48 = 0.125$$

$$0.125 \times 100 = 12.5$$

12.5% of the pages are Sports pages.

### Exercise 4.1

Do not use a calculator for questions 1 to 12.

**1** Change these percentages to fractions in their simplest form.
(a) 10%    (b) 25%    (c) 5%    (d) 35%    (e) 48%    (f) 12.5%

**2** Change these percentages to decimals.
(a) 20%    (b) 15%    (c) 1%    (d) 72%    (e) 87.5%    (f) 150%

**3** Change these fractions to percentages.
(a) $\frac{17}{50}$    (b) $\frac{12}{25}$    (c) $\frac{30}{200}$    (d) $\frac{4}{5}$    (e) $\frac{135}{500}$    (f) $\frac{13}{20}$    (g) $\frac{2}{3}$    (h) $\frac{2}{9}$

**4** Change these decimals to percentages.
(a) 0.15    (b) 0.32    (c) 0.125    (d) 0.07    (e) 1.12    (f) 0.015

**5** Write in order of size, lowest first:
(a) $\frac{1}{2}$   60%   $\frac{2}{5}$   0.55     (b) 43%   $\frac{9}{20}$   0.42   $\frac{11}{25}$     (c) $\frac{23}{80}$   28%   $\frac{57}{200}$   0.2805

**6** What is (a) 30 as a percentage of 50, (b) 42 as a percentage of 200?

**7** James saved £30 and then spent £9. What percentage of his savings did he spend?

**8** A Youth Club has 200 members. 80 of the members are boys.
(a) What percentage of the members are boys?
(b) What percentage of the members are girls?

**9** 240 people took part in a survey. 30 of them were younger than 18.
What percentage were younger than 18?

**10** A bar of chocolate has 32 squares. Jane eats 12 of the squares.
What percentage of the bar does she eat?

**11** Billy earns £9 per hour. He gets a wage rise of 27 pence per hour.
What is his percentage wage rise?

**12** Rohima achieved the following results.

| Geography: 32 out of 40 | English: 21 out of 25 | Maths: 17 out of 20 |
|---|---|---|

In which subject did she do best?

**13** In an ice hockey competition Team A won 8 out of the 11 games they played whilst Team B won 5 of their 7 games.

Which team has the better record in the competition?

**(14)** What is   (a)   6 minutes as a percentage of 1 hour,
               (b)   30 mm as a percentage of 5 cm,
               (c)   150 g as a percentage of 1 kg?

**(15)** A new car costs £13 500. The dealer gives a discount of £1282.50.
What is the percentage discount?

**(16)** There are 600 pupils in Years 9 to 13 of a High school.
360 pupils are in Years 10 and 11. 15% of pupils are in Years 12 and 13.
What percentage of pupils are in Year 9?

## Finding a percentage of a quantity

### EXAMPLE

Find 20% of £56.

Step 1     Divide by 100.
               £56 ÷ 100 = £0.56
Step 2     Multiply by 20.
               £0.56 × 20 = £11.20

So, 20% of £56 is £11.20.

> To find 1% of a quantity divide the quantity by 100.
> To find 20% of a quantity multiply 1% of the quantity by 20.
> This is the same as the method you would use to find
> $\frac{20}{100}$ of a quantity.

## Percentage change

### EXAMPLES

**1** A shirt normally priced at £24 is reduced by 15% in a sale.
How much does it cost in the sale?

Reduction in price = 15% of £24
$15 \div 100 \times 24 = 0.15 \times 24 = 3.6$
15% of £24 = £3.60
The shirt costs £24 − £3.60 = £20.40.

**2** A packet of cereals weighs 440 g.
A special offer packet weighs 30% more.
What is the weight of the special offer packet?

Extra contents = 30% of 440 g
                 = 440 ÷ 100 × 30
                 = 132 g
$440 + 132 = 572$

The special offer packet weighs 572 g.

## Exercise 4.2      Do not use a calculator for questions 1 to 10.

**1** Find
  (a)   20% of £80       (b)   75% of £20       (c)   30% of £220       (d)   15% of £350
  (e)   5% of £500       (f)   9% of 300 kg      (g)   45% of £25       (h)   60% of 20 m

**2** There are 450 seats in a theatre. 60% of the seats are in the stalls.
How many seats are in the stalls?

**3** Tony invests £400 in a building society. He earns 5% interest per year.
How much interest does he get in one year?

**4** Jenny gets a 15% discount on a theatre ticket. The normal cost is £18.
How much does she save?

**5** A salesman earns a bonus of 3% of his weekly sales.
How much bonus does the salesman earn in a week when his sales are £1400.

**6** Increase:
(a)  £50 by 60%          (b)  £10 by 30%          (c)  £15 by 10%          (d)  £50 by 15%

**7** Decrease:
(a)  £600 by 15%         (b)  £55 by 90%          (c)  £42 by 20%          (d)  £63 by 35%

**8** A mobile telephone company offers a 20% discount on calls made in March.
The normal cost of a peak time call is 50 pence per minute.
How much does a peak time call cost in March?

**9** Abdul earns £200 per week. He gets a wage rise of 7.5%. What is his new weekly wage?

**10** A packet of breakfast cereal contains 660 g. A special offer packet contains an extra 15%.
How many grams of breakfast cereal are in the special offer packet?

**Questions 11 to 16.**   Where appropriate give your answers to 3 significant figures.

**11** The price of a gold watch is £278. What does it cost with a 12% discount?

**12** The price of a used car is £5200. What does it cost with a 9.5% discount?

**13** Milk costs 35 pence a pint. How much does it cost after a 14% increase?

**14** Petrol costs 89.9 pence a litre. What does it cost after a 2.4% decrease?

**15** A car was valued at £13 500 when new. After one year it lost 22% of its value.
What was the value of the car after one year?

**16** In 2001 house prices increased by 19.6%. In 2002 house prices increased by 17.4%.
A house was valued at £78 000 at the beginning of 2001.
What was the value of the house at the end of 2002?

## Percentage increase and decrease

Sadik and Chandni took Maths tests in October and June.

My mark went up from 54% to 72%.

My mark went up from 42% to 60%.

Who has made the most improvement?

They have both improved by a score of 18% so by one measure they have both improved equally.
Another way of comparing their improvement is to use the idea of a percentage increase.

$$\text{Percentage increase} = \frac{\text{actual increase}}{\text{initial value}} \times 100\%$$

Comparing percentage increases is the best way to decide
whether Sadik or Chandni has made the most improvement.
*Explain why.*

**Remember:**
To calculate
% increase or % decrease
always use the initial value.

**For Sadik**
% increase = $\frac{18}{54} \times 100\% = 33.3\%$

**For Chandni**
% increase = $\frac{18}{42} \times 100\% = 42.9\%$

Both calculations are correct to one decimal place.

A percentage decrease can be calculated in a similar way.

$$\text{Percentage decrease} = \frac{\text{actual decrease}}{\text{initial value}} \times 100\%$$

## EXAMPLES

**1** A shop buys pens for 15 pence and sells them for 21 pence.
What is their percentage profit?

Actual profit = 21 pence − 15 pence
$\qquad$ = 6 pence

% profit = $\dfrac{\text{actual profit}}{\text{initial value}} \times 100$

$\qquad$ = $\dfrac{6}{15} \times 100 = 40\%$

**2** Pam buys a micro-scooter for £24.
She sells the micro-scooter for £15.
What is her percentage loss?

Actual loss = £24 − £15
$\qquad$ = £9

% loss = $\dfrac{\text{actual loss}}{\text{initial value}} \times 100$

$\qquad$ = $\dfrac{9}{24} \times 100 = 37.5\%$

## Exercise 4.3
Do questions 1 to 5 without a calculator.

**1** A shop buys calculators for £5 and sells them for £6. Find the percentage profit.

**2** Geri's wages of £7.50 per hour are increased to £9.00 per hour.
Find the percentage increase in her earnings.

**3** A man buys a boat for £25 000 and sells it for £18 000. Find his percentage loss.

**4** In October, Hinn scored 50% in an English test. In January he improved to 66%.
In the same tests, Becky scored 40% and 56%.
Who has made the most improvement? Explain your answer.

**5** The rent on Karen's flat increased from £80 to £90 per week.
(a) Find the percentage increase in her rent.

At the same time Karen's wages increased from £250 per week to £280 per week.
(b) Find the percentage increase in her wages.
Comment on your answers.

**6** The value of car A when new was £13 000. The value of car B when new was £16 500.
After one year the value of car A is £11 200 and the value of car B is £13 500.
Calculate the percentage loss in the values of cars A and B after one year.

**7** During 2004 the population of a village decreased from 323 to 260.
Find the percentage decrease in the population.

**8** At the start of May a flower was 12.3 cm high. In May it grew by 14.5%.
At the start of July it was 16.7 cm high.
What was its percentage growth during June?

**9** A rectangle has length 12 cm and width 8 cm.
The length is increased by 7.5% and the width decreased by 12.5%.
Find the change in area as a percentage of the original area of the rectangle.

**10** In 2003 Miles bought £2000 worth of shares.
In 2004 the value of his shares decreased by 10%.
In 2005 the value of his shares increased by 20%.
By what percentage has the value of his shares changed from 2003 to 2005?

**11** The price of a micro-scooter is reduced by 10%.
In a sale, the new price is reduced by a further 10%.
By what percentage has the original price of the micro-scooter been reduced in the sale?

**12** The price of telephone calls is increased by 15%.
Companies are given a 10% discount off the new price.
What is the percentage increase in the price of calls for companies?

## Reverse percentage problems

**1**  A shop sells videos with a 20% discount.
Petra buys a video and pays £10.
How much does the video normally cost?

Discount price is normal price less 20%.
So, 80% of normal price = £10.
So, 1% of normal price = £10 ÷ 80
$\qquad\qquad\qquad\qquad = £0.125$
So, normal price = £0.125 × 100
$\qquad\qquad\qquad = £12.50$

**2**  Tara gets a 5% wage rise.
Her new wage is £126 per week.
What was Tara's wage before her wage rise?

New wage = old wage + 5%
So, 105% of old wage = £126
1% of old wage is 126 ÷ 105 = £1.20
Old wage = 1.2 × 100 = £120

### Exercise 4.4

Do questions 1 to 4 without a calculator.

**1**  A special bottle of pop contains 10% more than a normal bottle.
The special bottle contains 660 ml.
How much does the normal bottle contain?

**2**  Jim saves 15% of his monthly salary. Each month he saves £90.
What is his monthly salary?

**3**  May gets a 20% wage rise. Her new wage is £264 per week.
What was May's wage before her wage rise?

**4**  In a high jump event, Nick jumps 1.8 metres.
This is 5% lower than the best height he can jump.
What is the best height he can jump?

**5**  A house is valued at £350 000.
This is a 12% increase on the value of the house a year ago.
What was the value of the house a year ago?

**6**  30 grams of a breakfast cereal provides 16.2 mg of vitamin C.
This is 24% of the recommended daily intake.
What daily intake of vitamin C is recommended?

**7**  Tom gets a 3% increase in his salary. His new salary is £1462.60 per month.
What was Tom's salary before his wage rise?

**8**  A one year old car is worth £6720. This is a decrease of 16% of its value from new.
What was the price of the new car?

**9**  Here is some data about the changes in the number of pupils in schools A and B.
School A's numbers increased by 4% to 442.
School B's numbers decreased by 6% to 423.
How many pupils were in schools A and B before the change in numbers?

**10**  John sells his computer to Dan and makes a 15% profit.
Dan then sells the computer to Ron for £391. Dan makes a 15% loss.
How much did John pay for the computer?
Explain why it is not £391.

**11**  Kim sells her bike to Sara.
Sara sells it to Tina for £121.50. Both Kim and Sara make a 10% loss.
How much did Kim pay for the bike?
Explain why it is not 20% more than £121.50.

## Wages

### Hourly pay

Many people are paid by the hour for their work. In most cases they receive a **basic hourly rate** for a fixed number of hours and an **overtime rate** for any extra hours worked.

---

#### EXAMPLE

A car-park attendant is paid £6.20 per hour for a basic 40-hour week.
Overtime is paid at time and a half.
One week an attendant works 48 hours.
How much does he earn?

| Basic Pay: | £6.20 × 40 | = £248.00 |
|---|---|---|
| Overtime: | 1.5 × £6.20 × 8 | = £74.40 |
| | Total pay | = £322.40 |

Overtime paid at 'time and a half' means 1.5 × normal hourly rate. In this example, the hourly overtime rate is given by:
1.5 × £6.20

Common overtime rates are 'time and a quarter', 'double time', etc.

---

## Income tax

The amount you earn for your work is called your **gross pay**.
Your employer will make deductions from your gross pay for income tax, National Insurance, etc.
Pay after all deductions have been made is called **net pay**.

The rates of tax and the bands (ranges of income) to which they apply vary.

The amount of **income tax** you pay will depend on how much you earn.
Everyone is allowed to earn some money which is not taxed, this is called a **tax allowance**.
Any remaining money is your **taxable income**.

---

#### EXAMPLE

George earns £6310 per year.
His tax allowance is £4895 per year and he pays tax at 10p in the £ on his taxable income.
How much income tax does George pay per year?

| Taxable income: | £6310 − £4895 = £1415 |
|---|---|
| Income tax: | £1415 × 0.10 = £141.50 |

George pays income tax of £141.50 per year.

An income tax rate of 10% is often expressed as '10p in the pound (£)'.

---

## Exercise 4.5

**1** A secretary earns £352.80 a week.
She is paid £9.80 per hour.
How many hours a week does she work?

**2** A chef is paid £12.40 per hour for a basic 38-hour week. Overtime is paid at time and a half.
How much does the chef earn in a week in which she works 50 hours?

**3** A hairdresser is paid £8.20 per hour for a basic 35-hour week.
One week she works two hours overtime at time and a half and $3\frac{1}{2}$ hours overtime at time and a quarter. How much is she paid that week?

**4** A driver is paid £68.85 for $4\frac{1}{2}$ hours of overtime. Overtime is paid at time and a half.
What is his basic hourly rate of pay?

**5** Lyn earns £6080 per year.
Her tax allowance is £4895 per year and she pays tax at 10p in the £ on her taxable income.
(a) What is her annual taxable income?
(b) How much income tax does she pay per year?

**6** Kay has an annual salary of £23 980.
Her tax allowance is £4895 per year.
She pays tax at 10p in the £ on the first £2090 of her taxable income and 22p in the £ on the remainder.
How much income tax does she pay per year?

**7** Les has an annual salary of £29 600. His tax allowance is £4895 per year.
He pays tax at 10p in the £ on the first £2090 of his taxable income and 22p in the £ on the remainder.
He is paid monthly. How much income tax does he pay per month?

**8** Alf's income is £25 800 per year.
He pays 9% of his gross income into a pension scheme on which he does not pay tax.
Alf also has a tax allowance of £4895 per year.
He pays tax at 10p in the £ on the first £2090 of his taxable income and 22p in the £ on the remainder.
Calculate how much income tax he pays per year.

**9** Reg has an annual salary of £49 880. His tax allowance is £4895 per year.
He pays tax at 10p in the £ on the first £2090 of his taxable income, 22p in the £ on the next £30 310 and 40p in the £ on the remainder.
Calculate how much income tax he pays per year.

**10** Alex has an annual salary of £41 240. Her tax allowance is £4895 per year.
She pays tax at 10p in the £ on the first £2090 of her taxable income, 22p in the £ on the next £30 310 and 40p in the £ on the remainder. She is paid monthly.
How much income tax does she pay per month?

## Spending

Spending money is part of daily life.
Every day people have to deal with many different situations involving money.
Money is needed to buy fares for journeys, for purchases at shops, for hiring cars and equipment and for buying large items such as furniture.

When a large sum of money is needed to make a purchase, **credit** may be arranged.
This involves paying for the goods over a period of time by agreeing to make a number of weekly or monthly repayments.
It may also involve paying a **deposit**. The cost of credit may be more than paying cash.

### EXAMPLE

A motor home costs £19 950.
It can be bought on credit by paying a deposit of £7000 and 36 monthly payments of £395.
How much more is paid for the motor home when it is bought on credit?

| | |
|---|---|
| Deposit: | £ 7 000 |
| Payments: £395 × 36 = | £14 220 |
| Credit Price: | £21 220 |

Difference: £21 220 − £19 950 = £1270
Credit price is £1270 more.

38

## Best buys

When shopping we often have to make choices between products which are packed in various sizes and priced differently. If we want to buy the one which gives the better value for money we must compare prices using the same units.

### EXAMPLE

Peanut butter is available in small or large jars, as shown.
Which size is the better value for money?

Compare the number of grams per penny for each size.
Small: $250 \div 58 = 4.31\ldots$ grams per penny.
Large: $454 \div 106 = 4.28\ldots$ grams per penny.

The small size gives more grams per penny and is better value.

## Household bills

The cost of living includes many bills for services provided to our homes. Electricity, gas and telephone charges are all examples of **quarterly bills** which are sent out four times a year.
Some bills are made up of two parts:
    A fixed (standing) charge, for providing the service.
    A charge for the quantity of the service used (amount of electricity, duration of telephone calls, etc.)

Other household bills include taxes payable to the local council, water charges and the cost of the insurance of the house (structure) and its contents.

## Exercise 4.6

1. Mr Jones pays £4.14 for 400 g of Brie and 250 g of Stilton. Stilton costs £7.60 per kilogram. How much per kilogram is Brie?

2. A washing machine costs £475. It can be bought on credit by paying a deposit of 10% of the cash price and 24 monthly payments of £19.50.
How much more is paid for the washing machine when it is bought on credit?

3. Jars of pickled onions are sold at the following prices: 460 g at 65p or 700 g at 98p. Which size is better value for money?

4. Mrs Dear checks her water bill. She has used 58 cubic metres of water at 97.04 pence per cubic metre and there is a standing charge of £11. How much is her bill?

5. George insures his house valued at £284 000 and its contents valued at £27 500.
The annual premiums for the insurance are:

> **Buildings: £1.35 per £1000 of cover,**    **Contents: 56p per £100 of cover.**

Calculate the total cost of the insurance premium.

6. Mr Peters has an annual council tax of £1982.28. He pays the council tax in 10 instalments. The first instalment is £200.28 and the remaining amount is payable in 9 instalments of equal value. How much is the second instalment?

7. Mr Jones receives an electricity bill for £56.84.
The bill includes a quarterly charge of £10.40 and the cost per unit is 6.85 pence.
Calculate to the nearest whole number, the number of units he has used.

8. Sheila rents a flat and pays £69.44 to insure its contents.
Contents insurance costs 56p for each £100 insured.
For how much are the contents insured?

## VAT

Some goods and services are subject to a tax called **value added tax**, or **VAT**, which is calculated as a percentage of the price or bill. Total amount payable = cost of item or service + VAT

For most purchases the rate of VAT is 17.5%. For gas and electricity the rate of VAT is 5%. Some goods are exempt from VAT.

### EXAMPLES

**1** A bill at a restaurant is £24 + VAT at 17.5%. What is the total bill?

VAT: £24 × 0.175 = £4.20

Total bill: £24 + £4.20 = £28.20

The total bill is £28.20.

**Remember:** $17.5\% = \frac{17.5}{100} = 0.175$

**2** An electricity bill of £49.14 includes VAT at 5%. How much VAT is paid?

Cost = cost without VAT + 5% VAT.
£49.14 = 105% of cost without VAT.

1% of cost without VAT is given by £49.14 ÷ 105 = £0.468

VAT = 5% of cost without VAT, so, VAT = £0.468 × 5 = £2.34.

### Exercise 4.7

Do not use a calculator for questions 1 and 2.

**1** Naomi's gas bill is £120 plus VAT at 5%. How much VAT does she have to pay?

**2** Joe receives an electricity bill for £70 plus VAT at 5%.
   (a) Calculate the amount of VAT charged.
   (b) What is the total bill?

**3** A car service costs £90 plus VAT at 17.5%.
   (a) Calculate the amount of VAT charged.
   (b) What is the total cost of the service?

**4** A bike costs £248 plus VAT at 17.5%. What is the total cost of the bike?

**5** James receives a telephone bill for £66 plus VAT at 17.5%. How much is the total bill?

**6** A loft conversion costs £23 000 plus VAT at 17.5%. What is the total cost?

**7** George buys vertical blinds for his windows.
He needs three blinds at £65 each and two blinds at £85 each.
VAT at 17.5% is added to the cost of the blinds.
How much do the blinds cost altogether?

**8** A car is hired for two days and driven 90 miles.
VAT at 17.5% is added to the hire charges.
How much does it cost to hire the car altogether?

HIRE A CAR

**£35 per day plus 10 pence per mile**

**9** A computer costs £1233.75 including VAT at 17.5%.
How much of the cost is VAT?

**10** A gas bill of £67.20 includes VAT at 5%. How much VAT is paid?

**11** VAT at 17.5% on a washing machine is £43.75.
What is the price of the washing machine including VAT?

**12** The bill for a new central heating boiler includes £436.10 VAT. VAT is charged at 17.5%.
What is the total bill?

## Savings

Money invested in a savings account or a bank or building society earns **interest**, which is usually paid once a year.

### Simple Interest

With **Simple Interest**, the interest is paid out each year and not added to your account.

> The amount of Simple Interest an investment earns can be calculated using:
>
> Simple Interest = $\dfrac{\text{Amount}}{\text{invested}} \times \dfrac{\text{Time in}}{\text{years}} \times \dfrac{\text{Rate of interest}}{\text{per year}}$

Banks and building societies advertise the **yearly rates** of interest payable.

For example, 6% per year.

Interest, usually calculated annually, can also be calculated for shorter periods of time.

### Compound Interest

With **Compound Interest**, the interest earned each year is added to your account and also earns interest the following year.

For example, an investment of 5% per annum means that the amount invested earns £5 for every £100 invested for one year.

So, after the first year of the investment, every £100 invested becomes £100 + 5% of £100.
£100 + 5% of £100 = £100 + £5 = £105
So, after the second year of the investment, every £100 of the original investment becomes
£105 + 5% of £105.
£105 + 5% of £105 = £105 + £5.25 = £110.25

This can also be calculated as: $100 \times (1.05)^2 = £110.25$
*Explain why this works.*

---

### EXAMPLES

**1** Find the Simple Interest paid on £600 invested for 6 months at 8% per year.

Simple Interest
$$= 600 \times \tfrac{6}{12} \times \tfrac{8}{100}$$
$$= 600 \times 0.5 \times 0.08$$
$$= £24$$
The Simple Interest paid is £24.

**Note:** Interest rates are given 'per year'. The length of time for which an investment is made is also given in years.
6 months = $\tfrac{6}{12}$ years.
*Explain why.*

**2** Find the Compound Interest paid on £600 invested for 3 years at 6% per year.

| 1st year | Investment | = £600 |
| | Interest: £600 × 0.06 | = £ 36 |
| | Value of investment after one year | = £636 |
| 2nd year | Investment | = £636 |
| | Interest: £636 × 0.06 | = £ 38.16 |
| | Value of investment after two years | = £674.16 |
| 3rd year | Investment | = £674.16 |
| | Interest: £674.16 × 0.06 | = £ 40.45 |
| | Value of investment after three years | = £714.61 |

Compound Interest = Final value − Original value
$$= £714.61 − £600 = £114.61$$

This could also be calculated as follows: $600 \times (1.06)^3 − 600 = £114.61$

Percentages and Money

41

Do not use a calculator for questions 1 to 7.

**1** Find the simple interest paid on £200 for 1 year at 5% per year.

**2** Calculate the simple interest on £500 invested at 6% per year after:
(a)   1 year,        (b)   6 months.

**3** Calculate the simple interest paid on an investment of £6000 at 7.5% per year after 6 months.

**4** Find the simple interest on £800 invested for 9 months at 8% per year.

**5** Calculate the simple interest on £10 000 invested for 3 months at 9% per year.

**6** Jenny invests £200 at 10% per annum compound interest.
What is the value of her investment after 2 years?

**7** Which of the following investments earn more interest?
(a)   £200 for 3 years at 5% compound.
(b)   £300 for 2 years at 5% compound.
Show your working.

**8** £10 000 is to be invested for 3 years.
Calculate the final value of the investment if the interest rate per annum is 6%.
Give your answer to a suitable degree of accuracy.

**9** Interest on a loan of £2000 is charged at the rate of 21% per annum.
Interest is calculated on the outstanding loan at the **start** of each year.
(a)   How much is owed immediately the loan is taken out?
Repayments are £600 per year.
(b)   How much is owed at the **start** of the third year of the loan?

**10** A bouncy ball is dropped from the top of a skyscraper 256 m high.
After each bounce it reaches a height 25% less than its previous height.
What is the height of the ball after 4 bounces?

**11** A man buys a new car for £13 000. The car loses value at the rate of 14% per annum.
(a)   (i)   What is its value after 3 years?
     (ii)   Express its value after 3 years as a percentage of its original value.
(b)   Repeat (a) for a new car originally valued at £20 000.
(c)   What do you notice about your answers to (a) and (b)?

**12** How long does it take £100 to double in value at 9% per annum?

## What you need to know

- 'Per cent' means 'out of 100'. The symbol for per cent is %. 10% can be written as $\frac{10}{100}$.
- To change a decimal or a fraction to a percentage - **multiply by 100**.
  For example:   0.12 as a percentage is $0.12 \times 100 = 12\%$.
  
  $\frac{3}{25}$ as a percentage is $\frac{3}{25} \times 100 = 3 \times 100 \div 25 = 12\%$.
- To change a percentage to a decimal or a fraction - **divide by 100**.
  For example:   18% as a decimal is $18 \div 100 = 0.18$.
  
  18% as a fraction is $\frac{18}{100}$ which in its simplest form is $\frac{9}{50}$.
- Percentage increase $= \dfrac{\text{actual increase}}{\text{initial value}} \times 100\%$    Percentage decrease $= \dfrac{\text{actual decrease}}{\text{initial value}} \times 100\%$
- **Hourly pay** is paid at a **basic rate** for a fixed number of hours.
  **Overtime pay** is usually paid at a higher rate such as time and a half,
  which means each hour's work is worth 1.5 times the basic rate.
- Everyone is allowed to earn some money which is not taxed. This is called a **tax allowance**.
- Tax is only paid on income earned in excess of the tax allowance. This is called **taxable income**.

- **Value added tax**, or **VAT**, is a tax on some goods and services and is added to the bill.
- Gas, electricity and telephone bills are paid **quarterly**.
  Some bills consist of a standing charge plus a charge for the amount used.
- When considering a **best buy**, compare quantities by using the same units.
  For example, find which product gives more grams per penny.
- Money invested in a savings account at a bank or building society earns **interest**,
  which is usually paid once a year.
  With **Simple Interest**, the interest is paid out each year and not added to your account.

$$\text{Simple Interest} = \frac{\text{Amount}}{\text{invested}} \times \frac{\text{Time in}}{\text{years}} \times \frac{\text{Rate of interest}}{\text{per year}}$$

With **Compound Interest**, the interest earned each year is added to your account and also earns interest the following year.

## Review Exercise 4

Do not use a calculator for questions 1 to 5.

**1** A bag contains 60 beads.
  (a) Emily uses 30% of the beads to make a necklace. How many beads does she use?
  (b) Laura uses 12 beads to make a bracelet. What percentage of the beads does she use?

**2** Mrs Wye pays 89p for 0.5 kg of carrots and 1 kg of onions. The onions cost 55p per kilogram.
  How much per kilogram are carrots?

**3** A roll of carpet is 20 m long. Beryl buys 18 m of carpet from the roll.
  What percentage of the roll did she buy?

**4** A train has 1200 seats. 85% of the seats are occupied.
  How many seats are unoccupied?

**5** A mobile phone company changes its line rental charges from £50 a year to £5 a month for
  12 months. Calculate the percentage increase. OCR

**6** A shop sells a computer for £936 plus VAT. VAT is charged at $17\frac{1}{2}\%$.
  Calculate the price including VAT. OCR

**7** My local shop sells boxes of teabags.
  The boxes come in three different sizes.

  Which size gives the best value for money? Show working to support your answer. OCR

**8** In 1850, a town in America introduced a 'Town Income Tax' on the earnings of all gold miners.
  In that year 1000 people lived in the town. $\frac{4}{5}$ of these were gold miners.
  The average earnings of a gold miner were $200. Their earnings were taxed at 5%.
  Calculate the amount of money collected in tax. OCR

**9** The basic price of a television set is £320. VAT at 17.5% is added to the basic price.
  Sanjit buys a television. He pays a deposit of 25% and 12 equal monthly payments.
  Calculate how much he pays each month. OCR

**10** Francis is paid £7.60 per hour for a basic 35-hour week.
  One week Francis also works overtime at time and a half.
  His total pay that week was £311.60.
  How many hours overtime did he work that week?

**11** An electricity company supplies electricity to a family with the following charges:

> Standing charge: 11.44 pence per day.   Electricity used: 6.85 pence per unit.
> VAT of 5% is added to the total.

The Green family receives a bill for 91 days.
In that time they had used a total of 1272 units of electricity.
Calculate the amount that the Greens have to pay.                                   OCR

**12** Mr Green asked GEMSURE how much it would cost to insure his house in 2006.
GEMSURE's original quote was £490, but Mr Green qualified for the No Claims Reduction
of 30% and a further 10% of the reduced cost because his house had a burglar alarm.

GEMSURE HOME INSURANCE
**30% No Claims Discount!**

(a)   Calculate the amount that Mr Green should pay GEMSURE.
(b)   Find the total percentage reduction on the original £490.                      OCR

**13** Hannah invests £360 in a building society account at 4.8% per year.
Find the simple interest paid on her investment after 4 months.

**14** Guy's house is in council Band G. He pays £1381.80 per year in council tax.
Properties in Band G pay 84% of the council tax for properties in Band H.
Calculate the council tax for properties in Band H.

**15** A clothing shop is having a sale. All goods are reduced by 25% in the sale.
(a)   The price of a coat in the sale is £60.
      Calculate the price of the coat before the sale.
(b)   In the final week all sale prices are reduced by 12%.
      Calculate the overall percentage reduction in prices.                         OCR

**16** Frankie invested £4000 in a high interest savings account.
The rate of compound interest was 7% per annum.
She left the money in the account for 3 years.
(a)   How much was in Frankie's account at the end of the 3 years?
(b)   She decides to leave all the money in the account.
      After how many **more** years will there be more than £8000 in her account?    OCR

**17** (a)   Kelly bought a television set.
      After a reduction of 15% in a sale, the one she bought cost her £319.60.
      What was the original price of the television?
(b)   A plant in a greenhouse is 10 cm high. It increases its height by 15% each day.
      How many days does it take to double in height?                               OCR

**18** Dipak's income is £48 564 per year. Dipak has a tax allowance of £4895 per year
and he also pays 15% of his income into a pension scheme on which he does not pay tax.
He pays tax at 10p in the £ on the first £2090 of his taxable income, 22p in the £ on the
next £30 310 and 40p in the £ on the remainder.
Calculate how much income tax he pays per year.

**19** Ros needs to insure her car. The full premium is £848.
Ros gets a 12.5% discount for agreeing to be the only driver.
She then gets a further 5% discount off the reduced price for agreeing to pay the
first £250 of any claim.
How much does Ros pay for her insurance?

**20** A population of tree ants decreases by 8% each year because of loss of habitat.
The population is now 50 000. What will the population be in 4 years' time?          OCR

# Working with Number

## Multiples

Numbers in the 4 times table are called **multiples** of 4.
**Multiples** of a number are found by multiplying the number by   1,   2,   3,   4,   …
For example, the multiples of 6 are:   6,   12,   18,   24,   …
The 8th **multiple** of 7 is   $8 \times 7 = 56$.

## Factors

Pairs of **whole numbers** which have a product of 6 are   $1 \times 6$   and   $2 \times 3$.
1,   2,   3,   and   6   are called **factors** of 6.
The **factors** of a number can be found from the multiplication facts that give the number.
For example:   $1 \times 12 = 2 \times 6 = 3 \times 4 = 12$.
The factors of 12 are   1,   2,   3,   4,   6,   12.

### Common factors

The factors of 20 are:   **1**,   **2**,   4,   **5**,   **10**,   20.
The factors of 50 are:   **1**,   **2**,   **5**,   **10**,   25,   50.
1,   2,   5   and   10   are factors of both 20 **and** 50.
They are called the **common factors** of 20 and 50.

### Prime numbers

Numbers like 7 are called **prime numbers**.
A prime number has exactly **two** factors, 1 and the number itself.
The first few prime numbers are:   2,   3,   5,   7,   11,   13,   …
The number 1 is not a prime number because it has only one factor.

## Exercise **5.1**          Do not use a calculator for this exercise.

**1**   (a)   Write down a multiple of 7 between 30 and 40.
   (b)   Write down a multiple of 8 between 40 and 50.

**2**   Cameron states that the sum of four consecutive numbers is always a multiple of 4.
   Give an example to show that this statement is not true.

**3**   3,   4,   5,   9,   14,   20,   27   and   35.
   Which of the above numbers are:
   (a)   multiples of 7,          (b)   factors of 20,          (c)   prime numbers?

**4**   (a)   What multiple of 6 is the third multiple of 4?
   (b)   What multiple of 8 is the fourth multiple of 4?
   (c)   What multiple of 20 is the tenth multiple of 10?
   (d)   What multiple of 24 is the fourth multiple of 18?

**5**   Find all the factors of:
   (a)   16          (b)      28          (c)   36          (d)   45          (e)   48          (f)   50

**6**   Find the common factors of:
   (a)   10 and 15,     (b)   12 and 20,     (c)   16 and 18,     (d)   24 and 36,     (e)   12, 18 and 36.

**7**   (a)   Find all the prime numbers between 30 and 40.
   (b)   Is 49 a prime number? Give a reason for your answer.

## Powers

Products of the same number, like
$$3 \times 3, \quad 5 \times 5 \times 5, \quad 10 \times 10 \times 10 \times 10 \times 10,$$
can be written in a shorthand form using **powers**.

For example:

$3 \times 3 = 3^2$        This is read as    '3 to the power of 2'.     $3^2$ has the value 9.

$5 \times 5 \times 5 = 5^3$        This is read as    '5 to the power of 3'.     $5^3$ has the value 125.

$10 \times 10 \times 10 \times 10 \times 10 = 10^5$    This is read as   '10 to the power of 5'.     $10^5$ has the value 100 000.

### Index form

Numbers written in shorthand form like $3^2$, $5^3$ and $10^5$ are said to be in **index form**.
This is sometimes called **power** form.

An expression of the form   $a \times a \times a \times a \times a$   can be written in index form as $a^5$.
$a^5$ is read as '$a$ to the **power** 5'.   $a$ is the **base** of the expression.    5 is the **index** or **power**.

## Prime factors

The factors of 18 are   1,   2,   3,   6,   9   and   18.
Two of these factors, 2 and 3, are prime numbers.
The **prime factors** of 18 are 2 and 3.

Those factors of a number which are prime numbers are called **prime factors**.

## Products of prime factors

All numbers can be written as the product of their prime factors.
For example:    $6 = 2 \times 3$          $20 = 2 \times 2 \times 5$         $168 = 2 \times 2 \times 2 \times 3 \times 7$

**Powers** can be used to write numbers as the product of their prime factors in a shorter form.
For example:    $20 = 2^2 \times 5$          $168 = 2^3 \times 3 \times 7$

A **factor tree** can be used to help write numbers as the product of their prime factors.

For example, this factor tree shows that:

$40 = 2 \times 20$

$40 = 2 \times 2 \times 10$

$40 = 2 \times 2 \times 2 \times 5$

$40 = 2^3 \times 5$

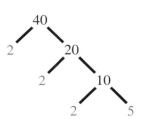

The branches of a factor tree stop when a prime factor is obtained.

So, 40 written as the product of its prime factors is   $2^3 \times 5$.

## Least common multiples

The **Least Common Multiple** of two numbers is the smallest number that is a multiple of both.

For example, to find the least common multiple of 36 and 48:

Write each number as a product of its prime factors.

$$36 = 2^2 \times 3^2 \qquad 48 = 2^4 \times 3$$

Circle the prime factor with the **highest** power for **each** prime factor.

$$36 = 2^2 \times \boxed{3^2} \qquad 48 = \boxed{2^4} \times 3$$

Multiply these numbers together.      $2^4 \times 3^2 = 16 \times 9 = 144$

The **least common multiple (LCM)** of 36 and 48 is 144.

## Highest common factors

The **Highest Common Factor** of two numbers is the largest number that is a factor of both.

For example, to find the highest common factor of 36 and 48:

Write each number as a product of its prime factors.

$$36 = 2^2 \times 3^2 \qquad 48 = 2^4 \times 3$$

Circle the prime factor with the **lowest** power for prime factors **common** to both numbers.

$$36 = \textcircled{$2^2$} \times 3^2 \qquad 48 = 2^4 \times \textcircled{3}$$

Multiply these numbers together. $\qquad 2^2 \times 3 = 4 \times 3 = 12$

The **highest common factor (HCF)** of 36 and 48 is 12.

### Exercise 5.2 — Do not use a calculator.

**1** Write these products of primes in index form.
   (a) $2 \times 2 \times 3 \times 3$
   (b) $2 \times 3 \times 3 \times 3 \times 5$
   (c) $2 \times 3 \times 5 \times 5$
   (d) $2 \times 2 \times 2 \times 3 \times 5 \times 5$
   (e) $5 \times 3 \times 3 \times 3 \times 5 \times 5$
   (f) $7 \times 7 \times 7 \times 7$

**2** Find the prime factors of:
   (a) 12    (b) 20    (c) 28    (d) 45    (e) 66    (f) 108

**3** Write the following numbers as products of their prime factors.
   (a) 12    (b) 20    (c) 28    (d) 45    (e) 66    (f) 108

**4** Write 128 as a product of its prime factors.

**5** Write 1000 as a product of its prime factors.

**6** A number written in terms of its prime factors is $2^3 \times 5^5$.
   (a) Calculate the number.
   (b) Write, in terms of its prime factors, a number which is 5 times the size.

**7** Write each of the numbers 24, 40, 56 and 88 as the product of their prime factors.
   What do you notice? Find the next three numbers.

**8** Find the least common multiple of:
   (a) 8 and 12
   (b) 5 and 32
   (c) 10 and 20
   (d) 15 and 18
   (e) 30 and 45
   (f) 4, 6 and 8
   (g) 5, 8 and 10
   (h) 45, 90 and 105

**9** Find the highest common factor of:
   (a) 12 and 66
   (b) 8 and 24
   (c) 16 and 18
   (d) 20 and 36
   (e) 33 and 88
   (f) 16, 20 and 28
   (g) 15, 39 and 45
   (h) 45, 90 and 105

**10** (a) Write 24 as a product of prime factors.
   (b) Write 54 as a product of prime factors.
   (c) What is the highest common factor of 24 and 54?
   (d) What is the least common multiple of 24 and 54?

**11** (a) Find the value of $x$ when $2^2 \times 3^x = 108$.
   (b) Write 162 as a product of prime factors.
   (c) What is the highest common factor of 108 and 162?
   (d) What is the least common multiple of 108 and 162?

**12** The bell at St. Gabriel's church rings every 6 minutes.
   At St. Paul's, the bell rings every 9 minutes.
   Both bells ring together at 9.00 am.
   When is the next time both bells ring together?

## Square numbers

**Whole numbers** raised to the power 2 are called **square numbers**.

For example:   $3^2 = 3 \times 3 = 9$     $3^2$ is read as '3 squared'.     9 is a square number.

Numbers that are not whole numbers can also be squared.
To **square a number** multiply it by itself.

For example:   $1.6^2 = 1.6 \times 1.6 = 2.56$
2.56 is **not** a square number. *Why not?*

> **Squaring on a calculator**
> $1.6^2$ is read as '1.6 squared'.
> To calculate $1.6^2$ use this sequence of buttons:
> [ 1 ] [ . ] [ 6 ] [ $x^2$ ] [ = ]

## Cube numbers

**Whole numbers** raised to the power 3 are called **cube numbers**.

For example:   $3^3 = 3 \times 3 \times 3 = 27$     $3^3$ is read as '3 cubed'.     27 is a cube number.

Numbers that are not whole numbers can also be cubed.

For example:   $1.6^3 = 1.6 \times 1.6 \times 1.6 = 4.096$
4.096 is **not** a cube number. *Why not?*

## Using a calculator

### Powers

The **squares** and **cubes** of numbers can also be calculated using the [ $x^y$ ] button on a calculator.

The [ $x^y$ ] button can be used to calculate the value of a number $x$ raised to the power of $y$.

For example, to calculate the value of $2.6^3$, enter the following sequence into your calculator:

[ 2 ] [ . ] [ 6 ] [ $x^y$ ] [ 3 ] [ = ]   This gives   $2.6^3 = 17.576$

## Reciprocals

The **reciprocal** of a number is the value obtained when the number is divided into 1.

For example, the reciprocal of 5 is $\frac{1}{5}$ (or 0.2).

On a calculator:   [ 5 ]

The reciprocal of a number $x$ is $\frac{1}{x}$.

A number times its reciprocal equals 1.

For example, the reciprocal of 2 is $\frac{1}{2}$, and   $2 \times \frac{1}{2} = 1$.

> To find the reciprocal of a number on a calculator use the [ $\frac{1}{x}$ ] button.
> 0 (zero) has no reciprocal.

## Square roots

The opposite of squaring a number is called finding the **square root**.

For example:
The square root of 16 is 4 because   $4^2 = 16$.

$\sqrt{\phantom{x}}$   This special symbol stands for the square root.

For example:   $\sqrt{9} = 3$     $\sqrt{2.56} = 1.6$

> **Square roots on a calculator**
> To calculate $\sqrt{2.56}$ use this sequence:
> [ $\sqrt{\phantom{x}}$ ] [ 2 ] [ . ] [ 5 ] [ 6 ] [ = ]

**Note:** $-3 \times -3 = 9$   and   $-1.6 \times -1.6 = 2.56$
So, the square root of a number can be **positive** or **negative**.
In most cases we only use the positive square root.

## Cube roots

The opposite of cubing a number is called finding the **cube root**.

For example:   The cube root of 27 is 3 because   $3^3 = 27$.

Do not use a calculator for questions 1 to 6.

**1** What is (a) the square of 7, (b) the cube of 5, (c) the reciprocal of 2?

**2** Jake says, "The square root of 55 lies between 7 and 8." Is he right? Explain your answer.

**3** Consider the numbers: | 8 16 27 36 64 100 |
Which of these numbers is both a square number **and** a cube number?

**4** Connie says that $2^2 + 3^2 = 5^2$. Is she right? Explain your answer.

**5** (a) Calculate the value of: (i) $(-3)^2$ (ii) $(-2)^3$ (iii) $(-4)^2$ (iv) $(-5)^3$
(b) What do you notice about the signs of your answers?

**6** Find the value of: (a) $\sqrt{64}$ (b) $\sqrt{49}$ (c) $\sqrt{3^2 + 4^2}$ (d) $\sqrt{13^2 - 12^2}$

**7** Find the cube root of (a) 8, (b) 64, (c) 125.

**8** Use the $\boxed{x^y}$ button on your calculator to find the value of:
(a) $2.5^2$ (b) $0.8^2$ (c) $15^3$ (d) $2.4^3$ (e) $7^5$ (f) $0.5^4$ (g) $6.5^6$

**9** Use the $\boxed{\frac{1}{x}}$ button on your calculator to find the reciprocals of:
(a) 4 (b) 20 (c) 25 (d) 0.5 (e) 0.25 (f) 0.4 (g) 0.16

**10** Show by means of an example, that a number times its reciprocal is equal to 1.

**11** Use your calculator to find $\sqrt{96}$. Give your answer to one decimal place.

**12** Calculate. (a) $\sqrt{5.3}$ (b) $\sqrt{300}$ (c) $\sqrt{4.8^2 - 2.7^2}$
Give your answers correct to one decimal place.

**13** Calculate the value of:
(a) $3^3 \times 10^3$ (b) $10^5 \div 5^3$ (c) $2.6 + \frac{1}{2.6}$ (d) $2.2^3$
(e) $8.5^2 - 1.3^2$ (f) $\frac{5}{(0.4)^2}$ (g) $(1.9 + 2.2)^2 \times 1.5$ (h) $0.8^2 \times \frac{1}{0.5}$
(i) $5^3 \times (4^5 - 4^2) + 6^3$ (j) $(8^7 - 8^5) \div (4^7 - 4^5)$

**14** (a) Show that $16^3 = 4^6$.
(b) Hence, or otherwise, solve the equation $2^x = 4^6$.

**15** Use trial and improvement to solve $5^x = 10$. Give your answer to 2 d.p.

## Multiplying and dividing numbers with powers

$3 \times 3 = 3^2$ and $5 \times 5 \times 5 = 5^3$ Both $3^2$ and $5^3$ are examples of numbers with powers.

These examples introduce methods for multiplying and dividing powers of the same number.

**1** Calculate the value of $6^5 \times 6^4$ in power form.
$6^5 = 6 \times 6 \times 6 \times 6 \times 6$ and $6^4 = 6 \times 6 \times 6 \times 6$
$6^5 \times 6^4 = (6 \times 6 \times 6 \times 6 \times 6) \times (6 \times 6 \times 6 \times 6)$
$\qquad = 6 \times 6 \times 6 \times 6 \times 6 \times 6 \times 6 \times 6 \times 6$
This gives: $6^5 \times 6^4 = 6^9$

**2** Calculate the value of $6^7 \div 6^4$ in power form.
$6^7 \div 6^4 = \dfrac{6^7}{6^4} = \dfrac{6 \times 6 \times 6 \times \cancel{6} \times \cancel{6} \times \cancel{6} \times \cancel{6}}{\cancel{6} \times \cancel{6} \times \cancel{6} \times \cancel{6}}$
$\qquad = 6 \times 6 \times 6 = 6^3$
This gives: $6^7 \div 6^4 = 6^3$

*Can you see a quick way of working out the index (power) for each example?*

## Rules of indices

When **multiplying**: powers of the same base are **added**. In general: $a^m \times a^n = a^{m+n}$

When **dividing**: powers of the same base are **subtracted**. In general: $a^m \div a^n = a^{m-n}$

### Raising a power to a power
$$(a^m)^n = a^{mn}$$

### Two special results
$$a^1 = a \qquad a^0 = 1$$

---

**EXAMPLES**     Simplify. Leave your answers in index form.

(a) $2^9 \times 2^4 = 2^{9+4} = 2^{13}$
Add indices

(b) $2^9 \div 2^4 = 2^{9-4} = 2^5$
Subtract indices

(c) $(4^9)^3 = 4^{9 \times 3} = 4^{27}$
Multiply indices

---

### Exercise 5.4     Do not use a calculator for this exercise.

**1** Simplify. Leave your answers in index form.
  (a) $2^3 \times 2^2$    (b) $3^5 \times 3^2$    (c) $5^6 \times 5^2$    (d) $7^3 \times 7$    (e) $9^5 \times 9^0$

**2** Simplify. Leave your answers in index form.
  (a) $2^3 \div 2^2$    (b) $3^5 \div 3^2$    (c) $5^6 \div 5^2$    (d) $7^3 \div 7$    (e) $9^5 \div 9^0$

**3** Simplify. Leave your answers in index form.
  (a) $3 \times 3^2 \times 3^3$    (b) $\dfrac{10 \times 10^3}{10^2}$    (c) $\dfrac{4^3 \times 4^3}{4}$    (d) $\dfrac{5^5 \times 5^2}{5^4}$

  (e) $\dfrac{2 \times 2^5}{2^3}$    (f) $\dfrac{5 \times 5^2}{5^3}$    (g) $\dfrac{7^3 \times 7^2}{7^7}$    (h) $\dfrac{3^5 \times 3^0}{3^2}$

**4** Simplify half of $2^{16}$.

**5** Simplify. Leave your answers in index form.
  (a) $(2^3)^2$    (b) $(3^5)^2$    (c) $(5^2)^3$    (d) $(7^3)^3$    (e) $(9^0)^5$

**6** Find $x$ in each of the following.
  (a) $2^3 \times 2^5 = 2^x$    (b) $3^5 \times 3^2 = 3^x$    (c) $7^2 \times 7^8 \times 7 = 7^x$    (d) $3^5 \div 3^2 = 3^x$
  (e) $8^7 \div 8^6 = 8^x$    (f) $6^5 \div 6 = 6^x$    (g) $(2^3)^2 = 2^x$    (h) $(5^4)^5 = 5^x$

  (i) $\dfrac{2^3 \times (2^2)^5}{2^8 \times 2^3} = 2^x$    (j) $\dfrac{(3^3 \times 3^2)^3}{3^7} = 3^x$    (k) $\dfrac{5^x \times 5^3 \times 5^4}{(5 \times 5^3)^3} = 5$    (l) $\dfrac{(3^x \times 3^2)^3}{(3 \times 3^5)^2} = 3^3$

---

## Negative powers and reciprocals

**Using patterns of powers**
This list shows the powers of two extended to include negative indices.

$2^3 = 2 \times 2 \times 2 = 8$
$2^2 = 2 \times 2 \quad\;\; = 4$
$2^1 = 2 \qquad\quad\; = 2$
$2^0 = 1 \qquad\quad\; = 1$
$2^{-1} = \dfrac{1}{2} \qquad = 0.5 \quad = \dfrac{1}{2^1}$
$2^{-2} = \dfrac{1}{4} \qquad = 0.25 \quad = \dfrac{1}{2^2}$
$2^{-3} = \dfrac{1}{8} \qquad = 0.125 = \dfrac{1}{2^3}$

**Using the rules of indices**
$\dfrac{1}{10} = 1 \div 10$    $\boxed{1 = 10^0 \\ 10 = 10^1}$
$\dfrac{1}{10} = 10^0 \div 10^1$
$\dfrac{1}{10} = 10^{0-1}$
$\dfrac{1}{10^1} = 10^{-1}$   $\boxed{a^m \div a^n = a^{m-n}}$

$\dfrac{1}{32} = 1 \div 32$    $\boxed{1 = 2^0 \\ 32 = 2^5}$
$\dfrac{1}{32} = 2^0 \div 2^5$
$\dfrac{1}{32} = 2^{0-5}$
$\dfrac{1}{2^5} = 2^{-5}$

All of the examples illustrate this general rule for negative indices.

$$a^{-m} = \dfrac{1}{a^m}$$

$\dfrac{1}{a^m}$ and, hence, $a^{-m}$,

is called the **reciprocal** of $a^m$.

## EXAMPLES

**1** Simplify $10^{-4} \div 10^{-2}$.

$$10^{-4} \div 10^{-2} = 10^{-4 - -2}$$
$$= 10^{-4 + 2}$$
$$= 10^{-2}$$

**2** Simplify $3^4 \times 2^3 \times 3^{-5} \times 2^5$.

$$3^4 \times 2^3 \times 3^{-5} \times 2^5 = 3^4 \times 3^{-5} \times 2^3 \times 2^5$$
$$= 3^{4 + -5} \times 2^{3 + 5}$$
$$= 3^{-1} \times 2^8$$

**3** Find the reciprocal of $\left(\frac{1}{6}\right)^{-2}$.

$$\left(\frac{1}{6}\right)^{-2} = \frac{1}{6^{-2}} = 6^2.$$
The reciprocal of $\left(\frac{1}{6}\right)^{-2}$ is $6^{-2}$.
This is equivalent to $\frac{1}{36}$.

**4** If $2^x \div 2^5 = \frac{1}{8}$ find the value of $x$.

$$\frac{1}{8} = \frac{1}{2^3} = 2^{-3}$$
$$2^{x-5} = 2^{-3}$$
So, $x - 5 = -3$
This gives $x = 2$.

**Remember:** When multiplying and dividing powers with different bases each base must be dealt with separately.

### Exercise **5.5**

Do not use a calculator for this exercise.

**1** Simplify. Leave your answers in index form.
   (a) $9^2 \times 9^{-2}$
   (b) $2^{-3} \times 2$
   (c) $5^5 \times 5^{-7}$
   (d) $8^{-2} \times 8^{-3}$
   (e) $2^{-3} \div 2$
   (f) $5^5 \div 5^{-7}$
   (g) $11^{-2} \div 11^3$
   (h) $7^{-4} \div 7^{-3}$

**2** Simplify. Leave your answers in index form.
   (a) $8^{-3} \times 8^5$
   (b) $7^2 \div 7^7$
   (c) $2.5^{-2} \div 2.5^{-1}$
   (d) $4^3 \times 4^2 \times 4^{-5}$
   (e) $10^{-3} \div 10^{-2}$
   (f) $6^{-3} \times 6^4 \div 6^5$
   (g) $0.1^{-7} \div 0.1^5$
   (h) $5^{-7} \div (5^2 \times 5^6)$
   (i) $4^2 \div (4^{-1} \times 4^{-2})$
   (j) $4^{-3} \times 4^5 \times 8^5 \times 8^2$
   (k) $4^{-1} \times 5^5 \times 5^{-7} \times 4^2$
   (l) $2^{-5} \times 5^3 \times 2^3 \times 5^2$
   (m) $\frac{3^5 \times 3^{-2}}{3^2}$
   (n) $\frac{5^{-3} \times 5^4}{5^{-2}}$
   (o) $\frac{2 \times 2^{-3} \times 2^{-1}}{2^2 \times 2}$

**3** Express with positive indices.
   (a) $3^{-2}$
   (b) $2^{-3}$
   (c) $3 \times 3^{-2}$
   (d) $5^{-2} \times 5^{-1}$
   (e) $\frac{1}{3^{-2}}$
   (f) $\frac{5}{5^{-1}}$
   (g) $2 \div 2^{-3}$
   (h) $3^{-3} \div 3^{-1}$
   (i) $(5^{-3})^2$
   (j) $(3^{-2})^{-3}$

**4** Write down the value of:
   (a) $5^0$
   (b) $3^{-1}$
   (c) $2^{-3}$
   (d) $\frac{1}{3^2}$
   (e) $\frac{1}{2^{-3}}$
   (f) $\frac{3}{3^{-2}}$

**5** Calculate each of the following.
   (a) $10 + 10^0 + 10^{-1}$
   (b) $2 + 2^{-1} + 2^{-2} + 2^{-3}$
   (c) $5^0 + 5^{-1} + 5^{-2}$
   (d) $3^{-1} + 2^{-1}$
   (e) $5^{-2} + 2^{-2}$
   (f) $5^{-2} \times 2^{-2}$
   (g) $5^{-2} \div 2^{-2}$
   (h) $5 \times 6^{-1} + 2 \times 5^{-1}$

**6** Find $x$ in each of the following.
   (a) $3^x = \frac{1}{81}$
   (b) $5^x = \frac{1}{25}$
   (c) $\left(\frac{1}{4}\right)^x = 16$
   (d) $\left(\frac{1}{6}\right)^x = 216$
   (e) $2^x = 0.5$
   (f) $5^x = 0.04$
   (g) $3 \times 10^x = 0.003$
   (h) $2 \times 5^x = 0.4$

**7** Calculate $\frac{4^5}{4^{-2}}$ giving your answer in the form $2^n$.

## Powers and roots

The inverse (opposite) of raising to a power is finding a **root**.
The inverse of squaring is finding the **square root**.
The inverse of cubing is finding the **cube root**.
The inverse of raising to the power 5 is finding the **fifth root**.
For example:

| | |
|---|---|
| The square root of 9 is 3 because $3^2 = 9$ | $\sqrt{6.25} = 2.5$ because $2.5^2 = 6.25$ |
| The cube root of 64 is 4 because $4^3 = 64$ | $\sqrt[3]{1.728} = 1.2$ because $1.2^3 = 1.728$ |
| The fifth root of 32 is 2 because $2^5 = 32$ | $\sqrt[6]{15625} = 5$ because $5^6 = 15625$ |

### The connection between powers and roots

If $a = b^n$, $\sqrt[n]{a} = \sqrt[n]{b^n} = b$

Using the rules of powers

$(b^n)^{\frac{1}{n}} = b^{n \times \frac{1}{n}} = b$

So, $(b^n)^{\frac{1}{n}}$ is the same as $\sqrt[n]{b^n}$.

So, $a^{\frac{1}{n}}$ is the same as $\sqrt[n]{a}$.

The inverse of "raising to the power $n$" is finding the $n$th root.

In general, finding the $n$th root of a number, $a$, can be written as:

$$\sqrt[n]{a} \quad \text{or} \quad a^{\frac{1}{n}}.$$

### EXAMPLES

**1** Calculate $81^{\frac{1}{4}}$.

$81^{\frac{1}{4}} = \sqrt[4]{81} = 3$
Because $3^4 = 81$.

**2** Calculate $25^{-\frac{1}{2}}$.

$25^{-\frac{1}{2}}$ is the **reciprocal** of $25^{\frac{1}{2}}$.

$25^{-\frac{1}{2}} = \frac{1}{25^{\frac{1}{2}}} = \frac{1}{\sqrt{25}} = \frac{1}{5} = 0.2$

**3** Calculate $512^{-\frac{1}{9}}$.

Use this key sequence: $\boxed{5}$ $\boxed{1}$ $\boxed{2}$ $\boxed{x^{1/y}}$ $\boxed{9}$ $\boxed{+/-}$ $\boxed{=}$

This gives $512^{-\frac{1}{9}} = 0.5$

## Harder fractional powers

This section deals with evaluating expressions of the form $a^{\frac{m}{n}}$ and $a^{-\frac{m}{n}}$.

In general, using the rules of indices:

$$a^{\frac{m}{n}} = \left(a^{\frac{1}{n}}\right)^m = \left(\sqrt[n]{a}\right)^m$$

$$a^{-\frac{m}{n}} = \frac{1}{a^{\frac{m}{n}}} = \frac{1}{\left(\sqrt[n]{a}\right)^m}$$

**To find the value of $a^{\frac{m}{n}}$:**

1. Find the $n$th root of $a$.

2. Raise the $n$th root of $a$ to the power $m$.

**To find the value of $a^{-\frac{m}{n}}$:**

Carry out the first two steps as before.

3. Write down the reciprocal of $a^{\frac{m}{n}}$.

**EXAMPLES**

**1** Find the value of $32^{\frac{4}{5}}$.

Find the 5th root of 32.

$32^{\frac{1}{5}} = 2$

Raise to the power of 4.

$2^4 = 16$

$32^{\frac{4}{5}} = 16$

**2** Find the value of $27^{-\frac{4}{3}}$.

$27^{-\frac{4}{3}}$ is the reciprocal of $27^{\frac{4}{3}}$.

So, first work out $27^{\frac{4}{3}}$.

$27^{\frac{4}{3}} = \left(27^{\frac{1}{3}}\right)^4 = 3^4 = 81$

The reciprocal of 81 is $\frac{1}{81}$.

So, $27^{-\frac{4}{3}} = \frac{1}{81}$.

**Exercise 5.6**    Do not use a calculator for questions 1 to 9.

**1** Find the value of each of the following.

(a) $\sqrt{400}$　　(b) $\sqrt[3]{27}$　　(c) $\sqrt[3]{1000}$　　(d) $\sqrt[4]{16}$　　(e) $\sqrt[3]{64}$　　(f) $\sqrt{6.25}$

**2** Find the value of each of the following.

(a) $64^{\frac{1}{2}}$　　(b) $8^{\frac{1}{3}}$　　(c) $81^{\frac{1}{4}}$　　(d) $32^{\frac{1}{5}}$　　(e) $625^{\frac{1}{4}}$　　(f) $36^{0.5}$

**3** Find the value of each of the following.

(a) $100^{-\frac{1}{2}}$　　(b) $49^{-0.5}$　　(c) $16^{-\frac{1}{4}}$　　(d) $125^{-\frac{1}{3}}$　　(e) $256^{-\frac{1}{4}}$　　(f) $243^{-\frac{1}{5}}$

**4** Find the value of each of the following.

(a) $1000^{\frac{2}{3}}$　　(b) $9^{\frac{3}{2}}$　　(c) $16^{\frac{3}{4}}$　　(d) $32^{\frac{2}{5}}$　　(e) $4^{\frac{5}{2}}$

(f) $9^{2.5}$　　(g) $125^{\frac{2}{3}}$　　(h) $16^{\frac{5}{4}}$　　(i) $243^{\frac{4}{5}}$　　(j) $36^{1.5}$

**5** Find the value of each of the following.

(a) $1000^{-\frac{2}{3}}$　　(b) $16^{-\frac{3}{2}}$　　(c) $8^{-\frac{2}{3}}$　　(d) $32^{-\frac{3}{5}}$　　(e) $4^{-\frac{3}{2}}$

(f) $100^{-\frac{5}{2}}$　　(g) $25^{-\frac{3}{2}}$　　(h) $16^{-\frac{3}{4}}$　　(i) $128^{-\frac{5}{7}}$　　(j) $125^{-\frac{2}{3}}$

**6** (a) Evaluate.　(i) $16^{0.5} \times 2^{-3}$　　(ii) $49^{-0.5} \times 81^{0.25}$

Give your answers as fractions.

(b) Work out.　(i) $\left(\sqrt{5}\right)^4$　　(ii) $27^{\frac{2}{3}}$

**7** Find $x$ in each of the following.

(a) $\sqrt[x]{27} = 3$　　(b) $\sqrt[x]{16} = 2$　　(c) $\sqrt[x]{32} = 2$　　(d) $25^x = 5$　　(e) $27^x = 9$

(f) $16^x = 2$　　(g) $16^x = 8$　　(h) $x^{\frac{3}{4}} = 64$　　(i) $x^{\frac{2}{3}} = 25$　　(j) $25^x = 125$

**8** Calculate each of the following.

(a) $2^{-1} + \left(\frac{1}{16}\right)^{\frac{1}{2}}$　　(b) $\left(\frac{1}{32}\right)^{-\frac{1}{5}} \times 8^{-\frac{2}{3}}$　　(c) $27^{\frac{2}{3}} \times 3^{-1}$　　(d) $49^{-\frac{1}{2}} + 16^{-\frac{3}{4}}$　　(e) $9^{\frac{3}{2}} \div 8^{\frac{2}{3}}$

**9** Use the rules of powers to show that:

(a) $0.25^{-\frac{7}{2}} = 16^{\frac{7}{4}}$　　(b) $32^{\frac{3}{5}} \times 4^{-\frac{3}{2}} = 1$　　(c) $25^{\frac{1}{2}} \times 36^{-\frac{1}{2}} = 8^{-\frac{1}{3}} + 3^{-1}$

**10** Use your calculator to find the value of each of the following, writing the full display.

(a) $\sqrt{\dfrac{59.6}{(0.4)^2}}$　　(b) $\left(\dfrac{3.51}{\sqrt{0.28}}\right)^3$　　(c) $\left(\dfrac{2.96 \times 8.7}{5.4 + 13.9}\right)^4$

(d) $\sqrt[3]{\dfrac{47.6}{8.51 - 6.79}}$　　(e) $\dfrac{9.3^2}{6.2 + \sqrt[3]{59.7}}$　　(f) $\dfrac{69.7}{2.9^2} - \dfrac{3.7}{\sqrt{5.4}}$

- **Multiples** of a number are found by multiplying the number by 1, 2, 3, 4, ...
  For example: the multiples of 8 are: $1 \times 8 = \mathbf{8}$, $2 \times 8 = \mathbf{16}$, $3 \times 8 = \mathbf{24}$, $4 \times 8 = \mathbf{32}$, ...

- **Factors** of a number are found by listing all the products that give the number.
  For example: $1 \times 6 = 6$ and $2 \times 3 = 6$. So, the factors of 6 are: 1, 2, 3 and 6.

- The **common factors** of two numbers are the numbers which are factors of **both**.

- A **prime number** is a number with only two factors, 1 and the number itself.
  The first few prime numbers are: 2, 3, 5, 7, 11, 13, 17, 19, 23, 29, 31, ...

- The **prime factors** of a number are those factors of the number which are prime numbers.

- The **Least Common Multiple** of two numbers is the smallest number that is a multiple of both.

- The **Highest Common Factor** of two numbers is the largest number that is a factor of both.

- An expression such as $3 \times 3 \times 3 \times 3 \times 3$ can be written in a shorthand way as $3^5$.
  This is read as '3 to the power 5'. The number 3 is the **base** of the expression. 5 is the **power**.

- Powers can be used to help write any number as the product of prime factors.

- Numbers raised to the power 2 are **squared**. Whole numbers squared are called **square numbers**.
  Squares can be calculated using the $\boxed{x^2}$ button on a calculator.
  The opposite of squaring a number is called finding the **square root**.
  Square roots can be calculated using the $\boxed{\sqrt{\phantom{x}}}$ button on a calculator.
  The square root of a number can be positive or negative.
  For example, the square root of 4 can be $+2$ or $-2$.
  The square root of a number can be written in index form. For example: $\sqrt{9} = 9^{\frac{1}{2}}$.

- Numbers raised to the power 3 are **cubed**. Whole numbers cubed are called **cube numbers**.
  The opposite of cubing a number is called finding the **cube root**.
  Cube roots can be calculated using the $\boxed{\sqrt[3]{\phantom{x}}}$ button on a calculator.
  The cube root of a number can be written in index form. For example: $\sqrt[3]{27} = 27^{\frac{1}{3}}$.

- **Powers**
  The squares and the cubes of numbers can be worked out on a calculator by using the $\boxed{x^y}$ button.
  The $\boxed{x^y}$ button can be used to calculate the value of a number $x$ raised to the power of $y$.

- **Roots** can be calculated using the $\boxed{x^{1/y}}$ button.

- **Reciprocals**
  The reciprocal of a number is the value obtained when the number is divided into 1.
  The reciprocal of a number can be found on a calculator by using the $\boxed{\frac{1}{x}}$ button.
  A number times its reciprocal equals 1. Zero has no reciprocal.
  The reciprocal of a number can be shown using an index of $-1$. For example: $5^{-1} = \frac{1}{5}$.

- **The rules of indices**

  | | | |
  |---|---|---|
  | Multiplying powers with the same base | $a^m \times a^n = a^{m+n}$ | |
  | Dividing powers with the same base | $a^m \div a^n = a^{m-n}$ | |
  | Raising a power to a power | $(a^m)^n = a^{mn}$ | |
  | Raising any number to the power zero | $a^0 = 1$ | (also $a^1 = a$) |
  | Negative powers and reciprocals | $a^{-m} = \dfrac{1}{a^m}$ | $a^{-m}$ is the reciprocal of $a^m$ |
  | Fractional powers and roots | $a^{\frac{1}{n}} = \sqrt[n]{a}$ | and $\quad a^{\frac{m}{n}} = \left(a^{\frac{1}{n}}\right)^m = \left(\sqrt[n]{a}\right)^m$ |

Do not use a calculator for questions 1 to 15.

**1** From this list of numbers | 8   10   13   15   16   18   21 | select:

(a) a square number,    (b) a factor of 24,    (c) a prime number.

**2** Joe says, "4 cubed is equal to 12." Is he right? Explain your answer.

**3** Write down (a) the square root of 81, (b) all the prime factors of 30.    OCR

**4** (a) Write down an even prime number.
(b) Write down a multiple of 9 which is between 100 and 110.
(c) What is the reciprocal of 4?

**5** Cameron states that the sum of four consecutive numbers is always a multiple of 4.
Give an example to show that this statement is not true.

**6** Work out $2^3 \times 5^2$.    OCR

**7** (a) Write as a product of its prime factors: (i) 32, (ii) 36.
(b) What is the highest common factor of 32 and 36?
(c) What is the least common multiple of 32 and 36?

**8** Lighthouse $L$ has a light which flashes every 12 seconds.
Lighthouse $M$ has a light which flashes every 10 seconds.
The two lights flash together at 2 am. How long will it be before they next flash together?    OCR

**9** Simplify $\dfrac{5^4 \times 5^6}{5^3}$. Give your answer as a single power of 5.    OCR

**10** $N$ is a negative number.
Is $N^2$ positive or negative? Explain your answer.    OCR

**11** Find $x$ in each of the following.
(a) $5^3 \times 5^2 = 5^x$    (b) $2^5 \div 2^4 = 2^x$    (c) $(7^3)^2 = 7^x$

**12** Write down the value of: (a) $5^{-1}$    (b) $7^0$    (c) $9^{-\frac{1}{2}}$    (d) $64^{\frac{1}{3}}$

**13** Find the value of each of the following. (a) $27^{\frac{2}{3}}$    (b) $25^{-\frac{3}{2}}$    (c) $81^{-\frac{3}{4}}$

**14** Calculate the value of: (a) $2^1 + 2^0 + 2^{-1}$    (b) $2^5 \times (8^3 - 4^5)$

**15** (a) Evaluate. (i) $225^{\frac{1}{2}}$    (ii) $36^{-0.5} \times 36^{\frac{1}{2}}$

(b) Given that $8^{\frac{2}{3}} \times 4^{-\frac{5}{2}} = 2^p$, find the value of $p$.    OCR

**16** Use your calculator to work out the values of the following.
(a) $2.7^2$    (b) $\sqrt{3}$ to 1 d.p.    (c) $\dfrac{9}{0.7^2}$ to 1 d.p.    (d) $3^6$    OCR

**17** (a) Use your calculator to find the value of $3.2^2 - \sqrt{4.84}$.

(b) (i) Use your calculator to find the value of $\dfrac{3.9^2 + 0.53}{3.9 \times 0.53}$, correct to 2 decimal places.

(ii) Write down a calculation you can do in your head to check your answer.
Write down your answer to this calculation.    OCR

**18** (a) Calculate $\dfrac{131.4 - 0.73}{2 - 4.5^2}$.

(b) Using indices, write 1089 as a product of its prime factor.    OCR

**19** Calculate $2.6^3 \times \sqrt{4.3 + 2.8}$. Give your answer correct to one decimal place.

**20** Calculate the value of: (a) $\left(\sqrt{7}\right)^6$    (b) $7^{-\frac{3}{4}}$    (c) $\sqrt[4]{\dfrac{5.7}{(0.3)^2}}$    (d) $\left(\dfrac{2.4}{\sqrt{1.5}}\right)^{-5}$
Give your answers correct to 3 significant figures.

**Standard index form** is a shorthand way of writing very large and very small numbers.
Standard index form is often called **standard form** or **scientific notation**.

## Large numbers and your calculator

Scientists who study the planets and the stars work with very large numbers.

Approximate distances from the Sun to some planets are:

Earth 149 000 000 km     Mars 228 000 000 km     Pluto 5 898 000 000 km

A calculator displays very large numbers in **standard form**.
To represent large numbers in standard form you need to use powers of 10.

| Number | 1 000 000 | 100 000 | 10 000 | 1000 | 100 | 10 |
|---|---|---|---|---|---|---|
| Power of 10 | $10^6$ | $10^5$ | $10^4$ | $10^3$ | $10^2$ | $10^1$ |

For example:   $2\,600\,000 = 2.6 \times 1\,000\,000 = 2.6 \times 10^6$
Therefore       $2\,600\,000 = 2.6 \times 10^6$ in **standard form**.

### Calculator displays

*Work out*   3 000 000 × 25 000 000   *on your calculator.*
*Write down the display.*

Most calculators will show the answer as: | 7.5          13 |

In **standard form** the answer should be written as   $7.5 \times 10^{13}$.

> A number written in standard form has **two** parts.
>
> The first part must be a number between 1 and 10.
>
> The second part is a power of 10.
>
> The two parts are connected by a multiplication sign.

### EXAMPLES

**1**  (a)   Write   370 000   in standard form.
$370\,000 = 3.7 \times 100\,000 = 3.7 \times 10^5$

(b)   Write   $5.6 \times 10^7$   as an ordinary number.
$5.6 \times 10^7 = 5.6 \times 10\,000\,000 = 56\,000\,000$

**2**  Write the calculator display | 7.3          05 |

(a)   in standard form,                    (b)   as an ordinary number.

(a)  | 7.3          05 |  means $7.3 \times 10^5$     (b)   $7.3 \times 10^5 = 7.3 \times 100\,000 = 730\,000$

## Exercise 6.1

1.  (a) Write 600 000 in standard form.
    (b) Write $9 \times 10^6$ as an ordinary number.

2.  Copy the table and fill in all the different forms of each number.

| | Ordinary number | Power of 10 | Standard form |
|---|---|---|---|
| | 300 000 | $3 \times 100\ 000$ | $3 \times 10^5$ |
| (a) | 75 000 | $7.5 \times 10\ 000$ | |
| (b) | | $8 \times 100\ 000\ 000$ | |
| (c) | | | $3.5 \times 10^{13}$ |
| (d) | 62 300 000 000 000 | | |

3.  Write each of these numbers in standard form.
    (a) 300 000 000 000    (b) 80 000 000    (c) 700 000 000    (d) 2 000 000 000
    (e) 42 000 000    (f) 21 000 000 000    (g) 3 700 000 000    (h) 630

4.  Change each of these numbers to an ordinary number.
    (a) $6 \times 10^5$    (b) $2 \times 10^3$    (c) $5 \times 10^7$    (d) $9 \times 10^8$
    (e) $3.7 \times 10^9$    (f) $2.8 \times 10^1$    (g) $9.9 \times 10^{10}$    (h) $7.1 \times 10^4$

5.  Write these calculator displays:
    (a) in standard form,
    (b) as an ordinary number.

    (i) | 4.5     03 |    (ii) | 7.8     07 |    (iii) | 5.3     05 |    (iv) | 3.25     04 |

6.  The table shows the estimated population for some countries in 2020.

| Country | Estimated population in 2020 |
|---|---|
| Albania | $5.3 \times 10^6$ |
| Brazil | $2.5 \times 10^8$ |
| Fiji | $9.0 \times 10^5$ |
| Greece | $1.2 \times 10^7$ |

    (a) (i) Which of these countries is estimated to have the largest population in 2020?
        (ii) Write the estimated population as an ordinary number.
    (b) In 2020, China is estimated to have a population of 1288 million people.
        Write 1288 million in standard form.

## Small numbers and your calculator

Scientists who study microbiology work with numbers that are very small.
The smallest living cells are bacteria which have a diameter of about 0.000 025 cm.
Blood cells have a diameter of about 0.000 75 cm.

A calculator displays small numbers in **standard form**.
It does this in the same sort of way that it does for large numbers.
To represent very small numbers in standard form you need to use powers of 10 for numbers less than 1.

| Number | 1000 | 100 | 10 | 1 | 0.1 | 0.01 | 0.001 | 0.000 1 |
|---|---|---|---|---|---|---|---|---|
| Power of 10 | $10^3$ | $10^2$ | $10^1$ | $10^0$ | $10^{-1}$ | $10^{-2}$ | $10^{-3}$ | $10^{-4}$ |

For example:   $0.000\ 037 = 3.7 \times 0.000\ 01 = 3.7 \times 10^{-5}$
Therefore       $0.000\ 037 = 3.7 \times 10^{-5}$ in **standard form**.

## Calculator displays

*Work out* 0.000 007 × 0.000 9 *on your calculator.*
*Write down the display.*

Most calculators will show the answer as: | 6.3       −09 |

In standard form the answer should be written as 6.3 × 10⁻⁹.

| | | |
|---|---|---|
| In **standard form** a number is written as: | a number between 1 and 10 × a power of 10 | |
| A **large** number has a **positive power**. | E.g. 160 000 000 = 1.6 × 10⁸ | |
| A **small** number has a **negative power**. | E.g. 0.000 000 06 = 6 × 10⁻⁸ | |

### EXAMPLES

**1** (a) Write 0.000 73 in standard form.
  0.000 73 = 7.3 × 0.000 1 = 7.3 × 10⁻⁴

 (b) Write 2.9 × 10⁻⁶ as an ordinary number.
  2.9 × 10⁻⁶ = 2.9 × 0.000 001 = 0.000 002 9

**2** Write the calculator display: | 1.5       −03 |

 (a) in standard form,  (b) as an ordinary number.

 (a) | 1.5       −03 | means 1.5 × 10⁻³  (b) 1.5 × 10⁻³ = 1.5 × 0.001 = 0.001 5

## Exercise 6.2

**1** (a) Write 0.000 35 in standard form.
 (b) Write 2.5 × 10⁻³ as an ordinary number.

**2** Copy and complete the following table.

| | Ordinary number | Power of 10 | Standard form |
|---|---|---|---|
| | 0.000 03 | 3 × 0.000 01 | 3 × 10⁻⁵ |
| (a) | 0.007 5 | 7.5 × 0.001 | |
| (b) | 0.000 008 75 | | |
| (c) | | | 3.5 × 10⁻⁹ |
| (d) | 0.000 000 000 006 23 | | |

**3** Write each of these numbers in standard form.
 (a) 0.007  (b) 0.04  (c) 0.000 000 005
 (d) 0.000 8  (e) 0.000 000 002 3  (f) 0.000 000 045
 (g) 0.023 4  (h) 0.000 000 002 34  (i) 0.006 7

**4** Change each of these numbers to an ordinary number:
 (a) 3.5 × 10⁻¹  (b) 5 × 10⁻⁴  (c) 7.2 × 10⁻⁵  (d) 6.1 × 10⁻³
 (e) 1.17 × 10⁻¹⁰  (f) 8.135 × 10⁻⁷  (g) 6.462 × 10⁻²  (h) 4.001 × 10⁻⁹

**5** Write these calculator displays:
 (a) in standard form,  (b) as an ordinary number.

 (i) | 3.4       −03 |  (ii) | 5.65       −05 |  (iii) | 7.2       −04 |  (iv) | 9.13       −01 |

## Using large and small numbers with a calculator

Calculations with large and small numbers can be done on a calculator by:
- changing the numbers to standard form,
- entering the numbers into the calculator using the $\boxed{\text{Exp}}$ button.

If your calculator works in a different way to the example shown refer to the instruction booklet supplied with the calculator or ask someone for help.

### EXAMPLE

Calculate the value of   $62\,500\,000\,000 \times 0.000\,000\,003$
Give your answer both as an ordinary number and in standard form.

$62\,500\,000\,000 \times 0.000\,000\,003 = (6.25 \times 10^{10}) \times (3 \times 10^{-9})$

To do the calculation enter the following sequence into your calculator.

$\boxed{6}\ \boxed{.}\ \boxed{2}\ \boxed{5}\ \boxed{\text{Exp}}\ \boxed{1}\ \boxed{0}\ \boxed{\times}\ \boxed{3}\ \boxed{\text{Exp}}\ \boxed{9}\ \boxed{+/-}\ \boxed{=}$

Giving:
$62\,500\,000\,000 \times 0.000\,000\,003$
$= 187.5$      (ordinary number)
$= 1.875 \times 10^2$  (standard form)

Some calculators display this result as: 187.5
Other calculators give this display: 1.875  *02*

**Remember:**
The calculator display **must** be changed to either **standard form** or an **ordinary number**.

### Exercise 6.3      Use your calculator to work out each of the following questions.

Write each of the answers:
    (i)     as on your calculator display,     (ii)    in standard form,    (iii)    as an ordinary number.

**1**
(a) $300\,000 \times 200\,000\,000$
(b) $120\,000 \times 80\,000\,000$
(c) $15\,000 \times 700\,000\,000$
(d) $65\,000 \times 2\,000\,000\,000$
(e) $480\,000 \times 500\,000\,000$
(f) $50\,000 \times 50\,000\,000$

**2**
(a) $0.000\,03 \times 0.000\,000\,2$
(b) $0.000\,045 \times 0.000\,003$
(c) $0.000\,75 \times 0.000\,000\,04$
(d) $0.002\,3 \times 0.000\,000\,05$
(e) $0.053 \times 0.000\,000\,08$
(f) $0.000\,006\,4 \times 0.000\,015\,2$

## Solving problems involving large and small numbers

Problems can involve numbers given in standard form.

### EXAMPLE

The following figures refer to the population of China and the USA in 1993.

China $1.01 \times 10^9$     USA $2.32 \times 10^8$

By how much did the population of China exceed that of the USA in 1993?

The greater the power …
… the bigger the number.

$1.01 \times 10^9$ is greater than $2.32 \times 10^8$.
You need to work out $1.01 \times 10^9 - 2.32 \times 10^8$
To do the calculation enter the following sequence into your calculator.

$\boxed{1}\ \boxed{.}\ \boxed{0}\ \boxed{1}\ \boxed{\text{Exp}}\ \boxed{9}\ \boxed{-}\ \boxed{2}\ \boxed{.}\ \boxed{3}\ \boxed{2}\ \boxed{\text{Exp}}\ \boxed{8}\ \boxed{=}$

Giving:   $1.01 \times 10^9 - 2.32 \times 10^8 = 778\,000\,000 = 7.78 \times 10^8$

**1** Give the answers to the following calculations as ordinary numbers.

(a) $(5.25 \times 10^9) \times (5 \times 10^{-5})$       (b) $(5.25 \times 10^9) \div (5 \times 10^{-5})$

(c) $(8.5 \times 10^6)^2$                    (d) $(5 \times 10^{-3})^3$

(e) $(7.2 \times 10^5) \div (2.4 \times 10^{-5})$       (f) $(9.5 \times 10^6) \div (1.9 \times 10^{-7})^2$

**2** Give the answers to the following calculations in standard form.

(a) 33 500 000 000 × 2 800 000 000       (b) 0.000 000 000 2 × 80 000 000 000

(c) 15 000 000 000 000²                   (d) 0.000 000 000 000 5³

(e) 48 000 000 000 ÷ 0.000 000 000 2       (f) 25 000 000 000 ÷ 500 000 000 000

**3** (a) In 1992 about 1 400 000 000 steel cans and about 688 000 000 aluminium cans were recycled.
What was the total number of cans that were recycled in 1992?
Give your answer in standard form.

(b) Alpha Centauri is about 40 350 000 000 000 km from the Sun.
Alpha Cygni is about 15 300 000 000 000 000 km from the Sun.
How much further is it from the Sun to Alpha Cygni than from the Sun to Alpha Centauri?
Give your answer in standard form.

**4** Here are the diameters of some planets.
        Saturn $1.2 \times 10^5$ km       Jupiter $1.42 \times 10^5$ km       Pluto $2.3 \times 10^3$ km

(a) List the planets in order of size starting with the smallest.

(b) What is the difference between the diameters of the largest and smallest planets?
Give your answer in standard form and as an ordinary number.

**5** Here are the areas of some of the world's largest deserts.

| | |
|---|---|
| The Sahara desert in North Africa | $8.6 \times 10^6$ km² |
| The Gobi desert in Mongolia and North East China | $1.166 \times 10^6$ km² |
| The Patagonian desert in Argentina | $6.73 \times 10^5$ km² |

(a) What is the total area of the Sahara and Patagonian deserts?

(b) What is the difference in area between the Gobi and the Patagonian deserts?
Give your answer in standard form.

**6** Calculate  $5.42 \times 10^6 \times 4.65 \times 10^5$
giving your answer in standard form correct to 3 significant figures.

**7** Calculate  $1.7 \times 10^3 \div 7.6 \times 10^7$
giving your answer in standard form correct to 2 significant figures.

**8** The area of the surface of the Earth is about $5.095 \times 10^9$ square miles.
Approximately 29.2% of this is land.
Use these figures to estimate the area of land surface on Earth.

**9** James wins a lottery prize of £$1.764 \times 10^6$. He pays £$5.29 \times 10^5$ for a house.
What percentage of his prize did he spend on the house?
Give your answer to a suitable degree of accuracy.

**10** The mass of an oxygen atom is $2.7 \times 10^{-23}$ grams.
The mass of an electron at rest is approximately 30 000 times smaller than this.
Estimate the mass of an electron at rest.

**11** The modern human appeared on the Earth about $3.5 \times 10^4$ years ago.
The Earth has been in existence for something like $1.3 \times 10^5$ times as long as this.
(a) Estimate the age of the Earth.

Reptiles appeared on the Earth about $2.3 \times 10^8$ years ago.
(b) How many times longer than the modern human have reptiles been alive?
Give your answer in standard form.

## Standard form calculations without a calculator

In some standard form problems the calculations can be handled without using a calculator.

### EXAMPLES

**1** Calculate the value of $(3 \times 10^2) + (4 \times 10^3)$.
Give your answer in standard form.

$3 \times 10^2 = 300 \qquad 4 \times 10^3 = 4000$
$(3 \times 10^2) + (4 \times 10^3) = 300 + 4000$
$= 4300$
$= 4.3 \times 10^3$

> When adding or subtracting numbers in standard form without a calculator change to ordinary numbers first.

**2** Calculate the value of $ab$ where
$a = 8 \times 10^3$ and $b = 4 \times 10^5$.

$ab = (8 \times 10^3) \times (4 \times 10^5)$
$= 8 \times 4 \times 10^3 \times 10^5$
$= 32 \times 10^8$
$= 3.2 \times 10 \times 10^8$
$= 3.2 \times 10^9$

> When **multiplying** the powers are **added**.
> $10^3 \times 10^5 = 10^{3+5} = 10^8$
> $10 \times 10^8 = 10^{1+8} = 10^9$

**3** Calculate the value of $x^2$ where $x = 7 \times 10^{-8}$.

$x^2 = (7 \times 10^{-8})^2$
$= 49 \times 10^{-16}$
$= 4.9 \times 10 \times 10^{-16}$
$= 4.9 \times 10^{-15}$

> **Remember:**
> $(7 \times 10^{-8})^2 = 7^2 \times (10^{-8})^2$
> $10 \times 10^{-16} = 10^{1-16} = 10^{-15}$

**4** Calculate the value of $(1.2 \times 10^3) \div (4 \times 10^{-8})$.

$(1.2 \times 10^3) \div (4 \times 10^{-8}) = (1.2 \div 4) \times (10^3 \div 10^{-8})$
$= 0.3 \times 10^{11}$
$= 3 \times 10^{-1} \times 10^{11}$
$= 3 \times 10^{10}$

> When **dividing** the powers are **subtracted**.
> $10^3 \div 10^{-8} = 10^{3--8} = 10^{11}$

### Exercise 6.5

Do not use a calculator. Give your answers in standard form.

**1** For each of the following calculate the value of $p + q$.
(a) $p = 5 \times 10^3$ and $q = 2 \times 10^2$
(b) $p = 4 \times 10^5$ and $q = 8 \times 10^6$
(c) $p = 3.08 \times 10^4$ and $q = 9.2 \times 10^3$
(d) $p = 4.25 \times 10^4$ and $q = 7.5 \times 10^3$

**2** For each of the following calculate the value of $p - q$.
(a) $p = 3 \times 10^3$ and $q = 2 \times 10^2$
(b) $p = 9.05 \times 10^5$ and $q = 5 \times 10^3$
(c) $p = 3.05 \times 10^7$ and $q = 5 \times 10^5$
(d) $p = 9.545 \times 10^8$ and $q = 4.5 \times 10^6$

**3** For each of the following calculate the value of $p \times q$.
(a) $p = 4 \times 10^3$ and $q = 2 \times 10^4$
(b) $p = 2 \times 10^4$ and $q = 3 \times 10^3$
(c) $p = 4 \times 10^5$ and $q = 6 \times 10^2$
(d) $p = 9 \times 10^9$ and $q = 3 \times 10^5$

**4** For each of the following calculate the value of $p \div q$.
(a) $p = 6 \times 10^5$ and $q = 2 \times 10^2$
(b) $p = 9 \times 10^5$ and $q = 3 \times 10^2$
(c) $p = 2.5 \times 10^5$ and $q = 5 \times 10^3$
(d) $p = 4 \times 10^8$ and $q = 2 \times 10^{-3}$
(e) $p = 1.2 \times 10^3$ and $q = 3 \times 10^{-3}$
(f) $p = 1.5 \times 10^{-5}$ and $q = 5 \times 10^{-3}$

**5** $x = 3 \times 10^4$ and $y = 5 \times 10^{-5}$. Work out the value of each of these expressions.
(a) $xy$ (b) $x^3$ (c) $x^2 y$ (d) $y^3$ (e) $\dfrac{x}{y}$

**6** Find the value of each of the following.
  (a) $(5 \times 10^6) \times (3 \times 10^4)$         (b) $(8 \times 10^{-5}) \times (3 \times 10^7)$
  (c) $(7 \times 10^{-5}) \times (6 \times 10^{-4})$       (d) $(8 \times 10^3)^2$
  (e) $(4 \times 10^5) \div (8 \times 10^3)$         (f) $(1.8 \times 10^3) \div (6 \times 10^{-7})$
  (g) $(5 \times 10^{-7}) \div (8 \times 10^{-2})$       (h) $(2 \times 10^4) \div (8 \times 10^{-1})$

## What you need to know

- **Standard index form**, or **standard form**, is a shorthand way of writing very large and very small numbers.
- In **standard form** a number is written as:  $a \times 10^n$  where $1 \le a < 10$ and $n$ is an integer.
  For large numbers, greater than 10, $n$ is **positive**.         E.g. $15\,000\,000 = 1.5 \times 10^7$
  For small positive numbers, less than 1, $n$ is **negative**.   E.g. $0.000\,06 = 6 \times 10^{-5}$

## Review Exercise 6

Do questions 1 to 3 without using your calculator.

**1** (a) Write in standard form.   (i)  $7\,800\,000$         (ii)  $0.000\,005$
  (b) Here are some numbers written in standard form.
        $1.7 \times 10^5$    $3.2 \times 10^{-3}$    $5.675 \times 10^4$    $9.75 \times 10^{-3}$
    (i) Which of these numbers is the largest?
        Write your answer as an ordinary number.
    (ii) Which of these numbers is the smallest?
        Write your answer as an ordinary number.

**2** (a) (i) Write sixty thousand in standard form.
      (ii) Hence, or otherwise, find the value of the square of sixty thousand.
        Give your answer in standard form.
  (b) Work out  $4.3 \times 10^{-3} + 2.7 \times 10^{-2}$.  Give your answer in standard form.         OCR

**3** During a total eclipse of the Sun, the Earth, Moon and Sun were in a straight line, as shown.

Earth            Moon                                    Sun

  (a) The Sun was 93 170 000 miles from the Earth.
    Write 93 170 000 in standard form.
  (b) The distance of the Moon from the Earth was $2.5 \times 10^5$ miles.
    Find the distance of the Moon from the Sun. Give your answer in standard form.         OCR

**4** (a) Work out  (i)  $\dfrac{3.6 \times 10^9}{4.5 \times 10^4}$,         (ii)  $\dfrac{4.5 \times 10^4}{3.6 \times 10^9}$.  Give your answers in standard form.

  (b) Calculate  30% of $7 \times 10^5$.  Give your answer in standard form.

**5** (a) Write 0.000 4 in standard form.

  (b) Work out  $\dfrac{(2.45 \times 10^5) \times (6 \times 10^4)}{1.5 \times 10^{-2}}$.  Give your answer in standard form.         OCR

**6** A quark weighs  $\dfrac{1}{1\,000\,000\,000\,000\,000\,000\,000\,000}$  of a grain of sand!

  (a) Write this fraction in standard form.
  (b) Write down, in standard form, a positive number which is smaller than this.         OCR

**7** The volume of water on Earth is approximately  $1.436 \times 10^9 \text{ km}^3$.
  About 94% of this is contained in the Earth's oceans.
  Use these figures to estimate the volume of water in the Earth's oceans.

# Ratio and Proportion ●●●●●

## Equivalent ratios

Ratios are used only to **compare** quantities. They do not give information about actual values.

For example.
A necklace is made using red beads and white beads in the ratio **3 : 4**.
This gives no information about the actual numbers of beads in the necklace.
The ratio **3 : 4** means that for every 3 red beads in the necklace there are 4 white beads.
The **possible** numbers of beads in the necklace are shown in the table.

| Red beads | 3 | 6 | 9 | 12 |
|-----------|---|---|---|----|
| White beads | 4 | 8 | 12 | 16 |
| Total beads | 7 | 14 | 21 | 28 |

*Make similar tables when the ratio of red beads to white beads in the necklace is:*

(a)  4 : 5      (b)  2 : 3      (c)  3 : 1

For the beads in this necklace:
The number of red beads is a **multiple** of 3.
The number of white beads is a **multiple** of 4.
The total number of beads is a **multiple** of 7.

The ratios  3 : 4,  6 : 8,  9 : 12,  …
are different forms of the **same** ratio.
They are called **equivalent** ratios.
They can be found by multiplying or dividing each part of the ratio by the **same** number.

## Simplifying ratios

To simplify a ratio divide both of the numbers in the ratio by the **same** number.
A ratio with whole numbers which cannot be simplified is in its **simplest form**.

### EXAMPLES

**1**  The ratio of boys to girls in a school is 3 : 4.
There are 72 boys. How many girls are there?

For the ratio 3 : 4, say 3 to 4.

$72 \div 3 = 24$
To find a ratio equivalent to 3 : 4 where the first number in the ratio is 72,
multiply each number in the ratio by 24.
$3 \times 24 : 4 \times 24 = 72 : 96$
The number of girls = 96.

**2**  Write the ratio 2 cm : 50 mm in its simplest form.

$2 \text{ cm} : 50 \text{ mm} = 20 \text{ mm} : 50 \text{ mm} = 20 : 50$
Divide both parts of the ratio by 10.
$20 \div 10 : 50 \div 10 = 2 : 5$
The ratio 2 cm : 50 mm in its simplest form is 2 : 5.

In its simplest form a ratio contains
**only** whole numbers. There are **no units**.
In order to simplify the ratio both
quantities in the ratio must be in the
**same units**.

## Exercise **7.1**          Do not use a calculator in this exercise.

**1**  Give the simplest form of each of these ratios.

   (a)  3 : 6          (b)  9 : 27          (c)  9 : 12          (d)  10 : 25          (e)  30 : 40
   (f)  22 : 55          (g)  9 : 21          (h)  18 : 8          (i)  36 : 81          (j)  35 : 15

**2** Each of these pairs of ratios are equivalent.
(a) 3 : 4 and 9 : n. (b) 2 : 7 and 8 : n. (c) 8 : n and 2 : 25. (d) 25 : n and 5 : 4.
In each case calculate the value of n.

**3** The heights of two friends are in the ratio 7 : 9. The shorter of the friends is 154 cm tall.
What is the height of the taller of the friends?

**4** Sugar and flour are mixed in the ratio 2 : 3.
How much sugar is used with 600 g of flour?

**5** The ratio of boys to girls in a school is 4 : 5. There are 80 girls.
How many boys are there?

**6** I earn £300 per week.  I earn £270 per week.
The amounts Jenny and James earn
is in the ratio of their ages.
Jenny is 20 years old. How old is James?

**7** A necklace contains 30 black beads and 45 gold beads.
What is the simplest form of the ratio of black beads to gold beads on the necklace?

**8** On Monday a hairdresser uses 800 ml of shampoo and 320 ml of conditioner.
Write in its simplest form the ratio of shampoo : conditioner used on Monday.

**9** Denise draws a plan of her classroom. On her plan Denise uses 2 cm to represent 5 m.
Write the scale as a ratio in its simplest form.

**10** On a map a pond is 3.5 cm long. The pond is actually 52.5 m long.
Write the scale as a ratio in its simplest form.

**11** Write each of these ratios in its simplest form.
(a) £2 : 50p (b) 20p : £2.50 (c) £2.20 : 40p (d) 6 m : 240 cm
(e) 2 kg : 500 g (f) 1 kg : 425 g (g) 90 cm : 2 m (h) 5 km : 200 m

**12** Sam spends 90p a week on comics. Tom spends £4 a week on comics.
Write the ratio of the amounts Tom and Sam spend on comics in its simplest form.

**13** An alloy is made of tin and zinc. 40% of the alloy is tin.
What is the ratio of tin : zinc in its simplest form?

**14** A box contains blue biros and red biros. $\frac{1}{3}$ of the biros are blue.
What is the ratio of blue biros to red biros in the box?

**15** A necklace is made from 40 beads. $\frac{2}{5}$ of the beads are white. The rest of the beads are red.
Find the ratio of the number of red beads to the number of white beads in its simplest form.

## Sharing in a given ratio

**EXAMPLE**

James and Sally share £20 in the ratio 3 : 2.
How much do they each get?

Add the numbers in the ratio. 3 + 2 = 5
For every £5 shared: James gets £3, Sally gets £2.
20 ÷ 5 = 4 There are 4 shares of £5 in £20.
James gets £3 × 4 = £12. Sally gets £2 × 4 = £8.
So, James gets £12 and Sally gets £8.

Do not use a calculator for questions 1 to 6.

**1**  (a)  Share 9 in the ratio 2 : 1.      (b)  Share 20 in the ratio 3 : 1.
    (c)  Share 35 in the ratio 1 : 4.      (d)  Share 100 in the ratio 9 : 1.

**2**  A bag contains 12 toffees. Bruce and Emily eat them at the ratio 1 : 2.
How many toffees does Emily eat?

**3**  A box contains gold coins and silver coins. The ratio of gold coins to silver coins is 1 : 9.
There are 20 coins in the box. How many silver coins are in the box?

**4**  Sunny and Chandni share £48 in the ratio 3 : 1. How much do they each get?

**5**  (a)  Share £35 in the ratio 2 : 3.      (b)  Share £56 in the ratio 4 : 3.
    (c)  Share £5.50 in the ratio 7 : 4.      (d)  Share £4.80 in the ratio 3 : 5.

**6**  A necklace contains 72 beads. The ratio of red beads to blue beads is 5 : 3.
How many red beads are on the necklace?

**7**  £480 is shared in the ratio 7 : 3.
What is the difference between the larger share and the smaller share?

**8**  A bag contains red beads and black beads in the ratio 1 : 3. What fraction of the beads are red?

**9**  A box contains red biros and black biros in the ratio 1 : 4.
What percentage of the biros are black?

**10**  In a school the ratio of the number of boys to the number of girls is 3 : 5.
What fraction of the pupils in the school are girls?

**11**  The ratio of non-fiction books to fiction books in a library is 2 : 3.
Find the percentage of fiction books in the library.

**12**  John is 12 years old and Sara is 13 years old. They share some money in the ratio of their ages.
What percentage of the money does John get?

**13**  In the UK there are 240 939 km² of land.
The ratio of agricultural land to non-agricultural land is approximately 7 : 3.
Estimate the area of land used for agriculture.

**14**  At the start of a game Jenny and Tim have 40 counters each.
At the end of the game the number of counters that Jenny and Tim each have is in the ratio 5 : 3.
    (a)  How many counters do Jenny and Tim have at the end of the game?
    (b)  How many counters did Jenny win from Tim in the game?

**15**  On a necklace, for every 10 black beads there are 4 red beads.
    (a)  What is the ratio of black beads to red beads in its simplest form?
    (b)  If the necklace has 15 black beads how many red beads are there?
    (c)  If the necklace has a total of 77 beads how many black beads are there?
    (d)  Why can't the necklace have a total of 32 beads?

**16**  The lengths of the sides of a triangle are in the ratio 4 : 6 : 9.
The total length of the sides is 38 cm. Calculate the length of each side.

**17**  To make concrete a builder mixes gravel, sand and cement in the ratio 4 : 2 : 1.
The builder wants 350 kg of concrete. How much gravel does the builder need?

**18**  The angles of a triangle are in the ratio 2 : 3 : 4. Calculate each angle.

**19**  A bag contains some red, green and black sweets. 30% of the sweets are red.
The ratio of the numbers of green sweets to black sweets is 5 to 9.
What percentage of the total number of sweets are black?

## Proportion

Some situations involve comparing **different** quantities.

### Direct proportion

When a motorist buys fuel, the more he buys the greater the cost.
In this situation the quantities can change but the ratio between the quantities stays the same.
As one quantity increases, so does the other.
The quantities are in **direct proportion**.

### Inverse proportion

By using more people to deliver a batch of leaflets, the time taken to complete the task is reduced.
In this situation, as one quantity increases the other quantity decreases.
The quantities are in **inverse proportion**.

---

### EXAMPLES

**1** 4 cakes cost £1.20.
Find the cost of 7 cakes.

4 cakes cost £1.20
1 cake costs   £1.20 ÷ 4 = 30p
7 cakes cost   30p × 7 = £2.10
So, 7 cakes cost £2.10.

> This is sometimes called the **unitary method**.
> (a)  **Divide** by 4 to find the cost of **1** cake.
> (b)  **Multiply** by 7 to find the cost of 7 cakes.

**2** 3 people take 8 hours to deliver some leaflets.
How long would it take 4 people?

3 people take 8 hours.
1 person takes 8 hours × 3 = 24 hours
4 people take 24 hours ÷ 4 = 6 hours
So, 4 people would take 6 hours.

> This assumes that time is **inversely proportional** to the number of people.
> (a)  **Multiply** by 3 to find how long **1** person would take.
> (b)  **Divide** by 4 to find how long 4 people would take.

---

### Exercise 7.3

Do not use a calculator for questions 1 to 6.

**1** 5 candles cost 80 pence.
   (a)  What is the cost of 1 candle?
   (b)  What is the cost of 8 candles?

**2** Alistair pays £1.90 for 2 cups of tea.
How much would he pay for 3 cups of tea?

**3** Lauren can buy 3 toffee apples at 60 pence each.
How many could she buy if they cost 45 pence each?

**4** The amount a spring stretches is proportional to the weight hung on the spring.
A weight of 5 kg stretches the spring by 60 cm.
   (a)  How much does a weight of 10 kg stretch the spring?
   (b)  What weight makes the spring stretch 24 cm?

**5** Jean pays £168 for 10 square metres of carpet.
How much would 12 square metres of carpet cost?

**6** Three people can deliver 1000 leaflets in 30 minutes.
How long would it take 5 people to deliver 1000 leaflets?

**7** These ingredients are needed to make 20 scones.

| 500 g flour | 100 g dried fruit | 250 g butter | water to mix |
|---|---|---|---|

(a) How much dried fruit is needed to make 50 scones?
(b) How much butter is needed to make 12 scones?

**8** Aimee pays £1.14 for 3 kg of potatoes.
How much would 7.5 kg of potatoes cost?

**9** A farmer estimates it will take 12 workers, 10 days to harvest his crop.
How many workers are needed to harvest the crop in 8 days?

**10** 9 metres of stair carpet cost £83.70. How much does 9.6 metres cost?

**11** It costs £15.60 each for 7 people to hire a minibus.
How much would each person pay if 12 people hired the minibus?

**12** A car travels 6 miles in 9 minutes. If the car travels at the same speed:
(a) how long will it take to travel 8 miles,
(b) how far will it travel in 24 minutes?

**13** 5 litres of paint cover an area of 30 m².
(a) What area will 2 litres of paint cover?
(b) How much paint is needed to cover 72 m²?

**14** Meg can make 30 monthly payments of £148.80 to repay a loan.
How many payments are needed if she can pay £186 a month?

**15** Mary phones her uncle in New York.
Phone calls to New York are charged at the rate of £2.20 for a 5-minute call.
(a) How much would a 7-minute call to New York cost?
(b) Mary's call cost £5.28. How long was her call?

**16** A school is organising three trips to the zoo.

Our trip is on Monday.
45 students are going.
The total cost is £468.

Our trip is on Tuesday.
25 students are going.

Our trip is on Wednesday.
The total cost is £332.80.

(a) How much does Tuesday's trip cost?
(b) How many students are going to the zoo on Wednesday?

**17** At 75 kilometres per hour a journey takes 40 minutes.
How long would the journey take at 60 kilometres per hour?

**18** A 42-litre paddling pool is filled at the rate of 12 litres of water every 5 minutes.
How long will it take to fill the pool?

**19** A piece of beef weighs 1.5 kg and costs £5.22.
How much would a piece of beef weighing 2.4 kg cost?
Give your answer to a suitable degree of accuracy.

**20** The lottery is won by 5 people and they each get £1 685 240.
How much would they each have got if only two people had won?

# What you need to know

- The ratio 3 : 2 is read '3 to 2'.
- A ratio is used only to **compare** quantities.
  A ratio does not give information about the exact values of quantities being compared.
- In its **simplest form**, a ratio contains whole numbers which have no common factor other than 1.
  All quantities in a ratio must have the **same units** before the ratio can be simplified.
  For example, £2.50 : 50p = 250p : 50p = 5 : 1.
- When two different quantities are always in the **same ratio** the two quantities are in
  **direct proportion**. For example, the amount and cost of fuel bought by a motorist.
- When, as one quantity increases the other decreases, the two quantities are in **inverse proportion**.
  For example, the number of people and the time taken to deliver a batch of leaflets.

## Review Exercise 7

Do not use a calculator for questions 1 to 5.

**1** These ingredients make 8 dumplings.

| 100 g flour | 50 g suet | water to mix |

(a) Write, in its simplest form, the ratio of flour to suet.
(b) How much flour would you need for 6 dumplings?
(c) How much suet would you need for 12 dumplings?

**2** (a) There were 48 biscuits in a packet. Karen ate 28 biscuits and Carl ate the remainder.
Write down the ratio, **number of biscuits Karen ate : number of biscuits Carl ate**,
in its lowest terms.
(b) Karen and Carl divided their next packet of 48 biscuits in the ratio 1 : 2.
How many of these biscuits did Carl receive?                OCR

**3** There were 1200 fans at the game between City and United.
The ratio of City fans to United fans was 3 : 2. How many fans of each team were there?  OCR

**4** What is the difference between the larger and smaller shares when £39 200 is shared in the
ratio 7 : 9?

**5** The cost of 5 metres of material is £18.40. What is the cost of 8 metres of the same material?

**6** At 60 mph Matt takes $1\frac{1}{4}$ hours to complete a journey.
How much longer would he take at 45 mph?

**7** A plan is drawn using a scale of 2 centimetres to represent 5 metres.
Write the scale as a ratio in the form 1 : $n$, where $n$ is a whole number.

**8** A charity collected 367 290 metal cans for recycling. The cans were either steel or aluminium.
They collected 5 times as many steel cans as aluminium cans.
How many steel cans were collected?

**9** Sam mixes concrete and uses this ratio.  **sand : gravel : cement = 2 : 3 : 1**
She mixes 1.5 m³ of concrete. How much sand does she use?                OCR

**10** Bag P contains silver coins and gold coins in the ratio 5 : 3.
Bag Q contains silver coins and gold coins in the ratio 3 : 2.
The number of coins in Bag P to the number of coins in Bag Q is in the ratio 2 : 1.
What is the smallest number of coins in each bag?

**11** Sasha, John and Dario went to a restaurant.
They agreed to split the cost in the ratio 4 : 3 : 5.
(a) The food cost £58.80. How much did Dario pay?
(b) They paid for the drinks in the same ratio. John paid £5.49.
How much did Sasha pay?

OCR

# Speed and Other Compound Measures

## Speed

**Speed** is a measurement of how fast something is travelling.
It involves two other measures, **distance** and **time**.
Speed can be worked out using this formula.

$$\text{Speed} = \frac{\text{Distance}}{\text{Time}}$$

**Speed** can be thought of as the **distance** travelled in **one unit of time** (1 hour, 1 second, …)

Speed can be measured in:

kilometres per hour (km/h),   metres per second (m/s),   miles per hour (mph),   and so on.

## Average speed

When the speed of an object is **constant** it means that the object doesn't slow down or go faster.
However, in many situations, speed is not constant.
For example:

A sprinter needs time to start from the starting blocks and is well into the race before running at top speed.
A plane changes speed as it takes off and lands.

In situations like this the idea of **average speed** can be used.
The formula for average speed is:

$$\text{Average speed} = \frac{\text{Total distance travelled}}{\text{Total time taken}}$$

The formula linking speed, distance and time can be rearranged and remembered as:

| (average) **speed** = (total) **distance** ÷ (total) **time** |
|---|
| (total) **distance** = (average) **speed** × (total) **time** |
| (total) **time** = (total) **distance** ÷ (average) **speed** |

$$S = D \div T$$
$$D = S \times T$$
$$T = D \div S$$

### EXAMPLES

**1** Robert drives a distance of 260 km. His journey takes 5 hours.
What is his average speed on the journey?

$$\text{Speed} = \frac{\text{Distance}}{\text{Time}} = \frac{260}{5} = 260 \div 5 = 52 \text{ km/h}$$

**2** Lisa drives at an average speed of 80 kilometres per hour on a journey that takes 3 hours.
What distance has she travelled?

$$\text{Distance} = \text{Speed} \times \text{Time} = 80 \times 3 = 240 \text{ km}$$   So, in 3 hours she travels 240 km.

**3** Lucy cycles at an average speed of 7 km/h on a journey of 28 km.
How long does she take?

$$\text{Time} = \text{Distance} \div \text{Speed} = 28 \div 7 = 4$$   So, her journey takes 4 hours.

**4** A cheetah takes 4 seconds to travel 100 m.
What is the speed of the cheetah?

$$\text{Speed} = \frac{\text{Distance}}{\text{Time}} = \frac{100}{4} = 100 \div 4 = 25 \text{ m/s}$$

Do not use a calculator.

**1** John cycles 16 miles in 2 hours. What is his average speed in miles per hour?

**2** Sue runs 21 km in 3 hours. What is her average speed in kilometres per hour?

**3** Joe swims 100 m in 4 minutes. What is his average speed in metres per minute?

**4** Calculate the average speed for each of the following journeys in kilometres per hour.

| | Total distance travelled | Total time taken |
|---|---|---|
| (a) | 60 km | 3 hours |
| (b) | 100 km | 2 hours |
| (c) | 10 km | $2\frac{1}{2}$ hours |

**5** Jackie runs 15 km in $1\frac{1}{2}$ hours. What is her average speed in kilometres per hour?

**6** Beverley walks for 2 hours at an average speed of 4 km/h. How many kilometres does she walk?

**7** Howard cycles for 5 hours at an average speed of 6 miles per hour. How far does he cycle?

**8** Aubrey runs at 6 km/h for $\frac{1}{2}$ hour. How far does he run?

**9** Calculate the total distance travelled on each of the following journeys.

| | Total time taken | Average speed |
|---|---|---|
| (a) | 3 hours | 50 km/h |
| (b) | 2 hours | 43 km/h |
| (c) | $\frac{1}{2}$ hour | 80 km/h |

**10** Ahmed drives 30 miles at an average speed of 60 miles per hour. How long does the journey take?

**11** Lauren cycles 100 m at 5 metres per second. How long does she take?

**12** A coach travels 75 km at an average speed of 50 km/h. How long does the journey take?

**13** Calculate the total time taken on each of the following journeys.

| | Total distance travelled | Average speed |
|---|---|---|
| (a) | 30 km | 10 km/h |
| (b) | 80 km | 40 km/h |
| (c) | 210 km | 60 km/h |

**14** Aimee cycles 27 km at 12 km/h. How long does she take?

**15** Penny cycles to work at 18 km/h. She takes 20 minutes. How far does she cycle to work?

**16** A train travels 100 km at an average speed of 80 km/h. How long does the journey take?

**17** Bristol is 40 miles from Gloucester.
(a) How long does it take to cycle from Bristol to Gloucester at 16 miles per hour?
(b) How long does it take to drive from Bristol to Gloucester at 32 miles per hour?

**18** A car travels 120 km in 2 hours.
(a) What is its average speed in kilometres per hour?
(b) How many hours would the car take to travel 120 km if it had gone twice as fast?

**19** Liam drives for 60 km at an average speed of 40 km/h. He starts his journey at 9.50 am. At what time does his journey end?

## Further problems involving speed

> **EXAMPLE**
>
> The Scottish Pullman travels from London to York, a distance of 302.8 km in 1 hour 45 minutes.
> It then travels from York to Edinburgh, a distance of 334.7 km in 2 hours 30 minutes.
> Calculate the average speed of the train between London and Edinburgh.
>
> Total distance travelled = 302.8 + 334.7 = 637.5 km
>
> Total time taken = 1 hr 45 mins + 2 hr 30 mins = 4 hr 15 mins = 4.25 hours
>
> Average speed = $\frac{637.5}{4.25}$ = 150 km/h

## Exercise **8.2**

**1**  On the first part of a journey a car travels 140 km in 3 hours.
On the second part of the journey the car travels 160 km in 2 hours.
(a)   What is the total distance travelled on the journey?
(b)   What is the total time taken on the journey?
(c)   What is the average speed of the car over the whole journey?

**2**  Lisa runs two laps of a 400 m running track.
The first lap takes 70 seconds. The second lap takes 90 seconds.
What is her average speed over the two laps?

**3**  Jenny sets out on a journey at 10.20 am.
She completes her journey at 1.05 pm. She travels a total distance of 27.5 km.
Calculate her average speed in kilometres per hour.

**4**  Harry drives for 40 km at an average speed of 60 km/h. He starts his journey at 9.50 am.
At what time does his journey end?

**5**  Sally cycles 38 km at an average speed of 23 km/h. She starts her journey at 9.30 am.
At what time does she finish? Give your answer to the nearest minute.

**6**  Chandni runs from Newcastle to Whitley Bay and then from Whitley Bay to Blyth.

| Newcastle to Whitley Bay | Time taken:   1 hr 20 min | Distance: 20 km |
| Whitley Bay to Blyth | Average speed: 0.2 km/min | Distance: 12 km |

(a)   Calculate Chandni's average speed over the whole journey.
(b)   Chandni left Newcastle at 10.50 am.
At what time did she arrive in Blyth?

**7**  Angela, Ben and Cathy drive from London to Glasgow.
Angela takes 12 hours 30 minutes driving at an average speed of 64 km/h.
Ben drives at an average speed of 100 km/h.
(a)   How long does Ben take?

Cathy takes 7 hours 12 minutes.
(b)   What is Cathy's average speed?

**8**  Ron runs 400 m in 1 minute 23.2 seconds.
Calculate his average speed in   (a)   metres per second,      (b)   kilometres per hour.

**9**  A cheetah runs at a speed of 90 km/h for 6 seconds.
How many metres does the cheetah run?

**10**  The distance from the Sun to the Earth is about 150 million kilometres.
It takes light from the Sun about 500 seconds to reach the Earth.
Calculate the speed of light in metres per second.

## Density

**Density** is a compound measure because it involves two other measures, **mass** and **volume**.
The formula for density is:

$$\text{Density} = \frac{\text{Mass}}{\text{Volume}}$$

The formula linking density, mass and volume can be rearranged and remembered as:

$$\text{Volume} = \frac{\text{Mass}}{\text{Density}}$$

$$\text{Mass} = \text{Density} \times \text{Volume}$$

For example, if a metal has a density of $2500 \, \text{kg/m}^3$ then $1 \, \text{m}^3$ of the metal weighs $2500 \, \text{kg}$.

### EXAMPLES

1. A block of metal has mass 500 g and volume $400 \, \text{cm}^3$.
   Calculate the density of the metal.
   Density $= \frac{500}{400} = 1.25 \, \text{g/cm}^3$

2. The density of a certain metal is $3.5 \, \text{g/cm}^3$. A block of the metal has volume $1000 \, \text{cm}^3$.
   Calculate the mass of the block.
   Mass $= 3.5 \times 1000 = 3500 \, \text{g}$.

## Population density

**Population density** is a measure of how populated an area is. The formula for population density is:

$$\text{Population density} = \frac{\text{Population}}{\text{Area}}$$

### EXAMPLE

Cumbria has a population of $\quad$ 489 700 $\quad$ and an area of $\quad$ $6824 \, \text{km}^2$.
Surrey has a population of $\quad$ 1 036 000 $\quad$ and an area of $\quad$ $1677 \, \text{km}^2$.
Which county has the greater population density?

The population densities are:

$\qquad$ Cumbria $\frac{489\,700}{6824} = 71.8$ people/km$^2$. $\qquad$ Surrey $\frac{1\,036\,000}{1677} = 617.8$ people/km$^2$.

Surrey has the greater population density.

## Exercise 8.3

1. A metal bar has a mass of 960 g and a volume of $120 \, \text{cm}^3$.
   Find the density of the metal in the bar.

2. A block of copper has a mass of 2160 g. The block measures 4 cm by 6 cm by 10 cm.
   What is the density of copper?

3. A paperweight is made of glass. It has a volume of $72 \, \text{cm}^3$ and a mass of 180 g.
   What is the density of the glass?

4. A silver necklace has a mass of 300 g. The density of silver is $10.5 \, \text{g/cm}^3$.
   What is the volume of the silver?

5. A can in the shape of a cuboid is full of oil.
   It measures 30 cm by 15 cm by 20 cm. The density of oil is $0.8 \, \text{g/cm}^3$.
   What is the mass of the oil?

**(6)** A copper plaque has a mass of 2.4 kg.
The density of copper is 3 g/cm³.
Calculate the volume of the plaque.

**(7)** A bag of sugar has a mass of 1 kg.
The average density of the sugar in the bag is 0.5 g/cm³.
Find the volume of sugar in the bag.

**(8)** A block of concrete has dimensions 15 cm by 25 cm by 40 cm.
The block has a mass of 12 kg.
What is the density of the concrete?

**(9)** Metal A has density 3 g/cm³ and metal B has density 2 g/cm³.
600 g of metal A and 300 g of metal B are melted down and mixed to make an alloy which is cast into a block.
(a) Calculate the volume of the block.
(b) Calculate the density of the alloy.

**(10)** The population of Northern Ireland is 1 595 000.
The area of Northern Ireland is 13 483 km².
Calculate the population density of Northern Ireland.

**(11)** The table shows the total population, land area and the population densities for some countries in Europe.

|  | Country | Area km² | Population | Population density people/km² |
|---|---|---|---|---|
| (a) | Belgium | ? | 9 970 000 | 326.6 |
| (b) | France | 543 960 | 56 700 000 | ? |
| (c) | UK | 244 090 | ? | 235.2 |

Calculate the missing figures in the table.

**(12)** Brass is an alloy made from zinc and copper.
The ratio of the volume of zinc to the volume of copper in the alloy is 1 : 3.
The density of zinc is 2.5 g/cm³. The density of copper is 3 g/cm³.
A brass ornament has a volume of 400 cm³.
Calculate the mass of the ornament.

## What you need to know

- **Speed** is a compound measure because it involves **two** other measures.
- **Speed** is a measure of how fast something is travelling. It involves the measures **distance** and **time**.

  $$\text{Speed} = \frac{\text{Distance}}{\text{Time}}$$

- In situations where speed is not constant, **average speed** is used.

  $$\text{Average speed} = \frac{\text{Total distance travelled}}{\text{Total time taken}}$$

- The formula linking speed, distance and time can be rearranged and remembered as:

  (average) **speed** = (total) **distance** ÷ (total) **time**
  (total) **distance** = (average) **speed** × (total) **time**
  (total) **time** = (total) **distance** ÷ (average) **speed**

- Two other commonly used compound measures are **density** and **population density**.

- **Density** is a compound measure which involves the measures **mass** and **volume**.

  $$\text{Density} = \frac{\text{Mass}}{\text{Volume}}$$

- **Population density** is a measure of how populated an area is.

  $$\text{Population density} = \frac{\text{Population}}{\text{Area}}$$

Do not use a calculator for questions 1 to 5.

**1** The chart shows the distances in kilometres between some towns.
Mrs Hill drove from Manchester to Southampton.
She completed the journey in 4 hours.
What was her average speed for the journey in kilometres per hour?

| London | | | |
|---|---|---|---|
| 326 | Manchester | | |
| 270 | 60 | Sheffield | |
| 129 | 376 | 334 | Southampton |

**2** A lorry travels from Middlesbrough to York in $1\frac{1}{4}$ hours. The distance is 50 miles.
Find the average speed of the lorry in miles per hour.

**3** Kath has to drive 18 km to work. Calculate her average speed for the journey when she leaves home at 0750 and gets to work at 0814.

**4** Flik lives 2.4 km from school.
How many minutes does she take to walk to school if her average walking speed is 4 km/h?

**5** Jane took part in a sponsored cycle ride.
She cycled from her home town to Blackpool and back.
The distance from her home town to Blackpool is 48 km.
Jane cycled to Blackpool at an average speed of 12 km/h.
(a) Find the time she took to cycle to Blackpool.

Her average speed for the return journey was 8 km/h.
(b) Calculate her average speed for the whole journey.

OCR

**6** Rajid swam 200 metres in a total time of 2 minutes 58 seconds.
Calculate his average speed, in metres per second.

OCR

**7** In June 1998 the speed limit on the Kingston bypass was reduced from 70 to 50 miles per hour.
The bypass is 7.3 miles long.
How much longer does it take to drive along the bypass at 50 mph than it did at 70 mph?
Show your method clearly and give your answer in minutes to 1 decimal place.

OCR

**8** Arnold runs 400 m in 1 minute. What is his average speed in km/h?

**9** A train travels from Bournemouth to Manchester at an average speed of 47 mph.
The train travels 268 miles. How long does the journey take in hours and minutes?

**10** Spencer cycles from Poole to Swanage in two stages.

| **Stage 1** Poole to Wareham | Distance: 22.4 km | Average speed: 14 km/h |
|---|---|---|
| **Stage 2** Wareham to Swanage | Time taken: 48 minutes | Average speed: 16 km/h |

Calculate Spencer's average speed for the whole of his journey from Poole to Swanage.

**11** Light travels at $1.863 \times 10^5$ miles per second.
Lights takes 43.3 minutes to travel from the Sun to Jupiter.
Calculate the distance of Jupiter from the Sun.

**12** A glass ornament has a mass of 350 g and a volume of 120 cm³.
Calculate the density of the glass.

**13** A gold bracelet has a mass of 84 g. The density of gold is 19.3 g/cm³.
What is the volume of the bracelet?

**14** The area of Singapore is 4290 km². The population density of Singapore is 676 people/km².
Calculate the population of Singapore, correct to two significant figures.

**15** Watcham has a population of 86 000 in an area of 104 square miles. To meet housing targets, it needs to aim to house an extra 14 000 people whilst increasing the area by only 6 square miles.
If this happens, by how much will the population density have increased?

OCR

# Extending the Number System

So far, we have looked at integers, fractions and decimals.
In this chapter we extend the number system to include **irrational numbers**.

All real numbers are either **rational** or **irrational**.

## Rational numbers

Numbers which can be written in the form $\frac{a}{b}$, where $a$ and $b$ are integers ($b \neq 0$) are **rational**.
Examples of rational numbers are:

$$2 \qquad -5 \qquad \frac{2}{5} \qquad 0.\dot{6} \qquad 3.47 \qquad 1\frac{3}{4}$$

$\frac{a}{b}$ is a **proper fraction** if $a < b$.

$\frac{a}{b}$ is an **improper fraction** (top heavy) if $a > b$.

All fractions can be written as decimals.

$\frac{3}{4}$ can be thought of as $3 \div 4$ and is equal to 0.75.

Some decimals have recurring digits.
These are shown by:

a single dot above a single recurring digit,
a dot above the first and last digit of a set of recurring digits.

For example:

$$\frac{1}{3} = 0.3333333\ldots = 0.\dot{3}$$

$$\frac{41}{70} = 0.5857142857142\ldots = 0.5\dot{8}5714\dot{2}$$

$$\frac{123}{999} = 0.123123123\ldots = 0.\dot{1}2\dot{3}$$

$$\frac{3}{11} = 0.27272727\ldots = 0.\dot{2}\dot{7}$$

## Changing recurring decimals to fractions

**Recurring decimals** can be converted to fractions.

Some are well known, such as $0.\dot{3} = \frac{1}{3}$ and $0.\dot{6} = \frac{2}{3}$.

**To convert a recurring decimal to a fraction**:

Let $x = $ the recurring decimal.
Multiply both sides by the power of 10 that corresponds to the number of digits in the recurring pattern.

E.g.   by $10^1 = 10$ if only 1 digit recurs,
by $10^2 = 100$ if 2 digits recur,
by $10^3 = 1000$ if 3 digits recur,
and so on.

Subtract the original equation from the new equation.

Solve the resulting equation for $x$.

Make sure that the answer is a fraction in its simplest form.

Write down the fraction, in its simplest form, which is equal to these recurring decimals.

(a)  $0.\dot{4}$          (b)  $0.\dot{5}\dot{7}$          (c)  $0.1\dot{2}3\dot{4}$

(a)  $x = 0.444\ldots$
Only 1 digit recurs, so, multiply both sides by 10.
$10x = 4.444\ldots$
Subtract the original equation from the new equation.
$9x = 4$
Divide both sides by 9.
$x = \frac{4}{9}$
$0.\dot{4} = \frac{4}{9}$

(b)  $x = 0.5757\ldots$
2 digits recur, so, multiply both sides by 100.
$100x = 57.5757\ldots$
Subtract the original equation from the new equation.
$99x = 57$
Divide both sides by 99.
$x = \frac{57}{99} = \frac{19}{33}$  (in its simplest form)
$0.\dot{5}\dot{7} = \frac{19}{33}$

(c)  $x = 0.1234234\ldots$
3 digits recur, so, multiply both sides by 1000.
$1000x = 123.4234234\ldots$
Subtract the original equation from the new equation.
$999x = 123.3$
Divide both sides by 999.
$x = \frac{123.3}{999}$
A fraction should consist of whole numbers.
So, multiply numerator and denominator by 10.
$x = \frac{1233}{9990} = \frac{137}{1110}$  (in its simplest form)
$0.1\dot{2}3\dot{4} = \frac{137}{1110}$

## Exercise 9.1

**1**  Convert these recurring decimals to fractions in their simplest form.

(a)  $0.\dot{7}$          (b)  $0.\dot{1}$          (c)  $0.\dot{8}$          (d)  $0.\dot{3}\dot{6}$          (e)  $0.\dot{8}\dot{2}$
(f)  $0.1\dot{3}\dot{5}$          (g)  $0.\dot{2}1\dot{6}$          (h)  $0.4\dot{2}\dot{5}$          (i)  $0.\dot{1}6\dot{2}$          (j)  $0.\dot{2}8571\dot{4}$

**2**  Write each of these numbers as a fraction in its simplest form.

(a)  $0.1\dot{6}$          (b)  $0.0\dot{3}$          (c)  $0.6\dot{1}$          (d)  $0.4\dot{6}$          (e)  $0.2\dot{3}$
(f)  $0.8\dot{3}$          (g)  $0.1\dot{8}\dot{2}$          (h)  $0.1\dot{3}\dot{6}$          (i)  $0.86\dot{1}$          (j)  $0.7\dot{7}2\dot{7}$

**3**  $0.\dot{1}17647058823529\dot{4}$
When the number above is written as a fraction the numerator and denominator are both less than 20. What is the fraction?

**4**  Look at the decimal expansions for the fractions $\frac{1}{a}$, where $1 < a < 21$ ($a$ is a whole number).
For what values of $a$ does the decimal not recur?
Find a condition so that a fraction with numerator 1 does not recur.

## Irrational numbers

Numbers are either **rational** or **irrational**.
An irrational number **cannot** be written as a fraction.
Irrational numbers include:
    square roots of non-square numbers,
    cube roots of non-cube numbers.
Examples of irrational numbers are:

$$\sqrt{2} \qquad \sqrt[3]{7} \qquad \pi \qquad \sqrt{13}$$

Real numbers are either rational
or irrational numbers.
You will meet imaginary numbers,
such as $\sqrt{-1}$, if you study Maths
beyond GCSE.

### EXAMPLES

**1** Show that $0.425$ and $0.\dot{2}$ are rational numbers.

$0.425$ is a **terminating decimal**.
$0.425 = \frac{425}{1000} = \frac{17}{40}$

$0.\dot{2}$ is a **recurring decimal**.
$$x = 0.222\ldots$$
$$10x = 2.222\ldots$$
$$9x = 2$$
$$x = \frac{2}{9}$$
$$0.\dot{2} = \frac{2}{9}$$

All terminating and recurring
decimals can be written in
the form $\frac{a}{b}$ so they are all
rational numbers.

**2** State whether each of the following are rational or irrational numbers.
Where a number is rational write it as a fraction in its simplest form.

| $0.6$ | $\pi$ | $\sqrt[3]{7}$ | $\sqrt{36}$ |
|---|---|---|---|

$0.6 = \frac{6}{10} = \frac{3}{5}$      rational      A rational number expressed in the form $\frac{a}{b}$ is in its simplest form if $a$ and $b$ have no common factor.

$\pi = 3.141592654\ldots$    irrational    $\pi$ is a non-recurring decimal and has no exact value.

$\sqrt[3]{7} = 1.91293118\ldots$    irrational    $\sqrt[3]{7}$ is a non-recurring decimal and has no exact value.

$\sqrt{36} = 6$      rational      Note: $\sqrt{36}$ means the positive square root of 36.

### Exercise 9.2      Do not use a calculator.

**1** These numbers are rational.
Write each number as a fraction in its simplest form.

(a) $0.5$      (b) $0.45$      (c) $0.3$      (d) $0.625$      (e) $2\frac{1}{4}$

(f) $-0.25$      (g) $0.\dot{2}\dot{7}$      (h) $\sqrt{49}$      (i) $\frac{\sqrt{0.49}}{2}$      (j) $0.\dot{2}2\dot{5}$

(k) $\frac{\sqrt{64}}{\sqrt{16}}$      (l) $-\frac{\sqrt{0.16}}{2}$      (m) $\sqrt[3]{64}$      (n) $\frac{\sqrt[3]{27}}{4}$      (o) $0.1\dot{2}$

**2** Which of these numbers are rational?

(a) $0.25$      (b) $0.\dot{5}$      (c) $\sqrt{5}$      (d) $\sqrt{25}$      (e) $\frac{1.8}{3}$

(f) $-\sqrt{0.25}$      (g) $\frac{\pi}{2}$      (h) $2.\dot{1}$      (i) $\sqrt[3]{8}$      (j) $\sqrt{1\frac{7}{9}}$

Express each of the rational numbers in the form $\frac{a}{b}$, where $a$ and $b$ are integers.

## Surds

Roots of rational numbers which **cannot** be expressed as rational numbers are called **surds**.
A surd is an irrational number.
These are examples of surds:

$$\sqrt{2} \qquad \sqrt{0.37} \qquad \sqrt[3]{10} \qquad 3 + \sqrt{2} \qquad \sqrt{7}$$

$\sqrt{a}$ means the positive square root of $a$.

Numbers like $\sqrt{64}$, $\sqrt{0.25}$, $\sqrt[3]{27}$ are not surds because the root of each number is rational.

$$(\sqrt{64} = 8, \quad \sqrt{0.25} = 0.5, \quad \sqrt[3]{27} = 3.)$$

## Manipulating and simplifying surds

Rules for surds.

$$\sqrt{ab} = \sqrt{a} \times \sqrt{b} \qquad m\sqrt{a} + n\sqrt{a} = (m + n)\sqrt{a} \qquad \sqrt{\frac{a}{b}} = \frac{\sqrt{a}}{\sqrt{b}}$$

To simplify surds look for factors that are square numbers.

### EXAMPLE

Simplify the following leaving the answers in surd form.

(a) $\sqrt{32}$ 　　　(b) $\sqrt{8} + \sqrt{18}$ 　　　(c) $\sqrt{108} - \sqrt{75}$ 　　　(d) $\sqrt{\dfrac{72}{20}}$

(a) $\sqrt{32} = \sqrt{16} \times \sqrt{2} = 4\sqrt{2}$

(b) $\sqrt{8} + \sqrt{18} = \sqrt{4} \times \sqrt{2} + \sqrt{9} \times \sqrt{2} = 2\sqrt{2} + 3\sqrt{2} = 5\sqrt{2}$

(c) $\sqrt{108} - \sqrt{75} = \sqrt{36} \times \sqrt{3} - \sqrt{25} \times \sqrt{3} = 6\sqrt{3} - 5\sqrt{3} = \sqrt{3}$

(d) $\sqrt{\dfrac{72}{20}} = \dfrac{\sqrt{72}}{\sqrt{20}} = \dfrac{\sqrt{36}\,\sqrt{2}}{\sqrt{4}\,\sqrt{5}} = \dfrac{6\sqrt{2}}{2\sqrt{5}} = \dfrac{3\sqrt{2}}{\sqrt{5}}$

## Exercise 9.3

**1** Which of the following are surds?

(a) $\sqrt{2}$ 　　　(b) $\sqrt{4}$ 　　　(c) $\sqrt[3]{8}$ 　　　(d) $\sqrt{0.4}$ 　　　(e) $\sqrt{0.09}$

**2** Write the following surds in their simplest form.

(a) $\sqrt{12}$ 　　　(b) $\sqrt{27}$ 　　　(c) $\sqrt{45}$ 　　　(d) $\sqrt{48}$ 　　　(e) $\sqrt{32}$

(f) $\sqrt{50}$ 　　　(g) $\sqrt{54}$ 　　　(h) $\sqrt{24}$ 　　　(i) $\sqrt{98}$ 　　　(j) $\sqrt{80}$

(k) $\sqrt{63}$ 　　　(l) $\sqrt{200}$ 　　　(m) $\sqrt{128}$ 　　　(n) $\sqrt{112}$ 　　　(o) $\sqrt{175}$

**3** Simplify.

(a) $\sqrt{2} + \sqrt{2}$ 　　　(b) $2\sqrt{5} - \sqrt{5}$ 　　　(c) $5\sqrt{3} + 2\sqrt{3}$

(d) $\sqrt{18} + \sqrt{8}$ 　　　(e) $\sqrt{50} - \sqrt{32}$ 　　　(f) $\sqrt{45} + \sqrt{80}$

(g) $\sqrt{75} - \sqrt{12}$ 　　　(h) $\sqrt{300} - \sqrt{48}$ 　　　(i) $\sqrt{50} + \sqrt{18} - \sqrt{8}$

(j) $3\sqrt{20} + 2\sqrt{45}$ 　　　(k) $2\sqrt{48} + 3\sqrt{12}$ 　　　(l) $3\sqrt{45} - 2\sqrt{20}$

**4** Simplify.

(a) $\sqrt{200} - 2\sqrt{18} + \sqrt{72}$     (b) $\sqrt{300} + \sqrt{48} - 3\sqrt{27}$     (c) $3\sqrt{18} - 2\sqrt{8} + \sqrt{2}$

**5** Simplify the following.

(a) $\sqrt{\dfrac{9}{4}}$     (b) $\sqrt{\dfrac{25}{16}}$     (c) $\sqrt{\dfrac{18}{8}}$     (d) $\sqrt{\dfrac{24}{9}}$     (e) $\sqrt{\dfrac{6}{4}}$     (f) $\sqrt{\dfrac{12}{15}}$

**6** Simplify the following.

(a) $\sqrt{3} \times \sqrt{3}$     (b) $\sqrt{3} \times 2\sqrt{3}$     (c) $2\sqrt{5} \times 3\sqrt{5}$     (d) $\sqrt{2} \times \sqrt{8}$

(e) $\sqrt{12} \times \sqrt{3}$     (f) $\sqrt{5} \times \sqrt{10}$     (g) $2\sqrt{6} \times \sqrt{3}$     (h) $2\sqrt{5} \times \sqrt{10}$

(i) $\sqrt{8} \times \sqrt{18}$     (j) $3\sqrt{2} \times 2\sqrt{3}$     (k) $4\sqrt{3} \times 2\sqrt{2}$     (l) $\sqrt{27} \times \sqrt{32}$

**7** Remove the brackets and simplify the following.

(a) $\sqrt{2}(\sqrt{2} + 1)$     (b) $\sqrt{3}(\sqrt{6} - \sqrt{3})$     (c) $\sqrt{5}(\sqrt{10} - \sqrt{5})$

## Rationalising denominators of fractions

When the denominator of a fraction is a surd it is usual to remove the surd from the denominator. This process is called **rationalising the denominator**.

For fractions of the form $\dfrac{a}{\sqrt{b}}$, multiply both the numerator (top) and the denominator (bottom) of the fraction by $\sqrt{b}$ and then simplify where possible.

### EXAMPLE

Rationalise the denominator and simplify where possible:     (a) $\dfrac{1}{\sqrt{2}}$,     (b) $\dfrac{3\sqrt{2}}{\sqrt{6}}$.

(a)  $\dfrac{1}{\sqrt{2}} = \dfrac{1}{\sqrt{2}} \times \dfrac{\sqrt{2}}{\sqrt{2}} = \dfrac{\sqrt{2}}{2}$

(b)  $\dfrac{3\sqrt{2}}{\sqrt{6}} = \dfrac{3\sqrt{2}}{\sqrt{6}} \times \dfrac{\sqrt{6}}{\sqrt{6}} = \dfrac{3\sqrt{2}\,\sqrt{6}}{6} = \dfrac{3\sqrt{2}\,\sqrt{2}\,\sqrt{3}}{6} = \dfrac{6\sqrt{3}}{6} = \sqrt{3}$

## Exercise 9.4

**1** Rationalise the denominator in each of the following and then simplify the fraction.

(a) $\dfrac{1}{\sqrt{3}}$   (b) $\dfrac{1}{\sqrt{5}}$   (c) $\dfrac{1}{\sqrt{7}}$   (d) $\dfrac{2}{\sqrt{2}}$   (e) $\dfrac{5}{\sqrt{5}}$   (f) $\dfrac{4}{\sqrt{2}}$   (g) $\dfrac{6}{\sqrt{3}}$

(h) $\dfrac{14}{\sqrt{7}}$   (i) $\dfrac{3}{\sqrt{6}}$   (j) $\dfrac{15}{\sqrt{5}}$   (k) $\dfrac{9}{\sqrt{3}}$   (l) $\dfrac{5}{\sqrt{15}}$   (m) $\dfrac{18}{\sqrt{6}}$   (n) $\dfrac{35}{\sqrt{5}}$

**2** Express each of the following in its simplest form with a rational denominator.

(a) $\dfrac{6}{\sqrt{8}}$   (b) $\dfrac{6}{\sqrt{24}}$   (c) $\dfrac{8}{\sqrt{32}}$   (d) $\dfrac{9}{\sqrt{18}}$   (e) $\dfrac{\sqrt{3}}{\sqrt{6}}$   (f) $\dfrac{\sqrt{12}}{\sqrt{3}}$

(g) $\dfrac{\sqrt{18}}{\sqrt{2}}$   (h) $\dfrac{\sqrt{5}}{\sqrt{20}}$   (i) $\dfrac{3\sqrt{5}}{\sqrt{15}}$   (j) $\dfrac{4\sqrt{6}}{\sqrt{12}}$   (k) $\dfrac{2\sqrt{8}}{\sqrt{32}}$   (l) $\dfrac{5\sqrt{7}}{\sqrt{35}}$

(m) $\dfrac{\sqrt{3}\,\sqrt{5}}{\sqrt{30}}$   (n) $\dfrac{\sqrt{2}\,\sqrt{3}}{\sqrt{18}}$   (o) $\dfrac{5}{2\sqrt{3}}$   (p) $\dfrac{\sqrt{8}}{2\sqrt{5}}$   (q) $\sqrt{\dfrac{9}{10}}$   (r) $\sqrt{\dfrac{4}{3}}$

- **Rational numbers** can be written in the form $\frac{a}{b}$, where $a$ and $b$ are integers ($b \neq 0$).
  Examples of rational numbers are: $2$, $\quad -5$, $\quad \frac{2}{5}$, $\quad 0.6$, $\quad 3.47$, $\quad 1\frac{3}{4}$.
- All fractions can be written as decimals.
  For example, $\frac{1}{3} = 0.3333333\ldots = 0.\dot{3}$, $\quad \frac{123}{999} = 0.123123123\ldots = 0.\dot{1}2\dot{3}$
- **Irrational numbers** cannot be written as fractions.
  Irrational numbers include:  square roots of non-square numbers,
  $\qquad\qquad\qquad\qquad\qquad$ cube roots of non-cube numbers.
  Examples of irrational numbers are: $\sqrt{2}$, $\quad \sqrt[3]{7}$, $\quad \pi$, $\quad \sqrt{13}$.
- All **terminating** and **recurring decimals** are rational numbers.
- A **surd** is the root of a rational number which is not rational.
  A surd is an irrational number.
- Rules for manipulating and simplifying surds:
$$\sqrt{ab} = \sqrt{a} \times \sqrt{b} \qquad m\sqrt{a} + n\sqrt{a} = (m + n)\sqrt{a} \qquad \sqrt{\frac{a}{b}} = \frac{\sqrt{a}}{\sqrt{b}}$$
- To **rationalise** the denominator of a fraction of the form $\frac{a}{\sqrt{b}}$ multiply both the numerator (top)
  and the denominator (bottom) of the fraction by $\sqrt{b}$.

### Review Exercise 9 $\qquad$ Do not use a calculator.

**1** (a) Change $\frac{5}{9}$ into a decimal.
$\quad$ (b) Find the fraction which is equal to $0.2\dot{5}$. Give your answer in its simplest form.

**2** Convert the recurring decimal $0.\dot{3}\dot{5}$ to a fraction. $\hfill$ OCR

**3** Simplify.
$\quad$ (a) $3\sqrt{5} - \sqrt{5}$ $\qquad\qquad$ (b) $\sqrt{\frac{36}{25}}$ $\qquad\qquad$ (c) $\sqrt{2} \times 3\sqrt{2}$

**4** Simplify the following, leaving the answers in surd form.
$\quad$ (a) $\sqrt{12}$ $\qquad\qquad$ (b) $2\sqrt{3} + 3\sqrt{3}$ $\qquad\qquad$ (c) $\sqrt{\frac{15}{12}}$

**5** (a) Where possible, write these decimals as fractions in their simplest form.
$\qquad$ (i) $0.1$ $\qquad\qquad$ (ii) $0.12112111211112\ldots$ $\qquad\qquad$ (iii) $0.\dot{1}2\dot{3}$
$\quad$ (b) Simplify $\sqrt{18} + \sqrt{72}$. $\hfill$ OCR

**6** Express the following in the form $p\sqrt{q}$ where $p$ and $q$ are integers and $q$ is as small as possible.
$\quad$ (a) $\sqrt{72}$ $\qquad\qquad$ (b) $\sqrt{20} \times \sqrt{15}$ $\qquad\qquad$ (c) $\dfrac{\sqrt{50} \times \sqrt{27}}{\sqrt{18}}$ $\hfill$ OCR

**7** (a) Expand and simplify $\sqrt{5}(2 - 2\sqrt{5})$.
$\quad$ (b) Given that $\sqrt{45} = k\sqrt{5}$, find the value of $k$.
$\quad$ (c) Rationalise the denominator of $\dfrac{20}{\sqrt{5}}$ and simplify your answer.

**8** Express $\dfrac{4}{\sqrt{2}}$ in the form $p\sqrt{q}$, where $p$ and $q$ are integers. $\hfill$ OCR

**9** (a) Simplify $\sqrt{27} + \sqrt{12}$.
$\quad$ (b) Hence, simplify $(\sqrt{27} + \sqrt{12})(\sqrt{27} - \sqrt{12})$.

**10** (a) Write the following in the form $a\sqrt{b}$, where $a$ and $b$ are whole numbers.
$\qquad$ (i) $\sqrt{6} \times \sqrt{8}$ $\qquad\qquad$ (ii) $\sqrt{18} + \sqrt{8}$
$\quad$ (b) Express $\dfrac{1}{2\sqrt{3}}$ in the form of $\dfrac{\sqrt{a}}{b}$, where $a$ and $b$ are whole numbers.

Do not use a calculator for this exercise.

**1**  Here are 4 calculations:  (a) $29 \times 52$   (b) $0.21 \times 0.27$   (c) $19^2$   (d) $1 \div 0.09$

Choose from the list below, the number which is closest to the answer of each calculation.
Use approximations to help you decide.

|  10   0.6   100   375   1000   0.06   37.5   1500 |
OCR

**2**  In a school of 980 students, 540 are girls.
Two thirds of the girls travel to school by bus.   45% of the boys travel to school by bus.
How many more girls than boys travel to school by bus?
OCR

**3**  My recipe for mint jelly uses $2\frac{1}{4}$ pints of water for 6 pounds of cooking apples.
I used only 4 pounds of cooking apples.
How much water did I use to make the jelly?
OCR

**4**  Mrs Brown has double glazing, costing £8000, installed in her house.
To pay for the double glazing she must first pay a deposit of 15% of the cost.
The rest of the cost is paid in 20 equal payments.
How much is one of these equal payments?
OCR

**5**  (a)  Write these fractions in order, smallest first.

$$\frac{1}{2} \quad \frac{1}{4} \quad \frac{1}{3} \quad \frac{2}{5} \quad \frac{3}{4} \quad \frac{2}{3}$$

(b)  Write down a fraction that lies between $\frac{2}{3}$ and $\frac{4}{5}$.

(c)  Work out.  (i) $\frac{2}{3} + \frac{4}{5}$   (ii) $\frac{2}{3}$ of 45   (iii) $\frac{4}{5} \div 8$   (iv) $\frac{2}{3} \times \frac{4}{5}$

**6**  A dealer bought a mobile phone for £75 and sold it to make a 30% profit.
For how much did he sell the phone?
OCR

**7**  Janet and Kyra share a flat and pay all bills in the ratio 1 to 2.
(a)  The telephone bill is £75.
     How much of this bill does Janet pay?
(b)  Janet's share of the electricity bill is £42.
     How much is Kyra's share of the electricity bill?
OCR

**8**  Given that   $1758 \times 28 = 49\,224$,   write down the values of:
(a)  $175.8 \times 0.028$   (b)  $49.224 \div 280$
OCR

**9**  Find the Simple Interest on £500 invested for 6 months at 4% per year.

**10**  The number of spaces is given to the nearest ten.
What is the minimum and maximum possible number of spaces?

> **Parking**
> **400 spaces**

**11**  (a)  Work out  $2^3 + \sqrt{100}$.
(b)  Which number is smaller,  $3^5$  or  $5^3$?  Show all your working.

**12**  John pays £3.24 for 200 g of jelly babies and 300 g of toffees.   100 g of jelly babies cost 48p.
What is the cost of 100 g of toffees?

**13**  Sam ate $\frac{2}{3}$ of the sweets in a bag.   Tom ate $\frac{1}{4}$ of the **remaining** sweets.
(a)  What fraction of the **original** number of sweets did Tom eat?
(b)  There were 9 sweets left after Sam and Tom had eaten their sweets.
     How many sweets were originally in the bag?
OCR

**14** Red tulips and yellow tulips are used for a flower display. The display uses 40 tulips.
The ratio of red tulips to yellow tulips is 3 : 5. How many tulips are red?

**15** Calculate an **estimate** of $\sqrt{(5.84^2 - 3.19^2)}$.  OCR

**16** (a) Find the value of 24 multiplied by the reciprocal of 24.
Show clear working to explain your answer.
(b) Jagdeep said, "The square root of a number is always smaller than the number itself."
Is he correct? Give an example to support your answer.  OCR

**17** The volume of a metal prism is $30\,cm^3$. The mass of the prism is $210\,g$.
What is the density of the metal in $g/cm^3$?

**18** Write 90 as the product of its prime factors.  OCR

**19** Andi tells Cato:

*"When driving your car, if you increase your speed by 10% and then decrease your*
*speed by 10% you will be travelling at a slower speed than you were to begin with."*

Is he correct? Explain your answer.

**20** A train completes a journey of $210\,km$ in $2\frac{1}{2}$ hours.
What is the average speed of the train in kilometres per hour?

**21** (a) Find the highest common factor of 48 and 72.
(b) Find the least common multiple of 48 and 72.

**22** Are these statements true or false?

> **A:** The product of two prime numbers is always a prime number.
> **B:** The sum of two consecutive numbers is always odd.

Explain each answer.

**23** (a) Write $\dfrac{9^5 \times 9^3}{9^4}$ as a single power of 9.

(b) Write $6.5 \times 10^5$ as an ordinary number.
(c) Write 0.000 025 in standard form.

**24** Appleby and Bunbury are two small villages.
(a) The population of Appleby is 120 and the population of Bunbury is 280.
Write the ratio of the populations, Appleby : Bunbury, in its simplest form.
(b) The two villages share a government grant of £80 000 in the ratio of their populations.
Work out how much each village receives.
(c) The distance between Appleby and Bunbury is 35 km, correct to the nearest km.
Write down the greatest and least possible distances between the two villages.  OCR

**25** Calculate $3\frac{2}{3} - 2\frac{1}{2}$.  OCR

**26** (a) Work out the value of $4^1 - 4^{-1}$.    (b) What is the reciprocal of 0.4?

**27** (a) Work out (i) $0.002 \times 0.6$,    (ii) $50 \div 0.05$.
(b) Work out $(3.0 \times 10^4) \times (6.0 \times 10^3)$, writing the answer in standard form.
(c) A terawatt is $10^{12}$ watts.
A power station produces $1.2 \times 10^8$ watts. Write this in terawatts.  OCR

**28** In a sale prices are reduced by 10%. The sale price of a tennis racket is £36.
What was the original price of the tennis racket?

**29** A grandmother decides to share out £6000 among her 5 grandchildren.
Alex receives $\frac{5}{12}$, Brenda 15% and the remainder is shared in the ratio 6 : 4 : 3 between
Christine, David and Ellie respectively. How much does each grandchild receive?

**30** (a) **Estimate** the value of $\sqrt{\dfrac{301.3^2}{892}}$.

(b) The maximum legal load a lorry can carry is 44 tonnes.
It is needed to carry crates that each weigh 6 tonnes to the nearest tonne.
The lorry driver wishes to carry 7 of these crates.
Can he be certain this load is legal? Show your working. OCR

**31** $A = 3 \times 10^4 \qquad B = 5 \times 10^{-2}$
(a) Calculate $A \times B$. Give your answer in standard form.
(b) Calculate $A \div B$. Give your answer in standard form.

**32** (a) Which one of the following is a recurring decimal? $\boxed{\dfrac{22}{25} \qquad \dfrac{17}{20} \qquad \dfrac{8}{11} \qquad \dfrac{2}{5}}$
(b) Express $\frac{5}{9}$ as a recurring decimal.
(c) You are given that $\frac{1}{27} = 0.\dot{0}3\dot{7}$. Express $\frac{4}{27}$ as a recurring decimal. OCR

**33** Simplify, leaving your answers where appropriate in surd form.

(a) $\sqrt{32}$ (b) $\sqrt{2\frac{1}{4}}$ (c) $3\sqrt{3} + \sqrt{12}$

**34** (a) Write the following as whole numbers or fractions. (i) $4^0$ (ii) $9^{\frac{1}{2}}$
(b) Evaluate $(3 \times 10^{-2}) \times (8 \times 10^6)$, giving your answer in standard form. OCR

**35** (a) Vic runs 50 m in 10 seconds.
What is his average speed? Give your answer in kilometres per hour.
(b) Jean also runs 50 m. The ratio of Jean's average speed to Vic's average speed is 4 : 5.
Calculate Jean's average speed in kilometres per hour.

**36** A running track is 100 m correct to the nearest metre.
Another running track is 400 m correct to the nearest metre.
Lauren runs four times around the 100 m track. Aimee runs once around the 400 m track.
What is the upper bound of the difference between the distance Lauren runs and
the distance Aimee runs?

**37** Light travels at $1.86282 \times 10^5$ miles per second.
The Earth is 92.5 million miles from the Sun.
Using suitable approximations, estimate the number of **minutes** light takes to travel
from the Sun to the Earth.

**38** Find the fractions equivalent to these recurring decimals. (a) $0.\dot{7}$ (b) $0.4\dot{7}$ OCR

**39** Work out the value of: (a) $8^{\frac{1}{3}} + 4^{\frac{3}{2}} - 16^{\frac{3}{4}}$, (b) $27^{-\frac{2}{3}}$.

**40** (a) Simplify, leaving your answer where appropriate in surd form.
(i) $\sqrt{27} + \sqrt{147}$ (ii) $5\sqrt{3} + \sqrt{108}$ (iii) $\sqrt{18} \times \sqrt{12}$

(b) Simplify $\sqrt{\dfrac{2}{45}}$, leaving your answer with a rational denominator.

**41** Express each of the following as a fraction in its simplest form.
(a) $2^{-4}$ (b) $144^{-\frac{1}{2}}$ (c) $\left(\frac{27}{64}\right)^{\frac{2}{3}}$

**42** (a) Express $\sqrt{99}$ in the form $a\sqrt{b}$, where $a$ and $b$ are prime numbers.
(b) Show that $\left(\sqrt{2} + \dfrac{1}{\sqrt{2}}\right)^2 = 4.5$.
(c) (i) If $x > 1$, write in ascending order $x^0$, $\sqrt{x}$, $\dfrac{1}{x}$, $x^2$.

(ii) If $0 < x < 1$, write in ascending order $x^0$, $\sqrt{x}$, $\dfrac{1}{x}$, $x^2$. OCR

**43** Write $0.\dot{2}1\dot{6}$ as a fraction in its simplest form.

Section Review

You may use a calculator for this exercise.

**1** (a) Alika pays £6.46 for some cheese. She buys 0.3 kg of Brie and 0.5 kg of Stilton.
The Brie costs £7.20 per kilogram.
How much per kilogram is Stilton?

(b) The weights and prices of two pots of
natural yogurt are shown.
Which pot is better value for money?
Show **all** your working.

**2** Calculate.

(a) $\sqrt{841}$  (b) $93.6 - 3.5 \times (6.2 + 2.6)$  (c) $\dfrac{13.25 + 35.51}{5.3}$  OCR

**3** In a maternity hospital, 200 babies were born during May. 110 of them were girls.
(a) What percentage of the babies were girls?
(b) What is the ratio Boy babies : Girl babies? Give your answer in its lowest terms.
(c) In June, the number of babies born in the hospital increased by 5%.
Calculate the total number of babies born in June.  OCR

**4** A hotel is building a swimming pool.
The volume of earth to be removed is 120 m³.
The digger removes 0.15 m³ with each scoop.
(a) How many scoops are needed to remove all the earth?
(b) The digger takes 2 minutes to take a scoop and dump it.
The digger is hired by the day. There are 8 hours in a working day.
For how many days should the digger be hired? Write down all your calculations.  OCR

**5** (a) James used his calculator to work out $\dfrac{3+5}{2.5+4}$. He said the answer was 9.

(i) Explain how you can see that James's answer is wrong **without** working out the
correct answer.
(ii) This is what James put into his calculator.

$$\boxed{3}\ \boxed{+}\ \boxed{5}\ \boxed{\div}\ \boxed{2}\ \boxed{.}\ \boxed{5}\ \boxed{+}\ \boxed{4}\ \boxed{=}$$

What has he forgotten to do?

(b) Use your calculator to find the value of this expression. $\dfrac{57.3 \times 0.08}{12.05 - 11.65}$  OCR

**6** Bushra has a mobile phone.
She pays a charge of £12.50 per month and the phone calls cost 3 pence per minute.
VAT of 17.5% is added to the total of the charge and the calls.
How much is Bushra's phone bill in a month when she has made calls for 170 minutes?  OCR

**7**

| **EXCHANGE RATES** . . . £1 WILL BUY |
|---|
| GERMANY . . . 1.40 EUROS   UNITED STATES . . . 1.80 DOLLARS |

The same computer can be bought in Germany and in the United States.
In the United States it costs 950 dollars. In Germany it costs 9% more.
How much does it cost to buy the computer in Germany?
Give your answer, in euros, to a suitable degree of accuracy.

**8** (a) Use your calculator to find the value of $\dfrac{19.8^2}{7.19 + 2.73}$

(b) Show how you can use approximation to check your answer.

9  Fiona and Hamish agree to share the profits of their business in the ratio 5 : 3.
   The total profit in 2005 was £60 480.
   Calculate Fiona's share of the profit.                                    OCR

10 (a)  Eddie drives from Barnsley to Cambridge.
        He travels 160 miles in 2 hours 30 minutes.
        Work out his average speed.

   (b)  Eddie also makes these journeys.

| Day | Monday | Tuesday |
|---|---|---|
| Journey | Cambridge to Rugby | Cambridge to Sheffield |
| Average Speed (mph) | 54 | 60 |
| Time taken | 1 hour 20 mins | 2 hours 15 mins |

        How much further is it from Cambridge to Sheffield than it is to Rugby?    OCR

11 Wyn has 600 yo-yo's to sell.  He sells $\frac{3}{5}$ of them at £2 each.
   He then reduces the price of the remaining yo-yo's by 40%.
   In the end he is left with 24 damaged yo-yo's which he cannot sell.
   Wyn paid £500 for the yo-yo's.
   Find the percentage profit which he made on the sale of these yo-yo's.

12 A sponsored walk is held in Boughton each year.
   The money raised is shared between three charities, A, B and C, in the ratio 5 : 4 : 3.
   (a)  In 2003, charity A was given £675.
        How much was given to charity B?
   (b)  In 2004, a total of £1800 was raised.
        (i)   How much was given to charity C?
        (ii)  In 2005, a total of £1975.50 was raised.
              Calculate the percentage increase in the amount raised from 2004 to 2005.    OCR

13 (a)  Write 62 500 000 in standard form.
   (b)  Write 0.375 as a fraction in its lowest terms.
   (c)  What is the least common multiple of 8 and 18?
   (d)  What is the highest common factor of 60 and 84?

14 Kelly invested £450 for 3 years at a rate of 6% per year Compound Interest.
   Calculate the total amount that the investment is worth at the end of the 3 years.    OCR

15 A gold bar has a mass of 1 kilogram. The density of gold is 19.3 g/cm³.
   What is the volume of the gold?

16 (a)  Use your calculator to work out these expressions.
        (i)   $\sqrt{15.1^2 - 2.81^3}$.  Give your answer correct to 3 significant figures.

        (ii)  $\dfrac{1.6 \times 10^{-4} + 8 \times 10^{-5}}{4.8 \times 10^{5}}$.  Give your answer in standard form.

   (b)  Jenny thinks that the reciprocal of a number is always smaller than the number itself.
        Is she correct? Give an example to support your answer.    OCR

17 (a)  A car takes 27 minutes to travel 45 km along a motorway.
        What is the speed of the car in kilometres per hour?
   (b)  A coach overtakes a lorry on the motorway. The speed of the coach is 60 miles per hour.
        The speed of the coach is 20% more than the speed of the lorry.
        What is the speed of the lorry?

18 An electricity bill is £154.56, including VAT at 5%.
   How much of the bill is VAT?                                    OCR

**19** An annual rate of interest between 7% and 8% would be required for a sum of money to double in ten years. Use a trial and improvement method to find this rate of interest. Give your answer as a percentage to 1 decimal place. Show your calculations.    OCR

**20** (a) (i) Write the reciprocal of $1\frac{1}{2}$ as a fraction.

(ii) Write the reciprocal of 40 as a decimal.

(b) Calculate the difference between $5^{-2}$ and $2^{-5}$. Give your answer in standard form.    OCR

**21** $P = 2^3 \times 3^2 \times 5$     $Q = 2 \times 3^3 \times 7$

(a) What number is the highest common factor of $P$ and $Q$?

(b) What number is the least common multiple of $P$ and $Q$?

**22** Evaluate $0.9^7$, giving your answer in standard form.

**23** Lake Reindeer in Canada covers an area of $6.3 \times 10^9 \, \text{m}^2$.

Lake Michigan in the United States of American covers an area of $5.8 \times 10^{10} \, \text{m}^2$.

(a) What is the total area covered by these two lakes?
Give your answer in standard form.

(b) What is the ratio of the area of Lake Reindeer to the area of Lake Michigan?
Give your answer in the form $1 : n$.    OCR

**24** A seal colony is decreasing at the rate of 15% per year.
At the beginning of 2003 there were 5000 seals.

(a) Calculate the number of seals in the colony at the end of 2005.

(b) In which year will the number of seals in the colony fall below 2000?

**25** (a) Calculate $\sqrt{\dfrac{14.7}{(0.7)^3}}$. Give your answer correct to two significant figures.

(b) The distance from the Earth to the Moon is $3.81 \times 10^5$ kilometres.
Light travels at a speed of $3 \times 10^8$ metres per second.
How long does it take light to travel from the Earth to the Moon?

**26** I wish to paint the outside walls of my house.
A tin of paint covers $25 \, \text{m}^2$, correct to the nearest $5 \, \text{m}^2$.
The outside walls of my house have an area of $320 \, \text{m}^2$, correct to the nearest $10 \, \text{m}^2$.
Calculate the maximum number of tins of paint I may have to buy.    OCR

**27** David travels from Manchester to London in $3\frac{1}{2}$ hours, measured to the nearest half hour.
The distance from Manchester to London is 200 miles, measured to the nearest 10 miles.
Calculate upper and lower bounds for the average speed for David's journey.
Give these bounds correct to 3 significant figures where appropriate.    OCR

**28** (a) During 2005 the population of Newtown increased by 5%.
At the end of the year the population was 18 417.
What was the population at the beginning of the year?

(b) The population of Calculand is expected to increase at an annual rate of 2%.
In 2005 the population was 147 million.
Calculate the expected population of Calculand 15 years later.    OCR

**29** (a) Write $0.\dot{2}\dot{7}$ as a fraction in its simplest form.

(b) $m$ is a whole number greater than 2.
Write down a possible value for $m$, when $\sqrt{m} \times \sqrt{2}$ is a whole number.

(c) Write $\dfrac{\sqrt{5}}{\sqrt{2}}$ in the form $\dfrac{\sqrt{a}}{b}$, where $a$ and $b$ are whole numbers.

**30** A formula used in science is $a = \dfrac{v - u}{t}$.
The quantities $v$, $u$ and $t$ are each measured correct to the nearest 0.1.
$$u = 17.4, \quad v = 30.3 \quad \text{and} \quad t = 2.6$$
Find the maximum possible value of $a$.    OCR

# Introduction to Algebra

**Algebra** is sometimes called the language of Mathematics.
Algebra uses letters in place of numbers.

A class of children line up. We cannot see how many
children there are altogether because of a tree.
We can say there are $n$ children in the line.
The letter $n$ is used in place of an unknown number.

Three more children join the line.
There are now   $n + 3$   children in the line.

This picture shows two lines of $n$ children.
So, there are   $n + n$   or   $2 \times n$   children altogether.
The simplest way to write this is $2n$.

Both   $n + 3$   and   $2n$   are examples of **algebraic expressions**.

---

## Exercise **10.1**      Write algebraic expressions for each of the following questions.

**1**  I have $m$ marbles in a bag. I put in another 6 marbles.
How many marbles are now in the bag?

**2**  I have $m$ marbles. I lose 12 marbles.
How many marbles do I have left?

**3**  I have 8 bags of marbles. Each bag contains $m$ marbles.
How many marbles do I have altogether?

**4**  There are $p$ pencils in a pencil case. I take one pencil out.
How many pencils are left in the pencil case?

**5**  There are $p$ pencils in a pencil case. I put in another 5 pencils.
How many pencils are now in the pencil case?

**6**  I have 25 pencil cases. There are $p$ pencils in each pencil case.
How many pencils do I have altogether?

**7**  I have 6 key rings. There are $k$ keys on each key ring.
How many keys do I have altogether?

**8**  What is the cost of $b$ biscuits costing 5 pence each?

**9**  Three cakes cost a total of $c$ pence. What is the cost of one cake?

**10**  Five kilograms of apples cost $a$ pence. What is the cost of one kilogram of apples?

**11**  A group of 36 students are split into $g$ groups. How many students are in each group?

## Expressions and terms

Consider this situation:

    $2n$ students start a typing course.
    3 of the students leave the course.
    How many students remain on the course?

$2n - 3$ students remain.
$2n - 3$ is an **algebraic expression**, or simply an **expression**.

An expression is just an answer made up of letters and numbers.
$+2n$   and   $-3$   are **terms** of the expression.

> **Note:**
> A term includes the sign, $+$ or $-$.
> $2n$ has the same value as $+2n$.

## Simplifying expressions

### Adding and subtracting terms

You can add and subtract terms with the same letter.
This is sometimes called **simplifying an expression**.

$a + a = 2a$
$5k + 3k = 8k$
$3p + 5 + p - 1 = 4p + 4$

$6a - 2a = 4a$
$2d - 3d = -d$
$4x - 4x = 0$

  $6 + a$   cannot be simplified.
$5p - 2q$   cannot be simplified.
  $x^2 + x$   cannot be simplified.
$ab + ba = 2ab$

> **Note that:**
> A simpler way to write $1d$ is just $d$.
>
> $-1d$ can be written as $-d$.
>
> $0d$ is the same as $0$.
>
> Just as with ordinary numbers, you can add terms in any order.
> $a - 2a + 5a = a + 5a - 2a = 4a$

### EXAMPLE

Write down an expression for the perimeter of this shape.
Give your answer in its simplest form.

Perimeter is the total distance round the outside of the shape.
$y + 2x - 1 + 2y + 2x + 3$
Simplify this expression to get:   $4x + 3y + 2$
The perimeter of the shape is   $4x + 3y + 2$.

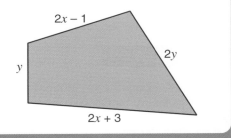

## Exercise 10.2

**1** Simplify these expressions.

  (a)   $n + n + n$
  (b)   $2y + 3y$
  (c)   $5g + g + 4g$
  (d)   $5y - y$
  (e)   $6m - m + 3m$
  (f)   $-2x - 3x + x$
  (g)   $2a - 5a - 12a + a$

**2** Which of these expressions cannot be simplified? Give a reason for each of your answers.

  (a)   $v + v$
  (b)   $v + 4$
  (c)   $2v + v + 4$
  (d)   $v + w$

**3** Simplify where possible.

  (a)   $5x + 3x + y$
  (b)   $w + 3v - v$
  (c)   $2a + b - 3b$
  (d)   $-a + b + 2a$
  (e)   $5 - 9k + 4k$
  (f)   $2a - a + 3$
  (g)   $3a - 5a + 2b + b$
  (h)   $3x - x + 5y - 2y$
  (i)   $2a - b + 3b - a$
  (j)   $-f + g - f - g$
  (k)   $2v - w - 3w - v$
  (l)   $7 - 2t - 9 - 3t$

**4** Simplify.

  (a)   $xy + yx$
  (b)   $3pq - qp$
  (c)   $5ab - 2ba - a + b$
  (d)   $3x^2 - x^2$
  (e)   $5y^2 + 4y^2 - y$
  (f)   $a^2 + 5a^2 - 2a^2 + a$
  (g)   $d^2 - 2g^2 - g^2 + d^2$
  (h)   $3t^2 + t + 2t^2 - 2t$
  (i)   $3m^2 - 4m^2 + 7m - m$

**5** Write down an expression for the perimeter of each shape.
Give each answer in its simplest form.

(a)

(b)

(c)

(d)

## Multiplying terms

Multiply the numbers and then letters in alphabetical order.

$a \times b = ab$      $3x \times y = 3xy$      $3a \times 2b = 6ab$

$a \times a = a^2$      $5c \times 4c = 20c^2$      $b \times b \times b = b^3$

$4a^2b \times 3abc^2 = 12a^3b^2c^2$      $(4 \times 3 = 12, \quad a^2 \times a = a^3, \quad b \times b = b^2, \quad c^2)$

## Dividing terms

Divide the numbers and then letters in alphabetical order.

$8a \div 2 = 4a$      $6y \div 2y = 3$      $9x \div x = 9$

$\dfrac{4p^2q}{12pq^2} = \dfrac{p}{3q}$    $\dfrac{4}{12} = \dfrac{1}{3}, \quad p^2 \div p = p, \quad q \div q^2 = q^{-1} = \dfrac{1}{q}$

 $\dfrac{4p^2q}{12pq^2}$ can be written as $4p^2q \div 12pq^2$

### Multiplying and dividing algebraic expressions with powers

$a^2$ and $b^3$ are examples of **algebraic expressions with powers**.
The rules for multiplying and dividing powers of the same number can be used to simplify algebraic expressions involving powers.

When multiplying or dividing expressions that include both numbers and powers:
**multiply** or **divide** the **numbers**, **add** or **subtract** the **powers**.
Deal with the powers of different bases **separately**.

### EXAMPLES

**1** Simplify.

(a) $x^3 \times x^8 = x^{3+8} = x^{11}$

(b) $2x^2 \times 5x^7 = (2 \times 5) \times (x^2 \times x^7) = 10 \times x^{2+7} = 10x^9$

(c) $x^3y^2 \times xy^4 = (x^3 \times x) \times (y^2 \times y^4) = x^{3+1} \times y^{2+4} = x^4y^6$

(d) $(x^3y^2)^2 = x^{3 \times 2} \times y^{2 \times 2} = x^6y^4$

(e) $(3x^4)^2 = (3 \times 3) \times (x^{4 \times 2}) = 9x^8$

$a^m \times a^n = a^{m+n}$
$a^m \div a^n = a^{m-n}$
$(a^m)^n = a^{m \times n}$

**2** Simplify.

(a) $x^8 \div x^5 = x^{8-5} = x^3$

(b) $6y^6 \div 2y^4 = (6 \div 2) \times (y^6 \div y^4) = 3 \times y^{6-4} = 3y^2$

### Exercise **10.3**

**1** Write these expressions in a simpler form.

(a) $3 \times a$      (b) $2 \times 4 \times c$      (c) $3 \times 3 \times d$      (d) $f \times 8$

(e) $3 \times 2p$      (f) $3q \times 5$      (g) $r \times r$      (h) $2g \times g$

(i) $2g \times 3g$      (j) $3t \times 4t$      (k) $5u \times 3u$      (l) $3d \times 3d$

**2** Simplify.

(a) $3 \times (-y)$      (b) $y \times (-5)$

(c) $(-2) \times (-y)$      (d) $3 \times (-2y)$

(e) $t \times (-t)$      (f) $2t \times (-t)$

(g) $(-2t) \times 5t$      (h) $(-2t) \times (-5t)$

**Remember:**
$$2 \times (-x) = -2x$$
$$(-2) \times (-x) = 2x$$

**3** Simplify.

(a) $10a \div 2$    (b) $12x \div x$    (c) $20y \div y$    (d) $8y \div 4y$

(e) $18p \div p$    (f) $18p \div 6$    (g) $18p \div 6p$    (h) $18k \div 2k$

(i) $28g \div 7g$    (j) $10m \div 2m$    (k) $20t \div 5t$    (l) $27x \div 3x$

**4** Simplify.

(a) $6y \div (-3)$      (b) $(-6y) \div 2$

(c) $(-5m) \div m$      (d) $(-5m) \div (-5)$

(e) $3a \div (-a)$      (f) $(-10d) \div 5d$

(g) $6g \div (-2g)$      (h) $(-3k) \div (-3k)$

**Remember:**
$$2x \div (-2) = -x$$
$$(-2x) \div 2 = -x$$
$$(-2x) \div (-2) = x$$

**5** Simplify.

(a) $a \times b$    (b) $y \times y$    (c) $2 \times p \times q$    (d) $2 \times a \times a$

(e) $3 \times g \times 4 \times h$    (f) $a \times b \times c$    (g) $m \times m \times m$    (h) $2 \times d \times d \times d$

(i) $2x \times 3x \times x$    (j) $5m \times m \times 2n$    (k) $3a \times b \times c$    (l) $2p \times 3q \times 3r$

**6** Simplify.

(a) $y^2 \times y$    (b) $t^3 \times t^2$    (c) $g^7 \times g^3$    (d) $m \times m^3 \times m^2$

(e) $3d^2 \times 2d^3$    (f) $4x^2 \times 2x^3$    (g) $2t \times t^2 \times 3t^2$    (h) $2r \times 3r^2 \times 4r^3$

(i) $mn \times m^2n$    (j) $a^2b \times ba^2$    (k) $3rs^3 \times 2r^2s$    (l) $2x^2y \times 5x^3y^2$

**7** Simplify.

(a) $(t^2)^3$    (b) $(y^3)^2$    (c) $(g^3)^3$    (d) $(x^4)^2$

(e) $(3a)^2$    (f) $(2h)^3$    (g) $2 \times (m^3)^2$    (h) $(2m^3)^2$

(i) $3 \times (d^3)^2$    (j) $(3d^3)^2$    (k) $(3a^2)^3$    (l) $(2k^3)^3$

(m) $(xy)^2$    (n) $(mn^2)^3$    (o) $(2st)^3$    (p) $(3p^2q)^2$

**8** Simplify.

(a) $y^3 \div y$    (b) $a^4 \div a^3$    (c) $x^5 \div x^5$    (d) $g \div g^2$

(e) $6b^3 \div b$    (f) $10m^3 \div 2m^2$    (g) $16t^3 \div 4t^2$    (h) $9h^2 \div 3h^3$

(i) $xy^2 \div xy$    (j) $m^3n \div mn^2$    (k) $2p^3q \div 3pq^2$    (l) $6r^2s^3 \div 2rs$

**9** Simplify and express with positive indices.

(a) $t^5 \times t^{-3}$    (b) $x^3 \times x \times x^{-2}$    (c) $2ab^{-4} \times 6a^{-1}b$

(d) $5p^2q^{-1} \times 3p^{-1}q^3$    (e) $x^7 \div x^{-3}$    (f) $a^{-3} \div a^{-2}$

(g) $6x^3 \div 2x^{-1}$    (h) $8t^{-3}w^2 \div 4t^2w^{-2}$    (i) $(a^{-2})^3$

(j) $(y^{-4})^{-1}$    (k) $5(m^3)^{-3}$    (l) $(3n^{-2})^{-2}$

**Remember:**
$$a^{-m} = \frac{1}{a^m}$$

**10** Simplify.

(a) $\dfrac{t^3}{t^2}$    (b) $\dfrac{g^2}{g^3}$    (c) $\dfrac{m^2 \times m}{m}$    (d) $\dfrac{y^2 \times y^3}{y^4}$

(e) $\dfrac{y \times y^3}{y^2}$    (f) $\dfrac{m^2 \times m^3}{m^6}$    (g) $\dfrac{2t^3 \times t}{t^2}$    (h) $\dfrac{6g^2 \times g}{2g^3}$

**11** Simplify the following by cancelling.

(a) $\dfrac{2uv}{u}$    (b) $\dfrac{12p^2}{3p}$    (c) $\dfrac{a^2bc^3}{2ab}$    (d) $\dfrac{20mn}{5m^2n}$

(e) $\dfrac{0.8w^3}{0.05w^5}$    (f) $\dfrac{3ab}{2ac} \times \dfrac{4bc}{6b^2}$    (g) $\dfrac{8a^2b \times 5ab^2}{10a^3b^3}$    (h) $\dfrac{8ab^2c^3 \times 6a^2bc^{-5}}{12a^2b^3c}$

## Brackets

Some expressions contain brackets. $2(a + b)$ means $2 \times (a + b)$.

You can multiply out brackets in an expression either by using a diagram or by expanding.

To multiply out $2(x + 3)$ using the **diagram method**:

        $2(x + 3)$ means $2 \times (x + 3)$.
        This can be shown using a rectangle.
        The areas of the two parts are $2x$ and 6.
        The total area is $2x + 6$.
        $2(x + 3) = 2x + 6$

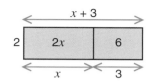

To multiply out $2(x + 3)$ by **expanding**:

        $2(x + 3) = 2 \times x + 2 \times 3$
                  $= 2x + 6$

### EXAMPLES

**1**   Multiply out the bracket $3(4a + 5)$.

**Diagram method**

$3(4a + 5) = 12a + 15$

**Expanding**

$3(4a + 5) = 3 \times 4a + 3 \times 5$
             $= 12a + 15$

**2**   Expand $x(x - 5)$.

$x \times x = x^2$ and $x \times -5 = -5x$
$x(x - 5) = x^2 - 5x$

## Exercise 10.4

**1**   Use the diagrams to multiply out the brackets.

(a)
$2(x + 5) = \ldots$

(b)
$3(a + 6) = \ldots$

(c)
$4(y + 3) = \ldots$

**2**   Draw your own diagrams to multiply out these brackets.

(a) $3(x + 2)$      (b) $2(y + 5)$      (c) $2(2x + 1)$      (d) $3(p + q)$

**3**   Use the diagrams to multiply out the brackets.

(a)
$a(a + 1) = \ldots$

(b)
$d(2 + d) = \ldots$

(c)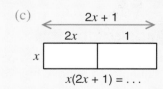
$x(2x + 1) = \ldots$

**4**   Multiply out the brackets by expanding.

(a) $2(x + 4)$      (b) $3(t - 2)$      (c) $2(3a + b)$      (d) $5(3 - 2d)$
(e) $x(x + 3)$      (f) $t(t - 3)$      (g) $g(2g + 3)$      (h) $m(2 - 3m)$

**5**   Multiply out the brackets by expanding.

(a) $2p(p + 3)$      (b) $3d(2 - 3d)$      (c) $m(m - n)$      (d) $5x(x + 2y)$

**To simplify an expression involving brackets:**
- Remove the brackets.
- Simplify by collecting like terms together.

$$3(t + 4) + 2$$
$$= 3t + 12 + 2$$ — Remove the brackets
$$= 3t + 14$$ — Simplify

**6** Multiply out the brackets and simplify.
- (a) $2(x + 1) + 3$
- (b) $3(a + 2) + 5$
- (c) $6(w - 4) + 7$
- (d) $4 + 2(p + 3)$
- (e) $3 + 3(q - 1)$
- (f) $1 + 3(2 - t)$
- (g) $4(z + 2) + z$
- (h) $5(t + 3) + 3t$
- (i) $3(c - 2) - c$
- (j) $2a + 3(a - 3)$
- (k) $y + 2(y - 5)$
- (l) $5x + 3(2 - x)$
- (m) $4(2a + 5) + 3$
- (n) $-2x + 4(3x - 3)$
- (o) $3(p - 5) - p + 4$
- (p) $3a + 2(a + b)$
- (q) $3(x + y) - 2y$
- (r) $2(p - q) - 3q$
- (s) $2x + x(3 - x)$
- (t) $a(a - 3) + a$
- (u) $y(2 - y) + y^2$

**7** Remove the brackets and simplify.
- (a) $2(x + 1) + 3(x + 2)$
- (b) $3(a + 1) + 2(a + 5)$
- (c) $4(y + 2) + 5(y + 3)$
- (d) $2(3a + 1) + 3(a + 1)$
- (e) $3(2t + 5) + 5(4t + 3)$
- (f) $3(z + 5) + 2(z - 1)$
- (g) $7(q - 2) + 5(q + 6)$
- (h) $5(x + 3) + 6(x - 3)$
- (i) $8(2e - 1) + 4(e - 2)$
- (j) $2(5d + 4) + 2(d - 1)$
- (k) $m(m - 2) + m(2m - 1)$
- (l) $a(3a + 2) + 2a(a - 3)$

**8** Multiply out the brackets and simplify.
- (a) $-3(x + 2)$
- (b) $-3(x - 2)$
- (c) $-2(y - 5)$
- (d) $-2(3 - x)$
- (e) $-3(5 - y)$
- (f) $-4(1 + a)$
- (g) $5 - 2(a + 1)$
- (h) $5d - 3(d - 2)$
- (i) $4b - 2(3 + b)$
- (j) $-3(2p + 3)$
- (k) $5m - 2(3 + 2m)$
- (l) $2(3d - 1) - d + 3$
- (m) $-a(a - 2)$
- (n) $2d - d(1 + d)$
- (o) $x^2 - x(1 - x) + x$
- (p) $-3g(2g + 3)$
- (q) $t^2 - 2t(3 - 3t)$
- (r) $2m - 2m(m - 3)$

**Remember:**
$$(-2) \times (+3) = -6$$
$$(-2) \times (-3) = +6$$

so, $-2(x + 3) = -2x - 6$
and $-2(x - 3) = -2x + 6$

**9** Expand the brackets and simplify.
- (a) $2(a + 1) - (3 - a)$
- (b) $3(y - 1) - 2(y + 1)$
- (c) $2(1 + m) - 3(1 - m)$
- (d) $5(x - 2) - 2(x - 3)$
- (e) $2(5 + d) - 3(3 + d)$
- (f) $4(t - 1) - 3(t + 2)$
- (g) $3(2m + 1) - 2(m - 3)$
- (h) $4(2x - 3) - 3(3x + 2)$
- (i) $2(4 + 3a) - 3(4a - 5)$

## Factorising

**Factorising** is the opposite operation to removing brackets.
For example: to remove brackets $2(x + 5) = 2x + 10$

To factorise $3x + 6$ we can see that $3x$ and 6 have a
**common factor** of 3 so,

$$3x + 6 = 3(x + 2)$$

A **common factor** can also be a **letter**.
Both $y^2$ and $5y$ can be divided by $y$.
To factorise $y^2 - 5y$ we take $y$ as the common factor,
so, $y^2 - 5y = y(y - 5)$

**Common factors:**
The **factors** of a number are all the
numbers that will divide exactly into
the number.
Factors of 6 are 1, 2, 3 and 6.

A **common factor** is a factor which
will divide into two or more terms.

In some instances the terms will have both a number and a letter as common factors and **both** must be taken out.

You can check that you have factorised an expression correctly by multiplying out the brackets.

**EXAMPLES**

**1** Factorise $4x - 6$.

Each term has a factor of 2.
So, the common factor is 2.
$4x - 6 = 2(2x - 3)$

**3** Factorise completely $2ab^2 - 6b^3$.

$2ab^2 - 6b^3 = 2b^2(a - 3b)$

**2** Factorise $2x^2 - 6x$.

Each term has a factor of 2.
Each term has a factor of $x$.
So, the common factor is $2x$.

$2x^2 - 6x = 2x(x - 3)$

## Exercise 10.5

**1** Copy and complete.
(a) $2x + 2y = 2(\ldots + \ldots)$    (b) $3a - 6b = 3(\ldots - \ldots)$    (c) $6m + 8n = 2(\ldots + \ldots)$
(d) $x^2 - 2x = x(\quad)$    (e) $ab + a = a(\quad)$    (f) $2x - xy = x(\quad)$
(g) $2ab - 4a = 2a(\quad)$    (h) $4x^2 + 6x = 2x(\quad)$    (i) $dg - dg^2 = dg(\quad)$

**2** Factorise.
(a) $2a + 2b$      (b) $5x - 5y$      (c) $3d + 6e$      (d) $4m - 2n$
(e) $6a + 9b$      (f) $6a - 8b$      (g) $8t + 12$      (h) $5a - 10$
(i) $4d - 2$      (j) $3 - 9g$      (k) $5 - 20m$      (l) $4k + 4$

**3** Factorise.
(a) $xy - xz$      (b) $fg + gh$      (c) $ab - 2b$      (d) $3q + pq$
(e) $a + ab$      (f) $gh - g$      (g) $a^2 + 3a$      (h) $5t - t^2$
(i) $d - d^2$      (j) $m^2 + m$      (k) $5r^2 - 3r$      (l) $3x^2 + 2x$

**4** Factorise completely.
(a) $3y + 6 - 9x$      (b) $t^3 - t^2 + t$      (c) $2d^2 + 4d$      (d) $3m - 6mn$
(e) $2fg + 4g^2$      (f) $4pq - 8q$      (g) $6y - 15y^2$      (h) $6x^2 + 4xy$
(i) $6n^2 - 2n$      (j) $4ab + 6b$      (k) $\frac{1}{2}a - \frac{1}{2}a^2$      (l) $20x + 4xy$
(m) $a^3 + a^5 + a^2$      (n) $2\pi r + \pi r^2$      (o) $20a^2b + 12ab^2$      (p) $3pq - 9p^2q$

## What you need to know

**You should be able to:**

- Write simple algebraic expressions.
- Simplify expressions by collecting like terms together.
  e.g. $2d + 3d = 5d$ and $3x + 2 - x + 4 = 2x + 6$
- Multiply simple expressions together. e.g. $2a \times a = 2a^2$ and $y \times y \times y = y^3$
- Recall and use these properties of powers:
  Powers of the same base are **added** when terms are **multiplied**.
  Powers of the same base are **subtracted** when terms are **divided**.
  Powers are **multiplied** when a power is raised to a power.

  $$a^m \times a^n = a^{m+n}$$
  $$a^m \div a^n = a^{m-n}$$
  $$(a^m)^n = a^{m \times n}$$

- Multiply out brackets. e.g. $2(x - 5) = 2x - 10$ and $x(x - 5) = x^2 - 5x$
- Factorise expressions. e.g. $3x - 6 = 3(x - 2)$ and $x^2 + 5x = x(x + 5)$

**1** Large sticks of rock cost $n$ pence each.
  (a)  Write an expression for the cost of 5 large sticks of rock.
  (b)  A small stick of rock costs 15 pence less than a large stick.
       Write an expression for the cost of a small stick of rock.

**2** (a)  Write each of the following expressions in its simplest form.
       (i)  $4b + 2b + 3b$     (ii)  $2 \times y \times 3$     (iii)  $t \times t \times t$
  (b)  Multiply out the following expression by removing the brackets.  $4(3x + 5)$     OCR

**3** The cost of one banana is $b$ pence. The cost of one grapefruit is $g$ pence.
  Write down an expression for the total cost of 3 bananas and 5 grapefruit.     OCR

**4** In the triangle $PQR$, the side $PQ$ has length $x$ centimetres.
  (a)  $PR$ is twice the length of $PQ$.
       Write an expression for the length of $PR$.
  (b)  $QR$ is 3 cm longer than $PQ$.
       Write an expression for the length of $QR$.
  (c)  Write an expression for the perimeter of the triangle.
       Give your answer in its simplest form.

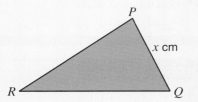

**5** Simplify.  (a)  $ab + 2ba$     (b)  $a^2 - a + 3a$     (c)  $3(x - 2) - x$     (d)  $3x + 2(x + 1)$

**6** (a)  Simplify.  $2x + 4y + 7x - y$
  (b)  Factorise.  $3x + 18$     OCR

**7** (a)  Simplify  $2n + 1 - n + 2n - 6$.
  (b)  Multiply out and simplify  $3(a - 1) + 2(a + 2)$.
  (c)  Factorise  $2x^2 + xy$.

**8** (a)  Simplify  $a^3 \times a^2$.
  (b)  Expand and simplify the expression  $5(2x - 1) + 3(4x - 3)$.     OCR

**9** Factorise.  (a)  $6x - 15$     (b)  $y^2 + 7y$

**10** Simplify.
  (a)  $a \times 2a \times 3a$          (b)  $a \times 2b \times 3a \times 4$          (c)  $(-2a) \times (+a) \times (-b)$

**11** (a)  Simplify  $7 - 2(x - 3)$.
  (b)  Factorise  (i)  $6xy - 2y$,          (ii)  $7y^2 + 14y$.
  (c)  Simplify  $(-5m) \times (-m)$.

**12** Multiply out the brackets and simplify.  (a)  $x^2 - x(1 - x)$          (b)  $4 - 3(x + 1)$

**13** Multiply out and simplify  $2(3x + 1) - 4(x - 3)$.     OCR

**14** Simplify.  (a)  $a^6 \times a^3$     (b)  $b^6 \div b^3$     (c)  $\dfrac{c^3 \times c}{c^2}$     (d)  $(d^3)^2$

**15** Simplify.  (a)  $p^4 \times p^3$     (b)  $\dfrac{12t^5}{3t^2}$     OCR

**16** (a)  Factorise fully.  (i)  $6xy - 3y^2$     (ii)  $4m^2 + 6m$
  (b)  Simplify.     (i)  $5y^3 \times 2y^2$     (ii)  $6x^6 \div 2x^2$     (iii)  $\dfrac{9a^3 \times 2b}{6ab^2}$

**17** Simplify.  (a)  $4(x - 3) - 2(x + 1)$     (b)  $\dfrac{4y^3 \times 3y^2}{6y}$     OCR

**18** Simplify.  (a)  $4(x + 2) - 4(2x + 1)$     (b)  $\dfrac{3a^6 \times 4a^2}{2a^3}$     OCR

# Solving Equations ●●●●●●●●●

## Activity

Can you solve these puzzles?

● **Nueve** is a Spanish number.
  If you add 1 to **nueve** you get 10.
  What is **nueve**?

● What number must be put in each shape to make the statements correct?

  $\Box + 3 = 8$ $\qquad$ $\bigcirc \times 3 = 30$ $\qquad$ $2 \times \bigcirc - 3 = 7$

These are all examples of **equations**.
Equations like these can be solved using a method known as **inspection**.
Instead of words or boxes, equations are usually written using letters for the unknown numbers.
**Solving** an equation means finding the numerical value of the letter which fits the equation.

---

### EXAMPLES

Solve these equations by inspection.

**1** $\quad x - 2 = 6$

$\quad x = 8$

Reason: $\mathbf{8} - 2 = 6$

**2** $\quad 2y = 10$

$\quad y = 5$

Reason: $2 \times \mathbf{5} = 10$

> **Remember:**
> A letter or a symbol stands for an unknown number.
>
> $2y$ means $2 \times y$.

---

## Exercise **11.1**

**1** What number must be put in the box to make each of these statements true?
  (a) $\Box + 4 = 7$ $\qquad$ (b) $15 - \Box = 11$ $\qquad$ (c) $13 = \Box + 4$ $\qquad$ (d) $11 = \Box - 5$

**2** Solve these equations by inspection.
  (a) $x + 2 = 6$ $\qquad$ (b) $a + 7 = 10$ $\qquad$ (c) $y - 4 = 4$
  (d) $6 + t = 12$ $\qquad$ (e) $h - 15 = 7$ $\qquad$ (f) $d + 4 = 5$
  (g) $z - 5 = 25$ $\qquad$ (h) $p + 7 = 7$ $\qquad$ (i) $c + 1 = 100$

**3** What number must be put in the box to make each of these statements true?
  (a) $3 \times \Box = 15$ $\qquad$ (b) $\Box \times 4 = 20$ $\qquad$ (c) $\Box \div 2 = 9$ $\qquad$ (d) $7 = \Box \div 3$

**4** Solve these equations by inspection.
  (a) $3a = 12$ $\qquad$ (b) $5e = 30$ $\qquad$ (c) $8 = 2p$ $\qquad$ (d) $4 = 8y$
  (e) $\frac{d}{2} = 5$ $\qquad$ (f) $\frac{t}{3} = 3$ $\qquad$ (g) $\frac{m}{7} = 4$ $\qquad$ (h) $\frac{x}{5} = 20$

**5** What number must be put in the box to make each of these statements true?
  (a) $2 \times \Box + 3 = 5$ $\qquad$ (b) $\Box \times 3 + 5 = 17$ $\qquad$ (c) $3 + \Box \times 2 = 11$
  (d) $5 \times \Box - 1 = 9$ $\qquad$ (e) $4 \times \Box - 5 = 7$ $\qquad$ (f) $\Box \times 3 - 6 = 9$

## Solving equations by working backwards

I think of a number and then subtract 3.
The answer is 5.
What is the number I thought of?

Imagine that $x$ is the number I thought of.
The steps of the problem can be shown in a diagram.

$x \longrightarrow$ subtract 3 $\longrightarrow$ Answer 5

Now work backwards, doing the opposite calculation.

8 $\longleftarrow$ add 3 $\longleftarrow$ 5

The number I thought of is 8.

**Remember:**

| Forwards | Backwards |
|----------|-----------|
| add | subtract |
| subtract | add |
| multiply | divide |
| divide | multiply |

---

### EXAMPLE

I think of a number, multiply it by 3 and add 4.
The answer is 19.
What is my number?

$x \longrightarrow$ multiply by 3 $\longrightarrow$ add 4 $\longrightarrow$ 19

5 $\longleftarrow$ divide by 3 $\longleftarrow$ 15 $\longleftarrow$ subtract 4 $\longleftarrow$ 19

The number I thought of is 5.

---

### Exercise 11.2

Solve these equations by working backwards.

**1** I think of a number and then multiply it by 2. The answer is 10. What is my number?

**2** Jan thinks of a number and then subtracts 5. Her answer is 9. What is her number?

**3** Lou thinks of a number. He multiplies it by 2 and then subtracts 5. The answer is 7. What is his number?

**4** I think of a number, subtract 5 and then multiply by 2. The answer is 12. What is my number?

**5** I think of a number, add 4 then multiply by 3. The answer is 24. What is my number?

**6** Steve thinks of a number. He multiplies it by 5 and then adds 2. The answer is 17. What is his number?

**7** I think of a number, multiply it by 3 and then subtract 5. The answer is 7. What is my number?

**8** Solve this puzzle.

> Begin with $x$. Double it and then add 3. The result is equal to 17. What is the value of $x$?

**9** Kathryn thinks of a number. She adds 3 and then doubles the result.
 (a) What number does Kathryn start with to get an answer of 10?
 (b) Kathryn starts with $x$. What is her answer in terms of $x$?

**10** Sarah thinks of a number. She subtracts 2 and multiplies by 3.
 (a) What number does Sarah start with to get an answer of 21?
 (b) Sarah starts with $x$. What is her answer in terms of $x$?

## The balance method

It is not always easy to solve equations by inspection.
To solve harder equations a better method has to be used.
Here is a method that works a bit like a balance.

① These scales are balanced.

② You can add the same amount to both sides and they still balance.

③ You can subtract the same amount from both sides and they still balance.

④ You can double (or halve) the amount on both sides and they still balance.

**Equations** work in the same way.
If you do the same to both sides of an equation, it is still true.

### EXAMPLES

**1** Solve $d - 13 = 5$.

$d - 13 = 5$
Add 13 to both sides.
$d = 18$

**2** Solve $x + 7 = 16$.

$x + 7 = 16$
Subtract 7 from both sides.
$x = 9$

**3** Solve $4a = 20$.

$4a = 20$
Divide both sides by 4.
$a = 5$

The aim is to find out what number the letter stands for, by ending up with **one letter** on one side of the equation and a **number** on the other side.

**4** Solve $4n + 5 = 17$.

$4n + 5 = 17$
Subtract 5 from both sides.
$4n = 12$
Divide both sides by 4.
$n = 3$

Look at the examples carefully.
The steps taken to solve the equations are explained.
Notice that, doing the same to both sides means:

**adding** the **same number** to both sides.
**subtracting** the **same number** from both sides.
**dividing** both sides by the **same number**.
**multiplying** both sides by the **same number**.

**1** Use the balance method to solve these equations.

(a) $y + 4 = 7$
(b) $n - 7 = 9$
(c) $9 + x = 11$
(d) $y - 12 = 7$
(e) $14 + b = 21$
(f) $x - 9 = 20$
(g) $7 + m = 11$
(h) $k - 2 = 3$
(i) $5 + y = 12$

**2** Use the balance method to solve these equations.

(a) $3c = 12$
(b) $5a = 20$
(c) $4f = 12$
(d) $\frac{d}{3} = 10$
(e) $\frac{e}{2} = 7$
(f) $\frac{m}{4} = 5$

**3** Solve these equations.

(a) $2p + 1 = 9$
(b) $4t - 1 = 11$
(c) $3h - 7 = 14$
(d) $3 + 4b = 11$
(e) $5d - 8 = 42$
(f) $2x + 3 = 15$
(g) $2 + 3c = 17$
(h) $3n - 1 = 8$
(i) $4x + 3 = 11$

## More equations

All the equations you have solved so far have had whole number solutions, but the solutions to equations can include negative numbers and fractions.

### EXAMPLES

**1** Solve $-4a = 20$.

$-4a = 20$
Divide both sides by $-4$.
$a = -5$

**2** Solve $6m - 1 = 2$.

$6m - 1 = 2$
Add 1 to both sides.
$6m = 3$
Divide both sides by 6.
$m = \frac{1}{2}$

**1** Solve these equations.

(a) $4k = 2$
(b) $2a = -6$
(c) $-3d = 12$
(d) $-8n = 4$
(e) $t + 3 = -2$
(f) $n - 3 = -2$
(g) $2m + 1 = 4$
(h) $3x - 2 = 5$
(i) $2y + 5 = 4$

**2** Solve these equations.

(a) $5x = -10$
(b) $2y + 7 = 1$
(c) $4t + 10 = 2$
(d) $5 - a = 7$
(e) $2 - d = 5$
(f) $3 - 2g = 9$
(g) $4t = 2$
(h) $2x = 15$
(i) $5d = 7$
(j) $4a - 5 = 1$
(k) $3 + 5g = 4$
(l) $2b - 5 = 4$

**3** Solve.

(a) $x - 1 = -3$
(b) $3 + 2n = 2$
(c) $2 - a = 3$
(d) $4 - 3y = 13$
(e) $2x - 1 = -3$
(f) $3 - 5d = 18$
(g) $4x + 1 = -5$
(h) $-2 - 3x = 10$
(i) $2 - 4x = 8$
(j) $5 - 4n = -1$
(k) $\frac{1}{2}z + 2 = 7$
(l) $-2 = 5m + 13$
(m) $-3 = 17 - 5n$
(n) $-6p - 1 = 8$
(o) $12 + \frac{v}{3} = 15$

## Equations with brackets

Equations can include brackets. Before using the balance method any brackets must be removed by multiplying out. This is called **expanding**.

**Remember:** $2(x + 3)$ means $2 \times (x + 3)$

$2(x + 3) = 2 \times x + 2 \times 3 = 2x + 6$

Once the brackets have been removed the balance method can be used as before.

### EXAMPLES

**1** Solve $3(x + 2) = 12$.

$3(x + 2) = 12$
Expand the brackets.
$3x + 6 = 12$
$3x = 6$
$x = 2$

**2** Solve $5(3y - 7) + 15 = 25$.

$5(3y - 7) + 15 = 25$
Expand the brackets.
$15y - 35 + 15 = 25$
$15y = 45$
$y = 3$

## Exercise 11.5

**1** Solve.

(a) $2(x + 3) = 12$     (b) $4(a + 1) = 12$     (c) $5(t + 4) = 30$
(d) $3(p - 2) = 9$      (e) $6(c - 2) = 24$     (f) $2(x - 1) = 4$
(g) $6(d - 3) = 36$     (h) $7(2 + e) = 49$     (i) $5(f + 2) = 30$

**2** Solve.

(a) $3(2w + 1) = 15$    (b) $2(4s + 5) = 34$    (c) $8(3t - 5) = 32$
(d) $5(3y + 2) = 25$    (e) $4(7 - 2x) = 4$     (f) $5(3y - 10) = 25$

**3** Solve these equations. The solution will not always be a whole number.

(a) $3(p + 2) = 3$      (b) $2(3 - d) = 10$     (c) $2(1 - 3g) = 14$
(d) $2(x - 5) = 7$      (e) $5(y + 1) = 7$      (f) $2(1 + 3t) = 5$
(g) $2(2t - 1) = 5$     (h) $3(2a - 3) = 6$     (i) $5(m - 2) = 3$

**4** Solve these equations.

(a) $2(x + 3) - 5 = 9$      (b) $3(a - 1) + 2 = 5$        (c) $5(3 - 2m) - 7 = 13$
(d) $5 + 2(y - 3) = 4$      (e) $2w + 3(1 + w) = -12$     (f) $e + 5(2e - 4) = 2$
(g) $3a - 7(1 - a) = 8$     (h) $2 - 3(t + 5) = 20$       (i) $5x - 2(3 - x) = 1$

## Equations with letters on both sides

In some questions letters appear on both sides of the equation.

### EXAMPLES

**1** Solve $3x + 1 = x + 7$.

$3x + 1 = x + 7$
Subtract 1 from both sides.
$3x = x + 6$
Subtract $x$ from both sides.
$2x = 6$
Divide both sides by 2.
$x = 3$

**2** Solve $4(3 + 2x) = 5(x + 2)$.

$4(3 + 2x) = 5(x + 2)$
$12 + 8x = 5x + 10$
$8x = 5x - 2$
$3x = -2$
$x = -\frac{2}{3}$

1. Solve the following equations.
   (a) $3x = 20 - x$       (b) $5q = 12 - q$       (c) $2t = 15 - 3t$
   (d) $5e - 9 = 2e$       (e) $3g - 8 = g$       (f) $y + 3 = 5 - y$
   (g) $4x + 1 = x + 7$       (h) $7k + 3 = 3k + 7$       (i) $3a - 1 = a + 7$
   (j) $3p - 1 = 2p + 5$       (k) $6m - 1 = m + 9$       (l) $3d - 5 = 5 + d$
   (m) $2y + 1 = y + 6$       (n) $3 + 5u = 2u + 12$       (o) $4q + 3 = q + 3$

2. Solve.
   (a) $3d = 32 - d$       (b) $3q = 12 - q$       (c) $3c + 2 = 10 - c$
   (d) $4t + 2 = 17 - t$       (e) $4w + 1 = 13 - 2w$       (f) $2e - 3 = 12 - 3e$
   (g) $2g + 5 = 25 - 2g$       (h) $2z - 6 = 14 - 3z$       (i) $5m + 2 = 20 + 2m$
   (j) $5a - 4 = 3a + 6$       (k) $3 + 4x = 15 + x$       (l) $6y - 11 = y + 4$

3. Solve these equations. The solution will not always be a whole number.
   (a) $3m + 8 = m$       (b) $2 - 4t = 12 + t$       (c) $5p - 3 = 3p - 7$
   (d) $5x - 7 = 3x$       (e) $3 + 5a = a + 5$       (f) $2b + 7 = 11 - 3b$
   (g) $4 - 4y = y$       (h) $7 + 3d = 10 - d$       (i) $f - 6 = 3f + 1$

4. Solve.
   (a) $2(x + 3) - 5 = 9$       (b) $2(a - 1) + a = 3$       (c) $4(3 - 2m) - 7 = 2m$
   (d) $3(a + 4) = 2 + a$       (e) $3(y - 5) = y - 4$       (f) $4(n + 2) = 2n + 5$
   (g) $4d + 3 = 2(d - 3)$       (h) $7k + 2 = 5(k - 4)$       (i) $2(4t + 5) = t - 18$
   (j) $5q - 2(q + 1) = 4$       (k) $x = 8 - 2(x + 3)$       (l) $4 - 3(a - 2) = a$

5. Solve.
   (a) $2(3h - 4) = 3(h + 1) - 5$       (b) $2(3 - 2x) = 2(6 - x)$
   (c) $2(3w - 1) + 4w = 28$       (d) $2(y + 4) + 3(2y - 5) = 5$
   (e) $3(2v + 3) = 5 - 4(3 - v)$       (f) $5c - 2(4c - 9) = 5 + 5(2 - c)$
   (g) $5(x + 2) + 2(2x - 1) = 7(x - 4)$       (h) $3(x - 4) = 5(2x - 3) - 2(3x - 5)$

## Equations with fractions

You have already met some equations with fractions.
This section deals with harder equations with fractions.

For example: $\frac{3}{4}x = \frac{2}{5}$

With equations like this, it is easier to get rid of the fractions first.
To do this multiply both sides of the equation by the least common multiple of the denominators of
the fractions.

Solve $\frac{3}{4}x = \frac{2}{5}$.

The multiples of 4 are: 4, 8, 12, 16, **20**, …
The multiples of 5 are: 5, 10, 15, **20**, …

The least common multiple of 4 and 5 is 20.
So, the first step is to multiply both sides of the equation by 20.

$$\frac{3}{4}x \times 20 = \frac{2}{5} \times 20$$

This is the same as: $x \times \frac{3}{4} \times 20 = \frac{2}{5} \times 20$

$$15x = 8$$

Divide both sides by 15.

$$x = \frac{8}{15}$$

**Remember:**
$\frac{3}{4} \times 20$ is the same as $\frac{3}{4}$ of 20.
To find $\frac{3}{4}$ of 20:

$20 \div 4 = 5$ gives $\frac{1}{4}$ of 20.

$5 \times 3 = 15$ gives $\frac{3}{4}$ of 20.

So, $\frac{3}{4} \times 20 = 15$.

## EXAMPLES

**1** Solve $\frac{x}{2} + \frac{2x}{3} = 7$.

$$\frac{x}{2} + \frac{2x}{3} = 7$$

Multiply both sides by 6.

$$6 \times \frac{x}{2} + 6 \times \frac{2x}{3} = 6 \times 7$$
$$3x + 4x = 42$$
$$7x = 42$$
$$x = 6$$

**2** Solve $\frac{x-1}{3} = \frac{x+1}{4}$.

$$\frac{x-1}{3} = \frac{x+1}{4}$$

Multiply both sides by 12.

$$4(x-1) = 3(x+1)$$
$$4x - 4 = 3x + 3$$
$$4x = 3x + 7$$
$$x = 7$$

## Exercise 11.7

**1** Solve these equations.

(a) $\frac{2}{3}x = 4$

(b) $\frac{2d}{5} = -4$

(c) $\frac{a}{8} = \frac{3}{4}$

(d) $\frac{2m}{8} = -\frac{3}{6}$

(e) $\frac{3t}{4} = \frac{1}{3}$

**2** Solve.

(a) $\frac{h+1}{4} = 3$

(b) $\frac{2x-1}{3} = 5$

(c) $\frac{3a+4}{5} = -1$

(d) $\frac{7-d}{4} = \frac{5}{2}$

(e) $\frac{2a+1}{2} = \frac{3}{5}$

(f) $\frac{2-3h}{3} = -\frac{5}{6}$

(g) $\frac{x+2}{5} = \frac{3-x}{4}$

(h) $\frac{a-1}{2} = \frac{a+1}{3}$

(i) $\frac{2x-1}{6} = \frac{2-x}{3}$

**3** Solve.

(a) $\frac{x}{2} + \frac{x}{4} = 1$

(b) $\frac{x}{2} - \frac{x}{3} = 2$

(c) $\frac{x}{4} + \frac{3x}{8} = -1$

(d) $\frac{2x}{3} - \frac{x}{6} = -2$

(e) $\frac{x+1}{2} + \frac{x-1}{3} = 1$

(f) $\frac{x+2}{3} - \frac{x+1}{4} = 2$

(g) $\frac{11-x}{4} = 2 - x$

(h) $\frac{x+2}{2} + \frac{x-1}{5} = \frac{1}{10}$

(i) $\frac{2x-3}{6} + \frac{x+2}{3} = \frac{5}{2}$

## Using equations to solve problems

So far, you have been given equations and asked to solve them.
The next step is to **form an equation** first using the information given in a problem.
The equation can then be solved in the usual way.

## EXAMPLE

The triangle has sides of length: $x$ cm, $2x$ cm and 7 cm.

(a) Write an expression, in terms of $x$,
for the perimeter of the triangle.
Give your answer in its simplest form.

(b) The triangle has a perimeter of 19 cm.
By forming an equation find the value of $x$.

$x$ cm     7 cm     $2x$ cm

(a) The perimeter of the triangle is: $x + 2x + 7$ cm
In its simplest form, the perimeter is: $(3x + 7)$ cm

(b) The perimeter of the triangle is 19 cm, so, $3x + 7 = 19$
$$3x = 12$$
$$x = 4$$

**1** The weights of three packages are shown.

   $k$ kilograms                     $2k$ kilograms                     $3k$ kilograms

   (a)   Write an expression, in terms of $k$, for the total weight of the packages.
   (b)   The packages weigh 15 kilograms altogether.
         By forming an equation find the weight of the lightest package.

**2** A bag contains $x$ yellow balls, $(2x + 1)$ red balls and $(3x + 2)$ blue balls.
   (a)   Write an expression, in terms of $x$, for the total number of balls in the bag.
   (b)   The bag contains 45 balls. How many yellow balls are in the bag?

**3** Dominic is 7 years younger than Marcie.
   (a)   Dominic is $n$ years old.
         Write an expression, in terms of $n$, for Marcie's age.
   (b)   The sum of their ages is 43 years.
         By forming an equation find the ages of Dominic and Marcie.

**4** The diagram shows the lengths of three rods.

   $(y - 5)$ centimetres            $y$ centimetres            $(2y + 3)$ centimetres

   (a)   Write an expression, in terms of $y$, for the total length of the rods.
   (b)   The total length of the rods is 30 centimetres.
         What is the length of the longest rod?

**5** Grace is given a weekly allowance of £$p$.
   Aimee is given £4 a week **more** than Grace.
   Lydia is given £3 a week **less** than Grace.
   (a)   Write an expression, in terms of $p$, for the amount given to
         (i)   Aimee,      (ii)   Lydia,      (iii)   all three girls.
   (b)   The three girls are given a total of £25 a week altogether.
         By forming an equation find the weekly allowance given to each girl.

**6** The cost of a pencil is $x$ pence. The cost of a pen is 10 pence more than a pencil.
   (a)   Write an expression, in terms of $x$, for the cost of a pen.
   (b)   Write an expression, in terms of $x$, for the total cost of a pencil and two pens.
   (c)   The total cost of a pencil and two pens is 65 pence.
         Form an equation in $x$ and solve it to find the cost of a pencil.

**7** A chocolate biscuit costs $x$ pence.
   A cream biscuit costs 4 pence less than a chocolate biscuit.
   Jamie pays 77 pence for 3 chocolate biscuits and 2 cream biscuits.
   By forming an equation find the cost of a cream biscuit.

**8** (a)   Write down a simplified expression, in terms of $x$, for the perimeter of the triangle.

   $(2x - 5)$ cm          $(2x - 1)$ cm
   $(3x + 2)$ cm

   (b)   The perimeter is 59 cm.
         Write down an equation and solve it to find the value of $x$.
   (c)   Use your answer to find the length of each side of the triangle.

**9** The length of a rectangle is $x$ cm. The width of the rectangle is 4 cm less than the length.
  (a) Write an expression, in terms of $x$, for the width of the rectangle.
  (b) Write an expression for the perimeter of the rectangle in terms of $x$.
  (c) The perimeter of the rectangle is 20 cm.
    By forming an equation find the value of $x$.

**10** Geoffrey knows that the sum of the angles of this shape adds up to 540°.
  (a) Write down an equation in $x$.
  (b) Use your equation to find the size
    of the largest angle.

**11** A drink costs $x$ pence.
  A cake costs 7 pence more than a drink.
  The total cost of two drinks and a cake is 97 pence.
  Form an equation in $x$ and solve it to find the cost of a cake.

**12** The areas of these rectangles are equal.

By forming and solving an equation in $x$, find the area of $A$.

**13**

  (a) Write down an expression, in terms of $x$, for the perimeter of the rectangle.
  (b) The perimeter of the rectangle is equal to the perimeter of the square.
    Form an equation and find the value of $x$.
  (c) What is the perimeter of the rectangle, in centimetres?

**14** John has $x$ CDs in his collection.
  Sarah has five times as many CDs as John.
  John and Sarah each collect another 12 CDs. Now Sarah has twice as many CDs as John.
  (a) Write down an expression, in terms of $x$, for the number of CDs Sarah has now.
  (b) Form an equation and solve it to find how many CDs Sarah has now.

## What you need to know

- The solution of an equation is the value of the unknown letter that fits the equation.

**You should be able to:**

- Solve simple equations by inspection.  e.g. $x + 2 = 5$,  $x - 3 = 7$,  $2x = 10$,  $\frac{x}{4} = 12$
- Solve simple equations by inspection by working backwards.
- Use the balance method to solve equations which are difficult to solve by inspection.
- Solve equations with brackets.  e.g. $4(3 + 2x) = 36$
- Solve equations with unknowns on both sides of the equals sign.  e.g. $3x + 1 = x + 7$
- Solve equations with fractions.  e.g. $\frac{1}{4}x + 1 = 7$,  $\frac{x + 3}{4} = 2$,  $\frac{x - 1}{3} + \frac{x + 1}{2} = \frac{1}{6}$
- Write, or form, equations using the information given in a problem.
- Use equations to solve problems.

**1** Georgina makes up this number game.

> Think of an odd number.
> Subtract 5.
> Halve the result.
> Tell me your answer.

(a) Naomi thinks of the number 11.
What is her answer?

(b) Jacob says his answer is 9.
What number did he start with?

(c) Alfie says his answer is 4.5.
Georgina tells him he has made a mistake. Explain how she knows this.

**2** Solve. (a) $\frac{x}{4} = 3$    (b) $5y = 20$    (c) $3y + 2 = 11$    (d) $2y + 5 = 2 - y$

**3** Solve. (a) $4p - 3 = 7$    (b) $\frac{k}{3} + 2 = 6$      OCR

**4** Solve. (a) $5m - 7 = 28$    (b) $3t + 3 = 5t - 7$    (c) $\frac{x - 3}{5} = 2$

**5** Solve the equations. (a) $2x + 9 = 3$    (b) $3y - 2 = y + 6$    OCR

**6** Solve the equations. (a) $4x - 1 = 7$    (b) $6x + 3 = x + 10$    OCR

**7** Solve. (a) $3(x - 2) = 9$    (b) $6x + 3 = x - 2$

**8** Solve these equations. (a) $4x + 5 = 23$    (b) $2(x - 1) = 14$    OCR

**9** Solve. (a) $3(a - 5) = 6a$    (b) $5(x + 2) = 14$    (c) $x + 8 = 3(2 - x)$

**10** Solve the equation $\frac{2x - 3}{5} = -1$.

**11** Solve these equations.
(a) $3 - 4q = 11$      (b) $4(2t - 3) + 4t = 6$      (c) $\frac{2x + 9}{5} = 6$

**12** (a) Hilda is twice as old as Evie. Their ages add up to 51 years.
How old is Hilda?

(b) Colin is 2 years older than John. Their ages add up to 36 years.
How old is Colin?

**13** The diagram shows two cans of oil.
The cans hold a total of 3 litres of oil.
By forming an equation find the amount of oil in the larger can.

$n$ litres        $(3n + 1)$ litres

**14** A drink costs $x$ pence.
A packet of crisps costs 15 pence **less** than a drink.
(a) Write an expression, in terms of $x$, for the cost of a packet of crisps.
(b) A drink and two packets of crisps cost 96 pence.
By forming an equation find the cost of a drink.

**15** Form and solve an equation to calculate the angles of this triangle.

$2x - 10$

$x$

$22 + x$

OCR

**16** Solve. (a) $\frac{3}{4x} = \frac{1}{8}$      (b) $\frac{x - 2}{2} = \frac{x + 3}{3}$

**17** Solve. $2(2x - 5) - 3(x + 2) = 5(2 - x)$

**18** Solve these equations. (a) $4(2x - 1) = 3x + 11$    (b) $\frac{x - 3}{4} + x = \frac{29}{8}$    OCR

**19** Solve. $\frac{2x - 1}{3} + \frac{x - 1}{4} = 4$      OCR

**20** Solve. (a) $\frac{(x - 2)}{3} - \frac{(x - 3)}{2} = 1$    (b) $\frac{2x - 1}{5} - \frac{x - 3}{4} = \frac{3}{2}$

# Formulae ●●●●●●●●●●●●●●●●

Most people at some time make use of **formulae** to carry out routine calculations.
A **formula** represents a rule written using numbers, letters and mathematical signs.
When using a formula you will need to **substitute** your own values for the letters in order to carry out your calculation.

## Substitution

### EXAMPLES

**1** Find the value of $a - 3$, when $a = 4$.

$a - 3$
$= 4 - 3$
$= 1$

**2** Find the value of $3m$, when $m = -4$.

$3m$
$= 3 \times -4$
$= -12$

**3** Find the value of $pq - 3$, when $p = 5$ and $q = -2$.

$pq - 3$
$= 5 \times (-2) - 3$
$= -10 - 3$
$= -13$

## Exercise 12.1    Do not use a calculator.

**1** $t = 5$.   Find the value of   (a) $3 - t$   (b) $2t$   (c) $3t - 4$   (d) $t \times t$

**2** $m = -3$.  Find the value of   (a) $m + 2$   (b) $m - 1$   (c) $4m$   (d) $2m + 9$

**3** $a = 6$ and $b = 3$.   Find the value of
   (a) $3a + 2b$   (b) $b - a$   (c) $\frac{a}{b}$   (d) $a \times b$   (e) $2(a + b)$

**4** $x = 15$ and $y = 6$.   Find the value of
   (a) $x + 2y$   (b) $x - 3y$   (c) $\frac{x}{y}$   (d) $xy$   (e) $6(x - y)$

**5** $p = -10$ and $q = 5$.   Find the value of
   (a) $p + q$   (b) $p - 2q$   (c) $\frac{p}{q}$   (d) $2pq$   (e) $\frac{p - q}{p + q}$

**6** $x = 15$ and $y = -6$.   Find the value of
   (a) $x + 2y$   (b) $y - x$   (c) $\frac{x}{y}$   (d) $\frac{xy}{10}$   (e) $6(x + y)$

**7** $a = -6$ and $b = -3$.   Find the value of
   (a) $3a + 2b$   (b) $b - a$   (c) $\frac{a}{b}$   (d) $a^2 + b$   (e) $\frac{ab}{2a - b}$

**8** Find the value of $pq + r$ when $p = 3$, $q = -5$ and $r = -2$.

## Writing expressions and formulae

A lollipop costs 15 pence.
How much will $n$ lollipops cost?
Write a formula for the cost, $C$, in pence, of $n$ lollipops.

Each lollipop costs 15 pence.

So, $n$ lollipops cost   $15 \times n$ pence $= 15n$ pence.   | $15n$ is an **algebraic expression**. |

If the cost of $n$ lollipops is $C$ pence, then   $C = 15n$.   | $C = 15n$ is a **formula**. |

Formulae can be used in lots of situations.

The grid shows the numbers from 1 to 50.
An **L** shape has been drawn on the grid.
It is called **L₁₄** because the lowest number is 14.

*What is the sum of the numbers in **L₁₄**?*

The **L** shape can be moved to different parts of the grid.
We can find the sum of the numbers for each shape.

| 1 | 2 | 3 | 4 | 5 | 6 | 7 | 8 | 9 | 10 |
|----|----|----|----|----|----|----|----|----|----|
| 11 | 12 | 13 | 14 | 15 | 16 | 17 | 18 | 19 | 20 |
| 21 | 22 | 23 | 24 | 25 | 26 | 27 | 28 | 29 | 30 |
| 31 | 32 | 33 | 34 | 35 | 36 | 37 | 38 | 39 | 40 |
| 41 | 42 | 43 | 44 | 45 | 46 | 47 | 48 | 49 | 50 |

A formula for the sum of the numbers, $S_n$,
can be written in terms of $n$ for shape $L_n$.

$S_n = n + (n + 10) + (n + 20) + (n + 21)$
$S_n = 4n + 51$

An **expression** is just an answer using letters and numbers.

A **formula** is an algebraic rule. It always has an equals sign.

---

### EXAMPLES

**1** A hedge is $l$ metres long. A fence is 50 metres longer than the hedge.
Write an **expression**, in terms of $l$, for the length of the fence.

The fence is $(l + 50)$ metres long.

**2** Boxes of matches each contain 48 matches.
Write down a **formula** for the number of matches, $m$, in $n$ boxes.

$m = 48 \times n$    This could be written as   $m = 48n$.

---

## Exercise 12.2

**1** I am $a$ years old.
   (a) How old will I be in 1 years time?
   (b) How old was I four years ago?
   (c) How old will I be in $n$ years time?

**2** Egg boxes hold 12 eggs each.
   How many eggs are there in $e$ boxes?

**3** A child is making a tower with toy bricks.
   He has $b$ bricks in his tower.
   Write an expression for the number of bricks in the tower after he takes 3 bricks from the top.

**4** Paul is $h$ cm tall.
   Sue is 12 cm taller than Paul.
   Write down an expression for Sue's height in terms of $h$.

**5** Write a formula for the perimeter, $P$, for each of these shapes in terms of the letters given.

(a) square with sides $g$, $g$, $g$, $g$

(b) rectangle with sides $y + 2$, $y$, $y$, $y + 2$

(c) triangle with sides $x - 3$, $x + 2$, $x$

(d) kite with sides $a$, $a$, $b$, $b$

**6** A caravan costs £25 per day to hire.
   Write a formula for the cost, $C$, in £s, to hire the caravan for $d$ days.

**7** A packet of biscuits costs $y$ pence.
Write down a formula for the cost, $P$ pence, of another packet which costs
(a) two pence less than the first packet,
(b) twice the cost of the first packet.

**8** The cost of hiring a ladder is given by:

> £12 per day, plus a delivery charge of £8

(a) Sam hired a ladder for 6 days. How much did he pay?
(b) Fred hired a ladder for $x$ days. Write down a formula for the total cost, £$C$, in terms of $x$.

**9** The grid shows the numbers from 1 to 50.
A **T** shape has been drawn on the grid.
It is called $\mathbf{T_{23}}$ because the lowest number is 23.

| 1 | 2 | 3 | 4 | 5 | 6 | 7 | 8 | 9 | 10 |
|---|---|---|---|---|---|---|---|---|----|
| 11 | 12 | 13 | 14 | 15 | 16 | 17 | 18 | 19 | 20 |
| 21 | 22 | 23 | 24 | 25 | 26 | 27 | 28 | 29 | 30 |
| 31 | 32 | 33 | 34 | 35 | 36 | 37 | 38 | 39 | 40 |
| 41 | 42 | 43 | 44 | 45 | 46 | 47 | 48 | 49 | 50 |

Calculate the sum of the numbers in:
(a) $\mathbf{T_{16}}$    (b) $\mathbf{T_{28}}$    (c) $\mathbf{T_2}$

(d) The diagram on the right shows $\mathbf{T_n}$.
Copy and complete the **T** shape in terms of $n$.

(e) Write a formula for the sum of the numbers, $\mathbf{S_n}$,
in terms of $n$, for shape $\mathbf{T_n}$.
Write your answer in its simplest form.

## Using formulae

The formula for the perimeter of a rectangle is $P = 2L + 2W$.
By **substituting** values for the length, $L$, and the width, $W$, you can calculate the value of $P$.

For example. To find the perimeter of a rectangle 5 cm in length and 3 cm in width,
substitute $L = 5$ and $W = 3$ into $P = 2L + 2W$.
$$P = 2 \times 5 + 2 \times 3$$
$$= 10 + 6$$
$$= 16 \qquad \text{The perimeter of the rectangle is 16 cm.}$$

### EXAMPLES

**1** Here is a formula for the area of a rectangle.

> **Area = length × width**

Use the formula to find the area of a rectangle
8 cm in length and 3 cm in width.
Area = length × width
$$= 8 \times 3$$
$$= 24 \text{ cm}^2$$

**2** $G = 4t - 1$.
Find the value of $G$ when $t = \frac{1}{2}$.
$$G = 4t - 1$$
$$= 4 \times \tfrac{1}{2} - 1$$
$$= 2 - 1$$
$$= 1$$

**3** $H = 3(4x - y)$
Find the value of $H$ when $x = 5$ and $y = 7$.
$$H = 3(4x - y)$$
$$= 3(4 \times 5 - 7)$$
$$= 3(20 - 7)$$
$$= 3(13)$$
$$= 39$$

**4** $W = x^2 + 2$
Find the value of $W$ when $x = 3$.
$$W = x^2 + 2$$
$$= 3 \times 3 + 2$$
$$= 9 + 2$$
$$= 11$$

**1** The number of points scored by a soccer team can be worked out using this formula.

> **Points scored = 3 × games won + games drawn**

A team has won 5 games and drawn 2 games. How many points have they scored?

**2** Here is a formula for the perimeter of a rectangle.

> **Perimeter = 2 × (length + width)**

A rectangle is 9 cm in length and 4 cm in width.
Use the formula to work out the perimeter of this rectangle.

**3** $T = 5a - 3$.    Find the value of $T$ when   $a = 20$.

**4** $M = 4n + 1$.  (a)  Work out the value of $M$ when   $n = -2$.
          (b)  Work out the value of $n$ when   $M = 19$.

**5** $H = 3g - 5$.  (a)  Find the value of $H$ when   $g = 2.5$.
          (b)  Find the value of $g$ when   $H = 13$.

**6** $F = 5(v + 6)$.    What is the value of $F$ when   $v = 9$?

**7** $V = 2(7 + 2x)$.    What is the value of $V$ when   $x = -3$?

**8** $P = 3(5 - 2d)$.    What is the value of $P$ when   $d = 0.5$?

**9** $C = 8(p + q)$.    What is the value of $C$ when   $p = -2$  and  $q = -3$?

**10** $S = ax + 4$.    What is the value of $S$ when   $a = 5$  and  $x = 0.4$?

**11** $T = a(x + 4)$.    What is the value of $T$ when   $a = -3$  and  $x = \frac{1}{2}$?

**12** $K = ab + c$.    Work out the value of $K$ when   $a = 5$,  $b = 3$  and  $c = -2$.

**13** $L = xy - z$.    Work out the value of $L$ when   $x = -4$,  $y = -2$  and  $z = 3$.

**14** The number of matches, $M$, needed to make a pattern of $P$ pentagons is given by the formula:  $M = 4P + 1$.
Find the number of matches needed to make 8 pentagons.

**15** The distance, $d$ metres, travelled by a lawn mower in $t$ minutes is given as:  $d = 24t$.
Find the distance travelled by the lawn mower in 4 minutes.

**16** Convert 30° Centigrade to Fahrenheit using the formula:  $F = C \times 1.8 + 32$

**17** $T = 45W + 30$  is used to calculate the time in minutes needed to cook a joint of beef weighing $W$ kilograms.
How many minutes are needed to cook a joint of beef weighing 2.4 kg?

**18** Convert 77 degrees Fahrenheit to Centigrade using the formula:  $C = (F - 32) \div 1.8$

**19** The voltage, $V$ volts, in a circuit with resistance, $R$ ohms, and current, $I$ amps, is given by the formula:  $V = IR$.
Find the voltage in a circuit when   $I = 12$  and  $R = 20$.

**20** A simple formula for the motion of a car is   $F = ma + R$.
Find $F$ when   $m = 500$,  $a = 0.2$  and  $R = 4000$.

**21** The cost, £$C$, of $n$ units of gas is calculated using the formula   $C = 0.08n + 8.5$.
Calculate the cost of 458 units of gas.

**22** The formula   $v = u + at$   gives the speed $v$ of a particle, $t$ seconds after it starts with speed $u$.
Calculate $v$ when   $u = 7.8$,  $a = -10$  and  $t = \frac{3}{4}$.

Do not use a calculator for questions 1 to 12.

**1**  $S = a^2 - 5$.   Find the value of $S$ when   $a = -3$.

**2**  $R = p^2 + 2p$.   Find the value of $R$ when   (a)  $p = 3$,   (b)  $p = -3$.

**3**  $K = m^2 - 5m$.   Work out the value of $K$ when   $m = -4$.

**4**  $S = 2a^2$.   Find the value of $S$ when   (a)  $a = 3$,   (b)  $a = -3$.

**5**  $S = (2a)^2$.   Find the value of $S$ when   (a)  $a = 3$,   (b)  $a = -3$.

**6**  $T = 3a^2 - 9$.   Find the value of $T$ when   $a = -4$.

**7**  $S = \frac{1}{2}p^2$.   Find the value of $S$ when   (a)  $p = 8$,   (b)  $p = -8$.

**8**  $S = \left(\frac{1}{2}p\right)^2$.   Find the value of $S$ when   (a)  $p = 8$,   (b)  $p = -8$.

**9**  $A = x^3$.   Find the value of $A$ when   (a)  $x = 2$,   (b)  $x = -3$.

**10**  $T = \sqrt{\dfrac{a}{b}}$   Work out the value of $T$ when   $a = 9$   and   $b = 16$.

**11**  $S = \sqrt[3]{pq}$   Work out the value of $S$ when
(a)  $p = 2$   and   $q = 32$,   (b)  $p = 2\frac{1}{4}$   and   $q = 1\frac{1}{2}$,   (c)  $p = 54$   and   $q = -0.5$.

**12**  $L = \sqrt{m^2 + n^2}$   Work out the value of $L$ when
(a)  $m = 6$   and   $n = 8$,   (b)  $m = 0.3$   and   $n = 0.4$.

**13**  The formula   $F = \dfrac{mv^2}{r}$   describes the motion of a cyclist rounding a corner.
Find $F$ when   $m = 80$,   $v = 6$   and   $r = 20$.

**14**  Use the formula   $R = \left(\dfrac{t}{s}\right)^2$   to calculate the value of $R$ when   $t = -0.6$   and   $s = \frac{2}{5}$.

**15**  Use the formula   $v = \sqrt{u^2 + 2as}$   to calculate the value of $v$ when
(a)  $u = 2.4$,   $a = 3.2$,   $s = 5.25$,   (b)  $u = 9.1$,   $a = -4.7$,   $s = 3.04$.
Give your answers correct to one decimal place.

## Writing and using formulae

**EXAMPLE**

(a)  Nick has a birthday party for 10 people.
How much does it cost?
(b)  Tony has a birthday party for $x$ people.
Write a formula for the cost £$T$, in terms of $x$.
(c)  Jean pays £140 for her birthday party.
How many people went to the party?

**Birthday Party Specials**
£20, plus £8 per person

(a)  Nick's party costs:   £20 + 10 × £8
                                   = £100

(b)  Cost for $x$ people in £ = $x \times 8 = 8x$
Total cost in £          = $20 + 8x$
Total cost is £$T$
So, formula is          $T = 20 + 8x$

(c)  Using the formula   $T = 20 + 8x$.
Jean's party costs £140, so,   $T = 140$.
                    $140 = 20 + 8x$
                      $8x = 120$
                        $x = 15$

15 people went to Jean's party.

**1** The cost of a taxi journey is:

> £3 plus £2 for each kilometre travelled

(a)   Alex travels 5 km by taxi.
      How much does it cost?
(b)   A taxi journey of $k$ kilometres costs £$C$.
      Write a formula for the cost, $C$, in terms of $k$.
(c)   Adrian paid £7 for a taxi journey.
      Use your formula to find the number of kilometres he travelled.

**2** A rule to find the cooking time, $C$ minutes, of a chicken which weighs $k$ kilograms, is:

> multiply the weight of the chicken by 40 and then add 20

(a)   Find the cooking time for a chicken which weighs 3 kg.
(b)   Write a formula for $C$ in terms of $k$.
(c)   Use your formula to find the weight of a chicken which has a cooking time of 100 minutes.

**3** An approximate rule for changing temperatures in degrees Celsius, $C$, to temperatures in degrees Fahrenheit, $F$, is given by the rule:

> double $C$ and add on 30

(a)   Find the value of $F$ when   $C = 6$.
(b)   Write down a formula for $F$ in terms of $C$.
(c)   Use your formula to find the value of $C$ when   $F = 58$.

**4** A teacher uses this rule to work out the number of exercise books he needs for Year 11 students.

> 3 books per student, plus 50 extra books

(a)   This year there are 120 students in Year 11.
      How many books are needed?
(b)   Using $b$ for the number of books and $n$ for the number of students, write down the
      teacher's rule for $b$ in terms of $n$.
(c)   For the next Year 11, he will need 470 books.
      How many students will be in Year 11 next year?

## Rearranging formulae

Sometimes it is easier to use a formula if you **rearrange** it first.

### EXAMPLES

**1**   $k = \frac{8m}{5}$

Rearrange the formula to give $m$ in terms of $k$.

$k = \frac{8m}{5}$

Multiply both sides by 5.
$5k = 8m$

Divide both sides by 8.
$\frac{5k}{8} = m$

We say we have **rearranged the formula**

$k = \frac{8m}{5}$   to make $m$ the **subject** of the formula.

**2**   $A = 3r^2$

Make $r$ the subject of the formula.

$A = 3r^2$

Divide both sides by 3.

$\frac{A}{3} = r^2$

Take the square root of both sides.

$\pm \sqrt{\frac{A}{3}} = r$

So,   $r = \pm \sqrt{\frac{A}{3}}$

## Exercise **12.6**

**1** Make $m$ the subject of these formulae.
  (a) $a = m + 5$
  (b) $a = x + m$
  (c) $a = m - 2$
  (d) $a = m - b$

**2** Make $x$ the subject of these formulae.
  (a) $y = 4x$
  (b) $y = ax$
  (c) $y = \frac{x}{2}$
  (d) $y = \frac{x}{a}$
  (e) $y = \frac{3x}{5}$

**3** Make $p$ the subject of these formulae.
  (a) $y = 2p + 6$
  (b) $t = 5p + q$
  (c) $m = 3p - 2$
  (d) $r = 4p - q$

**4** The cost, £$C$, of hiring a car for $n$ days is given by $C = 35 + 24n$.
  Make $n$ the subject of the formula.

**5** $V = IR$. Rearrange the formula to give $R$ in terms of $V$ and $I$.

**6** Make $c$ the subject of these formulae.
  (a) $y = c^2$
  (b) $y = \sqrt{c}$
  (c) $y = dc^2$
  (d) $y = \frac{\sqrt{c}}{3}$

  (e) $y = c^2 + x$
  (f) $y = x + \sqrt{c}$
  (g) $y = x + \frac{c^2}{d}$
  (h) $y = \frac{\sqrt{c}}{a} - x$

**7** Make $a$ the subject of these formulae.
  (a) $b = a + c^2$
  (b) $a^2 = b$
  (c) $p = ma + d$
  (d) $ma^2 = F$

**8** Make $x$ the subject of these formulae. (a) $3(x - a) = x$   (b) $2(a + x) = 3(b - x)$

**9** Make $a$ the subject of each of these formulae.
  (a) $3a - x = a + 2x$
  (b) $a - b = ax$
  (c) $a - 2 = ax + b$

**10** $R = \left(\frac{t}{s}\right)^2$. Rearrange the formula to give $t$ in terms of $R$ and $s$.

**11** $\frac{p + q}{3} = p - q$. Rearrange the formula to give $q$ in terms of $p$.

**12** Make $a$ the subject of each of these formulae.
  (a) $a + 2 = x(3 + a)$
  (b) $y = \frac{a - 3}{5 - a}$
  (c) $x(a - 1) = b(a + 2)$

  (d) $y(a - 1) = 3(2 - a)$
  (e) $\sqrt{\frac{a + x}{a - x}} = 2$
  (f) $\sqrt{\frac{a}{x - a}} = 2x$

## Solve problems by rearranging formulae

### EXAMPLE

A cuboid has length 8 cm and breadth 5 cm.
The volume of the cuboid is 140 cm³.
Calculate the height of the cuboid.

The formula for the volume of a cuboid is $V = lbh$,

so, $h = \frac{V}{lb}$ (by dividing both sides of $V = lbh$ by $lb$)

Substitute $V = 140$, $l = 8$ and $b = 5$ in $h = \frac{V}{lb}$.

$\qquad h = \frac{140}{8 \times 5} = 3.5$

The height of the cuboid is 3.5 cm.

The values to be substituted may include whole numbers, negative numbers, decimals or fractions.

**1** The perimeter of a square is $P = 4d$.
  (a) Rearrange the formula to give $d$ in terms of $P$.
  (b) Find $d$ when $P = 2.8$ cm.

**2** The area of a rectangle is $A = lb$.
  (a) Rearrange the formula to give $l$ in terms of $A$ and $b$.
  (b) Find $l$ when $A = 27$ cm² and $b = 4.5$ cm.

**3** The speed of a car is $S = \dfrac{D}{T}$.
  (a) (i) Change the subject to $D$.
     (ii) Find $D$ when $S = 48$ km/h and $T = 2$ hours.
  (b) (i) Change the subject to $T$.
     (ii) Find $T$ when $S = 36$ km/h and $D = 90$ km.

**4** The perimeter of a rectangle is $P = 2(l + b)$.
  (a) Change the subject to $b$.
  (b) Find $b$ when $P = 18$ cm and $l = 4.8$ cm.

**5** $y = mx + c$
  (a) Rearrange the formula to give $x$ in terms of $y$, $m$ and $c$.
  (b) Calculate $x$ when $y = 0.6$, $m = -0.4$ and $c = 1.8$.

**6** $A = \dfrac{bh}{2}$
  (a) Rearrange the formula to give $b$ in terms of $A$ and $h$.
  (b) Calculate $b$ when $A = 9.6$ and $h = 3$.

**7** $p^2 = q^2 + r^2$
  (a) Rearrange the formula to give $q$ in terms of $p$ and $r$.
  (b) Calculate $q$ when $p = 7.3$ and $r = 2.7$.

**8** $V = \dfrac{4}{3}\pi r^3$
  (a) Rearrange the formula to give $r$ in terms of $V$ and $\pi$.
  (b) Calculate $r$ when $V = 1.6 \times 10^5$ and $\pi = 3.14$.
     Give your answer to a suitable degree of accuracy.

**9** $\dfrac{x}{a} = \dfrac{b}{x}$
  (a) Make $x$ the subject of the formula.
  (b) Calculate $x$ when $a = 4.6 \times 10^3$ and $b = 3.5 \times 10^5$.
     Give your answer in standard form correct to two significant figures.

**10** $m = \dfrac{1 - n}{1 + n}$
  (a) Make $n$ the subject of the formula.
  (b) Calculate $n$ when $m = 8.5 \times 10^{-2}$.
     Give your answer in standard form to a suitable degree of accuracy.

## What you need to know

- A **formula** is an algebraic rule written using numbers, letters and mathematical signs.
**You should be able to:**
- Write algebraic expressions and formulae.
- Substitute positive and negative numbers in expressions and formulae.
- Use simple formulae to solve problems.
- Rearrange formulae to make another letter (variable) the subject.

**1** $V = a + bc$.    Find the value of $V$ when   $a = -5$,   $b = 3$   and   $c = 4$.

**2** $S = pq + r$.    Find the value of $S$ when   $p = -3$,   $q = 4$   and   $r = -2$.

**3** $P = 3(m + n)$.    Find the value of $P$ when   $m = 0.5$   and   $n = 2$.

**4** $P$ and $k$ are connected by the formula   $P = 20 + 4k$.
   (a)   Find the value of $P$ when   (i)   $k = 2$,      (ii)   $k = -3$.
   (b)   Find the value of $k$ when   $P = 72$.      OCR

**5** For the formula   $H = 17 - 0.5a$,   work out $H$ when   (a)   $a = 12$,      (b)   $a = -4$.     OCR

**6** What is the value of $3x^2$ when   $x = 6$?

**7** $P = ab + b^2$.   Work out the value of $P$ when   (a)   $a = 2$,   $b = 3$,      (b)   $a = 4$,   $b = -5$.
           OCR

**8** The cost of hiring a skip is:   $\boxed{\text{£15 PER DAY + £45 DELIVERY}}$

   (a)   Kay hires a skip for 3 days.
          How much does she have to pay?
   (b)   Write a formula for the cost, £$C$, of hiring a skip for $d$ days.

**9** Anita makes shirts in a factory. This formula is used to calculate her weekly wage.
$$w = 3s + 15$$
   where $s$ is the number of shirts she makes and $w$ is her weekly wage in pounds.
   (a)   One week she makes 80 shirts. Work out her weekly wage.
   (b)   Her wage one week was £207. How many shirts did she make that week?   OCR

**10** Find the exact value of   $\dfrac{1}{m} - \dfrac{1}{n}$   when   $m = \frac{2}{5}$   and   $n = \frac{3}{4}$.

**11** The cost of printing business cards is:   $\boxed{\text{£5 plus 15 pence a card}}$

   (a)   What is the total cost of printing 80 cards?
   (b)   Write a formula for the total cost, £$C$, of printing $n$ cards.
   (c)   Fred pays £77 for some business cards to be printed.
          How many cards did he have printed?

**12** The perimeter of a rectangle is given by the formula   $P = 2x + 13$.
   Rearrange the formula to find $x$ in terms of $P$.     OCR

**13** Make $x$ the subject of this formula.   $4(2x - y) = 2y + 5$     OCR

**14** You are given the formula   $a = \frac{1}{3}(b + c)d$.
   (a)   Work out the value of $a$ when   $b = 5$,   $c = -20$   and   $d = 0.5$.
   (b)   Express $d$ in terms of $a$, $b$ and $c$.

**15** Rearrange the formula   $P = \sqrt{6T}$   to make $T$ the subject.     OCR

**16** A formula is given as   $s = t - uv^2$.
   Calculate the value of $s$ when   $t = -6$,   $u = 50$   and   $v = 0.2$.

**17** Rearrange the formula   $s = \dfrac{t - u}{v^2}$   to give $v$ in terms of $s$, $t$ and $u$.

**18** Given that   $y + 4ax = 5y - 3x$,
   (a)   express $a$ in terms of $x$ and $y$,      (b)   express $x$ in terms of $y$ and $a$.   OCR

**19** Given that   $ay - b = cy - d$,   express $y$ in terms of $a$, $b$, $c$ and $d$.   OCR

**20** $p = \dfrac{mn}{m - n}$.   Express $m$ in terms of $p$ and $n$.

# Sequences ●●●●●●●●●●●●●●●

## Continuing a sequence

A **sequence** is a list of numbers made according to some rule.
For example:

$$5, \quad 9, \quad 13, \quad 17, \quad 21, \quad \dots$$

The first term is 5.
To find the next term in the sequence, add 4 to the last term.
The next term in this sequence is $21 + 4 = 25$.
*What are the next three terms in the sequence?*

The numbers in a sequence are called **terms**.
The start number is the **first term**, the next is the second term, and so on.

**To continue a sequence:**
1. Work out the rule to get from one term to the next.
2. Apply the same rule to find further terms in the sequence.

### EXAMPLES

Find the next three terms in each of these sequences.

**1**   5,   8,   11,   14,   17,   …

To find the next term in the sequence, add 3 to the last term.
$$17 + 3 = 20, \qquad 20 + 3 = 23, \qquad 23 + 3 = 26.$$
The next three terms in the sequence are: 20, 23, 26.

**2**   2,   4,   8,   16,   …

To find the next term in the sequence, multiply the last term by 2.
$$16 \times 2 = 32, \qquad 32 \times 2 = 64, \qquad 64 \times 2 = 128.$$
The next three terms in the sequence are: 32, 64, 128.

**3**   1,   1,   2,   3,   5,   8,   …

To find the next term in the sequence, add the last two terms.
$$5 + 8 = 13, \qquad 8 + 13 = 21, \qquad 13 + 21 = 34.$$
The next three terms in the sequence are: 13, 21, 34.
This is a special sequence called the **Fibonacci sequence**.

## Exercise **13.1**

**1**   Find the next three terms in these sequences.

(a)   1,   5,   9,   13,   …
(b)   6,   8,   10,   12,   …
(c)   28,   25,   22,   19,   …
(d)   3,   8,   13,   18,   23,   …
(e)   3,   6,   12,   24,   …
(f)   $\frac{1}{4}$,   $\frac{1}{2}$,   $\frac{3}{4}$,   1,   $1\frac{1}{4}$,   …
(g)   32,   16,   8,   4,   …
(h)   0.5,   0.6,   0.7,   0.8,   …
(i)   10,   8,   6,   4,   …
(j)   80,   40,   20,   10,   …
(k)   1,   3,   6,   10,   15,   …
(l)   1,   3,   4,   7,   11,   18,   …

**2** Find the missing terms from these sequences.

(a)  2,  4,  6,  __,  10,  12,  __,  16,  ...    (b)  2,  6,  __,  14,  18,  __,  26,  ...
(c)  1,  2,  4,  __,  16,  __,  64,  ...    (d)  28,  22,  __,  10,  4,  __,  ...
(e)  1,  4,  9,  __,  25,  __,  49,  ...    (f)  1,  2,  3,  5,  __,  13,  __,  34,  ...
(g)  __,  8,  14,  __,  __,  32,  38,  ...

**3** Write down the rule, in words, used to get from one term to the next for each sequence.
Then use the rule to find the next two terms.

(a)  2,  9,  16,  23,  30,  ...    (b)  3,  5,  7,  9,  11,  ...
(c)  1,  5,  9,  13,  17,  ...    (d)  31,  26,  21,  16,  ...
(e)  64,  32,  16,  8,  4,  ...    (f)  1,  3,  9,  27,  ...
(g)  −2,  −4,  −6,  −8,  ...    (h)  10,  7,  4,  1,  −2,  ...

**4** A sequence begins  1,  4,  7,  10,  ...
(a)  What is the 10th number in this sequence?
(b)  Explain how you found your answer.

**5** A number sequence begins  1,  2,  4,  ...
David says that the next number is 8.
Tony says that the next number is 7.
(a)  Explain why they could both be correct.
(b)  Find the 10th number in David's sequence.
(c)  Find the 10th number in Tony's sequence.

**6** Here is part of a number sequence:  3,  9,  15,  21,  ...
Is the number 50 in this sequence?
Explain your answer.

## Using rules

Sometimes you will be given a rule and asked to use it to find the terms of a sequence.

For example:
A sequence begins:  1,  4,  13,  ...
The rule for the sequence is:

> Multiply the last number by 3, then add 1

The next term in the sequence is given by:
$$13 \times 3 + 1 = 39 + 1 = 40$$

The following term is given by:
$$40 \times 3 + 1 = 120 + 1 = 121$$

So, the sequence can be extended to:   1,  4,  13,  40,  121,  ...

*Use the rule to find the next two terms in the sequence.*

The **same rule** can be used to make different sequences.

For example:
Another sequence begins:  2,  7,  22,  ...
Using the same rule, the next term is given by:
$$22 \times 3 + 1 = 66 + 1 = 67$$

The following term is given by:
$$67 \times 3 + 1 = 201 + 1 = 202$$

So, the sequence can be extended to:  2,  7,  22,  67,  202,  ...

*Use the rule to find the next two terms in the sequence.*

| EXAMPLE | This rule is used to find each number in a sequence from the number before it. |

Subtract 3 and then multiply by 4

Starting with 5 we get the following sequence:   5,   8,   20,   68,   …

(a)   Write down the next number in the sequence.
(b)   Using the same rule, but a different starting number, the second number is 16.
Find the starting number.

(a)   $(68 - 3) \times 4 = 65 \times 4 = 260$
Notice that, following the rule, 3 is subtracted first and the result is then multiplied by 4.
The next number in the sequence is 260.

(b)   Imagine the first number is $x$.

Working backwards.

7 ◄───── add 3 ◄──── 4 ◄──── divide by 4 ◄───── 16

The starting number is 7.

## Exercise 13.2

**1**   This rule is used to find each term of a sequence from the one before:

Subtract 3 then divide by 2

(a)   The first term is 45.
   (i)   What is the second term?       (ii)   What is the **fourth** term?
(b)   Using the same rule, but a different starting number, the second term is 17.
What is the starting number for the sequence?

**2**   This rule is used to find each term of a sequence from the one before:

Add 5 then multiply by 3

(a)   The first term is 7.
   (i)   What is the second term?       (ii)   What is the **third** term?
(b)   Using the same rule, but a different starting number, the second term is 45.
What is the starting number for the sequence?

**3**   A sequence is formed from this rule:

Add together the last two terms to find the next term

Part of the sequence is   …   5,   9,   14,   23,   …
(a)   Write down the next two terms after 23 in the sequence.
(b)   Write down the two terms that come before 5 in the sequence.

**4**   A sequence begins:   1,   −3,   …
The sequence is continued using the rule:

Add the previous two numbers and then multiply by 3

Use the rule to find the next two numbers in the sequence.

**5**   A sequence begins:   4,   7,   13,   25,   …
The next number in the sequence can be found using the rule:

"Multiply the last term by 2 then subtract 1."

(a)   Write down the next **two** terms in the sequence.
(b)   The 11th term in the sequence is 3073.
Use this information to find the 10th term in the sequence.

## Number sequences

A number sequence which increases (or decreases) by the same amount from one term to the next is called a **linear sequence**.

For example, terms in the sequence:  6,  11,  16,  21,  …   increase by 5 from one term to the next. We say that the sequence has a **common difference** of 5.

By comparing a sequence with multiples of the counting numbers:  1,  2,  3,  4,  …
we can write a rule to find the $n$ th term of the sequence.

Sequence:          6   11   16   21   …
Multiples of 5:    5   10   15   20   …

To get the $n$ th term add one to the multiples of 5.
So, the $n$ th term is   $5n + 1$.

Compare the sequence with multiples of the common difference.
In this case the common difference is 5, so, compare the sequence with multiples of 5.

A table can be used to find the $n$ th term of a sequence.

The sequence  2,  8,  14,  20,  …   has a common difference of 6.
The common difference is used to complete the table for terms 1, 2, 3, 4 and $n$.

| Term | Term × common difference | Sequence | Difference |
|------|--------------------------|----------|------------|
| 1 | $1 \times 6 = 6$ | 2 | $2 - 6 = -4$ |
| 2 | $2 \times 6 = 12$ | 8 | $8 - 12 = -4$ |
| 3 | $3 \times 6 = 18$ | 14 | $14 - 18 = -4$ |
| 4 | $4 \times 6 = 24$ | 20 | $20 - 24 = -4$ |
| $n$ | $n \times 6 = 6n$ | $6n - 4$ | |

Term:
1 represents the first term,
2 the second term, and so on.
$n$ represents the $n$ th term.

Common difference:
2nd term − 1st term
$= 8 - 2 = 6$.

Differences:
Check that each pair of entries gives the same result.

The $n$ th term of the sequence  2,  8,  14,  20,  …   is   $6n - 4$.

The rule for the $n$ th term can be used to find the value of any term in the sequence.
To find the fifth term, substitute   $n = 5$   into   $6n - 4$.
$6 \times 5 - 4 = 30 - 4 = 26$.
The fifth term is 26.

### EXAMPLE

(a)   Find the $n$ th term in the sequence   31,  28,  25,  22,  …
(b)   Find the value of the 10th term in the sequence.

(a)   The common difference is $-3$.

| Term | Term × common difference | Sequence | Difference |
|------|--------------------------|----------|------------|
| 1 | $1 \times (-3) = -3$ | 31 | $31 - (-3) = 34$ |
| 2 | $2 \times (-3) = -6$ | 28 | $28 - (-6) = 34$ |
| 3 | $3 \times (-3) = -9$ | 25 | $25 - (-9) = 34$ |
| 4 | $4 \times (-3) = -12$ | 22 | $22 - (-12) = 34$ |
| $n$ | $n \times (-3) = -3n$ | $-3n + 34$ | |

The $n$ th term is   $-3n + 34$.
This can also be written as   $34 - 3n$.

(b)   The $n$ th term is   $34 - 3n$.
Substitute   $n = 10$.
$34 - 3 \times 10 = 34 - 30 = 4$
The 10th term is 4.

Sequences · · · Sequences · · · Sequences · · ·

13

117

**1** Find the common differences of the following sequences.
   (a)  3,  6,  9,  12,  …        (b)  2,  5,  8,  11,  …        (c)  7,  13,  19,  25,  …
   (d)  12,  20,  28,  36,  …     (e)  20,  18,  16,  14,  …     (f)  7,  3,  −1,  −5,  …

**2** (a)  The multiples of 3 are  3,  6,  9,  12,  …
        What is the $n$ th multiple of 3?
   (b)  What is the $n$ th multiple of 8?

**3** A sequence of numbers starts:  4,  7,  10,  13,  …
   (a)  What is the common difference?
   (b)  Copy and complete this table.

| Term | Term × common difference | Sequence | Difference |
|------|--------------------------|----------|------------|
| 1 | $1 \times … =$ | 4 | $4 - … =$ |
| 2 | $2 \times … =$ | 7 | $7 - … =$ |
| 3 | $3 \times … =$ | 10 | $10 - … =$ |
| 4 | $4 \times … =$ | 13 | $13 - … =$ |
| $n$ | $n \times … = …n$ | $…n + …$ | |

   (c)  Write down the $n$ th term of the sequence.
   (d)  What is the value of the 8th term of the sequence?

**4** A sequence of numbers starts:  9,  11,  13,  15,  …
   (a)  What is the common difference?
   (b)  Copy and complete this table for the first four terms of the sequence.

| Term | Term × common difference | Sequence | Difference |
|------|--------------------------|----------|------------|
| 1 | 2 | 9 | 7 |
| 2 | 4 | 11 | … |
|  |  | 13 |  |

   (c)  Write down the $n$ th term of the sequence.
   (d)  What is the value of the 20th term of the sequence?

**5** A sequence of numbers starts:  20,  16,  12,  8,  …
   (a)  What is the common difference?
   (b)  Copy and complete this table for the first four terms of the sequence.

| Term | Term × common difference | Sequence | Difference |
|------|--------------------------|----------|------------|
| 1 | … | 20 | … |
|  |  | 16 |  |

   (c)  Write down the $n$ th term of the sequence.

**6** Find the $n$ th term of the following sequences.
   (a)  1,  4,  7,  10,  …        (b)  19,  16,  13,  10,  …     (c)  5,  9,  13,  17,  …
   (d)  4,  8,  12,  16,  …       (e)  1,  3,  5,  7,  …          (f)  7,  11,  15,  19,  …
   (g)  6,  4,  2,  0,  …         (h)  5,  8,  11,  14,  …       (i)  3,  8,  13,  18,  …
   (j)  40,  35,  30,  25,  …     (k)  0,  1,  2,  3,  …          (l)  −1,  1,  3,  5,  …

**7** Write down the first three terms of a sequence where the $n$ th term is   $n^2 + 3$.
   Explain how you found your answer.

## Activity

These patterns are made using squares.

| Pattern 1 | Pattern 2 | Pattern 3 |
| 3 squares | 5 squares | 7 squares |

How many squares are used to make:　(a)　Pattern 4,　　(b)　Pattern 10,　　(c)　Pattern 100?

The number of squares used to make each pattern forms a **sequence**.

Pattern 4 is made using 9 squares.
You could have answered this:　by drawing Pattern 4 or,
　　　　　　　　　　　　　by continuing the sequence of numbers　3,　5,　7,　…
It is possible to do the same for Pattern 10, though it would involve a lot of work, but it would be unreasonable to use either method for Pattern 100.
Instead we can investigate how each pattern is made.

2 × 1 + 1 = 3 squares　　　2 × 2 + 1 = 5 squares　　　2 × 3 + 1 = 7 squares

Each pattern is made using a **rule**.
The rule can be **described in words**.
To find the number of squares used to make a pattern use the rule:

"Double the pattern number and add 1."

| Pattern number | Rule | Number of squares |
| --- | --- | --- |
| 4 | 2 × 4 + 1 | 9 |
| 10 | 2 × 10 + 1 | 21 |
| 100 | 2 × 100 + 1 | 201 |

The same rule can be **written using symbols**.
We can then answer a very important question:　How many squares are used to make Pattern $n$?

Pattern $n$ will have　$2 \times n + 1$　squares.
This can be written as　$2n + 1$　squares.

## Special sequences of numbers

### Square numbers

　1　　　　4　　　　9　　　　16

The sequence starts:　1,　4,　9,　16,　…
The numbers in this sequence are called **square numbers**.

### Triangular numbers

　1　　　　3　　　　6　　　　10

The sequence starts:　1,　3,　6,　10,　…
The numbers in this sequence are called **triangular numbers**.

**1** A sequence of patterns is made using black and white counters.

**1 black, 3 white**  **2 black, 6 white**  **3 black, 9 white**

(a) How many white counters are there in a pattern with
(i) 5 black counters,  (ii) 10 black counters,  (iii) 100 black counters?
(b) How many white counters are there in a pattern with $n$ black counters?

**2** Linking cubes of side 1 cm are used to make rods.
This rod is made using 4 linking cubes.

The surface area of the rod is 18 square centimetres.
(4 squares on each of the long sides plus one square at each end.)
(a) What is the surface area of a rod made using 5 linking cubes?
(b) What is the surface area of a rod made using 10 linking cubes?
(c) What is the surface area of a rod made using $n$ linking cubes?

**3** A sequence of patterns is made using sticks.

**Pattern 1**  **Pattern 2**  **Pattern 3**  **Pattern 4**

(a) How many sticks are used to make Pattern 5?
(b) Pattern $n$ uses $T$ sticks. Write a formula for $T$ in terms of $n$.
(c) Use your formula to find the number of sticks used to make Pattern 10.
(d) One pattern uses 77 sticks. What is the pattern number?

**4** These patterns are made using matches.

**Pattern 1**  **Pattern 2**  **Pattern 3**

(a) How many matches are used to make Pattern 5?
(b) Which pattern uses 37 matches?
(c) Find a formula for the number of matches, $m$, in Pattern $p$.

**5** These are the first four **square numbers**.  1,  4,  9,  16, …
(a) What is the next square number?
(b) Copy and complete this list for the first 5 square numbers.
$$1^2 = 1, \quad 2^2 = 4, \quad 3^2 = 9, \quad \ldots = 16, \quad 5^2 = \ldots$$
(c) Write an expression for the $n$th square number.
(d) Find the 15th square number.

**6** (a) Find the next term in each of these sequences. Explain how you found your answers.
(i) 2, 5, 10, 17, 26, …  (ii) 0, 3, 8, 15, 24, …
(iii) 4, 7, 12, 19, 28, …  (iv) 2, 8, 18, 32, 50, …
(v) 2, 6, 12, 20, 30, …
(b) By comparing each of these sequences to the sequence of square numbers write an expression for the $n$th term of each sequence.

**7** A sequence of shapes is made using small squares.

Shape 1    Shape 2   Shape 3   Shape 4

(a) Shape $n$ uses $T$ small squares.
    Write a formula for $T$ in terms of $n$.
(b) Use your formula to find the number of small squares in Shape 10.

**8** These are the first four **triangular numbers**:  1,  3,  6,  10,  ...
(a) What is the next triangular number?
(b) Copy and complete this list for the first 5 triangular numbers.

$$\frac{1 \times 2}{2} = 1, \qquad \frac{2 \times 3}{2} = 3, \qquad \frac{3 \times 4}{2} = 6, \qquad \frac{\quad}{2} = 10, \qquad \ldots = \ldots$$

(c) Write an expression for the $n$th triangular number.
(d) Find the 10th triangular number.

**9** These are the first four **powers of 2**:  2,  4,  8,  16,  ...
(a) What is the next power of 2?
(b) Copy and complete this list for the first 5 powers of 2.

$$2^1 = 2, \qquad 2^2 = 4, \qquad 2^3 = 8, \qquad \ldots = 16, \qquad \ldots = \ldots$$

(c) Write an expression for the $n$th power of 2.
(d) Find the 10th power of 2.
(e) What power of 2 is equal to 256?

**10** (a) Write down the first 5 powers of 10.
(b) Write an expression for the $n$th power of 10.
(c) What power of 10 is equal to one million?

**11** (a) Write an expression for the $n$th term of this sequence:  3,  9,  27,  81,  ...
(b) Use your expression to find the 10th term of the sequence.

## What you need to know

- A **sequence** is a list of numbers made according to some rule.
  The numbers in a sequence are called **terms**.
- **To continue a sequence:** 1. Work out the rule to get from one term to the next.
                               2. Apply the same rule to find further terms in the sequence.
- A number sequence which increases (or decreases) by the same amount from one term to the next is called a **linear sequence**.
  The sequence:  2,  8,  14,  20,  26,  ...  has a **common difference** of 6.
- Special sequences  **Square numbers:**      1,  4,  9,  16,  25,  ...
                     **Triangular numbers:**  1,  3,  6,  10,  15,  ...
- Patterns of shapes can be drawn to represent a number sequence.
  For example, this pattern represents the sequence  3,  5,  7,  ...

**You should be able to:**
- Draw patterns of shapes which represent number sequences.
- Continue a given number sequence.
- Find an expression for the $n$th term of a sequence.

**1** (a) What is the next number in each of these sequences?
   (i) 1, 4, 7, 10, 13, ... (ii) 1, 2, 4, 8, 16, ... (iii) 10, 6, 2, −2, ...
   (b) The rule to continue sequence (i) is: **Add 3 to the last number.**
   Write down the rule to continue each of the other sequences.

**2** (a) Write down the next term in this sequence. 1, 7, 13, 19, ...
   (b) Will the number 81 be in the sequence? Give a reason for your answer.
   (c) What is the first number in the sequence which is greater than 100?

**3** These sequences all begin with the numbers 3, 6.
   Find the third number in each sequence.
   (a) 3, 6, ..., 12, ...     (b) 3, 6, ..., 24, ...     (c) 3, 6, ..., 15, ...

**4** Here are the rules for a sequence:
   **If the last number is odd, add 5.    If the last number is even, halve it.**
   A sequence begins with the number 9.
   (a) Write down the next three terms in the sequence.
   (b) Explain what will happen to the sequence if you continue.

**5**
> 1, 5, 13, 29, ...

One rule for finding the next number in this sequence is:

> **'Double the previous number and then add 3.'**

   (a) Find the next number in the sequence.
   (b) A later number in the sequence is represented by $x$.
   Write down the term in the sequence which comes after $x$.

   The first rule was: 'Double the previous number and then add 3.'
   (c) Describe in words a different rule for continuing the sequence.

                                                                                          OCR

**6** (a) Here are the first four terms of a sequence. 3  7  11  15
   Another term of the sequence is 3451. Work out the next term after 3451.
   (b) Here are the first four terms of another sequence. 2  4  8  16
   Another term of the sequence is 2048. Work out the term before 2048.
   (c) Here is a formula for the $n$th term of a different sequence. $n^2 + 1$
   Use it to find the first 3 terms of the sequence.

                                                                                          OCR

**7** Sticks are used to make patterns of squares.

   **Pattern 1**          **Pattern 2**                **Pattern 3**
   (a) How many sticks are needed to make **Pattern 4**?
   (b) How many **more** sticks are needed to make **Pattern 5** from **Pattern 4**?
   (c) Write an expression, in terms of $n$, for the number of sticks needed to make **Pattern $n$**.

**8** The first 5 terms of a sequence are: 4, 7, 10, 13, 16, ...
   (a) Write down the next 2 terms.
   (b) Explain how you worked out your answer to part (a).
   (c) Find the 20th term of the sequence.
   (d) Find the formula for the $n$th term of the sequence.

                                                                                          OCR

**9** Find the $n$th term of each of the following sequences.
   (a) 3, 6, 9, 12, 15, ...
   (b) 5, 9, 13, 17, 21, ...

                                                                                          OCR

# Straight Line Graphs ●●●●●●●

## Coordinates

**Coordinates** are used to describe the position of a point.

Two lines are drawn at right angles to each other.
The horizontal line is called the *x* **axis**.
The vertical line is called the *y* **axis**.
The plural of axis is **axes**.
The two axes cross at the point called the **origin**.

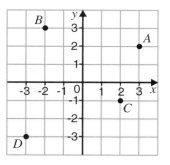

On the diagram, the coordinates of point *A* are (3, 2).
To find point *A*: start at the origin and go right 3 squares then up 2 squares.
The coordinates of point *B* are (−2, 3).

*What are the coordinates of the points C and D?*

## Linear functions

Look at these coordinates (0, 1), (1, 2), (2, 3), (3, 4).
*Can you see any number patterns?*

The same coordinates can be shown in a **table**.

| *x* | 0 | 1 | 2 | 3 |
|-----|---|---|---|---|
| *y* | 1 | 2 | 3 | 4 |

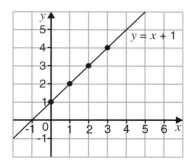

The diagram shows the coordinates plotted on a **graph**.
The points all lie on a **straight line**.

A **rule** connects the *x* coordinate with the *y* coordinate.
**All** points on the line obey the rule $y = x + 1$.

$y = x + 1$ is an example of a **linear function**.
The graph of a linear function is a **straight line**.

### Special graphs

This diagram shows the graphs: $x = 4$ $y = 1$
$x = -2$ $y = -5$

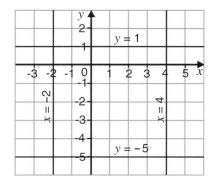

Notice that:
The graph of $x = 4$ is a **vertical** line.
All points on the line have *x* coordinate 4.

The graph of $y = 1$ is a **horizontal** line.
All points on the line have *y* coordinate 1.

$x = 0$ is the *y* axis.
$y = 0$ is the *x* axis.

## Drawing a graph of a linear function

To draw a linear graph:
● Find at least two corresponding values of *x* and *y*.
● Plot the points.
● Join the points with a straight line.

123

**1** (a) Complete the table of values for $y = 2x - 3$.

| $x$ | 0 | 1 | 2 | 3 |
|-----|---|---|---|---|
| $y$ |   |   | 1 |   |

(b) Draw the graph of the equation $y = 2x - 3$.

(a)

| $x$ | 0 | 1 | 2 | 3 |
|-----|----|----|---|---|
| $y$ | −3 | −1 | 1 | 3 |

When $x = 0$, $y = 2 \times 0 - 3 = -3$.
When $x = 1$, $y = 2 \times 1 - 3 = -1$.
When $x = 3$, $y = 2 \times 3 - 3 = 3$.

(b) Plot the points $(0, -3)$, $(1, -1)$, $(2, 1)$, and $(3, 3)$.

The straight line which passes through these points is the graph of the equation $y = 2x - 3$.

**2** (a) Draw the graph of the equation $y = 4 - 2x$.
(b) Use your graph to find the value of $y$ when $x = 2.5$.

(a) If values for $x$ are not given in the question you must choose at least two of your own.

When $x = -1$, $y = 4 - 2 \times (-1) = 4 + 2 = 6$.
When $x = 0$, $y = 4 - 2 \times 0 = 4 - 0 = 4$.
When $x = 3$, $y = 4 - 2 \times 3 = 4 - 6 = -2$.
Plot the points $(-1, 6)$, $(0, 4)$ and $(3, -2)$.

The straight line which passes through these points is the graph of the equation $y = 4 - 2x$.

(b) Using the graph:
From 2.5 on the $x$ axis, go down to meet the line $y = 4 - 2x$.
Then go left to meet the $y$ axis at $-1$.
When $x = 2.5$, $y = -1$.

---

## Exercise 14.1

**1** The diagram shows the positions of points $P$, $Q$ and $R$. Write down the coordinates of these points.

**2** Draw $x$ and $y$ axes from $-5$ to 5.
(a) Plot the points $S(3, -2)$ and $T(-5, 4)$. Join $ST$.
(b) Write down the coordinates of the midpoint of $ST$.

**3** Draw $x$ and $y$ axes from $-2$ to 4.
(a) Plot the points $A(3, 2)$, $B(3, -1)$ and $C(-1, -1)$.
(b) Points $A$, $B$ and $C$ are three corners of a rectangle.
Point $D$ is the fourth corner of the rectangle. Plot point $D$ on your diagram.
(c) What are the coordinates of point $D$?

**4**

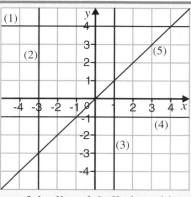

(a) Write down the equations of the lines labelled on this graph.
(b) What are the coordinates of the point where lines (1) and (3) cross?
(c) What are the coordinates of the point where lines (2) and (4) cross?

**5** Draw $x$ and $y$ axes from $-4$ to 4.
On your diagram, draw and label the graphs of these equations.
(a) $x = 3$      (b) $y = 2$      (c) $x = -2$      (d) $y = -1$

**6** (a) Copy and complete a table of values, like the one shown, for each of these equations.
    (i) $y = x + 2$
    (ii) $y = 2x$
    (iii) $y = -x$
    (iv) $y = 2 - x$

| $x$ | 0 | 1 | 2 | 3 |
|---|---|---|---|---|
| $y$ | | | | |

(b) Draw graphs for each of the equations in part (a).

**7** Draw tables of values and use them to draw graphs of:
(a) $y = x - 1$      (b) $y = 2x + 1$      (c) $y = 3 - x$      (d) $y = 6 - 2x$
Draw and label the $x$ axis from 0 to 4 and the $y$ axis from $-2$ to 10.

**8** (a) Copy and complete this table and use it to draw the straight line graph of $y = 4 - x$.

| $x$ | $-2$ | $-1$ | 0 | 1 | 2 |
|---|---|---|---|---|---|
| $y$ | | 5 | | | 2 |

Draw and label the $x$ axis from $-3$ to 3 and the $y$ axis from $-1$ to 6.
(b) Use your graph to find the value of:
    (i) $y$ when $x = 1.5$,      (ii) $y$ when $x = -0.5$.

**9** (a) Draw the graph of $y = 4x + 1$ for values of $x$ from $-2$ to 2.
(b) Use your graph to find the value of:
    (i) $y$ when $x = -1.5$,      (ii) $x$ when $y = 3$.

**10** (a) Draw the graph of $y = 2x - 1$ for values of $x$ from $-2$ to 3.
(b) Use your graph to find the value of $x$ when $y = 0$.

**11** (a) Draw the graph of $y = 5 - 2x$ for values of $x$ from $-2$ to 3.
(b) Use your graph to find the value of $x$ when $y = 8$.

**12** (a) Draw the graphs of $y = 2x - 3$ and $y = 3 - x$ on the same axes.
(b) Write down the coordinates of the point where the lines cross.

## Activity

Draw these graphs **on the same diagram**:

$$y = 2x + 2 \qquad y = 2x + 1 \qquad y = 2x \qquad y = 2x - 1$$

Draw and label the $x$ axis from 0 to 3 and the $y$ axis from $-1$ to 8.
What do they all have in common?
What is different?

The gradient of a straight line graph is found by drawing a right-angled triangle.

$$\text{Gradient} = \frac{\text{distance up}}{\text{distance along}}$$

distance up

distance along

The gradient of a line can be positive, zero or negative.

**Positive gradients**

**Zero gradients**

**Negative gradients**

The graphs of:
$y = 2x + 2$, $y = 2x + 1$, $y = 2x$, $y = 2x - 1$, go 2 squares up for every 1 square along.
The graphs are all parallel and have a gradient of 2.

Lines that are **parallel** have the same **slope** or **gradient**.

The point where a graph crosses the $y$ axis is called the **$y$-intercept**.

The $y$-intercept of the graph $y = 2x + 2$ is 2.
The $y$-intercept of the graph $y = 2x + 1$ is 1.

*What are the $y$-intercepts of the graphs $y = 2x$ and $y = 2x - 1$?*

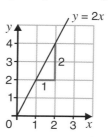

In general, the equation of any straight line can be written in the form

$$y = mx + c$$

where $m$ is the **gradient** of the line and $c$ is the **$y$-intercept**.

### EXAMPLES

**1** Write down the gradient and $y$-intercept for each of the following graphs.
   (a) $y = 3x + 5$
   (b) $y = 4x - 1$
   (c) $y = 6 - x$

   (a) Gradient = 3, $y$-intercept = 5.
   (b) Gradient = 4, $y$-intercept = $-1$.
   (c) Gradient = $-1$, $y$-intercept = 6.

**2** Write down the equation of the straight line which has gradient $-7$ and cuts the $y$ axis at the point $(0, 4)$.

   The general form for the equation of a straight line is $y = mx + c$.
   The gradient, $m = -7$, and the $y$-intercept, $c = 4$.
   Substitute these values into the general equation.
   The equation of the line is $y = -7x + 4$.
   This can be written as $y = 4 - 7x$.

**EXAMPLE**

**3** Find the equation of the line shown on this graph.

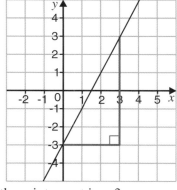

First, work out the gradient of the line.
Draw a right-angled triangle.

$$\text{Gradient} = \frac{\text{distance up}}{\text{distance along}}$$

$$= \frac{6}{3}$$

$$= 2$$

The graph crosses the $y$ axis at the point $(0, -3)$, so the $y$-intercept is $-3$.
The equation of the line is $y = 2x - 3$.

**Exercise 14.2**

**1** (a) Draw these graphs **on the same diagram**:
　　(i) $y = x + 2$　　(ii) $y = x + 1$　　(iii) $y = x$　　(iv) $y = x - 1$
　　Draw and label the $x$ axis from 0 to 3 and the $y$ axis from $-1$ to 5.
　(b) What do they all have in common? What is different?

**2** (a) Write down the gradient and $y$-intercept of $y = 3x - 1$.
　(b) Draw the graph of $y = 3x - 1$ to check your answer.

**3** Which of the following graphs are parallel?

　$y = 3x$ 　　　 $y = x + 2$ 　　　 $y = 2x + 3$ 　　　 $y = 3x + 2$

**4** Copy and complete this table.

| Graph | gradient | $y$-intercept |
|---|---|---|
| $y = 3x + 5$ | 3 | |
| $y = 2x - 3$ | | |
| $y = 4 - 2x$ | | 4 |
| $y = \frac{1}{2}x + 3$ | | |
| $y = 2x$ | | |
| $y = 3$ | | |

**5** (a) Write down the equation of the straight line which has gradient 5 and crosses the $y$ axis at the point $(0, -4)$.
　(b) Write down the equation of the straight line which has gradient $-\frac{1}{2}$ and cuts the $y$ axis at the point $(0, 6)$.

**6** Match the following equations to their graphs.

　(1) $y = x - 6$ 　　A　　　　B　　　　C　　　　D

　(2) $y = 6 - x$

　(3) $y = 2x + 1$　　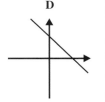

　(4) $y = 2x - 1$

**7** Find the equations of the lines shown on the following graphs.

(a)

(b)

(c)

**8** (a) Draw $x$ and $y$ axes from $-8$ to $8$.
(b) Plot the points $A(-2, -6)$ and $B(8, 4)$.
(c) Find the gradient of the line which passes through the points $A$ and $B$.
(d) Write down the coordinates of the point where the line crosses the $y$ axis.
(e) Find the equation of the line which passes through the points $A$ and $B$.

**9** (a) Draw $x$ and $y$ axes from $-8$ to $8$.
(b) Plot the points $P(-2, 3)$ and $Q(3, -7)$.
(c) Find the equation of the line which passes through the points $P$ and $Q$.

**10** What can you say about the slope of a line if the gradient is (a) 5, (b) $-5$, (c) 0?

**11** A line, with a gradient of 3, passes through the origin. What is the equation of the line?

**12** A plumber charges a fixed call-out charge and an hourly rate.
The graph shows the charges made for jobs up to 4 hours.

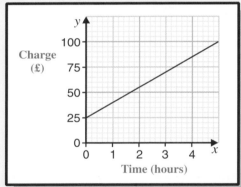

(a) What is the fixed call-out charge?
(b) What is the hourly rate?
(c) Write down the equation of the line in the form $y = mx + c$.
(d) Calculate the total charge for a job which takes 8 hours.

**13** The graph shows the taxi fare for journeys up to 3 km.

(a) What is the fixed charge?

(b) What is the charge per kilometre?

(c) Write down the equation of the line in the form $f = md + c$.

(d) Calculate the taxi fare for a journey of 5 km.

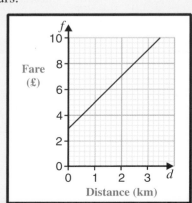

**Straight Line Graphs**

**EXAMPLE**

Draw the graph of the line given by the equation $x + 2y = 6$.

> By substituting $x = 0$ into the equation we can find the coordinates of the point where the line crosses the $y$ axis.

$x + 2y = 6$
Substitute $x = 0$.
$0 + 2y = 6$
$2y = 6$
$y = 3$

The line crosses the $y$ axis at the point $(0, 3)$.

> By substituting $y = 0$ into the equation we can find the coordinates of the point where the line crosses the $x$ axis.

$x + 2y = 6$
Substitute $y = 0$.
$x + 2 \times 0 = 6$
$x = 6$

The line crosses the $x$ axis at the point $(6, 0)$.

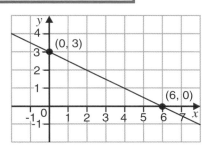

**To draw the graph of $x + 2y = 6$:**
1. Plot the points $(0, 3)$ and $(6, 0)$.
2. Using a ruler, draw a straight line which passes through the two points.

**Exercise 14.3**

**1** A straight line has equation $x + y = 7$.
  (a) By substituting $x = 0$ find the coordinates of the point where the line crosses the $y$ axis.
  (b) By substituting $y = 0$ find the coordinates of the point where the line crosses the $x$ axis.
  (c) Draw the graph of the line $x + y = 7$.

**2** (a) Draw these graphs on the same diagram.
    (i) $x + y = 2$      (ii) $x + y = 3$      (iii) $x + y = 5$
  (b) What do they all have in common?

**3** A straight line has equation $3x + y = 6$.
  (a) By substituting $x = 0$ find the coordinates of the point where the line crosses the $y$ axis.
  (b) By substituting $y = 0$ find the coordinates of the point where the line crosses the $x$ axis.
  (c) Draw the graph of the line $3x + y = 6$.

**4** Draw the graphs of lines with the following equations.
  (a) $x + 2y = 6$      (b) $2y = 4 - x$      (c) $2y = x + 4$

**5** A straight line has equation $3y + 5x = 15$.
  (a) By substituting $x = 0$ find the coordinates of the point where the line crosses the $y$ axis.
  (b) By substituting $y = 0$ find the coordinates of the point where the line crosses the $x$ axis.
  (c) Draw the graph of the line $3y + 5x = 15$.

**6** Draw the graphs of lines with the following equations, marking clearly the coordinates of the points where the lines cross the axes.
  (a) $5y + 4x = 20$      (b) $4x - y = 4$      (c) $3y + 2x = 12$

## Using graphs to solve linear equations

**EXAMPLE**

(a) Complete the tables for $y = x + 1$ and $y = 8 - x$.

| $x$ | 1 | 2 | 3 |
|---|---|---|---|
| $y = x + 1$ | | | |

| $x$ | 1 | 2 | 3 |
|---|---|---|---|
| $y = 8 - x$ | | | |

(b) Draw the graphs of $y = x + 1$ and $y = 8 - x$ on the same diagram.
(c) Use your graphs to solve the equation $8 - x = x + 1$.

(a)

| $x$ | 1 | 2 | 3 |
|---|---|---|---|
| $y = x + 1$ | 2 | 3 | 4 |

| $x$ | 1 | 2 | 3 |
|---|---|---|---|
| $y = 8 - x$ | 7 | 6 | 5 |

(b)

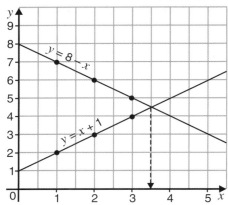

(c) The $x$ value of the point where the two graphs cross gives the solution of the equation $8 - x = x + 1$.
Reading from the graph: $x = 3.5$

*Check the graphical solution of the equation by solving $8 - x = x + 1$ algebraically.*

## Exercise 14.4

**1** (a) Copy and complete the tables for $y = x + 2$ and $y = 5 - x$.

| $x$ | 1 | 2 | 3 |
|---|---|---|---|
| $y = x + 2$ | | | |

| $x$ | 1 | 2 | 3 |
|---|---|---|---|
| $y = 5 - x$ | | | |

(b) Draw the graphs of $y = x + 2$ and $y = 5 - x$ on the same diagram.
(c) Write down the coordinates of the point where the two lines cross.
(d) Use your graphs to solve $x + 2 = 5 - x$.

**2** (a) Draw the graphs of $y = 3x + 1$ and $y = x + 6$ on the same diagram.
(b) Write down the coordinates of the point where the two lines cross.
(c) Use your graphs to solve the equation $3x + 1 = x + 6$.

**3** (a) Draw the graphs of $y = x$ and $y = 3x - 1$.
(b) Use your graphs to solve the equation $x = 3x - 1$.

**4** By drawing the graphs of $y = 2x$ and $y = 3 - x$, solve the equation $2x = 3 - x$.

**5** (a) Draw the graph of $y = 3 + 2x$.
(b) What graph should be drawn to solve the equation $3 + 2x = 9$?
(c) Draw the graph and use it to solve the equation $3 + 2x = 9$.

## Perpendicular lines

The diagram shows two lines, AB and CD.
The lines are **perpendicular**, at right angles, to each other.

Line AB has:

    gradient: 2

    $y$-intercept: $-3$

    equation: $y = 2x - 3$

Line CD has:

    gradient: $-\frac{1}{2}$

    $y$-intercept: 2

    equation: $y = -\frac{1}{2}x + 2$

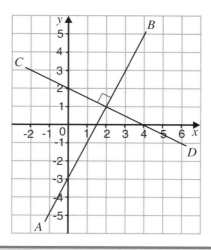

Notice that:

    Gradient of line $AB \times$ gradient of line $CD = -1$

In general, if two lines are perpendicular to each other, the product of their gradients $= -1$.

$$m_{AB} = \frac{-1}{m_{CD}}$$

This can be written as:

$m_{AB} \times m_{CD} = -1$    where $m_{AB}$ is the gradient of the line $AB$, and $m_{CD}$ is the gradient of the line $CD$.

14

### EXAMPLE

Write down the gradient of the line which is perpendicular to the line with equation $y = \frac{1}{5}x + 4$.

Gradient of the line $y = \frac{1}{5}x + 4$ is $\frac{1}{5}$.

Gradient of the line perpendicular to this line is $-1 \div \left(\frac{1}{5}\right) = -5$.

## Exercise 14.5

**1** Which of these lines are perpendicular to the line $y = x$?

    **A** $y = \frac{1}{2}x$      **B** $y = -x$      **C** $x + y = 3$      **D** $y = x - 1$

**2** Write down the gradient of a line which is perpendicular to:

    (a) $y = 3x + 1$      (b) $y = \frac{1}{4}x - 3$      (c) $y = 4 - 2x$

**3** (a) Find the equation of the line perpendicular to $y = x$ which passes through the point
        (i) $(0, 0)$,      (ii) $(0, 2)$.
    (b) Find the equation of the line perpendicular to $y = \frac{1}{2}x$, which passes through the point
        (i) $(0, 1)$,      (ii) $(1, 0)$.
    (c) Find the equation of the line through $(2, 2)$ which is perpendicular to $y = 2x$.

**4** Given the points $P(7, 4)$, $Q(9, -2)$, $R(-5, -20)$ and $S(-3, 4)$, show by means of gradients that $PR$ is perpendicular to $QS$.

**5** $L$ is the point $(-2, -1)$, $M(0, 5)$ and $N(4, -2)$.
    (a) Find the equation of the line through $N$ which is parallel to $LM$.
    (b) Find the equation of the line through $N$ which is perpendicular to $LM$.

**6** $ABCD$ is a rectangle, with $A$ at $(-3, 1)$ and $B$ at $(1, -1)$.
    Find the equations of the two sides $AB$ and $BC$ of the rectangle.

## Rearranging equations

The general equation for a straight line graph is $y = mx + c$.
When an equation is in this form the gradient and $y$-intercept are given by the values of $m$ and $c$.

The equation for a straight line can also be written in the form $px + qy = r$.
To find the gradient and $y$-intercept of this line we must first **rearrange** the equation.

For example, the graph of a straight line is given as $2y - 6x = 5$.
To rearrange: $2y - 6x = 5$

> Add $6x$ to both sides.
$$2y = 6x + 5$$
> Divide both sides by 2.
$$y = 3x + 2.5$$

Hence, the line has gradient 3 and $y$-intercept 2.5.

### EXAMPLES

**1** The graph of a straight line is given by the equation $4y - 3x = 8$.
    (a)   Write this equation in the form $y = mx + c$.
    (b)   Write down the gradient and the $y$-intercept of the line.

    (a)   $4y - 3x = 8$
        Add $3x$ to both sides.
          $4y = 3x + 8$
        Divide both sides by 4.
$$y = \tfrac{3}{4}x + 2$$

    (b)   The line has gradient $\tfrac{3}{4}$ and $y$-intercept 2.

**2** The equation of a straight line is $6x + 3y = 2$.
Write down the equation of another line which is parallel to this line.

Write the equation in the form $y = mx + c$.
$6x + 3y = 2$
Subtract $6x$ from both sides.
$$3y = -6x + 2$$
Divide both sides by 3.
$$y = -2x + \tfrac{2}{3}$$
The gradient of the line is $-2$.
To write an equation of a parallel line keep the same gradient and change the value of the $y$-intercept.
For example: $y = -2x + 5$

**3** Find the equation of the line through (2, 3) which is perpendicular to the line $y = 2x - 3$.

The equation of the line will be of the form $y = mx + c$.
The gradient of the line $y = 2x - 3$ is 2.

$m \times 2 = -1$  $(m_{AB} \times m_{CD} = -1)$
     $m = -\tfrac{1}{2}$

The line passes through the point (2, 3) and has gradient $-\tfrac{1}{2}$.
Substitute $x = 2$, $y = 3$ and $m = -\tfrac{1}{2}$ into $y = mx + c$.
$3 = -\tfrac{1}{2} \times 2 + c$
$3 = -1 + c$
$c = 4$
The equation of the line is $y = -\tfrac{1}{2}x + 4$.

**1** The graph of a straight line is given by the equation $2y - 3x = 6$.
Write this equation in the form $y = mx + c$.

**2** Write the equations of the following lines in the form $y = mx + c$.
(a) $2y + x = 4$     (b) $5y + 4x = 20$     (c) $4 - 3y = 2x$     (d) $2x - 7y = 14$

**3** Find the gradients of these lines.
(a) $2y = x$     (b) $x - y = 0$     (c) $2x - y = 0$
(d) $3y + x = 0$     (e) $4y - 3x = 0$     (f) $2x + 5y = 0$

**4** These lines cross the $y$ axis at the point $(0, a)$. Find the value of $a$ for each line.
(a) $y = x$     (b) $2y = x + 1$     (c) $3y + 6 = x$
(d) $2y - 5 = x$     (e) $4y - 3x = 8$     (f) $x + 5y = 2$

**5** Write down an equation which is parallel to each of these lines.
(a) $y = x$     (b) $y = 2x - 3$     (c) $2y = x - 4$

**6** The equation of a straight line is $2y + 3x = 4$.
Write down the equation of another line which is parallel to this line.

**7** Which of these pairs of lines are perpendicular to each other?
(a) $y = 4x,$     (b) $3y = x - 6,$     (c) $5y - 2x = 3,$
    $y = \frac{1}{4}x.$          $y = 1 - 3x.$         $2y = 5x.$

**8** The diagram shows a sketch of the line $2y = x + 4$.

(a) Find the coordinates of points $A$ and $B$.
(b) What is the gradient of the line?

Copy the diagram.
(c) (i) Draw the sketch of another line that has the same gradient as $2y = x + 4$.
     (ii) What is the equation of the line you have drawn?

**9**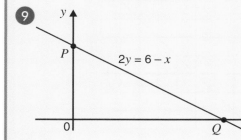

The diagram shows a sketch of the line $2y = 6 - x$.

(a) Find the coordinates of points $P$ and $Q$.
(b) What is the gradient of the line?

Copy the diagram.
(c) (i) Draw the sketch of another line that has the same gradient as $2y = 6 - x$.
     (ii) What is the equation of the line you have drawn?

**10** In each part, find the equation of the line, through $P$, which is
(a) parallel to the given line,
(b) perpendicular to the given line.
    (i) $P(0, 2),$   $y = x + 1.$
    (ii) $P(1, 3),$   $y = 2x - 1.$
    (iii) $P(-1, 5),$   $3y = x + 6.$
    (iv) $P(-4, -1),$   $4y + x = -8.$

**11** In the diagram, the lines $AB$ and $CD$ are perpendicular to each other and intersect at the point $(1, 4)$.
The line $AB$ crosses the $x$ axis at $(3, 0)$.

Calculate the coordinates of the points $P$ and $Q$.

# What you need to know

- **Coordinates** are used to describe the position of a point on a graph.
- The $x$ axis is the line $y = 0$.  The $y$ axis is the line $x = 0$.
- The graph of a **linear function** is a **straight line**.
  The general equation of a linear function is $y = mx + c$, where $m$ is the **gradient** of the line and $c$ is the **y-intercept**.
- The **gradient** of a line can be found by drawing a right-angled triangle.

  $$\text{Gradient} = \frac{\text{distance up}}{\text{distance along}}$$

  Gradient can be positive, zero or negative.

  distance up

  distance along

- If two lines are **perpendicular** to each other, the product of their gradients is $-1$.

  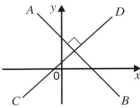

  $$m_{AB} \times m_{CD} = -1$$

  $$m_{AB} = \frac{-1}{m_{CD}}$$

- The points where a line crosses the axes can be found:
    by reading the coordinates from a graph,
    by substituting $x = 0$ and $y = 0$ into the equation of the line.
- Equations of the form $px + qy = r$ can be **rearranged** to the form $y = mx + c$.

**You should be able to:**
- Substitute values into given functions to generate points.
- Plot graphs of **linear functions**.
- Use graphs of linear functions to solve equations.
- Find the equation for a given line.

## Review Exercise 14

**1** (a) Write down the equations of the lines labelled on this graph.
   (b) What are the coordinates of the point where lines (1) and (2) cross?

**2** (a) Copy and complete the table of values for the equation $y = 2x + 1$.

| $x$ | $-2$ | $-1$ | 0 | 1 | 2 |
|-----|------|------|---|---|---|
| $y$ | $-3$ |      |   | 3 |   |

   (b) Draw the graph of $y = 2x + 1$.
   (c) Use your graph to find:  (i)  the value of $y$ when $x = -1.5$,
                                (ii) the value of $x$ when $y = 3.6$.

**3** (a) On the same diagram draw and label the lines: $y = 2x$ and $x + y = 6$.
   (b) Write down the coordinates of the point where the lines cross.

**4** Draw the graph of $y = 8 - 2x$ for values of $x$ from 0 to 5.     OCR

**5** (a) Write down the gradient of the line $y = 3x - 2$.
   (b) Find the coordinates of the point where the line $y = 3x - 2$ crosses the $y$ axis.

**6** The equation of the straight line drawn is $y = mx + c$.

Find the values of $c$ and $m$.

**7** The coordinates of three points on a straight line graph are shown in the table.

| $x$ | 1 | 2 | 3 |
|---|---|---|---|
| $y$ | 3 | 0 | $-3$ |

(a) Write down the value of $y$ when $x = 0$.
(b) Find the equation of the straight line.

OCR

**8** In an experiment, weights are added to a spring and the length of the spring is measured. The graph shows the results.

A line of best fit has been drawn.

(a) Estimate the length of the spring when no weight is added.
(b) Calculate the gradient of the line.
(c) Write down the equation of the line in the form $l = mw + c$.
(d) Use your equation to estimate the length of the spring for a weight of 300 g.

**9** The values in the table are connected by the equation $y = ax + b$.

| $x$ | 1 | 2 | 5 | 10 | 20 |
|---|---|---|---|---|---|
| $y$ | 2 | 5 | 14 | 29 | 59 |

Work out the values of $a$ and $b$.

OCR

**10** (a) The graph of a straight line is given by the equation $y - 3x = 2$.
    Write down the equation of a line parallel to this line which passes through the point (0, 5).
(b) The graph of a different line is given by the equation $3y - 2x = -6$.
    (i) What is the gradient of this line?
    (ii) Find the coordinates of the point where this line crosses the $y$ axis.

**11** Find the equation of the line passing through the points $(-1, 8)$ and $(2, -10)$.
Give your answer in the form $y = ax + b$.

OCR

**12** Find the gradient of the straight line with equation $5y - 2 = 3x$.

**13** Show that the lines $2y = x + 2$ and $y = 6 - 2x$ are perpendicular to each other.

**14** Find the equation of the line through (2, 3) which is perpendicular to $y = 4x - 5$.

**15** The diagram shows a sketch of a straight line which passes through $A (0, 4)$ and $B (6, 0)$.

Find the equation of the line:
(a) which passes through $A$ and $B$,
(b) which passes through (0, 2) and is parallel to $AB$,
(c) which passes through the midpoint of $AB$ and is perpendicular to $AB$.

Graphs are sometimes drawn to show real-life situations.
In most cases a quantity is measured over a period of time.

---

**EXAMPLE**

Craig drew a graph to show the amount of fuel in the family car as they travelled to their holiday destination. He also made some notes:

| Part of Graph | Event |
|---------------|-------|
| A             | Leave home. |
| A to B        | Motorway. |
| B to C        | Car breaks down. |
| C to D        | On our way again. |
| D to E        | Stop for lunch. |
| E to F        | Fill tank with fuel. |
| F to G        | Country roads. |
| G             | Arrive, at last! |

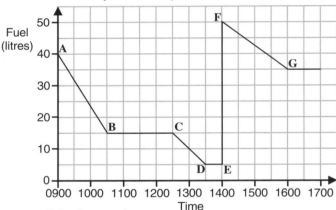

(a) How much fuel was in the tank at the start of the journey?
(b) At what time did the car break down?
(c) How long did the family stop for lunch?
(d) How much fuel was put into the tank at the garage?

(a) 40 litres       (b) 1030       (c) $\frac{1}{2}$ hour       (d) 45 litres

*Use the graph to work out how many litres of fuel were used for the journey.*

---

Notice that in this example and others involving graphs against time:

**A quantity increasing with time.**   **A quantity decreasing with time.**   **A quantity not changing, i.e. constant.**   **A quantity changing instantly.**

---

## Exercise **15.1**

**1**  A climber pulls a rucksack up a vertical cliff face using a rope.
Which of the graphs below could represent the motion of the rucksack against time?

A                          B                          C                          D

**2** Match the graphs to the situations. In each graph, the horizontal axis represents time and the vertical axis represents speed.

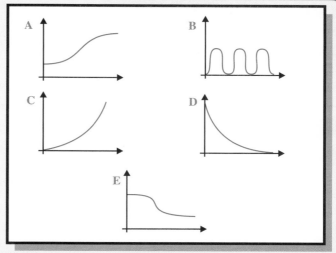

1 A runner starts from rest and begins to pick up speed.

2 A runner keeps having to stop and start.

3 A runner gets tired and has to slow down.

4 A runner sees the finish, builds up speed and sprints to the line.

**3** Cans of drink can be bought from a vending machine in the school canteen.
At 0900 one day the machine is three-quarters full.
During break, from 1045 to 1100, drinks are bought from the machine at a steady rate.
By the end of the break the machine is one-quarter full. At 1200 the machine is filled.
The lunch break is from 1230 to 1330. Someone complains at 1315 that the machine is empty.
The machine is filled at 1400, ready for the afternoon break from 1445 to 1500.
At 1600 the machine is three-quarters full.
Sketch a graph to show the number of drinks in the machine from 0900 to 1600.

**4** Two companies each use a formula to calculate the charge made for hiring out scaffolding.
Company A uses the formula   $c = 50 + 10d$,
Company B uses the formula   $c = 15d + 20$,
where   $c$ is the total charge, in pounds,
        $d$ is the length of the hire period, in days.
(a)   Draw the horizontal axis for $d$ from 0 to 10 and the vertical axis for $c$ from 0 to 180.
(b)   Draw the graph of   $c = 50 + 10d$.
(c)   Draw the graph of   $c = 15d + 20$.

Use your graph to answer the following.
(d)   From which company is it cheaper to hire scaffolding for 2 days?
(e)   From which company is it cheaper to hire scaffolding for 8 days?
(f)   For what number of days do both companies make the same charge?

**5** Water is poured into some containers at a constant rate.
Copy the axes given and sketch the graph of the depth of the water against time for each container as it is filled.

**Distance-time graphs** are used to illustrate journeys.

**Speed** is given by the gradient, or slope, of the line.
The faster the speed the steeper the gradient.
Zero gradient (horizontal line) means zero speed (not moving).

> **Calculations** involving speed, distance and time are covered in Chapter 8.

**EXAMPLES**

① The graph shows a bus journey.
   (a) How many times does the bus stop?
   (b) On which part of the journey does the bus travel fastest?

   (a) At zero speed the distance-time graph is horizontal.
       So, the bus stops 3 times.
   (b) The bus travels fastest when the gradient of the distance-time graph is steepest.
       So, the bus travels fastest between the second and third stops.

② What speed is shown by this distance-time graph?
   Give your answer in metres per second.

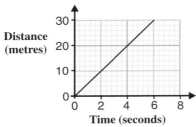

   A distance of 30 metres is travelled in a time of 6 seconds.
   Using Speed = Distance ÷ Time
        Speed = 30 ÷ 6
              = 5 metres per second

> **Remember:**
>
> **Speed** can be calculated from the gradient of a distance-time graph.
>
> When the distance-time graph is **linear** the **speed is constant**.
>
> When the distance-time graph is **horizontal** the **speed is zero**.
>
> Average speed = $\dfrac{\text{total distance}}{\text{total time}}$

**Exercise 15.2**

① The graph represents the journey of a cyclist from Hambone to Boneham.

   (a) What time did the cyclist leave Hambone?

   (b) The cyclist arrived in Boneham at 1200. How far is Boneham from Hambone?

   (c) The cyclist made one stop on his journey.
       (i) At what time did the cyclist stop?
       (ii) How far was the cyclist from Boneham when he stopped?

   (d) Calculate the average speed of the cyclist between 1130 and 1200.
       Give your answer in kilometres per hour.

2. (a) The graph represents the journey of a car. What is the speed of the car in kilometres per hour?

(b) The graph represents the journey of a train. What is the speed of the train in metres per second?

(c) The graph represents the speed of a cyclist. What is the speed of the cyclist in miles per hour?

3. This graph shows the progress made by a runner during the first 20 km of a marathon race.

Find the average speed of the runner:
(a) during the first 10 km of the race,
(b) during the second 10 km of the race,
(c) during the first 20 km of the race.

4. The graph represents a bus journey from Poole.

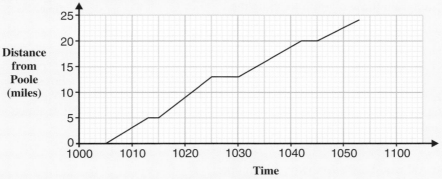

Calculate, in miles per hour, the average speed of the bus:
(a) between 1015 and 1025,  (b) for the whole journey.

5. Selby is 20 miles from York.
(a) Kathryn leaves Selby at 1030 and drives to York. She travels at an average speed of 20 miles per hour. Draw a distance-time graph to represent her journey.
(b) At 1030 Matt leaves York and drives to Selby. He travels at an average speed of 30 miles per hour.
   (i) On the same diagram draw a distance-time graph to represent his journey.
   (ii) At what time does Matt arrive in Selby?

**Using Graphs . . . . Using Graphs . . . .**

15

139

**6** Dan walks around Bolam Lake. He starts and finishes his walk at the car park beside the lake. The distance-time graph shows his journey.

(a) At what time did Dan start his walk?

(b) At what time did Dan reach the furthest distance from the car park?

(c) How many times did Dan stop during his walk?

(d) Dan stopped for lunch at 1330.
For how many minutes did he stop for lunch?

(e) Between what times did Dan walk the fastest?

(f) At what speed did Dan walk between 1530 and 1600?

**7** The graph represents the journey of a cyclist from Bournemouth to the New Forest.

(a) What is the average speed of the cyclist in miles per hour?

(b) Another cyclist is travelling from the New Forest to Bournemouth at an average speed of 12 miles per hour. At 1300 the cyclist is 15 miles from Bournemouth.

   (i) Copy the graph and on the same diagram draw a graph to show the journey of the cyclist to Bournemouth.

   (ii) At what time does the cyclist arrive in Bournemouth?

**8** Billy has a 10 km journey to school.
He leaves home at 8.05 am and takes 10 minutes to walk 1 km to Jane's house.
Billy gets a lift with Jane's mum at 8.20 am. Billy arrives at school at 8.45 am.

(a) Using 1 cm for 5 minutes on the time axis and 1 cm for 1 km on the distance axis draw a distance-time graph for Billy's journey.

(b) Find Billy's average speed for his whole journey in km/hour.

**9** Emby and Ashwood are two towns 14 km apart.
Kim leaves Emby at 1000 and walks at a steady pace of 6 km/hour towards Ashwood.
Ray leaves Ashwood at 1040 and cycles towards Emby.
Ray travels at a steady speed of 21 km/hour for the first 20 minutes and then at a slower steady speed for the rest of his journey.
Ray arrives at Emby at 1130.

(a) On the same diagram and using a scale of 1 cm for 10 minutes on the time axis and 1 cm for 1 km on the distance axis, draw a distance-time graph to show both journeys.

(b) Use your diagram to find:

   (i) the time that Kim arrives at Ashwood,

   (ii) the time that Kim and Ray pass each other,

   (iii) Ray's speed for the slower part of his journey.

## Speed-time graphs

**Acceleration** is the rate of change of speed.
Acceleration is given by the gradient, or slope, of the line.
The greater the acceleration, the steeper the gradient.
Zero gradient (horizontal line) means zero acceleration (moving at a constant speed).
Acceleration = speed ÷ time
Acceleration is measured in metres per second squared (m/s²).

> **Acceleration** can be calculated from the gradient of a speed-time graph.
>
> When the speed-time graph is **linear** the **acceleration is constant**.
>
> When the speed-time graph is **horizontal** the **speed is constant** and the **acceleration is zero**.
>
> The **area** enclosed by a speed-time graph represents the **distance** travelled.

### EXAMPLE

The graph shows Jane's speed plotted against time during a run.

(a)   Give a brief description of Jane's run.
(b)   Calculate Jane's acceleration during the first 20 seconds of her run.
(c)   Calculate Jane's deceleration during the last 50 seconds of her run.
(d)   How far did Jane run?

(a)   Jane accelerates at a constant rate for the first 20 seconds of her run.
      She then runs at a constant speed of 4 m/s for 30 seconds before slowing at a constant
      rate to a stop after 100 seconds.

(b)   Acceleration = speed ÷ time
                   = 4 ÷ 20
                   = 0.2 m/s²

> **From the graph:**
> **Positive** gradient = getting faster, **accelerating**.
> **Negative** gradient = slowing down, **decelerating**.

(c)   Deceleration = speed ÷ time
                   = 4 ÷ 50
                   = 0.08 m/s²

(d)   The area under the graph represents the distance travelled, in metres.
      Distance travelled = ½ (30 + 100) × 4
                         = 260 m

*Show that the distances Jane travels whilst accelerating, running at a constant speed and
decelerating, are 40 m, 120 m and 100 m respectively.*

Try to do questions 1 to 3 without using your calculator.

**1**   A car accelerated steadily from rest to 12 m/s in 15 seconds.
What was the acceleration of the car in m/s²?

**2**   Look at the points on this speed-time graph.

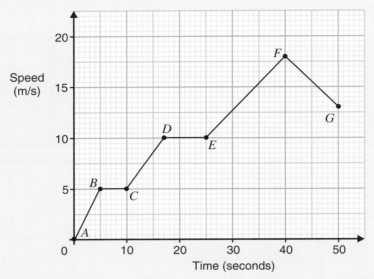

(a)   Between which points is:
   (i)    the speed constant,
   (ii)   the acceleration greatest,
   (iii)  the acceleration zero,
   (iv)   the acceleration negative?
(b)   Calculate the acceleration between points:
   (i)    E and F,
   (ii)   F and G.

**3**   The speed-time graph of an underground train travelling between two stations is shown.

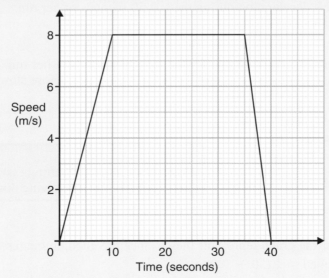

(a)   What was the maximum speed of the train?
(b)   Calculate the acceleration of the train at the beginning of the journey.
(c)   Calculate the deceleration of the train at the end of the journey.
(d)   Calculate the distance between the stations, in metres.

**4** The diagram shows a speed-time graph for a train travelling between station *A* and station *B*.

(a) For how long did the train accelerate at a constant rate at the start of its journey?
(b) What was the total time during the journey that the train was **not** accelerating?
(c) Show that the train was slowing down at a rate of approximately 0.9 m/s² as it approached station *B*.

**5** A car takes 12 seconds to accelerate uniformly from rest to 24 m/s.
It then travels at 24 m/s for 30 seconds before slowing down steadily to rest.
The whole journey takes 50 seconds.
(a) Draw the speed-time graph of the car.
(b) How far does the car travel?

**6** The speed-time graph shows the journey of a van between two road junctions.

(a) Calculate the acceleration of the van at the beginning of the journey.
(b) Calculate the time it takes the van to travel half the distance between the junctions.

## What you need to know

- A **gradient** measures the **rate of change** of one quantity with respect to another.
  A **positive** gradient represents a **rate of increase**.
  A **negative** gradient represents a **rate of decrease**.
- The gradient of a **distance-time graph** gives the speed.
  **Speed** is the rate of change of distance with respect to time.
  When the distance-time graph is **linear** the **speed is constant**.
  When the distance-time graph is **horizontal** the **speed is zero**.
- The gradient of a **speed-time graph** gives the acceleration.
  **Acceleration** is the rate of change of speed with respect to time.
  When the speed-time graph is **linear** the **acceleration is constant**.
  When the speed-time graph is **horizontal** the **speed is constant** and the **acceleration is zero**.
- The **area** enclosed by the graph on a speed-time graph represents the **distance** travelled.

**You should be able to:**
- Draw and interpret graphs which represent real-life situations.

**1** The graph illustrates a 10 km cycle race between Afzal and Brian.

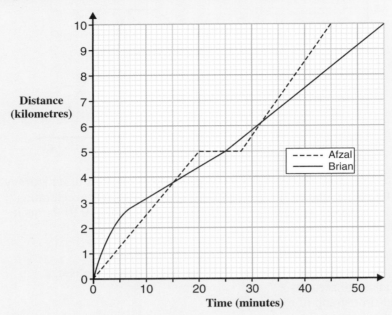

(a) Who was cycling faster at the beginning of the race?

(b) Which cyclist stopped?

(c) How far apart were the cyclists 10 minutes after the start of the race?

(d) Who won the race?

**2** Which graph matches each relationship?

**A**: The volume of a cube plotted against the length of its edge.

**B**: The cost of posting letters 1st class plotted against the number of letters posted.

**3** The distance from Ashby to Banborough is 16 km.
The distance from Banborough to Calby is 8 km.
John leaves Ashby at noon.
He walks towards Banborough for 1 hour at an average speed of 6 km/h and then rests for 20 minutes.
John then runs the remaining distance to Banborough at an average speed of 10 km/h.
At Banborough John talks to a friend for 20 minutes and borrows his bicycle.
He then cycles to Calby at an average speed of 16 km/h.
John leaves Calby at 1600.
He cycles home over the same route arriving at 1650.

Using a scale of 1 cm for 20 minutes and 1 cm for 2 km draw a distance-time graph for John's journey.

**4** The graph represents a coach journey from Bath.

The coach completed its journey at 1130.
(a) At what time did the coach leave Bath?
(b) How far did the coach travel?
(c) How many times did the coach stop on the journey?
(d) What was the average speed of the coach between 1030 and 1130?

**5** These two containers are full of water.
Both are emptied from taps at the bottom of each container.
Sketch the graph of the depth of water against time for each container as it is being emptied.

(a)       (b)

**6** It takes Samir 8 minutes to fill his bath.
The bath fills at 25 litres per minute for the first 2 minutes.
The rate of flow is 15 litres per minute for the next 2 minutes.
In the last 4 minutes, the bath fills at only 5 litres per minute.
(a) Show this information on a graph.
(b) Calculate the average rate of flow of the water in filling Samir's bath.

OCR

**7** The graph shows the speed of a marble rolling down a slope during a 5 second period.

(a) Work out the gradient of the line.
(b) What does the gradient of the line represent?

OCR

# Inequalities

## Activity

For all children who enter the competition we can say that
Age < 16 years

For anyone riding the Big Dipper we can say that
Height ≥ 1.2 m

For all items sold in the store we can say that
Cost ≤ £1

These are examples of inequalities.
*Can you think of other situations where inequalities are used?*

## Inequalities

An **inequality** is a mathematical statement, such as $x > 1$, $a \leq 2$ or $-3 \leq n < 2$.

In the following, $x$ is an integer.

| Sign | Meaning | Example | Possible values of $x$ |
|------|---------|---------|------------------------|
| < | is less than | $x < 4$ | 3, 2, 1, 0, −1, −2, −3, … |
| ≤ | is less than or equal to | $x \leq 4$ | 4, 3, 2, 1, 0, −1, −2, −3, … |
| > | is greater than | $x > 6$ | 7, 8, 9, 10, … |
| ≥ | is greater than or equal to | $x \geq 2$ | 2, 3, 4, 5, … |

An **integer** is a positive or negative whole number or zero.

Explain the difference between the meanings of the signs < and ≤.
Explain the difference between the meanings of the signs > and ≥.

## Number lines

Inequalities can be shown on a **number line**.

As you move to the right, numbers get bigger.
As you move to the left, numbers get smaller.

The number line below shows the inequality $-2 < x \leq 3$.

The circle at 3 is **filled** to show that 3 is **included**.
The circle at −2 is **not filled** to show that −2 is **not included**.

## EXAMPLES

**1** Draw number lines to show these inequalities:
  (a)  $x < 1.5$      (b)  $x \geqslant -2$      (c)  $x \leqslant 4$  and  $x > -1$

(a)  $x < 1.5$

The circle is:
**filled** if the inequality is **included**,
**not filled** if the inequality is **not included**.

(b)  $x \geqslant -2$

(c)  $x \leqslant 4$  and  $x > -1$.

$x$ has to satisfy two inequalities.

**2** (a)  Draw a number line to show the inequality   $3 \leqslant x < 8$.
  (b)  $x$ is an integer.
      Write down the values of $x$ which satisfy the inequality.

$3 \leqslant x < 8$
is a shorthand method
of writing
$3 \leqslant x$  **and**  $x < 8$.

(a)

(b)  The values of $x$ which satisfy the inequality  $3 \leqslant x < 8$  are:  3,  4,  5,  6,  7.

## Exercise **16.1**

**1** Write down the following mathematical statements and say whether each is true or false.
  (a)  $4 < 7$        (b)  $3 > -3$        (c)  $4 \geqslant 4$        (d)  $-2 > -1$
  (e)  $-8 \leqslant -8$      (f)  $1.5 \geqslant 2.1$      (g)  $3 \times 5 \leqslant 7 \times 2$      (h)  $-4 \times (-2) > -4 - 4$

**2** Write down an integer which could replace the letter.
  (a)  $x < 6$        (b)  $a \geqslant -2$        (c)  $c + 2 < 8$        (d)  $2d \leqslant 14$
  (e)  $f - 3 > 7$      (f)  $-2 < h < 0$      (g)  $t \leqslant 5$  **and**  $t > 4$   (h)  $r \geqslant -6$  **and**  $r < -1$

**3** In this question $x$ is an integer. Write down all the values of $x$ which satisfy these inequalities.
  (a)  $1 < x < 5$      (b)  $-2 < x \leqslant 3$      (c)  $-4 \leqslant x \leqslant -1$      (d)  $-1 \leqslant x < 3$

**4** Write down a mathematical statement, using inequalities, for each of these diagrams.

**5** Draw number lines to show the following inequalities.
  For each part, draw and label a number line from $-5$ to 5.
  (a)  $x > 2$                (b)  $x \leqslant 1$        (c)  $x \geqslant -4$        (d)  $x < -2$
  (e)  $-2 \leqslant x < 3$          (f)  $1 < x \leqslant 4$      (g)  $-3 < x < 0$      (h)  $x < -3$  and  $x \geqslant 1$

**Solve** means to find the values of $x$ which make the inequality true. The aim is to end up with **one letter** on one side of the inequality and a **number** on the other side of the inequality.

Solving inequalities is similar to solving equations.

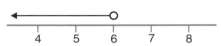

### EXAMPLES

**1** Solve the inequality $5x - 3 < 27$ and show the solution on a number line.

$5x - 3 < 27$
Add 3 to both sides.
$5x < 30$
Divide both sides by 5.
$x < 6$

The solution is shown on a number line as:

4   5   6   7   8

This means that the inequality is **true** for all values of $x$ which are less than 6.

**2** Solve the inequality $7a \geqslant a + 9$.

$7a \geqslant a + 9$
Subtract $a$ from both sides.
$6a \geqslant 9$
Divide both sides by 6.
$a \geqslant 1.5$

This means that the inequality is true for all values of $a$ which are equal to 1.5, or greater.

*Substitute $a = 1.5$, $a = 2$ and $a = 1$ into the original inequality. What do you notice?*

## Exercise 16.2

**1** Solve each of the following inequalities and show the solution on a number line.

(a) $3n > 6$      (b) $2x < -4$      (c) $a + 1 < 5$      (d) $a - 3 < 1$

(e) $2d - 5 \leqslant 1$      (f) $t + 2 < -1$      (g) $5 + 2g > 1$      (h) $4 + 3y \geqslant 4$

**2** Solve the following inequalities.
Show your working clearly.

(a) $a + 3 < 7$      (b) $5 + x \geqslant 3$      (c) $y + 2 < -1$      (d) $3c > 15$

(e) $2d < -6$      (f) $b - 3 \geqslant -2$      (g) $-2 + b \leqslant -1$      (h) $2c + 5 \leqslant 11$

(i) $3d - 4 > 8$      (j) $4 + 3f < -2$      (k) $8g - 1 \leqslant 3$      (l) $5h < h + 8$

(m) $3x < x - 6$      (n) $6j \geqslant 2j + 10$      (o) $7k > 3k - 16$      (p) $6m - 7 \leqslant m$

**3** (a) (i) Solve the inequality $3x + 5 \geqslant 2$.

(ii) Write down the inequality shown by the following diagram.

-2   -1   0   1   2   3   4

(b) Write down all the integers that satisfy both inequalities shown in part (a).

**4** Solve the following inequalities.

(a) $\frac{1}{2}a \geqslant 3$      (b) $\frac{1}{3}b < 5$      (c) $4m + 2 > 2m - 11$

(d) $7n - 3 \leqslant 13 - n$      (e) $3p - 2 > 6 + 2p$      (f) $4q + 5 > 12 - 3q$

(g) $6r + 1 \geqslant 4r - 2$      (h) $2t - 10 > t + 3$      (i) $2(u - 5) \leqslant 8$

(j) $3(4v + 1) < -15$      (k) $\frac{1}{2}w + 3 > 7$      (l) $\frac{1}{2}(5x - 1) < 3$

## Multiplying (or dividing) an inequality by a negative number

### Activity

$-2 < 3$

Multiply both sides by $-1$.
$-2 \times (-1) = 2$ and $3 \times (-1) = -3$

$2 > -3$

To keep the statement true we have to reverse the inequality sign.

Multiply both sides of these inequalities by $-1$.

**1** $3 > 2$

**2** $3 > -2$

**3** $-3 < -1$

**4** $5 \geqslant 4$

**5** $-4 \leqslant 5$

**6** $-4 \geqslant -5$

The same rules for equations can be applied to inequalities, with one exception:
When you **multiply** (or **divide**) both sides of an inequality by a negative number the inequality is reversed.

### EXAMPLES

**1** Solve $-3x < 6$.

Divide both sides by $-3$.
Because we are dividing by a negative number the inequality is reversed.
$x > -2$

**2** Solve $3a - 2 \geqslant 5a - 9$.

Subtract $5a$ from both sides.
$-2a - 2 \geqslant -9$
Add 2 to both sides.
$-2a \geqslant -7$
Divide both sides by $-2$.
$a \leqslant 3.5$

### Exercise 16.3

Solve the following inequalities. Show your working clearly.

**1** $-4a > 8$

**2** $-5b \leqslant -15$

**3** $-3c \geqslant 12$

**4** $3 - 2d < 5$

**5** $14 - 3e \leqslant 4e$

**6** $-5f > 4f - 9$

**7** $4g < 7g + 12$

**8** $5 - 3h \leqslant h - 3$

**9** $-5 - j \geqslant 12j - 18$

**10** $3 - 5k < 2(3 + 2k)$

**11** $3(m - 2) > 5m$

**12** $3(2n - 1) < 8n + 5$

**13** $3p \geqslant 5 - 6p$

**14** $2(q - 3) < 5 + 7q$

**15** $n - 5 > 2(n - 7)$

### Double inequalities

### EXAMPLE

Find the values of $x$ such that $-3 < x - 2 \leqslant 1$ and show the solution on a number line.

$-3 < x - 2 \leqslant 1$
Add 2 to each part of the inequality.
$-1 < x \leqslant 3$

The solution is shown on a number line as:

## EXAMPLE

Find the integer values of $n$ for which $-1 \leqslant 2n + 3 < 7$.

$-1 \leqslant 2n + 3 < 7$
Subtract 3 from each part.
$-4 \leqslant 2n < 4$
Divide each part by 2.
$-2 \leqslant n < 2$

Integer values which satisfy the inequality $-1 \leqslant 2n + 3 < 7$ are: $-2, -1, 0, 1$.

## Exercise 16.4

1. Solve each of the following inequalities and show the solution on a number line.
   (a) $5 < x + 4 \leqslant 9$
   (b) $-3 \leqslant x - 2 < 7$
   (c) $2 < 9 + x \leqslant 13$

2. Find the values of $x$ such that:
   (a) $2 < 2x \leqslant 6$
   (b) $-6 \leqslant 3x < 12$
   (c) $5 < 2x - 1 < 8$
   (d) $-2 \leqslant 3x - 1 \leqslant 11$
   (e) $12 < 5x + 2 \leqslant 27$
   (f) $-9 \leqslant 4x + 3 < 27$
   (g) $-16 < 7x - 2 < 12$
   (h) $-1 \leqslant 3x - 10 < 8$
   (i) $-4 \leqslant 5 + 2x \leqslant 3$

3. Find the integer values of $n$ for which:
   (a) $3 < n - 2 < 7$
   (b) $-2 < n + 1 \leqslant 5$
   (c) $-2 < 2n \leqslant 4$
   (d) $5 \leqslant 2n - 3 < 13$
   (e) $0 < 2n - 8 < 3$
   (f) $5 < 4n + 1 \leqslant 13$
   (g) $-4 \leqslant 5n + 6 < 11$
   (h) $-4 < 3n + 2 \leqslant 11$
   (i) $-5 \leqslant \frac{1}{2}n - 3 \leqslant 0$
   (j) $-12 < 5 - n \leqslant -3$
   (k) $-3 \leqslant 4 - 2n \leqslant 12$
   (l) $-5 < 3(n + 5) < 0$

## Graphs of inequalities

## Activity

Line A has equation $y = 2$.

Describe the $y$ coordinates of points **on** line A.
Describe the $y$ coordinates of points **below** line A.
Describe the $y$ coordinates of points **above** line A.

Above the line is the region $y > 2$.
Below the line is the region $y < 2$.

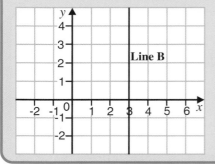

Line B has equation $x = 3$.

Use an inequality to describe the region to the right of line B.
Use an inequality to describe the region to the left of line B.

## Regions

A line divides the graph into two **regions**.
The region $x \leqslant 2$ is to the **left** of the line $x = 2$, including the line itself.
The region $x \geqslant 2$ is to the **right** of the line $x = 2$, including the line itself.

The region $y < -3$ is **below** the line $y = -3$.
The region $y > -3$ is **above** the line $y = -3$.

A **solid line** is used when the points on the line are included.
A **broken line** is used when the points on the line are not included.

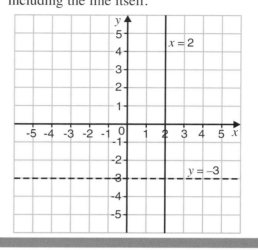

### EXAMPLE

On a sketch, show the region where the inequalities $x > -2$ and $y \leqslant 1$ are both true.
Label the region $R$.

**To do this:**
1 Draw the $x$ and $y$ axes.
2 Draw and label the line $x = -2$, using a broken line.
3 Show the region $x > -2$ by shading out the **unwanted** region.

4 Draw and label the line $y = 1$ using a solid line.
5 Show the region $y \leqslant 1$ by shading out the **unwanted** region.

6 Label the region, $R$, where $x > -2$ **and** $y \leqslant 1$.
Note that the region $R$ extends for ever to the right and downwards.

**Shading regions on a graph:**
Unless you are told to do otherwise, always shade out the **unwanted** region.

## Exercise 16.5

For each question, draw and label axes for $x$ and $y$ from $-5$ to 5.
Shade the unwanted regions. Leave the given region unshaded and label it $R$.

1 $x > 2$ and $y \geqslant 1$

2 $x \geqslant -3$ and $y < 4$

3 $x \geqslant -2$, $x < 1$ and $y > 2$

4 $x < 5$, $x \geqslant -1$ and $y \leqslant 3$

5 $x \leqslant 2$, $x > -2$, $y < 3$ and $y \geqslant 1$

6 $x \geqslant -2$, $x \leqslant 0$, $y \geqslant 1$ and $y \leqslant 4$

7 $x \leqslant 1.5$, $y > -1$ and $y \leqslant 2.5$

8 $x > -2.5$, $x \leqslant 1.5$ and $y \leqslant 2.5$

## Inequalities involving sloping lines

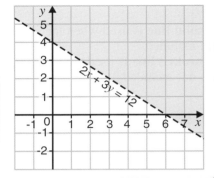
## Exercise 16.6

**1** Draw graphs to show the following. Leave unshaded the regions where the inequalities are true.
(a) $y \geqslant x$
(b) $y < 2x$
(c) $y < x + 1$
(d) $y \geqslant 2x - 1$
(e) $x + y \leqslant 3$
(f) $x + y > 2$
(g) $2x + y \geqslant 4$
(h) $x + 4y < 6$

**2** Draw graphs to show the following.
Label with the letter $R$ the region defined by the inequalities.
(a) $y < 3x$, $x < 2$ and $y > 0$
(b) $2x + 5y \leqslant 10$, $x \geqslant 0$ and $y \geqslant 0$
(c) $3x + 4y \geqslant 12$, $x < 3$ and $y < 4$
(d) $x + 3y < 6$, $x > -1$ and $y > 1$
(e) $2x + 3y \geqslant 6$, $1 < x \leqslant 3$ and $y < 4$

**3** Match each of these inequalities to its **unshaded** region.
**A** $2y < x + 2$    **B** $y > x$    **C** $2y < 4 - x$    **D** $y < 4 - x$

  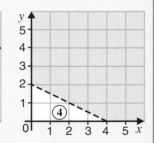

**4** The shaded area can be described by three inequalities,
one for each side of the shape.
One of the inequalities is $x < 3$.
Write down the other two inequalities.

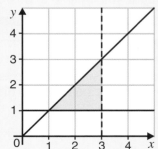

**5** A point $P$ has whole number coordinates and lies
in the region $y < 3$, $1 < x < 4$ and $2y > x$.
(a) Draw a diagram and show the region which satisfies these inequalities.
(b) Write down the coordinates of all the possible positions of $P$.

**6** Use inequalities to describe the shaded region in these diagrams.

(a)

(b)

(c)

(d)

**7** Draw and label axes for $x$ and $y$ from 0 to 8.
 (a) On your diagram, draw and label the lines $y = x + 2$ and $y = 6 - x$.
 (b) Write down the point, with whole number coordinates, which satisfies the inequalities:
  $y < x + 2$, $y < 6 - x$ and $y > 2$.

## What you need to know

- Inequalities can be described using words or numbers and symbols.

| Sign | Meaning |
|------|---------|
| < | is less than |
| ≤ | is less than or equal to |

| Sign | Meaning |
|------|---------|
| > | is greater than |
| ≥ | is greater than or equal to |

- Inequalities can be shown on a **number line**.

$$-2 < x \leq 3$$

The circle is:
    **filled** if the inequality is **included** (i.e. ≤ or ≥),
    **not filled** if the inequality is **not included** (i.e. < or >).

- Solving inequalities.
 **Solve** means find the values of $x$ which make the inequality true.
 The same rules for equations can be applied to inequalities, with one exception:
    When you **multiply** (or **divide**) both sides of an inequality by a negative number the
    inequality is reversed.
    For example, if $-3x < 6$ then $x > -2$.

- Inequalities can be shown on a graph. Replace the inequality sign by '=' and draw the line.
 For > and < the line is **broken**. For ≥ and ≤ the line is **solid**.
 Test a point on each side of the line to see whether its coordinates satisfy the inequality.
 Shade the **unwanted** region.

Inequalities . . . Inequalities . . . Inequalities . . .

**1** Draw number lines to show each of these inequalities.

(a) $x \leqslant -1$     (b) $x > 3$     (c) $4 < x \leqslant 9$     (d) $x < -2$ **and** $x > 5$

**2** Write down the inequalities shown on these number lines.

**3** Solve each of these inequalities and show the solution on a number line.

(a) $2x < 6$     (b) $3x \geqslant -15$     (c) $x + 1 \geqslant 5$     (d) $7x - 3 \leqslant 18$

**4** Solve $2x - 5 \geqslant 4$. Show your solution on a number line.     OCR

**5** Solve these inequalities and show the solution on a number line.

(a) $x - 3 < 1$     (b) $-2 < 2x \leqslant 4$     (c) $-1 \leqslant 3x + 2 < 5$     (d) $-1 < 2x + 5 < 3$

**6** Find the integer values of $n$ such that:

(a) $-4 < 2n \leqslant 8$     (b) $-3 \leqslant 3n + 6 < 12$     (c) $-4 \leqslant 5n + 6 \leqslant 1$

**7** (a) Write down the integer values of $n$ for which $-3 \leqslant 3n < 12$.

(b) Solve the inequality $4x + 3 \geqslant 23$.     OCR

**8** Solve this inequality. $2x + 3 < 5x + 12$     OCR

**9** (a) Find the values of the integer $n$ if $-4 \leqslant n \leqslant 3$ and $n \geqslant -2$.

(b) Solve the inequalities (i) $5 - 2x < 11$,     (ii) $4(x - 5) \geqslant \frac{1}{2}(x + 2)$.     OCR

**10** Solve this inequality. $5(x + 1) > 2x + 18$     OCR

**11** On separate diagrams, draw and label $x$ and $y$ axes from 0 to 6 and shade the regions where:

(a) $x > 2$,     (b) $y \leqslant 4$,     (c) $x + y \leqslant 4$.

**12** On a grid, indicate, by shading, the region **R** defined by these inequalities.

$$y \leqslant x + 3 \qquad y \geqslant 1 \qquad x \leqslant 2 \qquad x + y \leqslant 4$$     OCR

**13** Use inequalities to describe the shaded region in this diagram.

**14**

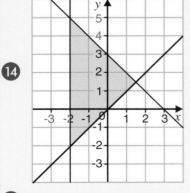

Write down the three inequalities which define the shaded region.

    OCR

**15** On a grid, shade the single region which satisfies both the inequalities

$$y \geqslant 3x \quad \text{and} \quad 3x + 2y \leqslant 12.$$     OCR

**16** (a) On the same diagram, represent the inequalities $x + y \leqslant 3$ and $y \leqslant 2x - 1$. Shade the **unwanted** region.

(b) Write down **all** the points with integer coordinates which satisfy the inequalities

$$x + y \leqslant 3, \quad y \leqslant 2x - 1 \quad \text{and} \quad y \geqslant 0.$$     OCR

# Further Graphs •••••••••

## Quadratic functions

Look at these coordinates: $(-3, 9)$, $(-2, 4)$, $(-1, 1)$, $(0, 0)$, $(1, 1)$, $(2, 4)$, $(3, 9)$.
*Can you see any number patterns?*

The diagram shows the coordinates plotted on a **graph**.
The points all lie on a **smooth curve**.

A **rule** connects the $x$ coordinate with the $y$ coordinate.
**All** points on the line obey the rule $y = x^2$.

$y = x^2$ is an example of a **quadratic function**.

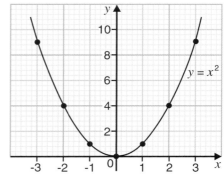

The graph of a **quadratic function** is always a smooth curve and is called a **parabola**.
The general equation of a quadratic function is $y = ax^2 + bx + c$, where $a$ cannot be equal to zero.

The graph of a quadratic function is symmetrical and has a **maximum** or a **minimum** value.

## Drawing a graph of a quadratic function

To draw a quadratic graph:
● Make a table of values connecting $x$ and $y$.
● Plot the points.
● Join the points with a smooth curve.

### EXAMPLE

Draw the graph of $y = x^2 - 3$ for values of $x$ from $-3$ to $3$.

First make a table of values for $y = x^2 - 3$.

| $x$ | $-3$ | $-2$ | $-1$ | $0$ | $1$ | $2$ | $3$ |
|---|---|---|---|---|---|---|---|
| $y$ | $6$ | $1$ | $-2$ | $-3$ | $-2$ | $1$ | $6$ |

Plot these points.
The curve which passes through these points
is the graph of the equation $y = x^2 - 3$.

● Quadratic graphs are always symmetrical.

● Join plotted points using smooth curves and
not a series of straight lines.

155

**1** (a) Copy and complete this table of values for $y = x^2 - 2$.

| $x$ | −3 | −2 | −1 | 0 | 1 | 2 | 3 |
|---|---|---|---|---|---|---|---|
| $y$ | | 2 | | | −1 | | 7 |

   (b) Draw the graph of $y = x^2 - 2$.
      Label the $x$ axis from −3 to 3 and the $y$ axis from −3 to 8.
   (c) Use your graph to find the value of $y$ when $x = -1.5$.

**2** (a) Draw the graph of $y = x^2 + 1$ for values of $x$ from −2 to 4.
   (b) Use your graph to find the value of $y$ when $x = 2.5$.
   (c) Use your graph to find the values of $x$ when $y = 4$.
   (d) Write down the coordinates of the point at which the graph has a minimum value.

**3** (a) Copy and complete this table of values for $y = 6 - x^2$.

| $x$ | −3 | −2 | −1 | 0 | 1 | 2 | 3 |
|---|---|---|---|---|---|---|---|
| $y$ | | 2 | | 6 | | | −3 |

   (b) Draw the graph of $y = 6 - x^2$ for values of $x$ from −3 to 3.
   (c) Write down the coordinates of the points where the graph of $y = 6 - x^2$
      crosses the $x$ axis.
   (d) Find the coordinates of the point at which the graph has a maximum value.

**4** Draw the graph of $y = 2x^2$ for values of $x$ from −2 to 2.

**5** Draw the graph of $y = x^2 - x + 2$ for values of $x$ from −2 to 3.

## Using graphs to solve quadratic equations

The diagram shows the graph of $y = x^2 - 4$.

The values of $x$ where the graphs of quadratic functions cross
(or touch) the $x$ axis give the **solutions to quadratic equations**.

At the point where the graph $y = x^2 - 4$ crosses the $x$ axis
the value of $y = 0$.

$$x^2 - 4 = 0$$

The solutions of this quadratic equation can be
read from the graph: $x = -2$ and $x = 2$

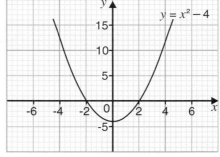

The graph $y = x^2 - 4$ could be used to solve other quadratic equations.

Solve $x^2 - 4 = 5$.
Draw the graph of $y = 5$ on the same diagram.
To solve $x^2 - 4 = 5$, read the values of $x$,
where the two graphs intersect.

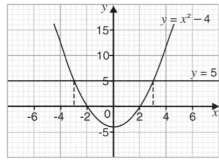

$$x = -3 \quad \text{and} \quad x = 3$$

Solve $x^2 - 4 = 3x$.
Draw the graph of $y = 3x$ on the same diagram.
To solve $x^2 - 4 = 3x$, read the values of $x$
where the two graphs intersect.

$$x = -1 \quad \text{and} \quad x = 4$$

**EXAMPLES**

**1** (a) Draw the graph of
$y = x^2 + 2x - 3$ for values of $x$ from $-4$ to 2.
(b) Use your graph to find the solutions of the
equation $x^2 + 2x - 3 = 0$.

(a) First make a table of values for $y = x^2 + 2x - 3$.

| $x$ | $-4$ | $-3$ | $-2$ | $-1$ | 0 | 1 | 2 |
|---|---|---|---|---|---|---|---|
| $y$ | 5 | 0 | $-3$ | $-4$ | $-3$ | 0 | 5 |

Plot these points.
The curve which passes through these points is the graph of the
equation $y = x^2 + 2x - 3$.
(b) To solve this equation, read the values of $x$ where the graph of $y = x^2 + 2x - 3$
crosses the $x$ axis. $x = -3$ and $x = 1$

**2** You are given the graph of $y = 2x - x^2$.
By drawing a suitable linear graph, on the same axes, find the solutions of $x^2 - 3x + 1 = 0$.

To find the linear graph:
Rearrange $x^2 - 3x + 1 = 0$ to give $1 - x = 2x - x^2$.
Hence, the linear graph is $y = 1 - x$.

Draw the graph of $y = 1 - x$ on the same diagram.

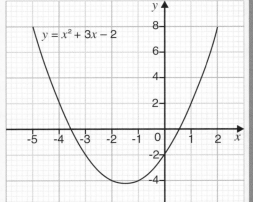

To solve $x^2 - 3x + 1 = 0$, read the values of $x$
where the two graphs intersect.

So, $x = 0.4$ and $x = 2.6$, correct to 1 d.p.

## Exercise 17.2

**1** The graph of $y = x^2 + 3x - 2$ is shown.
Use the graph to solve the equation $x^2 + 3x - 2 = 0$.
Give your answers correct to 1 d.p.

**2** (a) Draw the graph of $y = x^2 + x$
for values of $x$ from $-3$ to 2.
(b) Use your graph to solve the
equation $x^2 + x = 0$.
(c) Find the coordinates of the point at
which the graph has a minimum value.

**3** (a) Copy and complete this table of values for $y = x^2 - 2x + 1$.

| $x$ | $-2$ | $-1$ | 0 | 1 | 2 | 3 |
|---|---|---|---|---|---|---|
| $y$ | | | | | | |

(b) Draw the graph of $y = x^2 - 2x + 1$.
(c) Use your graph to solve the equation $x^2 - 2x + 1 = 0$.

**4** (a) Draw the graph of $y = 10 - x^2$ for values of $x$ from $-4$ to 4.
(b) Use your graph to solve the equation $10 - x^2 = 0$.
(c) Find the coordinates of the point at which the graph has a maximum value.

**5** Draw suitable graphs to solve the following equations.

    (a) $x^2 - 10 = 0$      (b) $5 - x^2 = 0$      (c) $y = x^2 - 3x + 2$      (d) $12 - 2x^2 = 0$

**6** (a) Copy and complete this table of values for $y = 2x^2 - 3x + 1$.

| $x$ | $-1$ | 0 | 1 | 2 | 3 |
|-----|------|---|---|---|----|
| $y$ |      | 1 |   |   | 10 |

    (b) Draw the graph of $y = 2x^2 - 3x + 1$.

    (c) Hence, solve the equation $2x^2 - 3x + 1 = 0$.

    (d) The graph of $y = 2x^2 - 3x + 1$ can also be used to solve the
        equation $2x^2 - 3x + 1 = 3$.

        (i) What other graph would you need to draw on the same axes to solve
            $2x^2 - 3x + 1 = 3$?

        (ii) Draw your graph in (d)(i) and hence, solve $2x^2 - 3x + 1 = 3$.

**7** (a) Draw the graph of $y = x^2 - x$ for values of $x$ from $-2$ to $3$.

    (b) Use your graph to solve the equation $x^2 - x = 0$.

    (c) By drawing a suitable linear graph on the same diagram:

        (i) solve the equation $x^2 - x = 4$,

        (ii) solve the equation $x^2 - x = 2x$.

**8** (a) On the same diagram draw the graphs $y = x^2$ and $y = x + 1$.

    (b) Use your graphs to solve the equation $x^2 - x - 1 = 0$.

**9** (a) Draw the graph of $y = x^2 + 2x - 2$ for values of $x$ from $-5$ to $3$.

    (b) Use your graph to solve the equations: (i) $x^2 + 2x - 2 = 0$,    (ii) $x^2 + 2x = 10$.

**10** (a) Draw the graph of $y = x^2 - 4x + 3$ for values of $x$ between $-1$ and $4$.

    (b) Use your graph to solve the equation $x^2 - 4x + 3 = 2$.

    (c) By drawing an appropriate linear graph on the same axes solutions to the
        equation $x^2 - 3x = 0$ can be found.

        (i) What is the equation of the linear graph?

        (ii) By drawing the graph given in (c)(i) find the solutions of $x^2 - 3x = 0$.

**11** (a) Draw the graph of $y = x^2 + x - 1$ for values of $x$ from $-2$ to $4$.

    (b) By drawing a suitable linear graph on the same axes solve the equation $x^2 - 2x - 3 = 0$.

**12** (a) Draw the graph of $y = x^2 - 4x + 1$ for values of $x$ between $-1$ and $4$.

    (b) Use your graph to solve the equation $x^2 - 4x + 1 = 0$.

    (c) By drawing an appropriate linear graph on the same axes find solutions to the
        equation $x^2 - 5x + 4 = 0$.

## Cubic graphs

The general form of a **cubic function** is $y = ax^3 + bx^2 + cx + d$, where $a$ cannot be equal to zero. As for quadratic graphs, the solutions of cubic equations can be found in a similar way.

## Exercise 17.3

**1** Draw the graphs of $y = x^3$, $y = x^3 - 2$ and $y = x^3 + x$ for values of $x$ from $-2$ to $2$.

**2** (a) Copy and complete this table of values for $y = x^3 - 6x$.

| $x$ | $-3$ | $-2$ | $-1$ | 0 | 1 | 2 | 3 |
|-----|------|------|------|---|---|----|---|
| $y$ | $-9$ |      | 5    | 0 |   | $-4$ |   |

    (b) Draw the graph of $y = x^3 - 6x$ for $-3 \leqslant x \leqslant 3$.

    (c) Use your graph to solve the equations (i) $x^3 - 6x = -6$,    (ii) $x^3 - 6x = 2$.

## The graph of the reciprocal function

The graph of the **reciprocal function** is of the form $y = \frac{a}{x}$ where $x$ cannot be equal to zero.

The diagram shows the graph of $y = \frac{1}{x}$.

The graph of $y = \frac{a}{x}$ does not cross either the $x$ axis or the $y$ axis.

*Explain this by investigating the values of y for very small and very large values of x.*

*Describe any symmetry you can see.*

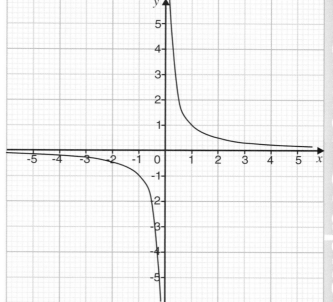

## The graph of the exponential function

The graph of the **exponential function** is of the form $y = a^x$.

The diagram shows the graph of $y = 2^x$.

The table shows values of $y$, given to 2 d.p.

| $x$ | $-3$ | $-2$ | $-1$ | 0 | 1 | 2 | 3 |
|---|---|---|---|---|---|---|---|
| $y$ | 0.13 | 0.25 | 0.5 | 1 | 2 | 4 | 8 |

○○○○○○○○○○○○○○○○○○○○○○
**Exponent** is an alternative term for **index**.

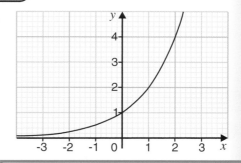

In general, the graph of $y = a^x$:
● does not touch the $x$ axis,
● crosses the $y$ axis at the point $(0, 1)$.

## Exercise 17.4

**1** (a) Draw the graph of $y = \frac{1}{x}$ for values of $x$ from $-5$ to 5.
   Label the $y$ axis from $-10$ to 10.

   (b) On the same axes, draw the graph of $y = 4 - x$.

   (c) Use your graph to find the values of $x$ for which $\frac{1}{x} = 4 - x$.

**2** (a) Draw the graph of $y = \frac{3}{x}$ for values of $x$ from $-6$ to 6.

   (b) On the same axes, draw the graph of $y = \frac{-3}{x}$.

   (c) Describe any patterns you can see.

**3** (a) Draw the graph of $y = 2^x$ for values of $x$ from $-5$ to 5.

   (b) On the same axes, draw the graph of $y = \left(\frac{1}{2}\right)^x$.

   (c) Compare and comment on the graphs drawn in parts (a) and (b).

**4** (a) Copy and complete this table of values for $y = 3^x$.
Give values of $y$ correct to 2 decimal places, where necessary.

| $x$ | $-3$ | $-2$ | $-1$ | 0 | 1 | 2 | 3 |
|---|---|---|---|---|---|---|---|
| $y$ | | | | | | | |

(b) Draw axes marked from $-3$ to 3 for $x$ and from 0 to 30 for $y$.
Draw the graph of $y = 3^x$ on your axes.

(c) Use your graph to find the value of
(i) $y$ when $x = 1.5$, (ii) $x$ when $y = 20$.

## The graph of a circle

The graph of a **circle** is of the form $x^2 + y^2 = r^2$.

The diagram shows the graph of $x^2 + y^2 = 16$.
The graph shows a circle with centre (0, 0) and
radius 4 units.

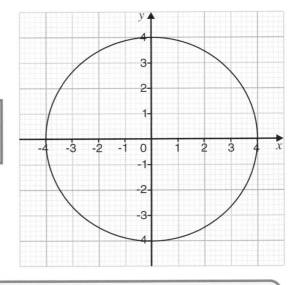

> In general, the graph of a circle is of the form:
> $$x^2 + y^2 = r^2$$
> where $r$ is the radius of the circle, with centre (0, 0).

## Exercise 17.5

**1** The graph of a circle is given by $x^2 + y^2 = 9$.
(a) What is the radius of the circle?
(b) Write down the coordinates of the points where the graph of $x^2 + y^2 = 9$
cuts the $x$ and $y$ axes.
(c) Draw the graph of $x^2 + y^2 = 9$.

**2** (a) Draw the graph of the circle with centre (0, 0) and radius 5 units.
(b) Write down the equation of the circle.
(c) On the same axes draw the graph of the line $y = 4$.
(d) Find the coordinates of the points of intersection of the circle with the line.

**3** (a) On axes for $x$ and $y$ marked from $-5$ to 5, draw the graph of $x^2 + y^2 = 16$.
(b) On the same axes, draw the graph of $y = 2x + 1$.
(c) Use your graph to find the values of $x$ where the graph of $x^2 + y^2 = 16$
cuts the graph of $y = 2x + 1$.

**4** (a) Draw the graph of the circle $x^2 + y^2 = 1$.
(b) On the same axes, draw the graph of $y = 2 - 2x$.
(c) Find the coordinates of the points where the graphs intersect.

**5** (a) Draw the graph of $x^2 + y^2 = 4$.
(b) On the same axes, draw the graph of $y = 1 - \frac{1}{2}x$.
(c) The graphs of $x^2 + y^2 = 4$ and $y = 1 - \frac{1}{2}x$ both cut the $x$ axis at the point (2, 0).
Use your graph to find the value of $x$ at the second point where the graphs intersect.

## Sketching graphs

You will need to be able to recognise and sketch **all** of these graphs.

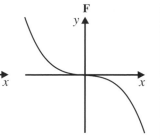

## Exercise 17.6

**1** Match the following equations to their graphs.

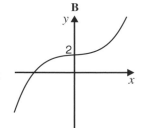

**(1)** $y = -x^3$

**(2)** $y = x^2 - 2$

**(3)** $y = 2x$

**(4)** $y = x^3 + 2$

**(5)** $y = 2x^2$

**(6)** $y = x - 2$

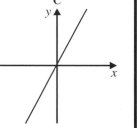

**2** Sketch the graphs of these equations.

   (a)  $y = x^2 + 3$      (b)  $y = x^3 - 3$      (c)  $y = -x$      (d)  $y = x - 3$

**3** The sketches of some graphs are shown. Write down the equation of each graph.

   (a)                (b)                (c)                (d)

# What you need to know

- The graph of a **quadratic function** is always a smooth curve and is called a **parabola**.
- The general form of a **quadratic function** is $y = ax^2 + bx + c$, where $a$ cannot be zero.

The graph of a quadratic function is symmetrical and has a **maximum** or **minimum** value.

- The general form of a **cubic function** is $y = ax^3 + bx^2 + cx + d$, where $a$ cannot be zero.

- The graph of the **reciprocal function** is of the form $y = \dfrac{a}{x}$  E.g.
  where $x$ cannot be equal to zero.

$y = \frac{1}{x}$

- The graph of the **exponential function** is of the form $y = a^x$.  E.g.

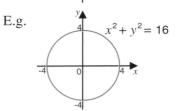
$y = 2^x$

- The graph of a **circle**, centre $(0, 0)$, is of the form $x^2 + y^2 = r^2$  E.g.
  where $r$ is the radius of the circle.

$x^2 + y^2 = 16$

**You should be able to:**
- **Substitute** values into given functions to generate points.
- Plot the graphs of **quadratic** and other functions.
- Use graphs of functions to solve equations.
  This may include drawing another graph and looking for points of intersection.
- Sketch the graphs of functions.

## Review Exercise 17

**1** The graph of $y = x^2 - 4x$ is shown.

Use the graph to:
(a) solve the equation $x^2 - 4x = 0$,
(b) find the coordinates of the point at which
    the graph has a minimum value.

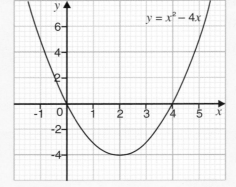
$y = x^2 - 4x$

**2** (a) Copy and complete the table of values for $y = x^2 - 4$.

| $x$ | $-3$ | $-2$ | $-1$ | 0 | 1 | 2 | 3 |
|---|---|---|---|---|---|---|---|
| $y$ | | 0 | | | $-3$ | | 5 |

(b) Draw the graph of $y = x^2 - 4$ between $x = -3$ and $x = 3$.
(c) Write down the coordinates of the lowest point on the curve.
(d) Write down the values of $x$ where the line $y = 3$ cuts the graph of $y = x^2 - 4$.  OCR

**3** (a) Copy and complete the table of values for $y = x^2 - 3x - 1$.

| $x$ | $-1$ | 0 | 1 | 2 | 3 | 4 |
|-----|------|---|---|---|----|---|
| $y$ | 3 | $-1$ | | | $-1$ | 3 |

(b) Draw the graph of $y = x^2 - 3x - 1$.

(c) Use your graph to solve the equation $x^2 - 3x - 1 = 0$.

OCR

**4** (a) Copy and complete the table below for $y = 2x^2 - 6x$.

| $x$ | $-1$ | 0 | 1 | 2 | 3 | 4 |
|-----|------|---|----|---|---|---|
| $y$ | | 0 | $-4$ | | | 8 |

(b) Draw the graph of $y = 2x^2 - 6x$.

(c) Use your graph to find the positive value of $x$ for which $2x^2 - 6x = 5$.

OCR

**5** Match each of these equations with its graph.

**A** $y = x^3$

**B** $y = 3^x$

**C** $y = 3x$

**D** $y = \dfrac{3}{x}$

P

Q

R

S

**6** (a) Draw the graph of $y = 2^x$ for values of $x$ from $-2$ to 3.

(b) Use your graph to solve $2^x = 6$.

OCR

**7** (a) Draw the graph of $y = x^2 - 3x + 1$ for values of $x$ from $-2$ to 4.

(b) Use your graph to solve the equation  (i) $x^2 - 3x + 1 = 0$,  (ii) $x^2 - 3x = 0$.

**8** (a) Draw the graph of $y = \dfrac{2}{x}$ for $-4 \leqslant x \leqslant 4$.

(b) On the same axes, draw the graph of $y = x + 1$ for $-4 \leqslant x \leqslant 4$.

(c) Use your graph to solve the equation $\dfrac{2}{x} = x + 1$.

**9** (a) Draw the graph of $y = x^2 + 2x - 3$ for values of $x$ from $-4$ to 2.

(b) By drawing a suitable straight line, find, graphically, the solution to
$x^2 + 2x - 3 = \frac{1}{2}x + 1$.

(c) What line would you draw to solve $x^2 + x - 5 = 0$?

OCR

**10** (a) Draw the graph of $y = x^3 + 5x$ for values of $x$ from $-2$ to 3.

(b) Use your graph to solve $x^3 + 5x = 10$.

OCR

**11** (a) Copy and complete this table for $y = x^3 - 3x + 1$.

| $x$ | $-2$ | $-1.5$ | $-1$ | $-0.5$ | 0 | 0.5 | 1 | 1.5 | 2 |
|-----|------|--------|------|--------|---|-----|---|-----|---|
| $y$ | $-1$ | 2.125 | | 2.375 | | $-0.375$ | $-1$ | | 3 |

(b) Draw the graph of $y = x^3 - 3x + 1$.

(c) Use your graph to estimate the values of $x$ when $y = 0$.

(d) Jane wants to use this graph to solve $x^3 + x - 1 = 0$.
Find the equation of the line she should draw.

OCR

**12** The circle $x^2 + y^2 = 25$ and the line $y = x + 7$ intersect at the points $P$ and $Q$.
Use a graphical method to find the coordinates of $P$ and $Q$.

# Direct and Inverse Proportion

## Direct proportion

If $x$ and $y$ are quantities such that $y : x$ is always constant, then $y$ is said to vary **directly** with $x$.

In this table, $y : x$ in its simplest form is always $2 : 5$.

| $x$ | 10 | 20 | 30 | 40 |
|-----|----|----|----|----|
| $y$ | 4  | 8  | 12 | 16 |

So, $y$ **varies directly** with $x$.

This can be expressed in words as:  $y$ is **proportional** to $x$  and expressed in symbols as:  $y \propto x$  where $\propto$ means "is proportional to".
The relationship between $x$ and $y$ can also be expressed as an equation.

$y = kx$  where $k$ is the **constant of proportionality**.

This equation can be rearranged to make $k$ the subject of the formula.

$$k = \frac{y}{x}$$

**Finding $k$**

Corresponding values of the proportional quantities can be used to find the value of $k$.

From the table:   when   $x = 10$,   $y = 4$.

Substitute these values into the equation   $y = kx$.

$4 = k \times 10$

Divide both sides by 10.

$k = 0.4$

The **equation connecting $x$ and $y$** is   $y = 0.4x$.

*Look at the table of values of $x$ and $y$:*

*What happens to $y$ when $x$ is doubled? What happens to $y$ when $x$ is trebled?*

> **Remember:**
> A ratio in its **simplest form** has only whole numbers that have no common factor other than 1.
> To **simplify a ratio** divide each part of the ratio by the highest common factor of the numbers.
> **Equivalent ratios** can be found by multiplying, or dividing, each part of the ratio by the **same** number.

> When two quantities are in direct proportion, as one quantity increases the other quantity **increases** at the **same rate**.

> Examples of quantities in **direct proportion**:
>
> When a vehicle travels at constant speed:
>    distance travelled ($d$) is proportional to time taken ($t$).   $d \propto t$      $d = kt$
>
> For any circle:
>    circumference ($C$) is proportional to radius ($r$).       $C \propto r$    $C = kr$
>
> *What is the constant of proportionality, $k$, in each of these examples?*

### EXAMPLE

1  The table shows values of $l$ and $m$. Show that $m$ is proportional to $l$.

| $l$ | 3   | 6  | 8  |
|-----|-----|----|----|
| $m$ | 7.5 | 15 | 20 |

If $m \propto l$, the ratio $m : l$ must be equivalent for **all** pairs of values of $m$ and $l$.

$\qquad 7.5 \div 3 = 2.5 \qquad\qquad 15 \div 6 = 2.5 \qquad\qquad 20 \div 8 = 2.5$

So,   $m : l$ is always equivalent to $1 : 2.5$.

So,   $m = 2.5 \times l$   which also means $m \propto l$.

**EXAMPLE**

**2**  The age of a tree, $A$ years, is proportional to the radius of its trunk, $r$ mm.
When the tree is 5 years old the radius of its trunk is 22 mm.
(a)  Find a formula connecting $A$ and $r$.
(b)  Find $A$ when  $r = 242$.
(c)  Find $r$ when  $A = 80$.

(a)  You are given that $A \alpha r$.
So,  $A = kr$
When  $A = 5$ years,  $r = 22$ mm.
$5 = k \times 22$
Divide both sides by 22.
$k = \frac{5}{22}$

The formula connecting $A$ and $r$ is  $A = \frac{5}{22} r$.

(b)  $A = \frac{5}{22} r$
When  $r = 242$.
$A = \frac{5}{22} \times 242$
$A = 55$

(c)  $A = \frac{5}{22} r$
When  $A = 80$.
$80 = \frac{5}{22} \times r$
$r = 352$

**Exercise 18.1**          Do not use a calculator.

**1**

| $a$ | 2 | 5 | 10 | 30 | 50 |
|---|---|---|---|---|---|
| $b$ | 3 | 7.5 | 15 | 45 | 75 |

| $e$ | 10 | 25 | 40 | 55 | 70 |
|---|---|---|---|---|---|
| $f$ | 2 | 3.5 | 5 | 6.5 | 8 |

| $c$ | 4 | 8 | 20 | 60 | 200 |
|---|---|---|---|---|---|
| $d$ | 0.2 | 0.4 | 1 | 3 | 10 |

| $g$ | 10 | 20 | 40 | 60 | 80 |
|---|---|---|---|---|---|
| $h$ | 0.35 | 0.7 | 1.4 | 2.1 | 2.8 |

Which of the following statements are true?
(a)  $b \alpha a$       (b)  $d \alpha c$       (c)  $f \alpha e$       (d)  $h \alpha g$
Give a reason for each answer.

**2**  In this table $p$ varies directly with $q$.

| $p$ | 1 | $a$ | 12 | $c$ | 70 |
|---|---|---|---|---|---|
| $q$ | 5 | 10 | $b$ | 40 | $d$ |

(a)  Find, in its simplest form, the ratio
(i)  $1 : a$       (ii)  $c : 40$
(b)  Calculate the values of $a$, $b$, $c$ and $d$.

**3**  $y = kx$  and  $y = 18$  when  $x = 3$.
(a)  Find the value of the constant $k$.
Hence, find the equation connecting $y$ and $x$.
(b)  Find $y$ when  $x = 8$.

**4**  $y$ varies directly as $x$, so,  $y = kx$.  When  $y = 2$,  $x = 10$.
(a)  Find the equation connecting $y$ and $x$.
(b)  Find $y$ when  $x = 45$.

**5**  $m$ varies directly as $n$, and  $m = 6$  when  $n = 4$.
(a)  Find the equation connecting $m$ and $n$.
(b)  Find  (i)  $m$ when  $n = 6$,       (ii)  $n$ when  $m = 15$.

**6**  In this table $p$ is proportional to $q$.
(a)  Find an equation connecting $p$ and $q$.
(b)  Find the values of $a$ and $b$.

| $p$ | 4 | 12 | $b$ |
|---|---|---|---|
| $q$ | 2.5 | $a$ | 20 |

**7**  In this table $y \alpha x$.
(a)  Find an equation expressing $y$ in terms of $x$.
(b)  Find the values of $a$ and $b$.

| $x$ | 25 | 100 | $b$ |
|---|---|---|---|
| $y$ | 1.25 | $a$ | 20 |

**8** The cost, £$C$, of building a wall is proportional to its area, $A\,\text{m}^2$.
A wall of area $20\,\text{m}^2$ costs £210.
    (a)   Find a formula giving $C$ in terms of $A$.
    (b)   Find the cost of a wall of area $55\,\text{m}^2$.
    (c)   A wall of height $1.6\,\text{m}$ costs £1155. How long is the wall?

**9** The distance travelled by a fixed wheel bicycle, $d$, is proportional to $n$, the number of times the pedal rotates. In a journey of $400\,\text{m}$ the pedal rotates 80 times.
    (a)   Find an equation expressing $d$ in terms of $n$.
    (b)   How far does the bicycle travel if the pedal rotates 200 times?
    (c)   How many times does the pedal rotate if the bicycle travels $3\,\text{km}$?

**10**  (a)   The extension, $e$, of a spring is proportional to $w$, the weight hung on the spring.
        When  $w = 2\,\text{kg}$,  $e = 60\,\text{mm}$.
        (i)    Find an equation expressing $e$ in terms of $w$.
        (ii)   Find $e$ when  $w = 5.3\,\text{kg}$.
        (iii)  Find $w$ when  $e = 96.6\,\text{mm}$.
    (b)   The extension of another spring is also proportional to the weight hung on it.
        Weights of $2.5\,\text{kg}$ and $8\,\text{kg}$ are hung on this spring and the extensions measured.
        What is the ratio of these two extensions in its simplest form?

## Inverse proportion

If $x$ and $y$ are quantities such that $y : \dfrac{1}{x}$ is always constant, then $y$ varies directly with $\dfrac{1}{x}$.
$y$ is also said to vary **inversely** with $x$.

In this table, $y : \dfrac{1}{x}$ in its simplest form is always $1 : 60$.

| $x$ | 1 | 2 | 5 | 10 | 12 | 15 |
|---|---|---|---|---|---|---|
| $y$ | 60 | 30 | 12 | 6 | 5 | 4 |

So, $y$ **varies directly** with $\dfrac{1}{x}$.

This can be expressed in words as:  $y$ is **inversely proportional** to $x$ and expressed in symbols as:  $y \propto \dfrac{1}{x}$

The relationship between $x$ and $y$ can also be expressed as an equation.

    $y = \dfrac{k}{x}$  or  $xy = k$  where $k$ is the **constant of proportionality**.

**Finding $k$**

Corresponding values of the proportional quantities can be used to find the value of $k$.
From the table:  When  $x = 1$,  $y = 60$.
Substitute these values into the equation  $y = \dfrac{k}{x}$.

$60 = \dfrac{k}{1}$,  giving  $k = 60$.

The equation connecting $x$ and $y$ is  $y = \dfrac{60}{x}$.  (This equation can also be written as  $xy = 60$.)

*Look at the table of values of $x$ and $y$:*
      *What happens to $y$ when $x$ is doubled? What happens to $y$ when $x$ is trebled?*

> When two quantities are in inverse proportion, as one quantity increases the other quantity **decreases** at the **same rate**.

> Examples of quantities in **inverse proportion**:
>
> For cars travelling the same distance:
>     average speed ($s$) is inversely proportional to time taken ($t$).  $s \propto \dfrac{1}{t}$    $st = k$
>
> For rectangles of constant area:
>     length ($l$) is inversely proportional to width ($w$).      $l \propto \dfrac{1}{w}$    $lw = k$

## EXAMPLE

In this table $y$ is inversely proportional to $x$. Express $y$ in terms of $x$ and find the value of $a$.

| $x$ | 5 | $a$ |
|-----|---|-----|
| $y$ | 20 | 4 |

$y \propto \dfrac{1}{x}$

So, $y = \dfrac{k}{x}$ and $xy = k$.

When $x = 5$, $y = 20$.

$k = 5 \times 20 = 100$

The equation connecting $x$ and $y$ is $y = \dfrac{100}{x}$

To find the value of $a$, $y = \dfrac{100}{x}$

can be rearranged as $x = \dfrac{100}{y}$.

$x = \dfrac{100}{y}$.

When $x = a$, $y = 4$.

$a = \dfrac{100}{4}$

$a = 25$

## Exercise 18.2

Do not use a calculator for this exercise.

**1**

| $a$ | 2 | 2.5 | 4 | 5 | 10 |
|-----|---|-----|---|---|----|
| $b$ | 5 | 4 | 2.5 | 2 | 1 |

| $c$ | 6 | 12 | 30 | 90 | 300 |
|-----|---|----|----|----|-----|
| $d$ | 0.2 | 0.4 | 1 | 3 | 10 |

Which of the following statements are true? Give a reason for each answer.    (a) $b \propto \dfrac{1}{a}$      (b) $d \propto \dfrac{1}{c}$

**2** The table shows values of $p$ and $q$.
  (a) Show that $q$ is inversely proportional to $p$.
  (b) Express $q$ in terms of $p$.

| $p$ | 2 | 10 | 50 |
|-----|---|----|----|
| $q$ | 0.25 | 0.05 | 0.01 |

**3** Copy and complete the table for the relationship $b \propto \dfrac{1}{a}$ and find the constant of proportionality.

| $a$ | 2 | 5 | 10 | 25 | 50 |
|-----|---|---|----|----|----|
| $b$ | 10 | | | | |

**4** (a) Given that $p \propto \dfrac{1}{q}$ and $p = 3$ when $q = 10$, find an equation connecting $p$ and $q$.

  (b) Hence, find $p$ when $q = 6$.

**5** In this table $y$ is inversely proportional to $x$.
  (a) Find an equation connecting $x$ and $y$.
  (b) Find the values of $a$ and $b$.

| $x$ | 5 | 12 | $b$ |
|-----|---|----|-----|
| $y$ | 9.6 | $a$ | 0.5 |

**6** $y$ is inversely proportional to $x$. $y = 12$ when $x = 3$. Find $y$ when $x = 4$.

**7** $s$ is inversely proportional to $r$. $s = 20$ when $r = 5$. Find $r$ when $s = 4$.

**8** In this table $M$ varies inversely with $L$.
  (a) Find an equation connecting $L$ and $M$.
  (b) Find the values of $a$ and $b$.

| $L$ | 8 | 12 | $b$ |
|-----|---|----|-----|
| $M$ | 1.8 | $a$ | 0.9 |

**9** The length of a rectangle, $l$, of constant area is inversely proportional to its width, $w$.
When $l = 20\,\text{cm}$, $w = 10\,\text{cm}$.
Find an equation expressing $l$ in terms of $w$.
Find the value of the constant of proportionality. What does it represent?

**10** A building contractor uses teams of workers to build sheds.
The time, $t$, for a team to build one shed is inversely proportional to the number of workers, $n$, in the team. A team of 2 take 6 days to build one shed.
  (a) Find an equation expressing $t$ in terms of $n$.
  (b) Find the time it takes a team of 6 to build one shed.
  (c) A team builds a shed in 4 days. How many workers are in the team?

## Other forms of proportion

**1** When $x = 4$, $y = 8$. Find an equation for $y$ in terms of $x$ if:

(a) $y$ is proportional to $x^2$,

(b) $y$ is proportional to the square root of $x$.

(a) $y \alpha x^2$ so, $y = kx^2$.

When $x = 4$, $y = 8$.

$8 = k \times 4^2$ which gives $k = \frac{1}{2}$.

$y = \frac{1}{2} x^2$

(b) $y \alpha \sqrt{x}$ so, $y = k\sqrt{x}$.

When $x = 4$, $y = 8$.

$8 = k\sqrt{4}$

$8 = 2k$ which gives $k = 4$.

$y = 4\sqrt{x}$

**2** A magnet is at a distance, $x$ cm, from a metal object.

The force, $F$ Newtons, exerted by the magnet on the metal object is inversely proportional to the square of $x$. When $x = 10$, $F = 2$.

(a) Find an equation expressing $F$ in terms of $x$.

(b) Find $F$ when $x = 20$.

(c) Find $x$ when $F = 8$.

(a) $F \alpha \frac{1}{x^2}$ so, $F = \frac{k}{x^2}$.

When $x = 10$, $F = 2$.

$2 = \frac{k}{10^2}$

$k = 10^2 \times 2$ which gives $k = 200$.

$F = \frac{200}{x^2}$

(b) When $x = 20$. $F = \frac{200}{20^2} = 0.5$

(c) When $F = 8$. $8 = \frac{200}{x^2}$

$x^2 = \frac{200}{8} = 25$

$x = 5$

---

### Exercise 18.3    You may use a calculator for this exercise.

**1** Write each of the following statements in words.

(a) $V \alpha t^2$    (b) $L \alpha \frac{1}{a}$    (c) $y \alpha x^3$    (d) $p \alpha \frac{1}{q^2}$    (e) $L \alpha \sqrt{m}$    (f) $b \alpha \frac{1}{c^3}$

**2** $y = kx^2$ and $y = 18$ when $x = 3$.

Find the constant, $k$, and hence, write an equation connecting $y$ and $x$.

**3** $y$ is proportional to the square of $x$.

(a) What happens to $y$ when $x$ is doubled?

(b) $y$ is multiplied by 25. What happens to $x$?

**4** $y$ is inversely proportional to $x^3$. When $x = 2$, $y = 8$.

Find an equation for $y$ in terms of $x$.

**5** Use the information given to find an equation connecting each of the following pairs of variables.

(a) $V$ is proportional to the square of $t$.    $V = 45$ when $t = 3$.

(b) $R$ is inversely proportional to the cube of $s$.    $R = 5$ when $s = 4$.

(c) $y$ is proportional to the square root of $x$.    $y = 40$ when $x = 16$.

(d) $A$ is inversely proportional to $b$.    $A = 20$ when $b = 5$.

(e) $L$ is proportional to the cube of $p$.    $L = 25$ when $p = 2$.

(f) $Q$ is proportional to the square root of $P$.    $Q = 100$ when $P = 64$.

**6** $y$ is inversely proportional to the square of $x$. When $x = 2$, $y = 20$.

(a) Find the constant of proportionality.

(b) Find $y$ when $x = 4$.

(c) Find $x$ when $y = 5$.

**7** Copy and complete the table for the relationships $b \propto a^2$

| $a$ | 1 | 2 | 10 |
|---|---|---|---|
| $b$ | 3 | | |

**8** This table shows values of $p$ and $q$ where $q$ is proportional to $p^3$. Calculate $A$ and $B$.

| $p$ | 2 | 5 | $B$ |
|---|---|---|---|
| $q$ | 16 | $A$ | 54 |

**9** $y = \dfrac{k}{x^2}$. When $x = 2$, $y = 0.4$.
  (a) Find the value of $k$.
  (b) Find $y$ when $x = 10$.

**10** $y = k\sqrt{x}$. When $x = 0.16$, $y = 4$.
  (a) Find the value of $k$.
  (b) Find $x$ when $y = 40$.

**11** $y$ is proportional to the cube of $x$. When $x = 10$, $y = 1$.
  (a) Find $y$ when $x = 20$.
  (b) Find $x$ when $y = 5$.

**12** For each part of this question find an equation connecting the variables $p$ and $q$.
Also find the values of the letters $a$ to $f$.

(a) $q$ varies inversely with the square of $p$.

| $p$ | 4 | 10 | $b$ |
|---|---|---|---|
| $q$ | 2.5 | $a$ | 0.1 |

(b) $q$ varies inversely with the cube of $p$.

| $p$ | 4 | 10 | $d$ |
|---|---|---|---|
| $q$ | 2.5 | $c$ | 20 |

(c) $q$ varies with the square of $p$.

| $p$ | 4 | 10 | $f$ |
|---|---|---|---|
| $q$ | 2.5 | $e$ | 10 |

**13** $y$ is inversely proportional to the square of $x$.
  (a) What happens to $y$ when $x$ is doubled?
  (b) $y$ is multiplied by 25. What happens to $x$?

**14** The time taken, $t$ seconds, for a skier to slide from rest down a ski slope is proportional to the square root of the distance travelled, $d$ metres. When $d = 100$, $t = 16$.
  (a) Find an equation for $t$ in terms of $d$.
  (b) Find the value of $t$ when $d = 25$.

**15** The height, $h$ m, that a stone reaches when it is thrown upwards varies directly with the square of its initial speed, $s$ metres per second. When $s = 10$, $h = 5$.
  (a) Find a formula expressing $h$ in terms of $s$.
  (b) Calculate $s$ when $h = 20$.
  (c) Calculate $h$ when $s = 50$.

**16** In cylinders of equal volume, the radius, $r$ cm, is inversely proportional to the square root of the height, $h$ cm. When $h = 4$, $r = 8$.
  (a) Find $h$ when $r = 4$.
  (b) What does the constant of proportionality represent?

**17** The radius, $r$, of a cone of fixed volume is inversely proportional to the square root of its height, $h$.
  (a) $r$ is doubled. What happens to $h$?
  (b) $h$ is multiplied by 16. What happens to $r$?

When $n$ is unknown, the graph of $y$ plotted against $x$ can be used to help find its value.

The general form of the relationships dealt within this chapter is $y \propto x^n$.
Values of $n > 0$ give **direct** proportionality.
Values of $n < 0$ give **inverse** proportionality.

When $n = 1$.

When $n > 1$.

- This relationship gives a straight-line graph which passes through the origin.
- As $x$ increases by a constant amount, $y$ increases by a constant amount.
- $k$, the constant of proportionality, is given by the gradient of the graph.

- This relationship gives a curved graph which passes through the origin.
- As $x$ increases by a constant amount, $y$ increases by amounts that increase.
- As $k$ increases the graph gets steeper.

When $0 < n < 1$.

When $n < 0$.

- This relationship gives a curved graph which passes through the origin.
- As $x$ increases by a constant amount, $y$ increases by amounts that decrease.
- As $k$ increases the graph gets steeper.

- This relationship gives a curved graph. The graph does not pass through the origin.
- As $x$ increases by a constant amount, $y$ decreases by amounts that decrease.
- As $k$ increases the graph gets steeper.

---

**EXAMPLE**

Use this table of values of $x$ and $y$ to find a formula connecting $x$ and $y$ where $y \propto x^n$.

| $x$ | 1 | 2 | 4 |
|---|---|---|---|
| $y$ | 12 | 3 | 0.75 |

Plot the points and draw the graph.

The graph shows inverse proportionality, so, $n < 0$.

$y \propto x^n$ so, $y = kx^n$
When $x = 1$, $y = 12$.
$\quad 12 = k \times 1^n$ giving $k = 12$.
So, $\quad y = 12 \times x^n$
When $x = 2$, $y = 3$.
$\quad 3 = 12 \times 2^n$
Dividing both sides by 12.
$\quad 0.25 = 2^n$
This gives $n = -2$.
So, $k = 12$, $n = -2$ and $y = 12x^{-2}$.

**1** Match each graph to a relationship.

**Graphs**

**Relationships**

(a) $y$ varies directly with the square of $x$.

(b) $y$ varies directly with $x$.

(c) $y$ varies inversely with the cube of $x$.

(d) $y$ varies directly with the square root of $x$.

**2** (a) What is the value of $n$ when $y \propto x^n$ and:
(i) $y$ varies directly with the cube of $x$,
(ii) $y$ varies inversely with $x$,
(iii) $y$ varies inversely with the square root of $x$?

In each of the relationships in (a) the constant of proportionality is 10.
(b) Draw the graph of each relationship for positive values of $x$.
(c) What happens to your graphs in (b):
(i) when $k < 10$, (ii) when $k > 10$?

**3** The relationship '$y$ is inversely proportional to the square of $x$' is of the form $y \propto x^n$.
Find the value of $n$.

**4** The graph of the relationship $y \propto x^n$ passes through the points $(0, 0)$, $(1, 0.25)$ and $(4, 4)$.
(a) Find the value of $n$.
(b) Find the constant of proportionality.
Repeat for a graph passing through the points $(1, 10)$, $(2, 2.5)$ and $(5, 0.4)$.

**5** Use this table of values of $p$ and $q$ to find a formula connecting $p$ and $q$ where $q \propto p^n$.

| $p$ | 1 | 2 | 5 |
|---|---|---|---|
| $q$ | 0.2 | 1.6 | 25 |

**6** Use this table of values of $s$ and $t$ to find a formula connecting $s$ and $t$ where $s \propto t^n$.

| $t$ | 1 | 4 | 25 |
|---|---|---|---|
| $s$ | 20 | 10 | 4 |

**7** The sketch shows a graph with equation $y = kx^n$.

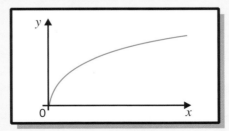

The graph passes through the points $(1, 5)$ and $(4, 10)$.
(a) Find the values of $k$ and $n$.
(b) Find the value of $x$ when $y = 15$.

# What you need to know

- If $x$ and $y$ are quantities such that $y : x^n$ is always constant, then $y$ varies **directly** with $x^n$.
- If $x$ and $y$ are quantities such that $y : \dfrac{1}{x^n}$ is always constant, then $y$ varies **inversely** with $x^n$.
- Direct and inverse proportion can be expressed:

| | in **words**: | in **symbols**: | as an **equation**: |
|---|---|---|---|
| **Direct proportion** | $y$ is **proportional** to $x^n$ | $y \propto x^n$ | $y = kx^n$ |
| **Inverse proportion** | $y$ is **inversely proportional** to $x^n$ | $y \propto \dfrac{1}{x^n}$ | $y = \dfrac{k}{x^n}$ |

The symbol $\propto$ means 'is proportional to'. $k$ is the constant of proportionality.

- The general form of a proportional relationship is $y \propto x^n$ or $y = kx^n$.

**Direct proportion**
$y = kx^n, \quad n > 0$

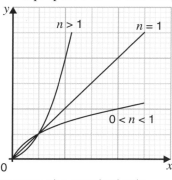

When:
$n = 1$: $y$ increases at a constant rate.
$0 < n < 1$: $y$ increases at a rate that decreases.
$n > 1$: $y$ increases at a rate that increases.

**Inverse proportion**
$y = kx^n, \quad n < 0$

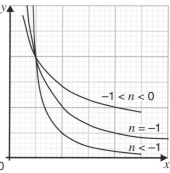

When:
$n = -1$: the graph is symmetrical about the line $y = x$.

## Review Exercise 18

**1** $m$ is directly proportional to the square of $n$. When $m = 18$, $n = 3$.
Find the value of $m$ when $n = 5$.

**2** $q$ is directly proportional to the square root of $p$.
Copy and complete the table.

| $p$ | 4 | | 100 |
|---|---|---|---|
| $q$ | | 4 | 5 |

**3** The distance, $d$ km, it is possible to see on a clear day is proportional to the square root of the height, $h$ m, above sea level.
Standing on a pier, 4 m above sea level, it is possible to see a distance of 10 km.
(a) Find a formula for $d$ in terms of $h$.
(b) Standing on top of the cliffs I can see a distance of 35 km.
How high are the cliffs?

OCR

**4** The amount of sag, $S$ cm, when a beam is carrying a load at its midpoint, is proportional to the cube of its length, $L$ m. The amount of sag is 2.4 cm for a beam of length 4 m.
(a) Find a formula for $S$ in terms of $L$.
(b) What is the amount of sag for a beam of length 6 m?
(c) For another beam the amount of sag is 0.3 cm. What is the length of this beam?

OCR

**5** The force, $F$ newtons, between two magnets is inversely proportional to the square of the distance, $d$ metres, between them.
When the magnets are 2 metres apart the force between them is 36 newtons.
Find (a) $F$ when $d = 5$, (b) $d$ when $F = 49$.

OCR

**6** $m$ is inversely proportional to the square root of $n$. When $m = 3$, $n = 16$.
Find the value of (a) $m$ when $n = 9$, (b) $n$ when $m = 2.4$?

172

## Brackets

You can multiply out brackets, either by using a diagram or by expanding.

**1** Multiply out $2(x + 3)$.

**Diagram method**

The areas of the two parts are $2x$ and $6$.
The total area is $2x + 6$.
$2(x + 3) = 2x + 6$

**Expanding**

$$2(x + 3) = 2 \times x + 2 \times 3$$
$$= 2x + 6$$

**2** Multiply out $x(x + 3)$.

The areas of the two parts are $x^2$ and $3x$.
$x(x + 3) = x^2 + 3x$

## More brackets

This method can be extended to multiply out $(x + 2)(x + 3)$.

The areas of the four parts are: $x^2$, $3x$, $2x$ and $6$.

$$(x + 2)(x + 3) = x^2 + 3x + 2x + 6$$

Collect like terms and simplify (i.e. $3x + 2x = 5x$)

$$= x^2 + 5x + 6$$

EXAMPLES

**1** Expand $(2x + 3)(x + 4)$.

|     | $x$    | $4$  |
| --- | ------ | ---- |
| $2x$| $2x^2$ | $8x$ |
| $3$ | $3x$   | $12$ |

$$(2x + 3)(x + 4) = 2x^2 + 8x + 3x + 12$$
$$= 2x^2 + 11x + 12$$

**2** Expand $(x + 3)(x - 5)$.

|     | $x$   | $-5$  |
| --- | ----- | ----- |
| $x$ | $x^2$ | $-5x$ |
| $3$ | $3x$  | $-15$ |

The diagram method works with negative numbers.

$$(x + 3)(x - 5) = x^2 - 5x + 3x - 15$$
$$= x^2 - 2x - 15$$

## Exercise 19.1

**Questions 1 to 6.** Use diagrams to multiply out the brackets.

**1** $(x + 3)(x + 4)$

**2** $(x + 1)(x + 5)$

**3** $(x - 5)(x + 2)$

**4** $(2x + 1)(x - 2)$

**5** $(3x - 2)(x - 6)$

**6** $(2x + 1)(3x + 2)$

**Questions 7 to 24.** Expand the following brackets. Only draw a diagram if necessary.

**7** $(x + 8)(x - 2)$

**8** $(x + 5)(x - 2)$

**9** $(x - 1)(x + 3)$

**10** $(x - 3)(x - 2)$

**11** $(x - 4)(x - 1)$

**12** $(x - 7)(x + 2)$

**13** $(2x + 1)(x + 3)$

**14** $(x + 5)(3x - 2)$

**15** $(5x - 3)(x - 1)$

**16** $(2x + 3)(2x - 1)$

**17** $(3x - 1)(2x + 5)$

**18** $(4x - 2)(3x + 5)$

**19** $(x + 3)(x - 3)$

**20** $(x + 5)(x - 5)$

**21** $(x + 7)(x - 7)$

**22** $(x + 5)^2$

**23** $(x - 7)^2$

**24** $(2x - 3)^2$

## Factorising

**Factorising** is the opposite operation to removing brackets.

For example,   $x^2 + 4x = x(x + 4)$

      and   $3x^2 + 6 = 3(x^2 + 2)$.

You can check that you have factorised an expression correctly by multiplying out the brackets.

## Factorising quadratic expressions

$x^2 + 8x + 15, \quad x^2 - 4$   and   $x^2 + 7x$   are examples of **quadratic expressions**.

You will need to be able to factorise quadratic expressions in order to solve quadratic equations.

The general form of a quadratic expression is $ax^2 + bx + c$, where $a$ cannot be equal to 0.

## Common factors

A **common factor** is a factor which will divide into each term of an expression.

For example,   $x^2 + 7x$   has a common factor of $x$.

        $x^2 + 7x = x(x + 7)$

## Difference of two squares

In the expression $x^2 - 4$,
$x^2 = x \times x$ and $4 = 2^2 = 2 \times 2$.

$x^2 - 4 = (x + 2)(x - 2)$
This result is called the **difference of two squares**.
In general: $a^2 - b^2 = (a + b)(a - b)$

○○○○○○○○○○○○○○○○○○○○

**Checking your work:**
To check your work, expand the brackets
and simplify, where necessary.
The result should be the same as the
original expression.

**EXAMPLES**

Factorise the following.

**1**  $x^2 - 100$
$= x^2 - 10^2$
$= (x + 10)(x - 10)$

**2**  $25 - x^2$
$= 5^2 - x^2$
$= (5 + x)(5 - x)$

**3**  $s^2 - t^2$
$= (s + t)(s - t)$

## Quadratics of the form $x^2 + bx + c$

The expression $x^2 + 8x + 15$ can be factorised.

From experience, we know that the answer is likely to be of the form:
$x^2 + 8x + 15 = (x + ?)(x + ?)$
where the question marks represent numbers.
Replacing the question marks with letters, $p$ and $q$, we get:
$x^2 + 8x + 15 = (x + p)(x + q)$

Multiply the brackets out, using either the diagram method or by expanding, and compare the results
with the original expression.

$$px + qx = x(p + q) = 8x$$
$$\textbf{and } p \times q = 15$$

$(x + p)(x + q)$

1  $x \times x = x^2$
2  $x \times q = qx$
3  $p \times x = px$
4  $p \times q = pq$

$(x + p)(x + q) = x^2 + qx + px + pq$
$= x^2 + (q + p)x + pq$
$= x^2 + 8x + 15$

Two numbers are required which: when multiplied give $+15$, **and** when added give $+8$.
$+5$ and $+3$ satisfy **both** conditions.
$x^2 + 8x + 15 = (x + 5)(x + 3)$

**EXAMPLES**

**1**  Factorise $x^2 + 6x + 9$.

$x^2 + 6x + 9 = (x + 3)(x + 3)$
$\qquad\qquad\quad = (x + 3)^2$

Because  $3 \times 3 = 9$
**and**  $3 + 3 = 6$.

**2**  Factorise $x^2 - 8x + 12$.

$x^2 - 8x + 12 = (x - 6)(x - 2)$

Because  $-6 \times -2 = 12$
**and**  $-6 + -2 = -8$.

**3**  Factorise $x^2 + 2x - 15$.

$x^2 + 2x - 15 = (x + 5)(x - 3)$

Because  $+5 \times -3 = -15$
**and**  $+5 + -3 = +2$.

**4**  Factorise $x^2 - 2x - 8$.

$x^2 - 2x - 8 = (x + 2)(x - 4)$

Because  $+2 \times -4 = -8$
**and**  $+2 + -4 = -2$.

19

Quadratic Equations

**1** Factorise these expressions.

(a) $x^2 + 5x$      (b) $x^2 - 7x$      (c) $y^2 - 6y$      (d) $2y^2 - 12y$

(e) $5t - t^2$      (f) $8y + y^2$      (g) $x^2 - 20x$      (h) $3x^2 - 60x$

**2** Factorise.

(a) $x^2 - 9$      (b) $x^2 - 81$      (c) $y^2 - 25$      (d) $y^2 - 1$

(e) $x^2 - 64$      (f) $100 - x^2$      (g) $36 - x^2$      (h) $x^2 - a^2$

**3** Copy and complete the following.

(a) $x^2 + 6x + 5 = (x + 5)(x + \dots)$      (b) $x^2 + 9x + 14 = (x + 7)(x + \dots)$

(c) $x^2 + 6x + 8 = (x + \dots)(x + 4)$      (d) $x^2 + 9x + 18 = (x + \dots)(x + 6)$

(e) $x^2 - 6x + 5 = (x - 5)(x - \dots)$      (f) $x^2 - 7x + 10 = (x - 5)(x - \dots)$

(g) $x^2 - 7x + 12 = (x - \dots)(x - 3)$      (h) $x^2 + 3x - 4 = (x + 4)(x - \dots)$

(i) $x^2 + 5x - 14 = (x + 7)(x - \dots)$      (j) $x^2 - 4x - 5 = (x - 5)(x + \dots)$

Multiply the brackets out mentally to check your answers.

**4** Factorise.

(a) $x^2 + 3x + 2$      (b) $x^2 + 8x + 7$      (c) $x^2 + 8x + 15$      (d) $x^2 + 8x + 12$

(e) $x^2 + 12x + 11$      (f) $x^2 + 9x + 20$      (g) $x^2 + 10x + 24$      (h) $x^2 + 13x + 36$

(i) $x^2 + 15x + 14$      (j) $x^2 + 10x + 16$

**5** Factorise.

(a) $x^2 - 6x + 9$      (b) $x^2 - 6x + 8$      (c) $x^2 - 11x + 10$      (d) $x^2 - 16x + 15$

(e) $x^2 - 8x + 15$      (f) $x^2 - 10x + 16$      (g) $x^2 - 12x + 20$      (h) $x^2 - 11x + 24$

(i) $x^2 - 13x + 12$      (j) $x^2 - 8x + 12$

**6** Factorise.

(a) $x^2 - x - 6$      (b) $x^2 - 5x - 6$      (c) $x^2 + 2x - 24$      (d) $x^2 + 5x - 24$

(e) $x^2 - 2x - 15$      (f) $x^2 + 3x - 18$      (g) $x^2 - 3x - 40$      (h) $x^2 - 4x - 12$

(i) $x^2 + 3x - 10$      (j) $x^2 - x - 20$

**7** Factorise.

(a) $x^2 - 4x + 4$      (b) $x^2 + 11x + 30$      (c) $x^2 + 2x - 8$      (d) $x^2 - 4x - 21$

(e) $x^2 + x - 20$      (f) $x^2 + 7x + 12$      (g) $x^2 + 8x + 16$      (h) $x^2 - 2x + 1$

(i) $x^2 - 49$      (j) $t^2 + 12t$      (k) $x^2 - 9x + 14$      (l) $x^2 - 7x + 6$

(m) $x^2 + 11x + 18$      (n) $x^2 + 11x + 24$      (o) $x^2 + 19x + 18$      (p) $x^2 - y^2$

(q) $x^2 + x - 6$      (r) $y^2 + 4y$      (s) $y^2 - 10y + 25$      (t) $x^2 - 12x + 36$

## Quadratics of the form $ax^2 + bx + c$

The expression $2x^2 + 11x + 15$ can be factorised.

First look at the term in $x^2$.

The coefficient of $x^2$ is 2, so, the brackets start: $(2x \dots \dots)(x \dots \dots)$

Next, look for two numbers which when multiplied give $+15$.

The possibilities are: 1 and 15 or 3 and 5.

Use these pairs of numbers to complete the brackets.

Multiply out pairs of brackets until the correct factorisation of $2x^2 + 11x + 15$ is found.

$(2x + 1)(x + 15) = 2x^2 + 30x + x + 15 = 2x^2 + 31x + 15$

$(2x + 15)(x + 1) = 2x^2 + 2x + 15x + 15 = 2x^2 + 17x + 15$

$(2x + 3)(x + 5) = 2x^2 + 10x + 3x + 15 = 2x^2 + 13x + 15$

$(2x + 5)(x + 3) = 2x^2 + 6x + 5x + 15 = 2x^2 + 11x + 15$

$2x^2 + 11x + 15 = (2x + 5)(x + 3)$

Rather than expanding brackets fully it is only necessary to look at two terms.

$(2x + 5)(x + 3)$

*Explain why.*

## EXAMPLES

**1** Factorise $3x^2 + 5x + 2$.

$3x^2 + 5x + 2 = (3x + 2)(x + 1)$

**2** Factorise $3a^2 + 7a + 2$.

$3a^2 + 7a + 2 = (3a + 1)(a + 2)$

*Multiply the brackets out mentally to check the answers.*

**3** Factorise $4x^2 + 19x - 5$.

$4x^2 + 19x - 5 = (4x - 1)(x + 5)$
The brackets contain different signs.
*Explain why.*

**4** Factorise $4x^2 - 16x + 15$.

$4x^2 - 16x + 15 = (2x - 5)(2x - 3)$
Each bracket contains a minus sign.
*Explain why.*

## Exercise 19.3

**1** Copy and complete the following.
   (a) $2x^2 + 12x + 18 = (2x + 6)(\ldots \ldots \ldots)$   (b) $2y^2 - 9y - 18 = (\ldots \ldots \ldots)(y - 6)$
   (c) $2a^2 + 5a - 18 = (2a + \ldots)(a - \ldots)$   (d) $2m^2 - 20m + 18 = (2m \ldots \ldots)(m \ldots \ldots)$
   (e) $4x^2 - 13x + 3 = (4x \ldots \ldots)(x \ldots \ldots)$   (f) $4d^2 + 4d - 3 = (2d - 1)(\ldots \ldots \ldots)$
   Multiply the brackets out mentally to check your answers.

**2** Factorise.
   (a) $2x^2 + 7x + 3$        (b) $2x^2 + 11x + 12$        (c) $2a^2 + 25a + 12$
   (d) $4x^2 + 4x + 1$        (e) $6y^2 + 7y + 2$        (f) $6x^2 + 17x + 12$
   (g) $11m^2 + 12m + 1$        (h) $3x^2 + 17x + 10$        (i) $5k^2 + 12k + 4$

**3** Factorise.
   (a) $2a^2 - 5a + 3$        (b) $2y^2 - 9y + 7$        (c) $4x^2 - 4x + 1$
   (d) $3x^2 - 5x + 2$        (e) $6d^2 - 11d + 3$        (f) $2x^2 - 3x + 1$
   (g) $2x^2 - 11x + 15$        (h) $9y^2 - 12y + 4$        (i) $4t^2 - 12t + 9$

**4** Factorise.
   (a) $2x^2 + x - 6$        (b) $2a^2 - a - 3$        (c) $3x^2 - 14x - 5$
   (d) $3t^2 + 14t - 5$        (e) $2y^2 - 5y - 7$        (f) $4y^2 + 7y - 2$
   (g) $9x^2 + 3x - 2$        (h) $10x^2 + 27x - 9$        (i) $5m^2 - 2m - 3$

## Further factorising

When factorising, work logically.
   Does the expression have a common factor?
   Is the expression a difference of two squares?
   Will the expression factorise into two brackets?

## EXAMPLES

Factorise the following.

**1** $2x^2 - 14x = 2x(x - 7)$

**2** $25 - 4y^2 = 5^2 - (2y)^2$
$= (5 + 2y)(5 - 2y)$

**3** $2x^2 - 18 = 2(x^2 - 9)$
$= 2(x + 3)(x - 3)$

**4** $2x^2 - 6x - 8 = 2(x^2 - 3x - 4)$
$= 2(x + 1)(x - 4)$

**1** Factorise.

(a) $3x + 12y$      (b) $t^2 - 16$      (c) $x^2 + 4x + 3$

(d) $y^2 - y$      (e) $2d^2 - 6$      (f) $p^2 - q^2$

(g) $a^2 - 2a$      (h) $x^2 - 2x + 1$      (i) $2y^2 - 8y$

(j) $a^2 - 6a + 9$      (k) $3m^2 - 12$      (l) $v^2 - v - 6$

(m) $ax^2 - ay^2$      (n) $-8 - 2x$      (o) $4 - 4k + k^2$

(p) $18 - 2x^2$      (q) $50 - 2x^2$      (r) $12x^2 - 27y^2$

(s) $6a^2 - 3a$      (t) $x^2 - 15x + 56$      (u) $x^2 + 2x - 15$

**2** Factorise.

(a) $3a^2 - 2a - 8$      (b) $3x^2 + 31x + 10$      (c) $64y^2 - 49$

(d) $3x^2 + 11x + 10$      (e) $7x^2 - 19x + 10$      (f) $6x^2 - 25x - 25$

(g) $5m^2 - 18m + 9$      (h) $8x^2 + 2x - 15$      (i) $13x - 20 - 2x^2$

(j) $4y^2 + 22y + 24$      (k) $6x^2 + 3x - 18$      (l) $28n - 10 + 6n^2$

## Solving quadratic equations

## Activity

I am thinking of two numbers.
I multiply them together.
The answer is zero.

Write down 2 numbers which could be Jim's numbers.
Now write down **four** more pairs.
What can you say about Jim's numbers?

You should have discovered that at least one of Jim's numbers must be **zero**.
We can use this fact to solve **quadratic equations**.

### EXAMPLES

**1** Find $x$ if:

(a) $x(x - 2) = 0$

Either $x = 0$ or $x - 2 = 0$

Because one of them must be zero.

$x = 0$ or $x = 2$

(b) $(x - 3)(x + 2) = 0$

$x - 3 = 0$ or $x + 2 = 0$

Because one of them must be zero.

$x = 3$ or $x = -2$

**2** Solve $x^2 - 5x + 6 = 0$

$x^2 - 5x + 6 = 0$

Factorise the quadratic expression first.

$(x - 2)(x - 3) = 0$

$x = 2$ or $x = 3$

> **To check solutions:**
> Does $(2)^2 - 5 \times (2) + 6 = 0$
> **and** $(3)^2 - 5 \times (3) + 6 = 0$?

**3** Solve these equations.

(a) $x^2 - 9 = 0$

$(x - 3)(x + 3) = 0$

$x = 3$ or $x = -3$

(b) $y^2 + 7y = 0$

$y(y + 7) = 0$

$y = 0$ or $y = -7$

(c) $a^2 + 4a - 5 = 0$

$(a - 1)(a + 5) = 0$

$a = 1$ or $a = -5$

**1** Solve these equations.

(a) $(x - 2)(x - 3) = 0$    (b) $(x + 4)(x + 6) = 0$    (c) $(x - 3)(x + 1) = 0$

(d) $(x - 5)(x + 2) = 0$    (e) $x(x - 4) = 0$    (f) $3x(x + 2) = 0$

**2** Solve.

(a) $x^2 - 3x + 2 = 0$    (b) $y^2 + 7y + 12 = 0$    (c) $m^2 - 2m - 8 = 0$

(d) $a^2 + a - 12 = 0$    (e) $n^2 - 5n - 36 = 0$    (f) $z^2 - 9z + 18 = 0$

(g) $k^2 + 8k + 15 = 0$    (h) $c^2 + 15c + 56 = 0$    (i) $b^2 + b - 20 = 0$

(j) $v^2 - 7v - 60 = 0$    (k) $w^2 + 8w - 48 = 0$    (l) $p^2 - p - 72 = 0$

**3** Solve.

(a) $x^2 - 5x = 0$    (b) $y^2 + y = 0$    (c) $p^2 + 3p = 0$

(d) $4a - a^2 = 0$    (e) $t^2 - 6t = 0$    (f) $g^2 - 4g = 0$

**4** Solve.

(a) $x^2 - 4 = 0$    (b) $y^2 - 144 = 0$    (c) $9 - a^2 = 0$

(d) $d^2 - 16 = 0$    (e) $x^2 - 100 = 0$    (f) $36 - x^2 = 0$

(g) $x^2 - 49 = 0$    (h) $2.25 - x^2 = 0$    (i) $2x^2 - 18 = 0$

**5** Solve these equations.

(a) $x^2 + 6x = 0$    (b) $x^2 + 5x + 4 = 0$    (c) $x^2 - 64 = 0$

(d) $x^2 - 4x + 3 = 0$    (e) $5x^2 - 10x = 0$    (f) $x^2 - x - 6 = 0$

(g) $x^2 + 2x - 15 = 0$    (h) $2x^2 - 8 = 0$    (i) $x^2 - 15x + 56 = 0$

**6** Solve these equations.

(a) $2x^2 + 7x + 5 = 0$    (b) $2x^2 - 11x + 5 = 0$    (c) $3x^2 - 17x - 28 = 0$

(d) $6y^2 + 7y + 2 = 0$    (e) $3x^2 + 7x - 6 = 0$    (f) $3z^2 - 5z - 2 = 0$

(g) $5m^2 - 8m + 3 = 0$    (h) $6a^2 + 3a - 63 = 0$    (i) $4y^2 - 3y - 10 = 0$

**7** Rearrange these equations and then solve them.

(a) $y^2 = 4y + 5$    (b) $x^2 = x$    (c) $x^2 = 8x - 16$

(d) $x^2 = 2x + 15$    (e) $n^2 - 10n = 24$    (f) $7 = 8m - m^2$

(g) $a(a - 5) = 24$    (h) $x^2 - 5x + 6 = 3 - x$    (i) $x = 6x^2 - 1$

(j) $15 - 7m = 2m^2$    (k) $6a^2 = 2 - a$    (l) $8x^2 = 3 - 2x$

## Using the quadratic formula

Some quadratic expressions do not factorise.

Consider the equation $x^2 - 5x + 2 = 0$.

It is not possible to find two numbers which:
when multiplied give $+2$ **and** when added give $-5$.

We could draw the graph of $y = x^2 - 5x + 2$
and use it to solve the equation $x^2 - 5x + 2 = 0$.
One solution lies between 0 and 1.
Another solution lies between 4 and 5.

*Graphical solutions have limited accuracy and
are time consuming. Explain why.*

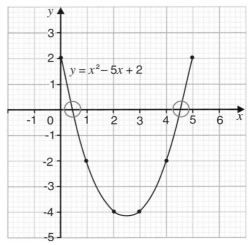

The solutions to a quadratic equation can be found using the **quadratic formula**.

$$\text{If } ax^2 + bx + c = 0 \text{ and } a \neq 0 \text{ then } x = \frac{-b \pm \sqrt{b^2 - 4ac}}{2a}$$

The quadratic formula can be used at any time, even if the quadratic expression factorises.

Solve $x^2 - 5x + 2 = 0$, giving the answers correct to three significant figures.

Using $x = \dfrac{-b \pm \sqrt{b^2 - 4ac}}{2a}$

Substitute: $a = 1$, $b = -5$ and $c = 2$.

$x = \dfrac{-(-5) \pm \sqrt{(-5)^2 - 4(1)(2)}}{2(1)}$

$x = \dfrac{5 \pm \sqrt{25 - 8}}{2}$

$x = \dfrac{5 \pm \sqrt{17}}{2}$

Either $x = \dfrac{5 + \sqrt{17}}{2}$ or $x = \dfrac{5 - \sqrt{17}}{2}$

$\qquad x = 4.5615\ldots$ or $x = 0.43844\ldots$
$x = 0.438$ or $4.56$, correct to 3 sig. figs.

*Check the answers by substituting the values of x into the original equation.*

---

**EXAMPLE**

Solve $6x = 3 - 5x^2$, giving the answers correct to two decimal places.

Rearrange $6x = 3 - 5x^2$ to get $5x^2 + 6x - 3 = 0$.

Using $x = \dfrac{-b \pm \sqrt{b^2 - 4ac}}{2a}$

Substitute: $a = 5$, $b = 6$ and $c = -3$.

$x = \dfrac{-6 \pm \sqrt{6^2 - 4(5)(-3)}}{2(5)}$

$x = \dfrac{-6 \pm \sqrt{36 + 60}}{10}$

$x = \dfrac{-6 \pm \sqrt{96}}{10}$

Either $x = \dfrac{-6 + \sqrt{96}}{10}$ or $x = \dfrac{-6 - \sqrt{96}}{10}$

$\qquad x = 0.3797\ldots$ or $x = -1.5797\ldots$

$x = -1.58$ or $0.38$, correct to 2 d.p.

---

## Exercise **19.6**

**1** Use the quadratic formula to solve these equations.
- (a) $x^2 + 4x + 3 = 0$
- (b) $x^2 - 3x + 2 = 0$
- (c) $x^2 + 2x - 3 = 0$

**2** Solve these equations, giving the answers correct to 2 decimal places.
- (a) $x^2 + 4x + 2 = 0$
- (b) $x^2 + 7x + 5 = 0$
- (c) $x^2 + x - 1 = 0$
- (d) $x^2 - 3x - 2 = 0$
- (e) $x^2 - 5x - 3 = 0$
- (f) $x^2 + 5x + 3 = 0$
- (g) $x^2 + 4x - 10 = 0$
- (h) $x^2 - 3x + 1 = 0$
- (i) $x^2 + 3x - 2 = 0$

**3** Use the quadratic formula to solve these equations.
- (a) $2x^2 + x - 3 = 0$
- (b) $2x^2 - 3x + 1 = 0$
- (c) $5x^2 + 2x - 3 = 0$

**4** Solve these equations, giving the answers correct to 2 decimal places.
- (a) $3x^2 - 5x + 1 = 0$
- (b) $2x^2 - 7x + 4 = 0$
- (c) $3x^2 + 23x + 8 = 0$
- (d) $3x^2 - 4x - 5 = 0$
- (e) $2z^2 + 6z + 3 = 0$
- (f) $3x^2 - 2x - 20 = 0$

**5** Rearrange the following to form quadratic equations.
Then solve the quadratic equations, giving answers correct to 2 decimal places.
- (a) $x^2 = 6x - 3$
- (b) $2x^2 - 6 = 3x$
- (c) $3x = 2x^2 - 4$
- (d) $2 = x + 5x^2$
- (e) $3(x + 1) = x^2 - x$
- (f) $x(2x + 5) = 10$
- (g) $3x(x - 4) = 2(x - 1)$
- (h) $(3x - 2)^2 = (x + 2)^2 + 12$
- (i) $5 = 2x(x - 1)$

**6**
- (a) Draw axes marked from $-3$ to 2 for $x$ and from $-2$ to 10 for $y$.
  Using the same axes draw the following graphs:
  $$y = 2x^2 + 4x + 1 \qquad y = 2x^2 + 4x + 2 \qquad y = 2x^2 + 4x + 3$$
  Use your graphs to solve the equations:
  $$2x^2 + 4x + 1 = 0 \qquad 2x^2 + 4x + 2 = 0 \qquad 2x^2 + 4x + 3 = 0$$
- (b) Use the quadratic formula to solve the following equations:
  $$2x^2 + 4x + 1 = 0 \qquad 2x^2 + 4x + 2 = 0 \qquad 2x^2 + 4x + 3 = 0$$
- (c) Compare your answers to parts (a) and (b).

## Completing the square

$16$, $x^2$, $9y^2$, $(m - 3)^2$ are all examples of **perfect squares**.

What must be added to $x^2 - 2x$ to make it a perfect square?
$(x - 1)^2 = x^2 - 2x + 1$
So, if $+1$ is added to $x^2 - 2x$ the result is $(x - 1)^2$.

The process of adding a constant term to a quadratic expression to make it a perfect square is called **completing the square**.

Consider the following.

$(x + 1)^2 = x^2 + 2x + 1$      $(x - 1)^2 = x^2 - 2x + 1$
$(x + 2)^2 = x^2 + 4x + 4$      $(x - 2)^2 = x^2 - 4x + 4$
$(x + 3)^2 = x^2 + 6x + 9$      $(x - 3)^2 = x^2 - 6x + 9$

In the expanded form the coefficient of $x$ is always **twice** the constant in the brackets or, to put it another way, the constant in the brackets is **half the coefficient of $x$**.

$(x + a)^2 = x^2 + 2ax + a^2$      $(x - a)^2 = x^2 - 2ax + a^2$

## Rearranging quadratics

Quadratics can be rearranged into a **square term** and a **constant value** (number).
This is sometimes called **completed square form** and can be used to solve quadratic equations.

> To write the quadratic $x^2 + bx + c$ in completed square form:
> write the **square term** as $(x + \frac{1}{2}$ the coefficient of $x)^2$ and then adjust for the **constant value**.

$x^2 + 6x + 10$ can be written in the form $(x + a)^2 + b$. Find $a$ and $b$.

The coefficient of $x$ is 6. $\frac{1}{2}$ of 6 is 3.
The **square term** is $(x + 3)^2$.
$(x + 3)^2 = x^2 + 6x + 9$
$x^2 + 6x + 10 = x^2 + 6x + 9 + 1 = (x + 3)^2 + 1$.
The **constant value** is $+1$.
So, $a = 3$ and $b = 1$.

> In general, the **vertex** of the graph
> $y = (x + a)^2 + b$ is at the point $(-a, b)$.

This change of form can still be done when the coefficient of $x^2$ is not 1.
Consider the following.

$(2x + 1)^2 = 4x^2 + 4x + 1$      $(2x - 1)^2 = 4x^2 - 4x + 1$
$(2x + 2)^2 = 4x^2 + 8x + 4$      $(2x - 2)^2 = 4x^2 - 8x + 4$
$(2x + 3)^2 = 4x^2 + 12x + 9$      $(2x - 3)^2 = 4x^2 - 12x + 9$

In general: $(px + q)^2 = p^2x^2 + 2pqx + q^2$
This can be used to change the form of quadratics.

$4x^2 + 20x + 31$ can be written in the form $(px + q)^2 + r$. Find $p$, $q$ and $r$.
Using $(px + q)^2 = p^2x^2 + 2pqx + q^2$.
$4x^2 + 20x + 31 = p^2x^2 + 2pqx + q^2$.

Comparing the coefficients of $x^2$.
$p^2 = 4$
$p = \sqrt{4} = 2$

Comparing the coefficients of $x$.
$2pq = 20$
But $p = 2$.
So, $4q = 20$
$q = 5$

$(2x + 5)^2 = 4x^2 + 20x + 25$
$4x^2 + 20x + 31 = 4x^2 + 20x + 25 + 6 = (2x + 5)^2 + 6$
The constant value, $r$, is $+6$.
So, $p = 2$, $q = 5$ and $r = 6$.

**EXAMPLES**

**1** Write these quadratics in the form
$(x + a)^2 + b$.

(a) $x^2 + 10x + 7$

$\frac{1}{2}$ of 10 is 5.

$(x + 5)^2 = x^2 + 10x + 25$
$x^2 + 10x + 7 = x^2 + 10x + 25 - 18$
$= (x + 5)^2 - 18$

(b) $x^2 - 8x - 5$

$\frac{1}{2}$ of $-8$ is $-4$.

$(x - 4)^2 = x^2 - 8x + 16$
$x^2 - 8x - 5 = x^2 - 8x + 16 - 21$
$= (x - 4)^2 - 21$

**2** Change $9x^2 + 24x + 5$
into the form $(px + q)^2 + r$.

Using $(px + q)^2 = p^2x^2 + 2pqx + q^2$.
$9x^2 + 24x + 5 = p^2x^2 + 2pqx + q^2$

$p^2 = 9$
$p = \sqrt{9} = 3$

$2pq = 24$
But $p = 3$.
So, $6q = 24$
$q = 4$

$(3x + 4)^2 = 9x^2 + 24x + 16$
$9x^2 + 24x + 5 = 9x^2 + 24x + 16 - 11$
$= (3x + 4)^2 - 11$

## Exercise 19.7

**1** What must be added to each expression to make a perfect square?
(a) $x^2 + 2x$     (b) $x^2 + 4x$     (c) $x^2 - 6x$
(d) $y^2 + 8y$     (e) $p^2 - 2p$     (f) $a^2 - 3a$
(g) $m^2 + 10m$     (h) $x^2 - 5x$

**2** Complete these squares.
(a) $x^2 + 6x + ... = (x + ...)^2$     (b) $a^2 - 4a + ... = (a - ...)^2$
(c) $b^2 + 2b + ... = (b + ...)^2$     (d) $m^2 - 8m + ... = (m - ...)^2$
(e) $n^2 - n + ... = (n - ...)^2$     (f) $x^2 + 5x + ... = (x + ...)^2$

**3** Change these quadratics into the form $(x + a)^2 + b$.
(a) $x^2 + 6x + 20$     (b) $x^2 + 6x + 5$     (c) $x^2 + 10x - 4$
(d) $x^2 - 4x + 5$     (e) $x^2 - 4x + 2$     (f) $x^2 - 4x - 4$
(g) $x^2 - 6x + 4$     (h) $x^2 - 8x$     (i) $x^2 + 12x$

**4** These quadratics can be written in the form $(x + a)^2 + b$.
State the values of $a$ and $b$.
(a) $x^2 + 6x + 15$     (b) $x^2 + 10x + 5$     (c) $x^2 - 6x - 5$
(d) $x^2 - 8x + 4$     (e) $x^2 + 12x + 4$     (f) $x^2 + 6x + 9$

**5** Change these quadratics into the form $(px + q)^2 + r$.
State the values of $p$, $q$ and $r$.
(a) $4x^2 + 16x + 5$     (b) $9x^2 + 12x + 3$     (c) $25x^2 - 40x - 3$
(d) $16x^2 + 32x - 5$     (e) $100x^2 + 60x + 3$     (f) $16x^2 - 40x + 9$

**6** The expression $x^2 - 4x - 1$ can be written in the form $(x + a)^2 + b$.
(a) Find the values of $a$ and $b$.
(b) What is the minimum value of the expression $x^2 - 4x - 1$?

**7** $x^2 - 6x + a = (x + b)^2 - 1$.
Find the values of $a$ and $b$.

**8** What is the minimum value of the expression $x^2 - 10x + 26$?

## Solving quadratic equations by completing the square

When a quadratic equation is expressed in the form $(x + m)^2 = n$, with $n > 0$, it is possible to solve the equation by taking the square roots of both sides.

### EXAMPLES

**1** Solve $x^2 + 2x = 8$.

$x^2 + 2x = 8$

Write the left-hand side (LHS) of the equation in the form $(x + a)^2 + b$ by completing the square.

$x^2 + 2x = (x + 1)^2 - 1$

$(x + 1)^2 - 1 = 8$

Add 1 to both sides.

$(x + 1)^2 = 9$

Take the square root of both sides of the equation.

$x + 1 = \pm\, 3$

Either $x + 1 = 3$ or $x + 1 = -3$

$\qquad\qquad x = 2$ or $\qquad x = -4$

**2** Solve $2x^2 - 12x = 9$, giving the answer correct to one decimal place.

$2x^2 - 12x = 9$

To solve a quadratic equation by completing the square we must first make the coefficient of $x^2$ unity (one).

Divide both sides of the equation by 2.

$x^2 - 6x = 4.5$

Complete the square on the LHS.

$(x - 3)^2 - 9 = 4.5$

$(x - 3)^2 = 4.5 + 9$

$(x - 3)^2 = 13.5$

$x - 3 = \pm\, \sqrt{13.5}$

Either $x = 3 + 3.7$ or $x = 3 - 3.7$

$\qquad x = 6.7$ or $-0.7$, correct to 1 d.p.

### Exercise 19.8

**1** Solve the following equations by completing the square.
- (a) $x^2 - 2x = 3$
- (b) $t^2 - 4t = 21$
- (c) $x^2 + 6x = 27$
- (d) $y^2 - 6y - 16 = 0$
- (e) $m^2 - 10m - 24 = 0$
- (f) $e^2 - 14e + 48 = 0$

**2** Solve the following equations by completing the square.
Give your answers correct to one decimal place.
- (a) $x^2 - 10x = 15$
- (b) $m^2 + 4m = 7$
- (c) $x^2 - 6x = -3$
- (d) $y^2 - 3y - 2 = 0$
- (e) $x^2 - 12x = 5$
- (f) $a^2 + 6a + 4 = 0$
- (g) $2n^2 + 2n = 1$
- (h) $2x^2 + 2x = 3$
- (i) $4z^2 - 12z + 3 = 0$
- (j) $3x^2 - 12x = -11$
- (k) $x^2 + 6x + 7 = 0$
- (l) $4x^2 - 4x - 15 = 0$

**3** (a) Write $x^2 - 4x + 1$ in the form $(x + a)^2 + b$.
(b) Hence, solve the equation $x^2 - 4x + 1 = 0$, leaving your answer in the form $c \pm \sqrt{d}$.

**4** The solutions of the equation $x^2 - 6x + 4 = 0$ can be given as $a \pm \sqrt{b}$ where $a$ and $b$ are prime numbers.
Find the values of $a$ and $b$.

**5** Solve the equation $2x^2 - 4x - 5 = 0$.
Give your answers in the form $p \pm \sqrt{q}$ where $p$ and $q$ are rational.

**6** The solutions of the equation $x^2 + mx + n = 0$ are $x = 3 \pm \sqrt{2}$.
Find the values of $m$ and $n$.

**7** The solutions of the equation $2x^2 + ax + b = 0$ are $x = \dfrac{4 \pm \sqrt{22}}{2}$.
Find the values of $a$ and $b$.

**8** Starting with $ax^2 + bx + c = 0$ prove the quadratic formula $x = \dfrac{-b \pm \sqrt{b^2 - 4ac}}{2a}$.

# Problems solved using quadratic equations

Some mathematical problems involve the forming of equations which are quadratic.
The equation is solved and the solutions are analysed to answer the original problem.

### EXAMPLES

**1** The sum of two numbers is 15 and their product is 56. Find the numbers.

If $x$ is one of the numbers then the other number is $(15 - x)$.

| | |
|---|---|
| Their product is 56, so, | $x(15 - x) = 56$ |
| Expand the brackets. | $15x - x^2 = 56$ |
| Rearrange to the form $ax^2 + bx + c = 0$. | $x^2 - 15x + 56 = 0$ |
| Factorise. | $(x - 7)(x - 8) = 0$ |
| Solve the equation. | $x = 7$ or $x = 8$ |

The numbers are 7 and 8.
**Check:** Does $7 + 8 = 15$ **and** $7 \times 8 = 56$?

**2** A rectangular lawn, 10 m by 8 m, is surrounded by a path which is $x$ m wide.
The total area of the path and lawn is 143 m².
Calculate the width of the path.

Drawing a **sketch diagram**, to which labels can be added, may help you to understand and solve problems.

$(8 + 2x)$ m

Total length $= (10 + 2x)$ m
Total width $= (8 + 2x)$ m
Total area $= 143$ m²

| | |
|---|---|
| Total length $\times$ total width = total area | $(10 + 2x)(8 + 2x) = 143$ |
| Expand the brackets. | $80 + 20x + 16x + 4x^2 = 143$ |
| Rearrange to the form $ax^2 + bx + c = 0$. | $4x^2 + 36x - 63 = 0$ |
| | $(2x - 3)(2x + 21) = 0$ |
| Either $2x - 3 = 0$ or $2x + 21 = 0$ | |
| $2x = 3$ or $2x = -21$ | |
| $x = 1.5$ or $x = -10.5$ | |

The quadratic equation has two solutions.
However, $x \neq -10.5$, as it is impossible to have a
path of negative width in the context of the problem.
So, $x = 1.5$
The width of the path is 1.5 m.
**Check:** Does $(10 + 2 \times 1.5) \times (8 + 2 \times 1.5) = 143$?

## Exercise 19.9

In this exercise form suitable equations and solve them using an appropriate method.

**1** This rectangle has an area of 21 cm².
(a) Form an equation in $x$.
(b) By solving your equation, find the value of $x$.

$x$ cm

$(x - 4)$ cm

**2** The product of $x$ and $(x - 2)$ is 63. By forming an equation, find the value of $x$.

**3** A right-angled triangle is cut from the corner of a rectangle as shown.
The shaded area is 7.5 cm².

(a) Form an equation in $x$ and show that it simplifies to $x^2 + 8x - 9 = 0$.
(b) By solving the equation $x^2 + 8x - 9 = 0$, find the value of $x$.

**4** Garden A consists of a lawn 8 m by 5 m with a path $x$ m wide on all sides.
Garden B consists of a lawn 15 m by 14.5 m with a path $x$ m wide on all sides.
Garden B is three times the area of Garden A.

(a) Form an equation in $x$.
(b) Solve it to find $x$ (the width of the path).
(c) Check that your value for $x$ gives the area of Garden B as three times the area of Garden A.

**5** The length of a rectangle is 5 cm greater than its width. The area of the rectangle is 40 cm².
Calculate the length and width of the rectangle.
Give your answer correct to two significant figures.

**6** The perimeter of a rectangle is 62 cm.
The length of the diagonal is 25 cm.
Calculate the dimensions of the rectangle.

**Hint:** In a right-angled triangle
"The square on the hypotenuse is equal to the sum of the squares on the other two sides."

**7** The perimeter of a rectangle is 20 m. The area is 20 m².
Calculate the dimensions of the rectangle. Give your answers correct to two decimal places.

**8** (a) Two positive numbers differ by 5. Their product is 234. What are the two numbers?
(b) The sum of two numbers is 12. Their product is 30. What are the two numbers?

**9** A canoe course is in the shape of a right-angled triangle.
The length of the course is 300 m.
The longest leg of the course is 125 m.
What are the lengths of the other two legs?

**10** Three numbers are in this sequence: $x$, $x + 3$, $x + 6$.
The sum of the squares of the two smaller numbers is equal to the square of the largest number.
What are the three numbers? (There are two solutions.)

**11** Consider these numbers: $x$, $x + 1$, $x + 3$ and $x + 7$.
The sum of the squares of the two smaller numbers is equal to the product of the two larger numbers.
(a) Form an equation and simplify it to a quadratic expression equal to 0.
(b) Solve the equation to find the numbers (two solutions).

**12** The $n$th triangular number is $\frac{1}{2} n(n + 1)$.
(a) Which triangular number is equal to 66?
(b) Which triangular number is equal to 120?

**13** Two numbers differ by 5. Their squares differ by 55. What are the two numbers?

## What you need to know

- Brackets, such as $(x + 2)(x + 5)$ can be multiplied out using:
    the **diagram method**,
    by **expanding**.
- **Factorising** is the opposite operation to removing brackets.
    When factorising, work logically.
    Does the expression have a **common factor**?
    Is the expression a difference of **two squares**?
    Will the expression factorise into **two brackets**?

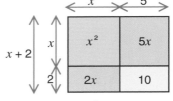

$(x + 2)(x + 5) = x^2 + 5x + 2x + 10$
$= x^2 + 7x + 10$

- A **common factor** is a factor which divides into two, or more, numbers (or terms). For example: $x^2 + 7x = x(x + 7)$
- **Difference of two squares**: $a^2 - b^2 = (a - b)(a + b)$
- **Quadratic equations** can be solved:
    by factorising, graphically, using the quadratic formula, by completing the square.
- The general form for a **quadratic equation** is $ax^2 + bx + c = 0$, where $a$ cannot be zero.
- The solutions to a quadratic equation can be found using the **quadratic formula**.

    If $ax^2 + bx + c = 0$ and $a \neq 0$ then $x = \dfrac{-b \pm \sqrt{b^2 - 4ac}}{2a}$

- Quadratic expressions, such as $x^2 + 8x + 20$, can be written in the form $(x + a)^2 + b$, where $a$ and $b$ are integers.
    In **completed square form**, $(x + a)^2 + b$:
        the value of $a$ is half the coefficient of $x$,
        the value of $b$ is found by subtracting the value of $a^2$ from the constant term of the original expression.
    For example: $x^2 + 8x + 20 = (x + 4)^2 + 4$
- Quadratic expressions, such as $4x^2 + 16x + 5$,
    where the coefficient of $x^2$ is not 1 can be written in the form $(px + q)^2 + r$.
    In completed square form, $(px + q)^2 + r$:
        the value of $p$ is the square root of the coefficient of $x^2$,
        the value of $q$ is the coefficient of $x$ divided by $2p$,
        the value of $r$ is found by subtracting the value of $q^2$ from the constant term of the original expression.
    For example: $4x^2 + 16x + 5 = (2x + 4)^2 - 11$

## Review Exercise 19

**1** Multiply out the brackets and simplify. $(x + 4)(x - 3)$ — OCR

**2** (a) Factorise. $x^2 + 5x$
(b) Remove the brackets and simplify. $(x + 3y)(x + 5y)$ — OCR

**3** Factorise (a) $2xy^2 + 4xy$, (b) $m^2 - 9m + 8$.

**4** Factorise fully. (a) $10a + 15ab - 20a^2$ (b) $x^2 - 4y^2$ (c) $5x^2 + 17x - 12$ OCR

**5** (a) Factorise. $x^2 + 10x + 24$ (b) Hence, solve. $x^2 + 10x + 24 = 0$ OCR

**6** Solve (a) $t^2 - 4t = 0$, (b) $y^2 + 3y + 2 = 0$.

**7** Solve by factorising. $x^2 + 9x - 10 = 0$ OCR

**8** (a) Solve this equation. $2x^2 + x - 3 = 0$
(b) Sketch the graph of $y = 2x^2 + x - 3$.
Show clearly where the graph crosses the $x$ axis. OCR

**9** Solve the equations (a) $x^2 - 9 = 0$, (b) $x^2 - 8x - 9 = 0$.

**10** The diagram shows a rectangle whose width is $x$ cm.
(a) The area of the rectangle is $50 \text{ cm}^2$.
Find an expression for the perimeter, $P$,
of the rectangle in terms of $x$.

$x$ cm

(b) The perimeter of the rectangle is 33 cm.
Show that $2x^2 - 33x + 100 = 0$.
(c) Solve the equation $2x^2 - 33x + 100 = 0$ to find the dimensions of the rectangle. OCR

**11** The sum of two numbers is 13. Their product is 36.
By forming an equation, find the two numbers.

**12** The expression $x^2 - 6x + 11$ can be written in the form $(x - p)^2 + q$.
(a) Find the values of $p$ and $q$.
(b) What is the minimum value of the expression?

**13** Solve the equation $x^2 - 11x + 8 = 0$. Give your answers correct to two decimal places.

**14** A rectangle has length $(x + 5)$ cm and width $(x - 1)$ cm.
A corner is removed from the rectangle, as shown.
(a) Show that the shaded area is given by
$x^2 + 4x - 11$.
(b) The shaded area is $59 \text{ cm}^2$.
(i) Show that $x^2 + 4x - 70 = 0$.
(ii) Calculate the value of $x$.

**15** Solve the equation $3x^2 + 2x - 2 = 0$.
Give your answers correct to two decimal places.

**16** An open box is made from a square of card of side $x$ cm, by removing squares of side 2 cm from each corner.

(a) Show that the volume, $V \text{ cm}^3$, of the box is given by $V = 2x^2 - 16x + 32$.
(b) Calculate the value of $x$ when $V = 60 \text{ cm}^3$.
Give your answer correct to one decimal place.

**17** (a) Show that the equation $2x - 3 = \dfrac{3(x + 1)}{x + 4}$ can be rearranged to $2x^2 + 2x - 15 = 0$.
(b) Solve the equation $2x^2 + 2x - 15 = 0$. OCR

# Simultaneous Equations

$x + y = 10$   is an equation with two unknown quantities $x$ and $y$.
Many pairs of values of $x$ and $y$ fit this equation.

For example.
$x = 1$   and   $y = 9$,   $x = 4$ and   $y = 6$,   $x = 2.9$   and   $y = 7.1$,   $x = 1.005$   and   $y = 8.995$,   ...
$x - y = 2$   is another equation with the **same** two unknown quantities $x$ and $y$.
Again, many pairs of values of $x$ and $y$ fit this equation.

For example.
$x = 4$   and   $y = 2$,   $x = 7$   and   $y = 5$,   $x = 2.9$   and   $y = 0.9$,   $x = -1$   and   $y = -3$,   ...

There is only **one** pair of values of $x$ and $y$ which fit **both** of these equations   ($x = 6$   and   $y = 4$).
Pairs of equations like   $x + y = 10$   and   $x - y = 2$   are called **simultaneous equations**.

To solve simultaneous equations you need to find values which fit **both** equations simultaneously.
Simultaneous equations can be solved using different methods.

## Using graphs to solve simultaneous equations

Consider the simultaneous equations   $x + 2y = 5$   and   $x - 2y = 1$.

Draw the graphs of   $x + 2y = 5$   and   $x - 2y = 1$.

For   $x + 2y = 5$:
When   $x = 1$,   $y = 2$.
This gives the point $(1, 2)$.

When   $x = 5$,   $y = 0$.
This gives the point $(5, 0)$.

To draw the graph of   $x + 2y = 5$
draw a line through the points
$(1, 2)$ and $(5, 0)$.

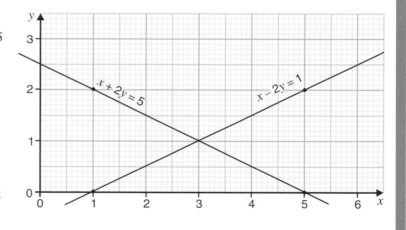

For   $x - 2y = 1$:
When   $x = 1$,   $y = 0$.
This gives the point $(1, 0)$.

When   $x = 5$,   $y = 2$.
This gives  the point $(5, 2)$.

To draw the graph of   $x - 2y = 1$
draw a line through the points
$(1, 0)$ and $(5, 2)$.

The values of $x$ and $y$ at the point where the lines cross give the solution to the
simultaneous equations.

The lines cross at the point $(3, 1)$.

This gives the solution   $x = 3$   and   $y = 1$.

To solve a pair of simultaneous equations plot the graph of each of the equations on the same diagram.
The coordinates of the point where the two lines cross:

- fit **both equations** simultaneously,
- give the **graphical solution** of the equations.

## EXAMPLE

Use a graphical method to solve this pair of simultaneous equations:   $5x + 2y = 20$
$y = 2x + 1$

Find the points that fit the equations   $5x + 2y = 20$   and   $y = 2x + 1$.

For   $5x + 2y = 20$:

When   $x = 0$,   $y = 10$.
This gives the point $(0, 10)$.

When   $y = 0$,   $x = 4$.
This gives the point $(4, 0)$.

Draw a line through the points $(0, 10)$ and $(4, 0)$.

For   $y = 2x + 1$:

When   $x = 0$,   $y = 1$.
This gives the point $(0, 1)$.

When   $x = 4$,   $y = 9$.
This gives the point $(4, 9)$.

Draw a line through the points $(0, 1)$ and $(4, 9)$.

The lines cross at the point $(2, 5)$.
This gives the solution   $x = 2$   and   $y = 5$.

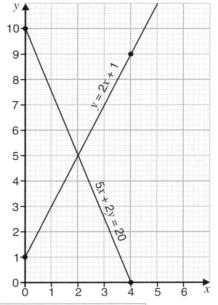

**Check:**
You can check a graphical solution by substituting
the values of $x$ and $y$ into the original equations.
When   $x = 2$   and   $y = 5$
$$5x + 2y = 5 \times 2 + 2 \times 5 = 20$$
$$y = 2x + 1 = 2 \times 2 + 1 = 5$$

## Exercise **20.1**

Use a graphical method to solve each of these pairs of simultaneous equations.
For each question use the sizes of axes given.
For example,   $0 \leqslant x \leqslant 8$   means draw and label the $x$ axis from 0 to 8 inclusive.

**1**   $x + y = 6$
$y = x - 2$
Axes   $0 \leqslant x \leqslant 8$,   $-3 \leqslant y \leqslant 7$

**2**   $x + y = 8$
$y - x = 2$
Axes   $0 \leqslant x \leqslant 10$,   $-3 \leqslant y \leqslant 10$

**3**   $x + 2y = 8$
$2x + y = 7$
Axes   $0 \leqslant x \leqslant 10$,   $0 \leqslant y \leqslant 8$

**4**   $3x + 2y = 12$
$y = x + 1$
Axes   $0 \leqslant x \leqslant 5$,   $0 \leqslant y \leqslant 8$

**5**   $x + 3y = 6$
$y = 2x - 5$
Axes   $0 \leqslant x \leqslant 10$,   $-6 \leqslant y \leqslant 4$

**6**   $3x + 4y = 24$
$2y = x + 2$
Axes   $-4 \leqslant x \leqslant 10$,   $-2 \leqslant y \leqslant 8$

**7**   $2x + y = -1$
$x + 2y = 4$
Axes   $-3 \leqslant x \leqslant 5$,   $-2 \leqslant y \leqslant 4$

**8**   $x + 2y = 6$
$x - 2y = 4$
Axes   $0 \leqslant x \leqslant 6$,   $-2 \leqslant y \leqslant 3$

## Simultaneous equations with no solution

Some pairs of simultaneous equations do not have a solution.

### EXAMPLE

Show that this pair of simultaneous equations do not have a solution.

$$y - 2x = 4$$
$$2y = 4x - 1$$

**Method 1**
Draw the graph of each equation.

$y - 2x = 4$
When $x = 0$, $y = 4$.
When $y = 0$, $x = -2$.
Plot and draw a line through the points $(0, 4)$ and $(-2, 0)$.

$2y = 4x - 1$
When $x = 0$, $y = -0.5$.
When $x = 2$, $y = 3.5$.
Plot and draw a line through the points $(0, -0.5)$ and $(2, 3.5)$.

The two lines are **parallel**.
This means they never cross and there are no values of $x$ and $y$ which fit both equations.
So, the simultaneous equations have no solution.

**Method 2**
Rearrange each equation to the form $y = mx + c$.

$y - 2x = 4$
Add $2x$ to both sides.
$y = 2x + 4$
The graph of this equation has a gradient ($m$) of 2 and a $y$-intercept ($c$) of 4.

$2y = 4x - 1$
Divide both sides by 2.
$y = 2x - 0.5$
The graph of this equation has a gradient ($m$) of 2 and a $y$-intercept ($c$) of $-0.5$.

Both lines have the same gradient (2) and different $y$-intercepts which shows that the lines are parallel.

### Exercise 20.2

**1** Draw graphs to show that each of these pairs of simultaneous equations have no solution.
   (a) $x + y = 6$      (b) $y - 4x = 8$      (c) $3x + 4y = 12$      (d) $5y - 2x = 10$
        $y = 2 - x$          $y = 4x + 2$          $8y = 24 - 6x$         $5y = 2x + 20$

**2** By rearranging each of these pairs of simultaneous equations to the form $y = mx + c$ show that they do not have a solution.
   (a) $2x + y = 6$      (b) $2y - 4x = 7$      (c) $5x - 2y = 8$      (d) $4y + 12x = 5$
        $y = 3 - 2x$         $y - 2 = 2x$        $4y = 10x + 7$        $1 - 2y = 6x$

**3** Two of these pairs of simultaneous equations have no solution.
   (a) $5x + y = 6$      (b) $5x = 8 + y$      (c) $2y - 10x = 5$      (d) $y + 1 = -5x$
        $y - 5x = 2$         $y - 5x = 2$         $4y + 20x = 5$        $2y + 10x = 5$

   Use an appropriate method to find which ones.
   Use a graphical method to solve the other two.

## Using the elimination method to solve simultaneous equations

The graphical method of solving simultaneous equations can be quite time consuming.
Sometimes, due to the equations involved, the coordinates of the points where the lines intersect can be difficult to read accurately.
For these reasons, other methods of solving simultaneous equations are often used.

Consider again the simultaneous equations $x + 2y = 5$ and $x - 2y = 1$.
Both equations have the same number of $x$'s and the same number of $y$'s.
If the two equations are added together the $y$'s will be **eliminated** as shown.

$$x + 2y = 5$$
$$\underline{x - 2y = 1}$$

Adding gives $\quad 2x \quad = 6$

So, $\quad\quad x \quad = 3$

**Remember:** $+2y + -2y = 2y - 2y = 0$

By **substituting** the value of this letter ($x$) into one of the original equations we can find the value of the other letter ($y$).

$$x + 2y = 5$$
$$3 + 2y = 5$$
$$2y = 2$$
$$y = 1$$

This gives the solution $x = 3$ and $y = 1$.

**Remember:** If you do the same to both sides of an equation it is still true.

---

### EXAMPLES

**1** Use the elimination method to solve this pair of simultaneous equations: $\quad 2x - y = 1$
$\quad\quad\quad\quad\quad\quad\quad\quad\quad\quad\quad\quad\quad\quad\quad\quad\quad\quad\quad\quad\quad\quad\quad\quad\quad\quad\quad 3x + y = 9$

Each equation has the **same number** of $y$'s but the **signs** are **different**.
To eliminate the $y$'s the equations must be **added**.

$$5x = 10$$
$$x = 2$$

Substitute $x = 2$ into $3x + y = 9$.
$$3 \times 2 + y = 9$$
$$6 + y = 9$$
$$y = 3$$

The solution is $x = 2$ and $y = 3$.

**Check:**
Substitute $x = 2$ and $y = 3$ into $2x - y = 1$
$$2 \times 2 - 3 = 1$$
$$4 - 3 = 1$$
$$1 = 1$$
The equation is true, so, the solution
$x = 2$ and $y = 3$ is correct.

**2** Use the elimination method to solve this pair of simultaneous equations: $\quad 2x + 3y = 9$
$\quad\quad\quad\quad\quad\quad\quad\quad\quad\quad\quad\quad\quad\quad\quad\quad\quad\quad\quad\quad\quad\quad\quad\quad\quad\quad\quad 2x + y = 7$

Each equation has the **same number** of $x$'s and the **signs** are the **same**.
To eliminate the $x$'s one equation must be **subtracted** from the other.

Subtract $2x + y = 7$ from $2x + 3y = 9$.
$$2y = 2$$
$$y = 1$$

Substitute $y = 1$ into $2x + y = 7$.
$$2x + 1 = 7$$
$$2x = 6$$
$$x = 3$$

The solution is $x = 3$ and $y = 1$.

**Check:**
Substitute $x = 3$ and $y = 1$ into $2x + 3y = 9$.
*Do this and make sure the solution is correct.*

Use the elimination method to solve each of these pairs of simultaneous equations.

**1** $3x - y = 1$
$x + y = 3$

**2** $2x - y = 2$
$x + y = 7$

**3** $4x + y = 9$
$2x - y = 3$

**4** $-x + 2y = 13$
$x + y = 8$

**5** $2x + y = 7$
$x + y = 4$

**6** $3x + y = 9$
$2x + y = 7$

**7** $2x + y = 12$
$x + y = 7$

**8** $x + 5y = 14$
$x + 2y = 8$

**9** $x + 2y = 13$
$x + 4y = 21$

**10** $x + 4y = 11$
$x + y = 5$

**11** $2x + 5y = 13$
$2x + y = 9$

**12** $5x + 3y = 26$
$2x + 3y = 14$

**13** $5x + 4y = 22$
$5x + y = 13$

**14** $2x - y = 10$
$3x + y = 10$

**15** $5x - 2y = 13$
$3x + 2y = 3$

**16** $x + 5y = 14$
$-x + 2y = 7$

**17** $2x + 3y = 8$
$2x + y = -4$

**18** $2x + y = 4$
$4x - y = 11$

**19** $3x + 4y = -8$
$x + 4y = 4$

**20** $3x + 2y = 6$
$x - 2y = 6$

**21** $x - 3y = 8$
$x + 2y = -7$

**22** $2x - 2y = 9$
$4x - 2y = 16$

**23** $3x - y = 5$
$3x + y = 4$

**24** $5x - 3y = 5$
$5x + y = -5$

## Further use of the elimination method

Look at this pair of simultaneous equations:

$$5x + 2y = 11$$
$$3x - 4y = 4$$

$5x + 2y = 11$      Equation A
$3x - 4y = 4$      Equation B

> A useful technique is to use capital letters to label the equations.

These equations do not have the same number of $x$'s or the same number of $y$'s.

To make the number of $y$'s the same we can multiply equation A by 2.

A × 2 gives    $10x + 4y = 22$     Equation C
B × 1 gives      $3x - 4y = 4$     Equation D

C + D gives         $13x = 26$
                  $x = 2$

> The number of $y$'s in equations C and D is the **same** but the **signs** are **different**. To eliminate the $y$'s the equations must be **added**.

Substitute $x = 2$ into $5x + 2y = 11$.
$$5 \times 2 + 2y = 11$$
$$10 + 2y = 11$$
$$2y = 1$$
$$y = 0.5$$

The solution is $x = 2$ and $y = 0.5$.

> In this example eliminating the $y$'s rather than the $x$'s is less likely to produce an error.
> *Try to solve the equations by eliminating the $x$'s.*

*Check the solution by substituting $x = 2$ and $y = 0.5$ into $3x - 4y = 4$.*

## EXAMPLE

Solve this pair of simultaneous equations:

$$3x + 7y = -2$$
$$4x + 9 = -3y$$

Rearrange and label the equations.

$$3x + 7y = -2 \quad \text{A}$$
$$4x + 3y = -9 \quad \text{B}$$

○○○○○○○○○○○○○○○○○○○○

Both equations must be in the form $px + qy = r$ before the elimination method can be used. You may have to **rearrange** the equations you are given.

$4x + 9 = -3y$ can be rearranged as $4x + 3y = -9$.

These equations do not have the same number of $x$'s or the same number of $y$'s. So, the multiplying method can be used.

**Method 1**

Eliminating the $x$'s.

A × 4 gives $\quad 12x + 28y = -8 \quad$ C

B × 3 gives $\quad 12x + \phantom{2}9y = -27 \quad$ D

C − D gives $\qquad 19y = -8 - -27$
$$\qquad\qquad 19y = -8 + 27$$
$$\qquad\qquad 19y = 19$$
$$\qquad\qquad\quad y = 1$$

Substitute $y = 1$ into $3x + 7y = -2$.

$$3x + 7 \times 1 = -2$$
$$3x + 7 = -2$$
$$3x = -9$$
$$x = -3$$

The solution is $x = -3$ and $y = 1$.

**Method 2**

Eliminating the $y$'s.

A × 3 gives $\quad 9x + 21y = -6 \quad$ C

B × 7 gives $\quad 28x + 21y = -63 \quad$ D

D − C gives $\qquad 19x = -63 - -6$
$$\qquad\qquad 19x = -63 + 6$$
$$\qquad\qquad 19x = -57$$
$$\qquad\qquad\quad x = -3$$

Substitute $x = -3$ into $3x + 7y = -2$.

$$3 \times -3 + 7y = -2$$
$$-9 + 7y = -2$$
$$7y = 7$$
$$y = 1$$

*Check the solution by substituting $x = -3$ and $y = 1$ into $4x + 9 = -3y$.*

## Exercise 20.4

Solve each of these pairs of simultaneous equations.

**1** $\quad 3x + 2y = 8$
$\quad\phantom{3}2x - \phantom{2}y = 3$

**2** $\quad x + \phantom{3}y = 5$
$\quad 5x - 3y = 1$

**3** $\quad 2x + 3y = 9$
$\quad\phantom{2}x + 4y = 7$

**4** $\quad x + 3y = 10$
$\quad 2x + 5y = 18$

**5** $\quad 5x + 2y = 8$
$\quad 2x - \phantom{2}y = 5$

**6** $\quad 3x + \phantom{2}y = 9$
$\quad\phantom{3}x - 2y = 10$

**7** $\quad 3x - 4y = 10$
$\quad\phantom{3}x + 2y = 5$

**8** $\quad x + 6y = 0$
$\quad 3x - 2y = -10$

**9** $\quad 2x + 3y = 11$
$\quad 3x + \phantom{3}y = 13$

**10** $\quad 2x + \phantom{2}y = 10$
$\quad -x + 2y = 9$

**11** $\quad 2x + 3y = 9$
$\quad 4x - \phantom{3}y = 4$

**12** $\quad 2x + 3y = 8$
$\quad 3x + 2y = 7$

**13** $\quad 3x + 4y = 23$
$\quad 2x + 5y = 20$

**14** $\quad 2x - 3y = 8$
$\quad\phantom{2}x - 5y = 11$

**15** $\quad\phantom{-}3x + 4y = 5$
$\quad -2x + 5y = 12$

**16** $\quad 3x - 2y = 4$
$\quad\phantom{3}x + 4y = 6$

**17** $\quad -3x + 2y = 5$
$\quad\phantom{-}4x + 3y = -1$

**18** $\quad 3x + 4y = 6$
$\quad 3y = 7 - x$

**19** $\quad 5x + 3y = 16$
$\quad 2y = 13 - x$

**20** $\quad 5x - 4y = 24$
$\quad 2x = y + 9$

**21** $\quad 2x + 3y = 14$
$\quad 8x - 5y = 5$

**22** $\quad 4x - 7y = 15$
$\quad 5x - 12 = 2y$

**23** $\quad 8x + 3y = 2$
$\quad 5x = 1 - 2y$

**24** $\quad 9x = 4y - 20$
$\quad 5x = 6y - 13$

## Using the substitution method to solve simultaneous equations

For some pairs of simultaneous equations a method using **substitution** is sometimes more convenient.

### EXAMPLE

Solve this pair of simultaneous equations: $5x + y = 9$
$$y = 4x$$

$5x + y = 9$      Equation A
$\quad\quad y = 4x$      Equation B

Substitute $y = 4x$ into Equation A
$$5x + 4x = 9$$
$$9x = 9$$
$$x = 1$$

Substitute $x = 1$ into $y = 4x$.
$$y = 4 \times 1$$
$$y = 4$$

The solution is $x = 1$ and $y = 4$.

*Check the solution by substituting $x = 1$ and $y = 4$ into $5x + y = 9$.*

## Exercise 20.5

Use the substitution method to solve these pairs of simultaneous equations.

**1**   $2x + y = 10$
$\quad\quad\quad y = 3x$

**2**   $3x - y = 9$
$\quad\quad\quad y = 2x$

**3**   $x + 5y = 18$
$\quad\quad\quad x = 4y$

**4**   $x + 2y = 15$
$\quad\quad\quad y = 2x$

**5**   $2x + y = 17$
$\quad\quad\quad y = 6x + 1$

**6**   $3x + 2y = 4$
$\quad\quad\quad x = y - 2$

**7**   $5x + 6y = 34$
$\quad\quad\quad y = x + 2$

**8**   $5x - 2y = 23$
$\quad\quad\quad x = y + 1$

**9**   $5x - y = 12$
$\quad\quad\quad y = 32 - 6x$

**10**   $x + 5y = 13$
$\quad\quad\quad x = 3y + 9$

**11**   $5x - 3y = 26$
$\quad\quad\quad y = 2x + 14$

**12**   $x + 4y = 32$
$\quad\quad\quad x = 2y - 4$

## Solving problems using simultaneous equations

### EXAMPLE

Billy buys 5 first class stamps and 3 second class stamps at a cost of £2.13.
Jane buys 3 first class stamps and 5 second class stamps at a cost of £1.95.
Calculate the cost of a first class stamp and the cost of a second class stamp.

Let $x$ pence be the cost of a first class stamp, and let $y$ pence be the cost of a second class stamp.

Billy's purchase of the stamps gives this equation.   $5x + 3y = 213$     Equation A
Jane's purchase of the stamps gives this equation.   $3x + 5y = 195$     Equation B

This gives a pair of simultaneous equations which can be solved using the elimination method.
$$5x + 3y = 213 \quad\quad A$$
$$3x + 5y = 195 \quad\quad B$$

A × 5 gives $25x + 15y = 1065$    C
B × 3 gives $\quad 9x + 15y = 585$    D
C − D gives $16x = 480$
$$x = 30$$

Substitute $x = 30$ into $5x + 3y = 213$.
$$5 \times 30 + 3y = 213$$
$$3y = 63$$
$$y = 21$$

So, the cost of a first class stamp is 30 pence and the cost of a second class stamp is 21 pence.

*Check the solution by substituting the values for x and y into the original problem.*

**1** Pencils cost $x$ pence each and pens cost $y$ pence each.
Pam buys 6 pencils and 3 pens for 93 pence.
Ray buys 2 pencils and 5 pens for 91 pence.
(a) Write down two equations connecting $x$ and $y$.
(b) By solving these simultaneous equations find the cost of a pencil and the cost of a pen.

**2** Apples are $x$ pence per kg.
Oranges are $y$ pence each.
5 kg of apples and 30 oranges cost £9.00.
10 kg of apples and 15 oranges cost £12.60.
(a) Write down two equations connecting $x$ and $y$.
(b) By solving these simultaneous equations find the cost of a kilogram of apples and the cost of an orange.

**3** Standard eggs cost $x$ pence per dozen.
Small eggs cost $y$ pence per dozen.
10 dozen standard eggs and 5 dozen small eggs cost £13.60.
5 dozen standard eggs and 8 dozen small eggs cost £11.31.
By forming two simultaneous equations find the values of $x$ and $y$.

**4** A group of children and adults went on a coach trip to a theme park.
Ticket prices for the theme park were £20 for adults and £15 for children.
Ticket prices for the coach were £10 for adults and £6 for children.
The total cost of the tickets for the theme park was £560.
The total cost of the coach tickets was £232.
How many children and adults went on the trip?

**5** Jenny types at $x$ words per minute.
Stuart types at $y$ words per minute.
When Jenny and Stuart both type for 1 minute they type a total of 170 words.
When Jenny types for 5 minutes and Stuart types for 3 minutes they type a total of 710 words.
Calculate $x$ and $y$.

**6** At a café, John buys 3 coffees and 2 teas for £4.30 and Susan buys 2 coffees and 3 teas for £4.20.
Calculate the price of a coffee and the price of a tea.

**7** Standard coaches hold $x$ passengers and first class coaches hold $y$ passengers.
A train with 5 standard coaches and 2 first class coaches carries a total of 1040 passengers.
A train with 7 standard coaches and 3 first class coaches carries a total of 1480 passengers.
By forming two simultaneous equations find the values of $x$ and $y$.

**8** Nick writes a number in each of these boxes:   $x = \boxed{\phantom{0}}$    $y = \boxed{\phantom{0}}$
When he adds 5 to $x$ the result is 2 times $y$.
When he adds 17 to $y$ the result is 2 times $x$.
Find the two numbers.

**9** In a game you score $p$ points if you win and $q$ points if you lose.
Matt plays. He wins 2 games and loses 3 games. He scores 4 points.
Kath plays. She wins 3 games and loses 2 games. She scores 11 points.
By forming two simultaneous equations find the values of $p$ and $q$.

**10** A local pop band hold two gigs.
Tickets for the gigs cost £$x$ and CDs cost £$y$.
At the first gig they sell 92 tickets and 8 CDs for a total of £1186.
At the second gig they sell 104 tickets and 16 CDs for a total of £1372.
Find the cost of a ticket and the cost of a CD.

## Simultaneous equations in which one equation is linear and one is quadratic

### Using graphs

To solve a pair of simultaneous equations, where one is **linear** and one is **quadratic**, plot the graph of each equation on the same diagram.
The coordinates at the **points of intersection** give the solutions to the equations.

> **EXAMPLE**
>
> Solve the simultaneous equations $y = x + 2$ and $y = 4 - x^2$.
>
> Draw the graph of $y = x + 2$.
>
> Draw the graph of $y = 4 - x^2$.
>
>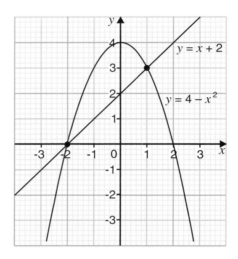
>
> The graphs intersect (cross) at the points $(-2, 0)$ and $(1, 3)$.
>
> This gives the solutions:
> $$x = -2, \quad y = 0$$
> **and** $\quad x = 1, \quad y = 3$.

### Exercise 20.7

Use a graphical method to solve each of these pairs of simultaneous equations.

**1** $y = x + 2$
$y = x^2$

**2** $y = 1 - x$
$y = x^2 - 1$

**3** $y = x - 3$
$y = 3x - x^2$

**4** $y = 2x - 3$
$y = x^2 - 3x + 3$

**5** $y = x$
$x^2 + y^2 = 8$

**6** $y - 2x = 0$
$x^2 + y^2 = 5$

### Using the method of substitution

In Exercise 20.5 we used the method of substitution to find the solutions of simultaneous equations where both equations were linear.
We can now use the same method to solve simultaneous equations where one is **linear** and one is **quadratic**.

**EXAMPLES**

 Solve the simultaneous equations $x - y = 2$ and $x^2 + 3y = 12$.

Rearrange the linear equation, $x - y = 2$, to make $y$ the subject of the equation.
$x - y = 2$
Add $y$ to both sides.
$x = 2 + y$
Subtract 2 from both sides.
$x - 2 = y$

Substitute $y = x - 2$ into the quadratic equation $x^2 + 3y = 12$.
$x^2 + 3(x - 2) = 12$
Simplify.
$x^2 + 3x - 6 = 12$
$x^2 + 3x - 18 = 0$

Solve the quadratic equation for $x$.
$$(x + 6)(x - 3) = 0$$
$x + 6 = 0$ or $x - 3 = 0$
$x = -6$ or $x = 3$.

Using $x - y = 2$.
When $\quad x = -6$.
$\quad -6 - y = 2$
$\quad\quad y = -8$
When $\quad x = 3$.
$\quad 3 - y = 2$
$\quad\quad y = 1$

This gives the solutions: $x = -6$, $y = -8$ **and** $x = 3$, $y = 1$.

 Solve the simultaneous equations $y = x - 2$ and $x^2 + y^2 = 10$.

Substitute $y = x - 2$ into $x^2 + y^2 = 10$.
$\quad x^2 + (x - 2)^2 = 10$
$x^2 + x^2 - 4x + 4 = 10$
$\quad 2x^2 - 4x - 6 = 0$
Divide both sides by 2.
$x^2 - 2x - 3 = 0$

$(x + 1)(x - 3) = 0$
$x = -1$ or $x = 3$.

Using $y = x - 2$.
When $x = -1$.
$\quad y = -1 - 2$
$\quad y = -3$
When $x = 3$.
$\quad y = 3 - 2$
$\quad y = 1$

This gives the solutions: $x = -1$, $y = -3$ **and** $x = 3$, $y = 1$.

*Simultaneous Equations*

Use the method of substitution to solve each of these pairs of simultaneous equations.

**1**
$$x = 3$$
$$x^2 + y^2 = 13$$

**2**
$$y = 6$$
$$3x^2 = 2y$$

**3**
$$y = x + 1$$
$$y = x^2 + x$$

**4**
$$y = x^2 + 2$$
$$y + 3x = 0$$

**5**
$$y = 5x$$
$$y = x^2 - x + 5$$

**6**
$$x^2 + y^2 = 18$$
$$x + y = 0$$

**7**
$$x^2 + y^2 = 20$$
$$x = 2y$$

**8**
$$y = \frac{4}{x}$$
$$y = 5 - x$$

**9**
$$xy = 5$$
$$y = 2x + 3$$

**10**
$$2x^2 - y = 5$$
$$x + y = 1$$

**11**
$$5x^2 - xy = 6$$
$$y - 2x = 3$$

**12**
$$3x^2 = y$$
$$y - 2 = 5x$$

**13**
$$y = 2x$$
$$y^2 + 7x = 2$$

**14**
$$y + 2 = 11x$$
$$y = 5x^2$$

**15**
$$x^2 + y^2 = 13$$
$$2x + y = 1$$

**16**
$$4y + x = 3$$
$$x + \frac{2}{y} = 1$$

**17**
$$xy + 2x^2 = 5$$
$$x + 2y = 1$$

**18**
$$2x^2 + 3xy - y^2 = 2$$
$$x - 2 = y$$

## What you need to know

- A pair of **simultaneous equations** are linked equations with the same unknown letters in each equation.
- To solve a pair of simultaneous equations find values for the unknown letters that fit **both** equations.
- Simultaneous equations can be solved either **graphically** or **algebraically**.
- Solving simultaneous equations **graphically** involves:
    drawing the graphs of both equations, finding the point(s) where the graphs cross.
  When the graphs of the equations are parallel, the equations have no solution.
- Solving simultaneous equations **algebraically** involves using either:
    the **elimination** method   or   the **substitution** method.

## Review Exercise 20

**1** (a) Copy and complete the table of values for   (i)  $y = 3x - 2$  and  (ii)  $y = 3 - x$.

(i)

| x | 0 | 1 | 2 |
|---|---|---|---|
| y |   |   |   |

(ii)

| x | 0 | 1 | 3 |
|---|---|---|---|
| y |   |   |   |

Draw the lines   $y = 3x - 2$   and   $y = 3 - x$   on the same grid.
(b) Hence, solve the simultaneous equations   $y = 3x - 2$   and   $y = 3 - x$. OCR

**2** The diagram shows the graph of the line   $3y = 6 - 2x$.
Copy the diagram.
(a) On the same axes draw the graph of   $y = x - 1$.
(b) Use the graphs to solve the simultaneous
equations:   $3y = 6 - 2x$
$$y = x - 1$$

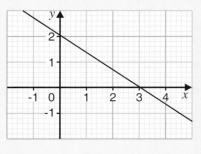

**3** Use a graphical method to solve the
simultaneous equations:   $y - 2x = -1$   and   $x + 2y = 4$.

**4** Use an algebraic method to solve these simultaneous equations:   $2x + y = 8$
$$x + y = 5$$

**5** Solve these simultaneous equations. $4x + y = 14$
$2x + y = 8$

OCR

**6** Solve each of these simultaneous equations.
(a)  $2x + 3y = 11$      (b)  $4x + y = 6$      (c)  $x - y = -3$      (d)  $x + 2y = 9$
  $2x + y = 5$         $2x - y = 6$         $x + 4y = 7$         $5x - 2y = 3$

**7** Solve these simultaneous equations. $2x + y = 14$
$3x + 2y = 22$

OCR

**8** Solve these simultaneous equations. $3x + y = 9$
$4x - 2y = 2$

OCR

**9** Solve these simultaneous equations. $4x + 3y = 6$
$3x - 2y = 13$

OCR

**10** (a) Show that the simultaneous equations $y = 2x - 2$ and $2y - 4x = 3$
have no solution.
(b) Show that the simultaneous equations $4y = x + 1$ and $8y - 2x = 3$
have no solution.
(c) The simultaneous equations $y = 3x + 2$ and $y = ax + b$ have no solution.
What can you say about the values of $a$ and $b$?
(d) The simultaneous equations $y = 3x + 2$ and $py + qx = r$ have no solution.
Find some possible values for $p$, $q$ and $r$.

**11** The equation of the straight line passing through the points (3, 2) and (9, 11)
is given by $px + qy = 5$.
(a) Explain why $3p + 2q = 5$.
(b) Write down another equation in terms of $p$ and $q$.
(c) Solve these to find the value of $p$ and the value of $q$.

OCR

**12** The diagram shows a window formed from
rectangular sections.
The window is 185 cm long and 105 cm high.
(a) Write down a pair of equations in terms of $x$ and $y$.
(b) Solve, algebraically, these simultaneous equations.

OCR

**13** Peaches cost $x$ pence each and oranges cost $y$ pence each.
4 peaches and one orange cost 58p. 6 peaches and 2 oranges cost 92p.
(a) Write down two equations connecting $x$ and $y$.
(b) Solve these simultaneous equations to find the values of $x$ and $y$.

**14** David collected 1p and 2p coins in a jar.
There are 374 coins in the jar. The coins have a total value of £5.02.
Use algebra to find how many 1p and 2p coins there are in the jar.

OCR

**15** Use a graphical method to solve the simultaneous equations: $2y + x = 4$ and $2y = x^2$.

**16** Use an algebraic method to solve the simultaneous equations: $3x + y = 17$ and $xy = 20$.

**17** Solve the simultaneous equations: $2x + y = 7$ and $x^2 + y^2 = 13$.

**18** Solve the simultaneous equations: $4y = 5x + 3$ and $y = 6 - x^2$.

**19** Solve, algebraically. $x^2 + y^2 = 34$
$y = x + 8$

OCR

**20** The graphs of $x^2 + y^2 = 25$ and $y = 7 - x$ intersect at points $P$ and $Q$.
Find the coordinates of $P$ and $Q$.

# Algebraic Methods

When solving problems or simplifying expressions it is necessary to be able to manipulate algebra.

## Simplifying expressions

### EXAMPLES

**1** Expand and simplify $(2x + 1)^2 - (x - 2)^2$.

$(2x + 1)^2 - (x - 2)^2$

Expand the brackets.

$= 4x^2 + 4x + 1 - (x^2 - 4x + 4)$

The second bracket was expanded and kept within a bracket because of the minus sign.

Remove the bracket.

$= 4x^2 + 4x + 1 - x^2 + 4x - 4$

Simplify.

$= 3x^2 + 8x - 3$

> The effect of a minus sign in front of a bracket is to change **all** signs inside the bracket.
> *Explain why.*

**2** Expand and simplify $(x + 2y)^2 + (2x - y)^2$.

$= x^2 + 4xy + 4y^2 + 4x^2 - 4xy + y^2$

$= 5x^2 + 5y^2$

$= 5(x^2 + y^2)$     (In factorised form.)

## Identities

A house has a front and a back garden.
The front garden consists of a square flower bed, 3 m by 3 m, surrounded by a path, $x$ m wide.
The back garden consists of a rectangular lawn, 9 m by 5 m, surrounded by a path, $x$ m wide.
Show that the total area of both gardens is given by: $2(4x^2 + 20x + 27)$.

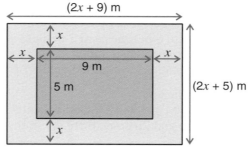

> **Sketch diagrams** are drawn to help write expressions for the total length and total width of each garden.
> *Explain how each expression is obtained.*

The area of the front garden is $(2x + 3)^2$.
The area of the back garden is $(2x + 9)(2x + 5)$.
The total area $= (2x + 3)^2 + (2x + 9)(2x + 5)$

$= (2x + 3)(2x + 3) + (2x + 9)(2x + 5)$

$= 4x^2 + 6x + 6x + 9 + 4x^2 + 10x + 18x + 45$

$= 8x^2 + 40x + 54$

$= 2(4x^2 + 20x + 27)$

This has shown that $(2x + 3)^2 + (2x + 9)(2x + 5) = 2(4x^2 + 20x + 27)$.
Although this looks like an equation it is called an **identity** because it is true for all values of $x$.
An identity is the same expression written in another form.

## EXAMPLES

**1** Show that $(x - 5)(x + 4) + (x - 3)(x - 2) = 2(x^2 - 3x - 7)$.

LHS $= (x - 5)(x + 4) + (x - 3)(x - 2)$
Expand the brackets.
$= x^2 + 4x - 5x - 20 + x^2 - 2x - 3x + 6$
Simplify.
$= 2x^2 - 6x - 14$
Factorise. Common factor 2.
$= 2(x^2 - 3x - 7)$
$=$ RHS

**Abbreviations:**
LHS = left-hand side
RHS = right-hand side

To show that an identity is true, either: start with the LHS and show that it is equal to the RHS, or start with the RHS and show that it is equal to the LHS.

LHS = RHS, so, $(x - 5)(x + 4) + (x - 3)(x - 2) = 2(x^2 - 3x - 7)$.

**2** Show that $(x + y)^2 - (x - y)^2 = 4xy$.

LHS $= (x + y)^2 - (x - y)^2$
$= x^2 + 2xy + y^2 - (x^2 - 2xy + y^2)$
$= x^2 + 2xy + y^2 - x^2 + 2xy - y^2$
$= 4xy$
$=$ RHS

LHS = RHS, so, $(x + y)^2 - (x - y)^2 = 4xy$.

## Exercise 21.1

**1** Expand and simplify.
(a) $(x + 5)(x + 2) + (x - 4)(x - 6)$
(b) $(4x + 1)(x - 1) - (x + 2)(x - 3)$
(c) $(x - 5)(x - 5) - (x - 4)(x - 6)$
(d) $(2x + 3)(3x + 4) - (4x - 5)(5x - 6)$

**2** Expand and simplify.
(a) $3(2x + 3y - 4z) - 4(3x - 5y + 3z)$
(b) $4(3x - 6y + 9z) - 3(4x - 8y + 12z)$
(c) $(x + 3y)^2 + (3x + y)^2$
(d) $(2x + 3y)^2 + (3x + 2y)^2$

**3** Show that:
(a) $(x + 2)(x + 4) + (x - 3)(x - 4) = 2x^2 - x + 20$
(b) $(3x - 1)(x + 1) + (x + 4)(2x + 1) = 5x^2 + 11x + 3$
(c) $(x + 5)(x - 6) - (x - 4)(x - 3) = 6(x - 7)$
(d) $(2x + 1)(3x - 4) - (6x + 5)(x - 3) = 8x + 11$

**4** Show that:
(a) $4(2x + 3y) - 2(3x - 4y) = 2(10y + x)$
(b) $3(s + 2t) + 2(3s + t) = 9s + 8t$
(c) $(x + y)^2 + (x - y)^2 = 2(x^2 + y^2)$
(d) $(x + 3y)^2 - (3x + y)^2 = 8(y + x)(y - x)$

**5** Prove these identities.
(a) $(x + ay)^2 + (ax - y)^2 = (a^2 + 1)(x^2 + y^2)$
(b) $(x + ay)^2 - (ax + y)^2 = (a^2 - 1)(y^2 - x^2)$
(c) $(ax + by)^2 + (bx - ay)^2 = (a^2 + b^2)(x^2 + y^2)$

## Algebraic fractions

**Algebraic fractions** have a numerator and a denominator (just as an ordinary fraction) but at least one of them is an expression involving an unknown.

e.g. $\dfrac{1}{x}$ $\qquad$ $\dfrac{x}{2}$ $\qquad$ $\dfrac{2}{x-5}$ $\qquad$ $\dfrac{x+1}{x-6}$ $\qquad$ $\dfrac{3}{x+7}$ $\qquad$ $\dfrac{x^2+2x+1}{x^2-1}$

Algebraic fractions can be simplified, added, subtracted, multiplied, divided and used in equations in the same way as numerical fractions.

## Simplifying algebraic fractions

Fractions can be simplified if the numerator and the denominator have a common factor.
In its **simplest form**, the numerator and denominator of an algebraic fraction have no common factor other than 1.

The numerator and denominator of $\frac{15}{25}$ have a highest common factor of 5.

$$\frac{15}{25} = \frac{15 \div 5}{25 \div 5} = \frac{3}{5}$$

3 and 5 have no common factors, other than 1.

$$\frac{15}{25} = \frac{3}{5} \text{ in its simplest form.}$$

Algebraic fractions work in a similar way.

To write an algebraic fraction in its simplest form:
● factorise the numerator and denominator of the fraction,
● divide the numerator and denominator by their highest common factor.
This is sometimes called **cancelling** a fraction.

### EXAMPLES

Write the following in their simplest form.

**1** $\quad \dfrac{3x-6}{3} = \dfrac{3(x-2)}{3} = x-2$

**2** $\quad \dfrac{3x+9}{4x^2+12x} = \dfrac{3(x+3)}{4x(x+3)} = \dfrac{3}{4x}$

**3** $\quad \dfrac{x^2y+3xy^2}{xy-2x^2y^2} = \dfrac{xy(x+3y)}{xy(1-2xy)} = \dfrac{x+3y}{1-2xy}$

**4** $\quad \dfrac{x^2+5x+6}{x^2-2x-8} = \dfrac{(x+2)(x+3)}{(x+2)(x-4)} = \dfrac{x+3}{x-4}$

**5** $\quad \dfrac{x^2+2x+1}{x^2-1} = \dfrac{(x+1)^2}{(x+1)(x-1)} = \dfrac{x+1}{x-1}$

**6** $\quad \dfrac{9-3y}{y-3} = \dfrac{3(3-y)}{y-3} = \dfrac{-3(y-3)}{y-3} = -3$

## Exercise 21.2

**1** Simplify these algebraic fractions.

(a) $\dfrac{4d+6}{2}$

(b) $\dfrac{9x+6}{3}$

(c) $\dfrac{8a+10b}{2}$

(d) $\dfrac{15m-10n}{5}$

(e) $\dfrac{8x-4y}{2}$

(f) $\dfrac{ax+bx}{x}$

(g) $\dfrac{x^2-x}{x}$

(h) $\dfrac{2x^2-4}{2}$

(i) $\dfrac{12}{3x-9}$

(j) $\dfrac{5x+10}{15}$

(k) $\dfrac{2x+4y+6z}{4x-6y+2z}$

(l) $\dfrac{-2x-4}{-6x-4}$

(m) $\dfrac{2x}{6x-4}$

(n) $\dfrac{3x}{6x^2-3}$

(o) $\dfrac{3x}{6x^2-3x}$

(p) $\dfrac{2x-1}{6x^2-3x}$

(q) $\dfrac{3m-6}{2m-4}$

(r) $\dfrac{m^2+3m}{3m+9}$

(s) $\dfrac{x^2-3x}{x^2+2x}$

(t) $\dfrac{5x-10}{6-3x}$

**2** Match the algebraic fractions with the values **A** to **E**.

(a) $\dfrac{3x + 6}{4x + 8}$     (b) $\dfrac{5x - 15}{2x - 6}$     (c) $\dfrac{8 - 4y}{6 - 3y}$     (d) $\dfrac{8x + 10}{4x + 5}$

(e) $\dfrac{-2x - 4}{-4x - 8}$     **A** $2$    **B** $\dfrac{4}{3}$    **C** $2\dfrac{1}{2}$    **D** $\dfrac{1}{2}$    **E** $\dfrac{3}{4}$

**3** Simplify these algebraic fractions.

(a) $\dfrac{x^2y + 5xy^2}{3xy + 4x^2y^2}$     (b) $\dfrac{x^2 + xy + 2xz}{2x^2 - 3xy + xz}$     (c) $\dfrac{a^2b^2 - 3ab}{ab^2 + a^2b}$     (d) $\dfrac{ax + ab + ay}{a^2b - 2ay}$

**4** Simplify these algebraic fractions.

(a) $\dfrac{x^2 + 3x}{x^2 + 4x + 3}$     (b) $\dfrac{x^2 + 3x + 2}{x^2 + 4x + 3}$     (c) $\dfrac{x^2 - 2x}{x^2 + x - 6}$

(d) $\dfrac{x^2 - x - 20}{x^2 + 7x + 12}$     (e) $\dfrac{x^2 - 4x + 4}{x^2 - 5x + 6}$     (f) $\dfrac{x^2 - 5x}{x^2 + 4x}$

(g) $\dfrac{x^2 - 1}{x + 1}$     (h) $\dfrac{x - 2}{x^2 - 4}$     (i) $\dfrac{x^2 - 2x - 3}{2x - 6}$

(j) $\dfrac{2x^2 - 2x - 12}{2x^2 - 18}$     (k) $\dfrac{2x^2 - 7x - 15}{2x^2 - 5x - 12}$     (l) $\dfrac{6x^2 - 13x - 5}{9x^2 - 1}$

## Arithmetic of algebraic fractions

The same methods used for adding, subtracting, multiplying and dividing numeric fractions can be applied to algebraic fractions.

### Multiplication

Numeric

$$\frac{8}{9} \times \frac{3}{14} = \frac{\cancel{2} \times 4}{3 \times \cancel{3}} \times \frac{\cancel{3}}{\cancel{2} \times 7} = \frac{4}{21}$$

Algebraic

$$\frac{2x + 2}{5x - 15} \times \frac{3x - 9}{4x + 4} = \frac{\cancel{2}(x + 1)}{5\cancel{(x - 3)}} \times \frac{3\cancel{(x - 3)}}{\cancel{4}(x + 1)} = \frac{3}{10}$$

### Division

Numeric

$$\frac{3}{7} \div \frac{9}{14} = \frac{3}{7} \times \frac{14}{9}$$

$$= \frac{\cancel{3}}{7} \times \frac{2 \times \cancel{7}}{3 \times \cancel{3}}$$

$$= \frac{2}{3}$$

Algebraic

$$\frac{7x - 7}{3x} \div \frac{4 - 4x}{x} = \frac{7x - 7}{3x} \times \frac{x}{4 - 4x}$$

$$= \frac{7\cancel{(x - 1)}}{3\cancel{x}} \times \frac{\cancel{x}}{-4\cancel{(x - 1)}}$$

$$= -\frac{7}{12}$$

### Addition

Numeric

$$\frac{4}{11} + \frac{2}{5} = \frac{4 \times 5 + 2 \times 11}{11 \times 5}$$

$$= \frac{42}{55}$$

Algebraic

$$\frac{4}{x - 3} + \frac{2}{x + 2} = \frac{4(x + 2) + 2(x - 3)}{(x - 3)(x + 2)}$$

$$= \frac{6x + 2}{(x - 3)(x + 2)}$$

### Subtraction

Numeric

$$\frac{4}{7} - \frac{2}{5} = \frac{4 \times 5 - 2 \times 7}{7 \times 5}$$

$$= \frac{6}{35}$$

Algebraic

$$\frac{4}{x - 3} - \frac{2}{2x + 1} = \frac{4(2x + 1) - 2(x - 3)}{(x - 3)(2x + 1)}$$

$$= \frac{8x + 4 - 2x + 6}{(x - 3)(2x + 1)}$$

$$= \frac{6x + 10}{(x - 3)(2x + 1)}$$

$$= \frac{2(3x + 5)}{(x - 3)(2x + 1)}$$

## EXAMPLE

Simplify  $\dfrac{x}{x-1} + \dfrac{2-x}{x+2}$

$$\dfrac{x}{x-1} + \dfrac{2-x}{x+2} = \dfrac{x(x+2) + (2-x)(x-1)}{(x-1)(x+2)}$$

$$= \dfrac{x^2 + 2x + 2x - 2 - x^2 + x}{(x-1)(x+2)}$$

$$= \dfrac{5x - 2}{(x-1)(x+2)}$$

It is common practice to leave the denominators of algebraic fractions in their factorised forms.

## Exercise 21.3

**1**  Simplify.

(a)  $\dfrac{4x-2}{15-3x} \times \dfrac{5-x}{2x-1}$

(b)  $\dfrac{5+5y}{y-3} \times \dfrac{6-2y}{8y+8}$

(c)  $\dfrac{7}{y} \times \dfrac{y^2}{14}$

**2**  Simplify.

(a)  $\dfrac{4x-2}{15-3x} \div \dfrac{2x-1}{5-x}$

(b)  $\dfrac{4+y}{7-y} \div \dfrac{2y+8}{y-7}$

(c)  $\dfrac{10-2x}{x^2} \div \dfrac{x-5}{x}$

**3**  Simplify.

(a)  $\dfrac{3}{x+5} + \dfrac{4}{x-4}$

(b)  $\dfrac{5}{2x+3} + \dfrac{6}{5x-3}$

(c)  $\dfrac{x+4}{x+2} + \dfrac{2x-1}{x-3}$

**4**  Simplify.

(a)  $\dfrac{4}{x+5} - \dfrac{3}{x-4}$

(b)  $\dfrac{5}{2x+3} - \dfrac{6}{5x-3}$

(c)  $\dfrac{2x-1}{x-3} - \dfrac{x+4}{x+2}$

**5**  If  $\mathbf{p} = \dfrac{2}{x}$,  $\mathbf{q} = \dfrac{3}{2x-6}$  and  $\mathbf{r} = \dfrac{x-3}{2x}$,  calculate

(a)  $\mathbf{p} + \mathbf{q}$      (b)  $\mathbf{p} - \mathbf{r}$      (c)  $\mathbf{q} + \mathbf{r}$      (d)  $\mathbf{p} \div \mathbf{r}$      (e)  $\mathbf{q} \times \mathbf{r}$      (f)  $\mathbf{r} \div \mathbf{p}$

## Solving equations involving algebraic fractions

### EXAMPLE

**1**  Solve the equation  $\dfrac{7}{x} + \dfrac{6}{x+5} = 2$.

$$\dfrac{7}{x} + \dfrac{6}{x+5} = 2$$

Multiply throughout by  $x(x+5)$.

$$\dfrac{7}{x} \times x(x+5) + \dfrac{6}{(x+5)} \times x(x+5) = 2 \times x(x+5)$$

$$7(x+5) + 6x = 2x(x+5)$$
$$7x + 35 + 6x = 2x^2 + 10x$$
$$13x + 35 = 2x^2 + 10x$$
$$2x^2 - 3x - 35 = 0$$

Solve the quadratic equation.

$$(2x+7)(x-5) = 0$$

Either  $2x + 7 = 0$     or  $x - 5 = 0$

$$x = -3\tfrac{1}{2} \quad \text{or} \quad x = 5$$

Solution:  $x = -3\tfrac{1}{2}$  or  5

The final answers can always be checked by substituting the solutions, in turn, into the original equation.

$$\dfrac{7}{x} + \dfrac{6}{x+5} = 2$$

Substitute  $x = -3\tfrac{1}{2}$

*Does*  $\dfrac{7}{-3\tfrac{1}{2}} + \dfrac{6}{-3\tfrac{1}{2} + 5} = 2$ ?

*Check the solution*  $x = 5$.

### EXAMPLE

**2** Henry took part in a sponsored walk between Aylestone and Bedrock.
He walked from Aylestone to Bedrock, a distance of 12 km, at a steady speed of $x$ km/h.
His average speed for the return part of the walk was 2 km/h slower.

(a) Write down, in terms of $x$, the time taken for the whole journey.

(b) Henry walked for a total of $3\frac{1}{2}$ hours.
Write an equation in $x$.
Show that the equation can be written as
$7x^2 - 62x + 48 = 0$.

(c) What was Henry's speed from Aylestone to Bedrock?

Sometimes, questions are set in the form of a problem. Use the information given in the question to **form an equation.**

**Solve** the equation.

**Analyse** the solutions to answer the original problem.

(a) Using Time = Distance ÷ Speed

Total time $= \dfrac{12}{x} + \dfrac{12}{x-2}$

(b) $\dfrac{12}{x} + \dfrac{12}{x-2} = 3\frac{1}{2}$

Add the algebraic fractions. $\qquad\qquad \dfrac{12(x-2) + 12x}{x(x-2)} = 3\frac{1}{2}$

Multiply both sides by $x(x-2)$. $\qquad 12x - 24 + 12x = 3\frac{1}{2}\,x(x-2)$

Simplify the left-hand side. $\qquad\qquad 24x - 24 = 3\frac{1}{2}\,x(x-2)$

Multiply both sides by 2. $\qquad\qquad 48x - 48 = 7x(x-2)$

Expand the right-hand side. $\qquad\qquad 48x - 48 = 7x^2 - 14x$

Rearrange into the form $ax^2 + bx + c = 0$. $\quad 7x^2 - 62x + 48 = 0$

(c) $7x^2 - 62x + 48 = 0$

$(7x - 6)(x - 8) = 0$

Either $7x - 6 = 0$ or $x - 8 = 0$

$\qquad\quad 7x = 6$ or $\qquad x = 8$

$\qquad\quad x = \frac{6}{7}$

The value of $\frac{6}{7}$ is a possible solution to the equation **but** it gives a negative speed for the return journey.
So, the solution which fits the problem is $x = 8$.
Henry's speed for the first part of the journey is 8 km/h.

## Exercise 21.4

**1** Solve the equation $\dfrac{4}{3x-1} - \dfrac{2}{x} = 1$.

**2** (a) Show that the equation $\dfrac{12}{x-3} + \dfrac{7}{x+1} = 5$ can be rearranged to give the
equation $5x^2 - 29x - 6 = 0$.

(b) Solve $5x^2 - 29x - 6 = 0$ to find solutions for $x$.

**3** (a) Show that the equation $\dfrac{6}{x+1} - \dfrac{5}{x+2} = 2$ can be rearranged to give the
equation $2x^2 + 5x - 3 = 0$.

(b) Hence, solve the equation $\dfrac{6}{x+1} - \dfrac{5}{x+2} = 2$.

**4** Solve these equations, giving answers correct to 3 significant figures where necessary.

(a) $\dfrac{5}{x+1} + \dfrac{9}{x+2} = 8$ $\qquad\qquad$ (b) $\dfrac{8}{x+4} - \dfrac{4}{x-2} = 5$

(c) $\dfrac{5}{2x+1} + \dfrac{4}{x+1} = 3$ $\qquad\qquad$ (d) $\dfrac{10}{x-1} + \dfrac{12}{x+2} = 3\frac{1}{2}$

**5** A motorist completes a 75 mile journey on country lanes at an average speed of $v$ miles per hour.

(a) Write an expression, in terms of $v$, for the time taken in hours.

On his return journey the motorist uses the motorway and completes the 75 mile journey at an average speed of 5 miles per hour faster.

(b) Write an expression, in terms of $v$, for the time taken on his return journey in hours.

His return journey took 10 minutes less to complete.

(c) By forming an equation calculate his average speed on country lanes.

**6** A car travels 60 km at a speed of $x$ km/h.
It then travels a further 90 km at a speed 6 km/h faster.

The whole journey takes $5\frac{1}{2}$ hours.

(a) Form an equation involving $x$.

(b) Show that this equation can be written as $11x^2 - 234x - 720 = 0$.

(c) Solve this equation to find the speed, $x$.

## Iteration

The solutions to a variety of equations can be found using a process called iteration.

The process of iteration has three stages.

**1** Rearranging an equation to form an **iterative formula**. Sometimes the formula is given.

**2** Choosing a **starting value**, $x_1$. Sometimes the starting value is given.

**3** **Substituting** the value of $x_1$ into the iterative formula.
This produces a value called $x_2$ which is then substituted into the iterative formula.
Substituting a value for $x_n$ produces the next value to be used, $x_{n+1}$.
The process is continued, producing values $x_3$, $x_4$, ... until the required degree of accuracy is obtained.

### EXAMPLE

Find a solution to the equation $x^2 - 5x + 3 = 0$, correct to 3 significant figures, using **iteration**.

Use $x_1 = 4$ as a starting value.

$$x^2 - 5x + 3 = 0$$
$$x^2 = 5x - 3$$

Take the square root of both sides. $\quad x = \sqrt{5x - 3}$

Write the iterative formula. $\quad x_{n+1} = \sqrt{5x_n - 3}$

To form an iterative formula, rearrange the equation so that one side has the variable on its own, e.g. '$x = ...$'

$x_1 = 4$ (this was given)

$x_2 = \sqrt{5 \times 4 - 3} \qquad = 4.1231...$

$x_3 = \sqrt{5 \times 4.1231... - 3} = 4.1970...$

$x_4 = \sqrt{5 \times 4.1970... - 3} = 4.2409...$

$x_5 = \sqrt{5 \times 4.2409... - 3} = 4.2666...$

$x_6 = \sqrt{5 \times 4.2666... - 3} = 4.2817...$

$x_7 = \sqrt{5 \times 4.2817... - 3} = 4.2905...$

$x_8 = \sqrt{5 \times 4.2905... - 3} = 4.2956...$

$x_9 = \sqrt{5 \times 4.2956... - 3} = 4.2986...$

$x_{10} = \sqrt{5 \times 4.2986... - 3} = 4.3003...$

The efficient use of the memory facilities of a calculator can help to reduce greatly the time taken to perform lengthy calculations.

At this stage the answer is not changing from 4.30 (correct to 3 sig. figs.).

**1** (a) Show how the equation $x^2 - 5x + 3 = 0$ can be rearranged to give:

$x = \dfrac{5x - 3}{x}$ and hence, the iterative formula $x_{n+1} = \dfrac{5x_n - 3}{x_n}$.

(b) Starting with the value $x = 4$ find a solution to the equation using iteration, correct to 3 significant figures. Show all calculations.

(c) A solution to the equation $x^2 - 5x + 3 = 0$ was found in the example using a different iterative formula. Compare the two iterative processes.

**2** (a) Show how the equation $6x^2 - 7x - 2 = 0$ can be rearranged to give:

$x = \sqrt{\dfrac{7x + 2}{6}}$ and hence, the iterative formula $x_{n+1} = \sqrt{\dfrac{7x_n + 2}{6}}$.

(b) Starting with the value $x_1 = 1$ find a solution to the equation using iteration, correct to 3 significant figures. Show all calculations.

(c) Show how this equation can also be rearranged to give: $x = \dfrac{7x + 2}{6x}$

and hence, the iterative formula $x_{n+1} = \dfrac{7x_n + 2}{6x_n}$.

Use a starting value of $x_1 = 1$ and this formula.
Which is the more efficient iterative formula?

**3** When finding a solution to $x^2 + 7x - 10 = 0$ the following iterative formula is used:
$x_{n+1} = \sqrt{10 - 7x_n}$. The starting value $x_1 = 1$ is used. What happens?

**4** Use iteration to find a solution to the equation $x^2 - x - 5 = 0$.
Show your iterative formula and use $x_1 = 3$ as a starting point.
Give your answer correct to two decimal places.

**5** Find a solution to the equation $x^2 + 7x = 100$ (correct to 3 sig. figs.) by using iteration.
Show your rearrangement giving an iterative formula and a good starting value.

**6** Find a solution to the equation $x^2 + 3x - 8 = 0$ by using iteration.
Give your answer to an appropriate degree of accuracy.

## Trial and improvement

Some equations cannot be solved directly.
Numerical solutions can be found by making a guess and improving the accuracy of the guess by **trial and improvement**.
This can be a time-consuming method of solving equations and is often used only as a last resort for solving equations which cannot be easily solved by algebraic or graphical methods.

A solution to the equation
$x^3 - 4x = 7$ lies between 2 and 3.
Find this solution to 1 decimal place.

Because the solution lies between 2 and 3, notice that:

when $x = 2$ $2^3 - 4(2) = 0$ Answer is less than 7.
when $x = 3$ $3^3 - 4(3) = 15$ Answer is greater than 7.

We are trying to find a value for $x$ which produces the answer 7.

First guess: $x = 2.5$ $2.5^3 - 4(2.5) = 5.625$ Too small.
Second guess: $x = 2.6$ $2.6^3 - 4(2.6) = 7.176$ Too big.

The solution lies between 2.5 and 2.6, but 2.6 gives an answer closer to 7.
The answer is probably 2.6, correct to 1 d.p.
To be certain, try $x = 2.55$. $2.55^3 - 4(2.55) = 6.381375$ Too small.

The solution lies between 2.55 and 2.6.
2.6 is the solution, correct to 1 d.p.

**1** Use trial and improvement to solve $x^3 = 54$, correct to one decimal place.
The working can be shown in a table.

| $x$ | $x^3$ | |
|---|---|---|
| 3 | 27 | Too small |
| 4 | 64 | Too big |
| 3.5 | | |

**2** Use trial and improvement to solve these equations. Show all your trials in a table.
(a) $w^3 = 72$       (b) $4x^3 = 51$

**3** A solution to the equation $x^3 + 2x = 40$ lies between 3 and 4.
Use trial and improvement to find this solution to 1 decimal place.

| $x$ | $x^3 + 2x$ | |
|---|---|---|
| 3 | 33 | Too small |
| 3.5 | 49.875 | Too big |

**4** A solution to the equation $x^3 + 5x = 880$ lies between 9 and 10.
Use trial and improvement to find this solution to 1 decimal place. Show your trials.

**5** Show that a solution to $x^3 - 5x^2 = 47$ lies between 6 and 7.
Use trial and improvement to find this solution, showing your trials,
(a) to 1 decimal place,     (b) to 2 decimal places.

**6** This cuboid has dimensions: $x$, $x + 2$ and $2x$.
(a) Write down an expression, in terms of $x$,
for the volume of the cuboid.
(b) The volume of the cuboid is $400\,cm^3$.
Form an equation and use trial and improvement
to find $x$, correct to 1 d.p.

**7** A solution to $x^4 + 5x - 20 = 0$ lies between 1 and 2.
Use trial and improvement to find this solution correct to 2 decimal places. Show your trials.

## What you need to know

- An **identity** is true for all values of $x$. An identity is the same expression written in another form.
  For example: $(2x + 3)^2 + (2x + 9)(2x + 5) = 2(4x^2 + 20x + 27)$.
  To show that an identity is true, either:
  - start with the LHS and show that it is equal to the RHS, or
  - start with the RHS and show that it is equal to the LHS.
- **Algebraic fractions** have a numerator and a denominator (just as an ordinary fraction) but at least one of them is an expression involving an unknown.
- To write an algebraic fraction in its **simplest form**:
  - factorise the numerator and denominator of the fraction,
  - divide the numerator and denominator by their highest common factor.
- The same methods used for adding, subtracting, multiplying and dividing numeric fractions can be applied to algebraic fractions.
- The solutions to a variety of equations can be found using a process called **iteration**.
  The process of iteration has three stages.
  1 Rearranging an equation to form an **iterative formula**.
  2 Choosing a **starting value**, $x_1$.
  3 **Substituting** the starting value, and then values of $x_n$ into the iterative formula.
    Continuing the process until the required degree of accuracy is obtained.
- **Trial and improvement** is a method used to solve equations. The accuracy of the value of the unknown letter is improved until the required degree of accuracy is obtained.

**1**  (a)  Factorise  (i)  $x^2 - 9$,        (ii)  $2x^2 - 5x - 3$.

   (b)  Hence, simplify  $\dfrac{x^2 - 9}{2x^2 - 5x - 3}$.

**2**  Simplify.  $\dfrac{x^2 + 3x}{x^2 + 2x - 3}$        OCR

**3**  Show that the equation  $\dfrac{2}{x + 1} + \dfrac{1}{x - 3} = 1$  can be written in the form  $x^2 - 5x + 2 = 0$.

**4**  Simplify.  $\dfrac{n + 4}{5n - 1} - \dfrac{4}{4n - 1}$        OCR

**5**  Prove that  $\dfrac{n + 2}{n} - \dfrac{n}{n - 1} = \dfrac{n - 2}{n(n - 1)}$.        OCR

**6**  Sachin cycled from his home town to Blackpool and back.
He cycled to Blackpool at an average speed of $x$ km/h.
He returned at an average speed of 5 km/h slower than on the outward journey.
The distance from his home town to Blackpool is 48 km.
The total journey took him 8 hours.
   (a)  Write down an equation in $x$ and show that it simplifies to  $\dfrac{6}{x} + \dfrac{6}{x - 5} = 1$.
   (b)  Find the solutions to the equation in part (a).
   (c)  Hence, find Sachin's average speed for the journey from Blackpool to his home.        OCR

**7**  A company was contracted to make 840 vans in 90 days.
After they made 540, the manager worked out the average production per day.
He worked out that, if they could increase this average by 1 van per day, they could
fulfil the contract in exactly 90 days.
Let the average for the first 540 be $x$ vans per day.
   (a)  Write down an equation in $x$ and show that it simplifies to  $\dfrac{18}{x} + \dfrac{10}{x + 1} = 3$.
   (b)  Use algebra to solve the equation.
      Hence, find the average production for the first 540 vans.        OCR

**8**  Solve the equation  $\dfrac{4}{(x + 1)} + \dfrac{3}{(x - 1)} = 1$.        OCR

**9**  (a)  Simplify the following expression.  $\dfrac{x^2 + x - 2}{x^2 - 4}$
   (b)  Solve.  $\dfrac{2x + 1}{x - 1} = \dfrac{7x + 3}{4x - 3}$        OCR

**10**  The equation  $x^3 - 5x = 50$  has a solution between 4 and 5.
Use trial and improvement to find the solution correct to 1 decimal place.
Show your trials.        OCR

**11**  Use a trial and improvement method to find the value of $x$ correct to one decimal place
when  $x^3 + x^2 = 30$.
Show clearly your trials and their outcomes.        OCR

**12**  The length of a rectangular carpet is 2 metres more than its width. Its area is 27 m².

To find the width, $x$, this iterative formula is used.  $x_{n+1} = \dfrac{27}{x_n + 2}$

Starting with  $x = 4$,  find the width, $x$, correct to one decimal place.

**13**  Solve the equation  $\dfrac{3}{x + 1} + \dfrac{1}{2x - 1} = 2$.

**14**  Solve the equation  $\dfrac{1}{2 - x} - \dfrac{1}{3} = x$.  Give your answers correct to two decimal places.

**15**  Solve the equation  $\dfrac{5}{2x - 1} + \dfrac{6}{x + 1} = 3$.  Give your answer correct to 2 decimal places.        OCR

# Transforming Graphs

**Transformations,** such as **translations** and **stretches,** can be used to change the position and size of a graph.

The equation of the transformed (new) graph is related to the equation of the original graph.

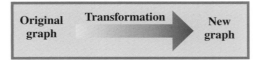

## Translating a graph

The graph of $y = x^2$ is transformed to the graph of $y = x^2 + 2$ by a **translation.**

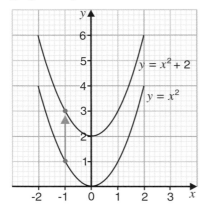

All points on the original graph are moved the **same distance** in the **same direction** without twisting or turning.

The translation has vector $\begin{pmatrix} 0 \\ 2 \end{pmatrix}$.

This means that the curve moves 2 units vertically up.

**Original graph:** $y = x^2$

**Transformation:** translation with vector $\begin{pmatrix} 0 \\ 2 \end{pmatrix}$.

**New graph:** $y = x^2 + 2$

---

*Draw the following graphs:*

$$y = x^2 \qquad \text{for} \quad -2 \leqslant x \leqslant 2,$$
$$y = x^2 - 3 \quad \text{for} \quad -2 \leqslant x \leqslant 2.$$

*Describe how the graph of $y = x^2$ is transformed to the graph of $y = x^2 - 3$.*

---

The graph of $y = x^2$ is transformed to the graph of $y = (x + 3)^2$ by a **translation.**

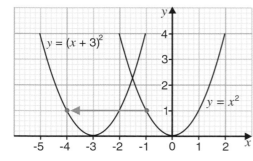

The translation has vector $\begin{pmatrix} -3 \\ 0 \end{pmatrix}$.

This means that the curve moves 3 units horizontally to the left.

**Original graph:** $y = x^2$

**Transformation:** translation with vector $\begin{pmatrix} -3 \\ 0 \end{pmatrix}$.

**New graph:** $y = (x + 3)^2$

---

*Draw the following graphs:*

$$y = x^2 \qquad \text{for} \quad -2 \leqslant x \leqslant 2,$$
$$y = (x - 2)^2 \quad \text{for} \quad 0 \leqslant x \leqslant 4.$$

*Describe how the graph of $y = x^2$ is transformed to the graph of $y = (x - 2)^2$.*

## Stretching a graph

The graph of $y = x^2$ is transformed to the graph of $y = 2x^2$ by a **stretch**.

The stretch is **from** the $x$ axis and is **parallel** to the $y$ axis.
The stretch has scale factor 2.

This means that $y$ coordinates on the graph of $y = x^2$ are doubled to obtain the corresponding $y$ coordinates on the graph of $y = 2x^2$.

**Original graph:** $y = x^2$

**Transformation:** stretch from $x$ axis, parallel to $y$ axis, scale factor 2.

**New graph:** $y = 2x^2$

> *Draw the following graphs:*
>
> $$y = x^2 \quad for \quad -2 \leqslant x \leqslant 2,$$
> $$y = 3x^2 \quad for \quad -2 \leqslant x \leqslant 2.$$
>
> *Describe how the graph of $y = x^2$ is transformed to the graph of $y = 3x^2$.*

The graph of $y = x^2$ is transformed to the graph of $y = (2x)^2$ by a **stretch**.

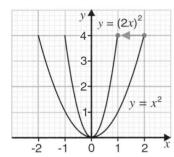

The stretch is **from** the $y$ axis and is **parallel** to the $x$ axis.
The stretch has scale factor $\frac{1}{2}$.

This means that $x$ coordinates on the graph of $y = x^2$ are halved to obtain the corresponding $x$ coordinates on the graph of $y = (2x)^2$.

**Original graph:** $y = x^2$

**Transformation:** stretch from $y$ axis, parallel to $x$ axis, scale factor $\frac{1}{2}$.

**New graph:** $y = (2x)^2$

> *Draw the following graphs:*
>
> $$y = x^2 \quad for \quad -2 \leqslant x \leqslant 2,$$
> $$y = (4x)^2 \quad for \quad -0.5 \leqslant x \leqslant 0.5.$$
>
> *Describe how the graph of $y = x^2$ is transformed to the graph of $y = (4x)^2$.*

**In general**

| Original graph | New graph | Transformation |
|---|---|---|
| $y = x^2$ | $y = x^2 + a$ | **translation**, vector $\begin{pmatrix} 0 \\ a \end{pmatrix}$. |
| $y = x^2$ | $y = (x + a)^2$ | **translation**, vector $\begin{pmatrix} -a \\ 0 \end{pmatrix}$. |
| $y = x^2$ | $y = ax^2$ | **stretch**, from the $x$ axis, parallel to the $y$ axis, scale factor $a$. |
| $y = x^2$ | $y = (ax)^2$ | **stretch**, from the $y$ axis, parallel to the $x$ axis, scale factor $\frac{1}{a}$. |

The general rules for translating and stretching the graph of $y = x^2$ apply to **all** graphs.

You may find it helpful to use a graphical calculator.

**1** (a) Complete tables of values for:
  (i)   $y = x^3$ for $-2 \le x \le 2$,   (ii)  $y = x^3 + 2$ for $-2 \le x \le 2$,
  (iii) $y = (x - 3)^3$ for $1 \le x \le 5$,   (iv) $y = 2x^3$ for $-2 \le x \le 2$.

  (b) Use your tables of values to draw graphs of each of the equations in (a).

  (c) Describe how the graph of $y = x^3$ is transformed to:
  (i)   the graph of $y = x^3 + 2$,   (ii)  the graph of $y = (x - 3)^3$,
  (iii) the graph of $y = 2x^3$.

  (d) Write down the equations of the graphs obtained when the graph of
  $y = x^3$ is transformed by:
  (i)   a translation with vector $\begin{pmatrix} 0 \\ -5 \end{pmatrix}$,

  (ii)  a translation with vector $\begin{pmatrix} 2 \\ 0 \end{pmatrix}$.

**2** In this diagram, each of the graphs labelled **a**, **b**, **c** and **d** is a transformation of the graph $y = x^2$.

What are the equations of graphs **a**, **b**, **c** and **d**?

**3** In this diagram, each of the graphs **a**, **b** and **c** is a stretch of the graph of $y = x^2$.

What are the equations of graphs **a**, **b** and **c**?

**4** The graph of $y = 4 - x^2$ for $-2 \le x \le 2$ is transformed by:

  (a) a translation of $\begin{pmatrix} 0 \\ 5 \end{pmatrix}$,

  (b) a stretch from the $x$ axis, parallel to the $y$ axis, with scale factor 2,
  (c) a stretch from the $y$ axis, parallel to the $x$ axis, with scale factor 2.
  In each case draw the original graph and its transformation.
  Write down the equation of each transformed graph.

**5** The graph of $y = x^2 - x$ for $-2 \le x \le 2$ is transformed by:

  (a) a translation of (i) $\begin{pmatrix} 0 \\ -5 \end{pmatrix}$, (ii) $\begin{pmatrix} 3 \\ 0 \end{pmatrix}$.

  (b) a stretch from the $x$ axis, parallel to the $y$ axis, with scale factor $\frac{1}{2}$.

  (c) a stretch from the $y$ axis, parallel to the $x$ axis, with scale factor 2.
  In each case write down the equation of the transformed graph.
  Check each equation by drawing its graph.

## Function notation

**Function notation** is an alternative way of expressing the relationship between two variables.

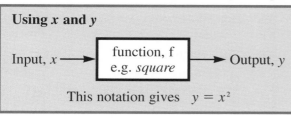

**Using $x$ and $y$**

Input, $x$ ⟶ | function, f e.g. *square* | ⟶ Output, $y$

This notation gives $y = x^2$

**Using function notation**

Input, $x$ ⟶ | function, f e.g. *square* | ⟶ Output, $f(x)$

This notation gives $f(x) = x^2$

$f(x)$ means 'a function of $x$'.
In general, $y = f(x)$.
For example:
The equation $y = x^5$ can be expressed in function notation as $f(x) = x^5$, where $y = f(x)$.

Letters other than f can be used.
For example:
The equation $y = \dfrac{1}{x^2 + 1}$ can be expressed in function notation as $g(x) = \dfrac{1}{x^2 + 1}$, where $y = g(x)$.

### EXAMPLES

**1** The function f is defined as $f(x) = x^2$.
Describe how each of the following graphs are related to the graph of $y = f(x)$.

(a) $y = f(x) + 2$
(b) $y = f(2x)$

(a) Because, $f(x) = x^2$, $y = f(x) + 2$ is equivalent to $y = x^2 + 2$.
So, the graph of $y = f(x)$ is transformed to the graph of $y = f(x) + 2$ by:
a **translation** with vector $\begin{pmatrix} 0 \\ 2 \end{pmatrix}$.

$f(x) = x^2$
Substitute $(2x)$ for $x$.
$f(2x) = (2x)^2$

(b) $y = f(2x)$ is equivalent to $y = (2x)^2$.
So, the graph of $y = f(x)$ is transformed to the graph of $y = f(2x)$ by:
a **stretch** from the $y$ axis, parallel to the $x$ axis, scale factor $\frac{1}{2}$.

**2** The diagram shows the graph of $y = f(x)$.

On separate diagrams show the graphs of:
(a) $y = f(x)$ and $y = f(x + 3)$,
(b) $y = f(x)$ and $y = 2f(x)$.

(a)

(b)

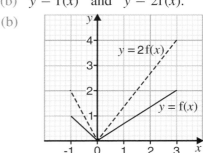

**In general**

| Original | New graph | Transformation | Note |
|---|---|---|---|
| $y = f(x)$ | $y = f(x) + a$ | **translation**, vector $\begin{pmatrix} 0 \\ a \end{pmatrix}$. | If $a$ is **positive**, curve moves $a$ units **up**.<br>If $a$ is **negative**, curve moves $a$ units **down**. |
| $y = f(x)$ | $y = f(x + a)$ | **translation**, vector $\begin{pmatrix} -a \\ 0 \end{pmatrix}$. | If $a$ is **positive**, curve moves $a$ units **left**.<br>If $a$ is **negative**, curve moves $a$ units **right**. |
| $y = f(x)$ | $y = af(x)$ | **stretch**, from the $x$ axis, parallel to the $y$ axis, scale factor $a$. | The $y$ coordinates on the graph of $y = f(x)$ are **multiplied** by $a$. |
| $y = f(x)$ | $y = f(ax)$ | **stretch**, from the $y$ axis, parallel to the $x$ axis, scale factor $\frac{1}{a}$. | The $x$ coordinates on the graph of $y = f(x)$ are **divided** by $a$. |

## Reflecting a graph

The diagram shows the graphs of $y = f(x)$ and $y = -f(x)$.

The graph of $y = f(x)$ is transformed to the graph of $y = -f(x)$ by:
a **stretch** from the $x$ axis, parallel to the $y$ axis, scale factor $-1$.
This transformation is equivalent to a **reflection** in the $x$ axis.

The diagram shows the graphs of $y = f(x)$ and $y = f(-x)$.

The graph of $y = f(x)$ is transformed to the graph of $y = f(-x)$ by:
a **stretch** from the $y$ axis, parallel to the $x$ axis, scale factor $-1$.
This transformation is equivalent to a **reflection** in the $y$ axis.

### EXAMPLE

**1** The graph of the function f, where
$f(x) = x^3 + 2$, is shown together
with the graphs of two related functions g and h.
Find equations for $g(x)$ and $h(x)$.

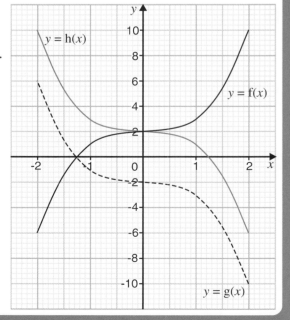

The graph of $y = g(x)$ is a reflection of the
graph of $y = f(x)$ in the $x$ axis.
This means that $g(x) = -f(x)$
So, $g(x) = -(x^3 + 2)$
So, $g(x) = -x^3 - 2$

The graph of $y = h(x)$ is a reflection of the
graph of $y = f(x)$ in the $y$ axis.
This means that $h(x) = f(-x)$
So, $h(x) = (-x)^3 + 2$
So, $h(x) = -x^3 + 2$

**EXAMPLE**

② The diagram shows the graphs of $y = \sin x$ and two related functions **a** and **b**. Find equations for the functions **a** and **b**.

The graph of $y = \sin x$ is transformed to the graph of function **a** by: a **stretch** from the $x$ axis, parallel to the $y$ axis, scale factor 2. So, the equation of function **a** is $y = 2\sin x$.

The graph of function **a** is transformed to the graph of function **b** by: a **translation** with vector $\begin{pmatrix} 0 \\ 1 \end{pmatrix}$. So, the equation of function **b** is $y = 2\sin x + 1$.

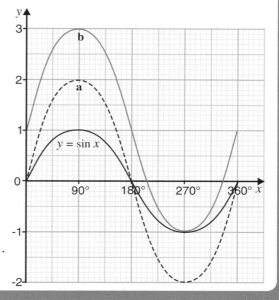

## Exercise 22.2

① Given that $f(x) = x^2$, sketch on separate diagrams the graphs of
  (a) $y = -f(x)$,  (b) $y = f(2 - x)$,  (c) $y = f(x) - 2$,  (d) $y = f(2x)$,  (e) $y = 2f(x)$.

② The diagram shows the graph of the function $y = f(x)$.

  (a) Copy the diagram, drawing axes marked from $-4$ to $4$ for $x$ and $y$.
      Draw the graph of the function $y = f(x) + 2$.
  (b) Describe fully how the graph of $y = f(x)$ is transformed to the graph of $y = f(x) + 2$.
  (c) Repeat parts (a) and (b) for each of these functions:
      (i)   $y = f(x) - 1$          (ii)   $y = f(x - 3)$        (iii)  $y = f(x + 2)$
      (iv)  $y = 0.5f(x)$          (v)    $y = 2f(x)$           (vi)   $y = f(0.5x)$
      (vii) $y = f(2x)$            (viii) $y = -f(x)$           (ix)   $y = f(-x)$
      (x)   $y = f(2x) + 1$        (xi)   $y = 2f(x + 1)$       (xii)  $y = 1 - f(x)$

③ The graph of $y = f(x)$ is shown.
  On separate diagrams sketch:

  (a) $y = f(x)$ and $y = f(x) + 2$

  (b) $y = f(x)$ and $y = f(x + 2)$

  (c) $y = f(x)$ and $y = 2f(x)$

  (d) $y = f(x)$ and $y = f\left(\frac{x}{2}\right)$

  (e) $y = f(x)$ and $y = -f(x)$

**4** The graph shows $y = h(x)$.
On separate diagrams sketch:

(a) $y = h(x) + 1$

(b) $y = h(x - 90)$

(c) $y = h(2x)$

(d) $y = 2h(x)$

(e) $y = -h(x)$

**5** The graph of the function $y = f(x)$ is transformed to each of the graphs **a**, **b** and **c**. Find, in terms of $f(x)$, equations for the graphs **a**, **b** and **c**.

**6** The diagram shows a sketch of $y = \sin x$ and three related functions.

(a) Describe how the graph of $y = \sin x$ is transformed to
  (i) the graph of function **a**,
  (ii) the graph of function **b**.

(b) Describe how the graph of function **b** is transformed to the graph of function **c**.

(c) Describe how the graph of $y = \sin x$ is transformed to the graph of function **c**, by using a combination of **two** transformations.

(d) What are the equations of the graphs **a**, **b** and **c**?

**7** The diagram shows the graphs of the functions $y = f(x)$, $y = g(x)$ and $y = h(x)$. Express $g(x)$ and $h(x)$ in terms of $f(x)$.

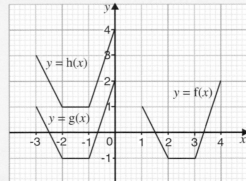

## Using graphs to find relationships

Graphs can be used to help find the relationship between two variables.
This is particularly useful when looking for rules to fit the results of scientific experiments.

### Linear functions

Linear functions have straight line graphs.
Straight line graphs have equations of the form $y = mx + c$, where $m$ is the gradient and $c$ is the $y$-intercept.

### EXAMPLE

The table shows the speed, $v$ (m/s), of a vehicle at various times, $t$ (sec), after it starts to decelerate.

| $t$ (sec) | 10 | 20 | 30 | 40 | 50 |
|-----------|----|----|----|----|----|
| $v$ (m/s) | 35 | 27 | 19 | 11 | 3 |

(a) Find an equation connecting $v$ and $t$.
(b) Use your equation to find:
  (i) $v$ when $t = 25$,
  (ii) $t$ when $v = 0$.

(a) **Step 1**

Plot the data and draw a line of best fit, by eye, to show the relationship between the variables speed and time.

**Step 2**

Find the equation of the line.
The equation is of the form
$v = mt + c$.
Find the gradient, $m$.
Draw a suitable right-angled triangle.
$m = \dfrac{-16}{20} = -0.8$

Find the intercept, $c$.
The line passes through the point $(0, 43)$.
$c = 43$.

The line slopes "downhill" so the gradient is negative.

**Step 3**

Substitute values for $m$ and $c$ into $v = mt + c$.
$m = -0.8$ and $c = 43$.
So, the equation connecting $v$ and $t$ is: $v = -0.8t + 43$.

(b) (i) Using $v = -0.8t + 43$.
  When $t = 25$.
   $v = -0.8 \times 25 + 43$
   $v = 23$
 (ii) Using $v = -0.8t + 43$.
  When $v = 0$.
   $0 = -0.8t + 43$
   $0.8t = 43$
  Divide both sides by 0.8.
   $t = 53.75$

## Non-linear functions

This section looks at **non-linear functions** of the form $y = ax^n + b$.

**To find the values of $a$ and $b$:**

1. Write $y = ax^n + b$ as the **linear function** $y = az + b$, by substituting $z = x^n$.

2. Draw the graph of $y$ against $z$.

3. Use the graph to find:
   the gradient, $a$,
   the $y$-intercept, $b$.

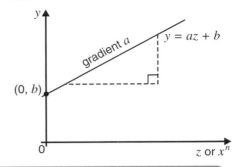

---

### EXAMPLE

The table shows values of $x$ and $y$ which are connected by an equation of the form $y = ax^2 + b$.
Find the values of $a$ and $b$.

| $x$ | 0 | 0.5 | 1 | 1.5 | 2 |
|---|---|---|---|---|---|
| $y$ | $-4$ | $-3.25$ | $-1$ | 2.75 | 8 |

Substituting $z = x^2$ in $y = ax^2 + b$ gives the linear function $y = az + b$.
So, draw the graph of $y$ against $z$.
Since $z = x^2$, values of $z$ are found by squaring the given values of $x$ in the table.

This table shows the values of $z$ and $y$.

| $z(=x^2)$ | 0 | 0.25 | 1 | 2.25 | 4 |
|---|---|---|---|---|---|
| $y$ | $-4$ | $-3.25$ | $-1$ | 2.75 | 8 |

The graph has gradient 3 and $y$-intercept $-4$.
So, $a = 3$ and $b = -4$.

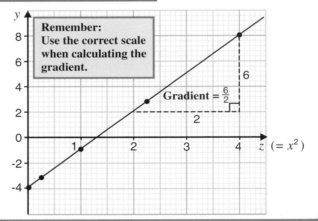

Remember:
Use the correct scale when calculating the gradient.

Gradient $= \frac{6}{2}$

---

### Exercise 22.3

**1** These tables show the data collected in two experiments.

| $x$ | 0.4 | 0.8 | 1.2 | 1.6 | 2 |
|---|---|---|---|---|---|
| $y$ | 24.2 | 35.4 | 46.6 | 57.8 | 69.0 |

| $p$ | 0.4 | 0.8 | 1.2 | 1.6 | 2 |
|---|---|---|---|---|---|
| $q$ | 35.2 | 30.1 | 24.9 | 19.8 | 14.1 |

(a) In each case assume that the variables are connected by a linear function and use a graphical method to find its equation.

(b) Use your equations to find:    (i) $y$ when $x = 2.7$,    (ii) $p$ when $q = 7.6$.

**2** In an experiment, Kym hangs weights, $w$ grams, on the end of a spring and measures its length, $l$ centimetres.
This graph shows Kym's results.

(a) Find an equation expressing $l$ in terms of $w$.
(b) Use your equation to find:
   (i) $l$ when $w = 500$,
   (ii) $w$ when $l = 55$.

**3** Two variables, $x$ and $y$, are connected by the equation $y = ax^2 + b$.
Some pairs of values of $x$ and $y$ are shown in the table.

| $x$ | 2 | 4 | 6 | 8 | 10 |
|---|---|---|---|---|---|
| $y$ | 2.8 | 4 | 6 | 8.8 | 12.4 |

By drawing an appropriate graph find the values of $a$ and $b$.

**4** A vehicle starts from rest and accelerates with a constant acceleration of $a$ m/s$^2$.
The formula $s = at^2$ gives the distance travelled, $s$ metres, after time, $t$ seconds.
The table shows pairs of values of $s$ and $t$.

| $t$ | 2 | 4 | 6 | 8 | 10 |
|---|---|---|---|---|---|
| $s$ | 8.4 | 33.6 | 75.6 | 134.4 | 210 |

Use a graphical method to find the acceleration.

**5** Wyn and Les perform an experiment. The results are shown in the table.

| $x$ | 0.4 | 0.8 | 1.2 | 1.6 | 2 |
|---|---|---|---|---|---|
| $y$ | 24.3 | 35.5 | 65.9 | 125.1 | 222.7 |

Wyn thinks that $x$ and $y$ are connected by a rule of the form $y = ax^2 + b$.
Les thinks the rule is of the form $y = ax^3 + b$.

Wyn uses the substitution $u = x^2$.

| $u(=x^2)$ | 0.16 | 0.64 | 1.44 | 2.56 | 4 |
|---|---|---|---|---|---|
| $y$ | 24.3 | 35.5 | 65.9 | 125.1 | 222.7 |

Les uses the substitution $v = x^3$.

| $v(=x^3)$ | 0.064 | 0.512 | 1.728 | 4.096 | 8 |
|---|---|---|---|---|---|
| $y$ | 24.3 | 35.5 | 65.9 | 125.1 | 222.7 |

(a) Draw the graph of $y$ against $u$ and, if possible, use it to find the values of $a$ and $b$.

(b) Draw the graph of $v$ against $y$ and, if possible, use it to find the values of $a$ and $b$.

**6** Two variables, $x$ and $y$, are connected by the equation $y = ax^3 + b$.
Some pairs of values of $x$ and $y$ are shown in the table.

| $x$ | 2 | 4 | 6 | 8 | 10 |
|---|---|---|---|---|---|
| $y$ | 2.8 | 6.0 | 13.2 | 28.0 | 52.4 |

By drawing an appropriate graph find the values of $a$ and $b$.

# What you need to know

- **Function notation** is a way of expressing a relationship between two variables.
  For example

  Input, $x$ ⟶ | function, f
  e.g. *cube* | ⟶ Output, f($x$)

  This notation gives $f(x) = x^3$

  f($x$) means 'a function of $x$'.
  In the example above, $f(x) = x^3$ is equivalent to the equation $y = x^3$ where $y = f(x)$.

- **Transformations,** such as **translations** and **stretches**, can be used to change the position and size of a graph.
  The equation of the transformed (new) graph is related to the equation of the original graph.

**In general**

| Original | New graph | Transformation | Note |
|---|---|---|---|
| $y = f(x)$ | $y = f(x) + a$ | **translation**, vector $\begin{pmatrix} 0 \\ a \end{pmatrix}$. | If $a$ is **positive**, curve moves $a$ units **up**. If $a$ is **negative**, curve moves $a$ units **down**. |
| $y = f(x)$ | $y = f(x + a)$ | **translation**, vector $\begin{pmatrix} -a \\ 0 \end{pmatrix}$. | If $a$ is **positive**, curve moves $a$ units **left**. If $a$ is **negative**, curve moves $a$ units **right**. |
| $y = f(x)$ | $y = af(x)$ | **stretch**, from the $x$ axis, parallel to the $y$ axis, scale factor $a$. | The $y$ coordinates on the graph of $y = f(x)$ are **multiplied** by $a$. |
| $y = f(x)$ | $y = f(ax)$ | **stretch**, from the $y$ axis, parallel to the $x$ axis, scale factor $\frac{1}{a}$. | The $x$ coordinates on the graph of $y = f(x)$ are **divided** by $a$. |
| $y = f(x)$ | $y = -f(x)$ | **reflection** in the $x$ axis. | The $y$ coordinates on the graph of $y = f(x)$ **change signs**. |
| $y = f(x)$ | $y = f(-x)$ | **reflection** in the $y$ axis. | The $x$ coordinates on the graph of $y = f(x)$ **change signs**. |

- **Finding relationships between variables**:
  **Linear functions** have straight line graphs, such as $y = ax + b$.
  From the graph of **$y$ against $x$**, the gradient $= a$ and the $y$-intercept $= b$.

  **Non-linear functions**, such as $y = ax^n + b$, can be written as the linear function $y = az + b$ by substituting $z = x^n$.
  From the graph of **$y$ against $x^n$**, the gradient $= a$ and the $y$-intercept $= b$.

## Review Exercise 22

**1** The graph of $y = \sin x$ is shown.
Sketch the graphs of
   (a) $y = 2\sin x$,
   (b) $y = \sin x + 2$,
   (c) $y = \sin 2x$,
   (d) $y = -\sin x$.

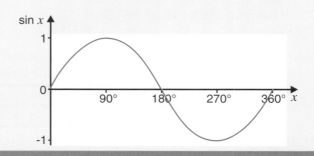

**2** A sketch of the function $y = f(x)$ is shown.

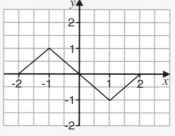

(a) On separate diagrams sketch
   (i) $y = -f(x)$,
   (ii) $y = 2f(x)$,
   (iii) $y = f(x - 2)$.

(b) Which one of these sketches is of the form $y = f(x) + a$, where $a$ is a constant? What is the value of $a$?

**P**

**Q**

**R**

**3** The diagram shows the graph of the function $y = f(x)$. Sketch graphs of each of the following functions.

(a) $y = f(x) - 3$

(b) $y = f(x + 2)$

OCR

**4**

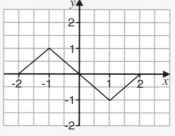

Graph **A** has equation $y = f(x)$. Write down the equations of

(a) graph **P**,

(b) graph **Q**,

(c) graph **R**.

OCR

**5** The values of $x$ and $y$ given in the table were obtained from an experiment.

| $x$ | 1.0 | 1.6 | 2.0 | 2.8 | 3.2 | 4.0 |
|-----|-----|-----|-----|-----|-----|-----|
| $y$ | 1.7 | 2.5 | 3.2 | 5.1 | 6.3 | 9.2 |

It is known that these values obey the rule $y = px^2 + q$, where $p$ and $q$ are constants. Plot the graph of $y$ against $x^2$, and use your graph to estimate the values of $p$ and $q$.

**6** In an experiment, it is thought that $x$ and $y$ are connected by a formula of the type $y = \dfrac{a}{x} + b$. Some values of $x$ and $y$ are given in the following table.

| $x$ | 2 | 4 | 6 | 8 | 10 |
|-----|----|----|----|----|----|
| $y$ | 33 | 18 | 14 | 11 | 9 |

By drawing a suitable graph, find the values of $a$ and $b$.

OCR

**Transforming Graphs**

Do not use a calculator for this exercise.

**1** Write each of the following expressions in its simplest form.
   (a) $f + g + f + f + g$   (b) $y \times t \times 3$   (c) $r \times r$   OCR

**2** (a) What is the value of $2xy$ when $x = 3$ and $y = 4$?
   (b) Work out the value of $ab + c$ when $a = 3$, $b = -2$ and $c = 5$.

**3** (a) Solve. (i) $a + 5 = 3$ (ii) $12 - b = 7$ (iii) $4c - 3 = 19$ (iv) $5d - 2 = 5 - 4d$
   (b) Multiply out $-4(f - 3)$.   OCR

**4** Mrs Crawley drove from her home to the supermarket, did her shopping and then returned home. The distance-time graph shows her journey.

   (a) At what time did Mrs Crawley leave home?
   (b) How far is the supermarket from Mrs Crawley's home?
   (c) How many minutes did Mrs Crawley spend at the supermarket?
   (d) Work out Mrs Crawley's average speed on her journey home?
       Give your answer in kilometres per hour.

**5** Multiply out the brackets and simplify. $3(4x + 1) + 2(2x - 1)$   OCR

**6** (a) Using the values $u = 4$, $v = -3$ and $w = 5$, work out: (i) $u^2 + v^2$  (ii) $\dfrac{uv}{2w}$
   (b) Multiply out the brackets. (i) $7(3x + 2y)$   (ii) $a(a - 3)$
   (c) Factorise. (i) $4a + 2b$   (ii) $3t - t^2$

**7** (a) Buns cost $x$ pence each. How much will 2 buns cost?
   (b) A doughnut costs 5 pence more than a bun. How much will 3 doughnuts cost?
   (c) The cost of buying 2 buns and 3 doughnuts is 95 pence.
       By forming an equation find the cost of a bun.

**8** (a) Draw the graph of $y + 2x = 5$ for values of $x$ from $-1$ to 4.
   (b) Use your graph to find the value of $x$ when $y = -2$.

**9** (a) Solve the equations (i) $3t - 1 = 17$,   (ii) $3(x - 2) = 27$.
   (b) These are the first 5 terms of a sequence. 3, 4, 5, 6, 7, ...
       Write down the $n$th term of the sequence.   OCR

**10** (a) Simplify. (i) $4(x - 3) - 2(x + 1)$   (ii) $\dfrac{y^3 \times y^2}{y}$
   (b) Solve the equation $3(z - 2) = 18$.   OCR

**11** Solve the equations. (a) $\dfrac{12}{x} = 2$   (b) $\dfrac{12}{\sqrt{x}} = 2$   OCR

**12** (a) Solve the inequality $3x - 5 < 7$.
(b) An equality is shown on the number line.

Write down the inequality.

**13** Expand the brackets and simplify $(x + 4)(x + 1)$.  OCR

**14** (a) Copy and complete the table of values for the curve $y = x^2 - 10$.

| $x$ | $-4$ | $-3$ | $-2$ | $-1$ | 0 | 1 | 2 | 3 | 4 |
|-----|------|------|------|------|---|---|---|---|---|
| $y$ | 6 | $-1$ | | | | $-9$ | $-6$ | $-1$ | |

(b) Draw the graph of $y = x^2 - 10$.
(c) Use your graph to find the values of $x$ for which $x^2 - 10 = 0$.  OCR

**15** A sequence begins $7, \ 4, \ 1, \ -2, \ \ldots$
What is (a) the next term in the sequence, (b) the $n$th term of the sequence?

**16** (a) Solve the equation $4(x + 3) = 22 + x$
(b) (i) Write down the integer values of $n$ for which $2 < 5n \leqslant 12$.
  (ii) Solve the inequality $5x + 3 \geqslant 4$.
(c) Solve the simultaneous equations: $3x + y = 13$
  $2x - y = 7$

**17** (a) Use the formula $y = mx + c$ to find the value of $y$
  when $m = 2$, $x = -3$ and $c = 11$.
(b) Rearrange the formula $y = mx + c$ to make $x$ the subject.  OCR

**18** A delivery driver has this table to work out how much a job costs.

| Number of hours | 1 | 2 | 3 | 4 | 5 |
|-----------------|---|---|---|---|---|
| Cost (£) | 32 | 44 | 56 | 68 | 80 |

(a) Draw a line graph to represent this information.
(b) How much is the cost of a job that lasts 6 hours?

The cost of a job is made up of a fixed charge plus an amount for each hour that the job lasts.
(c) How much is the fixed charge?
(d) The cost, £$C$, can be written as a formula in terms of the fixed charge,
  the amount per hour and the number of hours, $h$.
  Complete the formula: $C = \ldots\ldots\ldots + \ldots\ldots\ldots \times h$  OCR

**19** (a) Simplify $\dfrac{t^6}{t^2}$.
(b) Solve these equations. (i) $2(x + 3) = 15 - 3x$  (ii) $\dfrac{2x}{3} = 10$
(c) Factorise completely $5x^2 - 10xy$.
(d) (i) Factorise $x^2 - 6x + 8$.
  (ii) Hence, solve the equation $x^2 - 6x + 8 = 0$.  OCR

**20** Solve these simultaneous equations. $2x - \ y = 7$
  $3x + 2y = 7$  OCR

**21** Simplify. (a) $8x^2 \div 4x$  (b) $3a^2 \times 5a^3$  (c) $(5t^3)^2$

**22** Solve the equations. (a) $y^2 + 5y = 0$  (b) $m^2 - 7m + 12 = 0$

**23** (a) Simplify. $\dfrac{a^2 + 2a}{5a + 10}$  (b) Factorise. $2x^2 - 18$

**24** (a) Find the equation of the straight line that passes through the points $(2, -1)$ and $(5, 8)$.
(b) State the gradient of a line perpendicular to the line in part (a).  OCR

**25** Simplify.
  (a)  $2a^3b^2 \times 3a^2b$
  (b)  Half of $2^{18}$
  (c)  $2x(x - 5y) - y(2x + 5y)$
  (d)  $\dfrac{x - x^2}{x^2 + 5x - 6}$     OCR

**26** Sketch the graphs of each of these equations. Accurate plotting is **not** required.

  (a)  $y = 4 - 2x$
  (b)  $y = -2x^2$
  (c)  $y = \dfrac{10}{x}$     OCR

**27** (a)  Solve, algebraically, these simultaneous equations.  $5x + 3y = 14$
                                                                                $3x - 2y = 16$
  (b)  Solve.  $15 + 4n \geqslant 3 - 2n$
  (c)  Solve by factorising.  $2x^2 + 5x + 2 = 0$     OCR

**28** A rectangle has length $(x + 2)$ cm and width $(x + 1)$ cm.
The rectangle has an area of $6 \, \text{cm}^2$.
Form an equation and show that it can be simplified to
      $x^2 + 3x - 4 = 0$.

**29** (a)  Draw the graph of  $y = x^2 - 3x + 1$  for values of $x$ from $-1$ to $4$.
  (b)  Draw a suitable straight line and find, graphically, the solution to  $x^2 - 3x + 1 = x - 1$.
  (c)  What line would you draw to solve  $x^2 - x - 1 = 0$?     OCR

**30** (a)  Solve the equation.  $\dfrac{2}{x - 3} + \dfrac{5}{x + 3} = 1$

  (b)  Make $x$ the subject of the formula.  $z = \dfrac{x + 2y}{y - 2x}$     OCR

**31** $y$ is proportional to the square of $x$.  $y = 12$  when  $x = 2$.
  (a)  Find an equation connecting $y$ and $x$.
  (b)  Find the value of $y$ when  $x = 4$.     OCR

**32** The diagram shows a square $ABCD$.
  (a)  Find the gradients of the line segments $AC$ and $BD$.
  (b)  Find the equation of the line parallel to $AC$
       which passes through $D$.
  (c)  Find the equation of the line perpendicular to $AC$
       which passes through $A$.

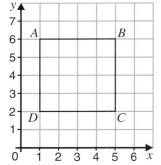

**33** Solve the simultaneous equations
$y + x^2 = 2$  and  $x = 2 - y$.

**34** (a)  Simplify.  (i)  $\dfrac{7(x - 3)}{(x - 3)^2}$
        (ii)  $\left(\dfrac{3x^2}{y^3}\right)^4$
        (iii)  $\dfrac{4x - x^2}{16 - x^2}$

  (b)  Prove that  $\dfrac{2n - 1}{n} + \dfrac{5n}{2n + 1} = \dfrac{(3n + 1)(3n - 1)}{n(2n + 1)}$.     OCR

**35** Rearrange the formula  $\dfrac{x - m}{y} = \dfrac{y - m}{x}$  to give $m$ in terms of $x$ and $y$.

**36** (a)  By completing the square, find the integers $p$ and $q$ such that  $x^2 + 6x - 1 = (x + p)^2 + q$.
  (b)  Hence, solve  $x^2 + 6x - 1 = 0$,  leaving the roots in surd form.     OCR

**37** This is the graph of a function  $y = f(x)$.

Sketch the graphs of the following:

  (a)  $y = f(x - 1)$,

  (b)  $y = \frac{1}{2} f(x)$.

OCR

224

# Algebra
# Calculator Paper

You may use a calculator for this exercise.

**1** (a) Simplify (i) $n \times n \times n$, (ii) $3a \times 2b$.
(b) Multiply out the brackets $6(2x - 3)$.                           OCR

**2** (a) On the same diagram, draw and label the lines $y = x$ and $y = 6 - x$.
(b) What are the coordinates of the point where the two lines cross?

**3** An approximate conversion between temperatures in Fahrenheit (F) and Celsius (C) is given by the formula $F = 2C + 30$.
Use this formula to find the value of $C$ when $F = 68$.                           OCR

**4** (a) Simplify $3x + 4y - 2x + 7y$.
(b) Solve the equations (i) $2(3x - 2) = 50$, (ii) $7x = 6 + 3x$.                           OCR

**5** (a) Write, as simply as possible, an expression for the total length of these rods.
(b) The total length of the rods is 23 cm. By forming an equation find the value of $a$.

**6** (a) Multiply out the brackets and simplify $4(x - 5) + 2(3x - 1)$.
(b) Find the integer values of $n$ which satisfy the inequality $0 < 3n < 14$.                           OCR

**7** (a) Find the eighth term of the sequence whose $n$th term is $4n - 1$.
(b) The first three patterns in a sequence are shown below.

Pattern 1          Pattern 2          Pattern 3

Write down, in terms of $n$, the number of ticks when there are $n$ crosses.                           OCR

**8** (a) Copy and complete this table of values for the graph $y = x^2 - 7$.

| $x$ | $-3$ | $-2$ | $-1$ | 0 | 1 | 2 | 3 |
|---|---|---|---|---|---|---|---|
| $y$ | 2 | | | $-7$ | | $-3$ | 2 |

(b) Draw the graph of $y = x^2 - 7$.
(c) Use your graph to find the values of $x$ for which $x^2 - 7 = 0$.

**9** (a) In this question $a = 5$, $b = -4$ and $c = 3$. Work out. (i) $a^2 + b$ (ii) $\dfrac{ab}{2c - b}$
(b) Multiply out the brackets. (i) $7(2x + 3y)$ (ii) $x(x^2 - 2x)$                           OCR

**10** (a) Factorise. (i) $8x + 12$ (ii) $ab + ac$
(b) Solve these equations. (i) $4x + 7 = 2x + 20$ (ii) $\dfrac{10 + 2x}{3} = 7$                           OCR

**11** Write down an expression for the $n$th term of these sequences.
(a) 3, 6, 9, 12, ... (b) 4, 7, 10, 13, ...

**12** The equation $x^3 - 15x + 3 = 0$ has a solution between 3 and 4.
Use trial and improvement to find this solution.
Give your answer to one decimal place. Show clearly the outcomes of your trials.                           OCR

**13** (a) Simplify. (i) $t^2 \times t^3$ (ii) $\dfrac{t^2}{t^4}$
(b) Expand. $x(x^2 + 3)$
(c) Expand and simplify. $(x + 3)(x - 4)$                           OCR

**14** (a) Solve the inequality $3x - 5 > 4$.
  (b) List the values of $x$, where $x$ is an integer, such that $-1 \leqslant x + 2 < 1$.
  (c) Rearrange the formula $y = 5x + 10$ to make $x$ the subject.
  (d) Solve. (i) $\frac{2t + 3}{3} = 7$    (ii) $5(x - 3) = 3x + 1$

**15** (a) Solve the equation $5x - 7 = 3(x + 1)$.
  (b) Solve the simultaneous equations $x - y = 3$ and $3x + y = -1$.
  (c) Simplify. (i) $x^2 y^3 \times \frac{x^3}{y}$    (ii) $(p^2)^3$

**16** The area, $y$, of this rectangle is given by $y = x^2 + x$.

  (a) Copy and complete the table of values for $y$.

| $x$ | 0 | 1 | 2 | 3 | 4 | 5 | 6 |
|---|---|---|---|---|---|---|---|
| $y$ | 0 |   | 6 |   | 20 |   | 42 |

  (b) Draw the graph of $y = x^2 + x$.
  (c) Use your curve to find the value of $x$ if the area of the rectangle is 35 cm².
  (d) The rectangle is the base of a cuboid with volume, $V$, given by $V = x^3 - x$.
    Use trial and improvement to find the value of $x$ when $V = 400$ cm³.
    Give your answer to one decimal place.                                      OCR

**17** (a) On the same diagram, draw and label the lines $y = x$ and $y = 3 - x$
    for values of $x$ from 0 to 3.
  (b) Explain how you can use your graph to solve the equation $x = 3 - x$.
  (c) Shade the region that is satisfied by all of the inequalities
    $$y \geqslant x, \quad y \leqslant 3 - x \quad \text{and} \quad x \geqslant 0.$$

**18** (a) Expand and simplify.    $x(2x - 1) - 2(x - 3)$
  (b) Factorise this expression.    $x^2 - 3x - 10$
  (c) Solve this inequality.    $2x + 1 < 3 - 3x$                              OCR

**19** The equation of the straight line drawn on the axes is $y = mx + c$.

  (a) Find the values of $c$ and $m$.

  (b) Find the coordinates of point $A$.

**20** You are given the formula $V = \sqrt{\frac{P}{R}}$.

  (a) Work out the value of $V$ when $P = 0.35$ and $R = \frac{5}{7}$.
  (b) Rearrange the formula to give $P$ in terms of $V$ and $R$.

**21** (a) Solve. $\frac{11 - x}{8} = x - 2$

  (b) Solve, algebraically, these simultaneous equations.    $2x + 6y = 11$
                                                              $3x - 4y = 10$

  (c) Solve $x^2 + 7x + 5 = 0$, giving the roots correct to 2 decimal places.    OCR

**22** In the table, $y$ is inversely proportional to $x^2$.

| $x$ | 1 | 2 | 3 | $r$ |
|---|---|---|---|---|
| $y$ | 36 | 9 | $p$ | 1 |

  (a) Find (i) $p$, (ii) $r$.
  (b) Write down an equation connecting $x$ and $y$.                           OCR

226

**23** (a) Which of the following equations are illustrated by the graphs shown?

$$xy = 1 \qquad y = 2 - x \qquad x^2 + y^2 = 3 \qquad y = x^3 \qquad y = 1 - x^2 \qquad 2y = 2 + x$$

(i)  (ii)  (iii)  (iv)

(b) Draw a graph of $y = 2^x$ for $-3 \le x \le 3$.

**24** (a) The line $L$ is parallel to $y + 2x = 3$ and passes through the point $(0, 4)$.
Write down the equation of $L$ in the form $y = mx + c$.
(b) The line $M$ is perpendicular to $y + 2x = 3$. Write down the gradient of the line $M$.
(c) Show that, where the curve $y = x^2 - 1$ intersects the line $y + 2x = 3$, $x^2 + 2x - 4 = 0$.
(d) Solve $x^2 + 2x - 4 = 0$, giving your answers to two decimal places.
(e) Hence, find the coordinates of the points of intersection of $y = x^2 - 1$ and $y + 2x = 3$.
OCR

**25** (a) Make $x$ the subject of the formula $y = \dfrac{x + 3}{x}$.

(b) Simplify $\dfrac{2x}{x + 1} - \dfrac{6}{x - 3}$. 
OCR

**26** The diagram shows the speed-time graph of an underground train between two stations.

(a) Calculate the acceleration of the train between 0 and 10 seconds.
(b) Calculate the time it takes to travel half the distance between the stations.

**27** (a) Simplify $(3xy^3)^2$.
(b) Solve the equation $2x^2 - 5x - 4 = 0$. Give your answers correct to 2 d.p.
(c) $P$ is inversely proportional to the square root of $Q$.
If $P = 12$ when $Q = 49$, find an expression for $P$ in terms of $Q$.
OCR

**28** In this question, all lengths are in metres.
A rectangular garden 20 by 18 consists of a
rectangular lawn surrounded by a concrete path
of uniform width $x$.

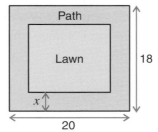

(a) Write down an expression in terms of $x$
for the area of the path.

The area of the path is one-quarter of the area of the whole garden.
(b) (i) Use your answer to (a) to form an equation in $x$.
(ii) Show that the equation simplifies to $2x^2 - 38x + 45 = 0$.
(c) Solve this equation to find the width of the path. 
OCR

**29** Solve the equation $\dfrac{3}{x + 1} + \dfrac{1}{x - 2} = 1$. Give your answers correct to 2 d.p.

**30** Solve, algebraically, these simultaneous equations. $y = 7 - 3x$ and $x^2 + y^2 = 43$ OCR

# Angles and 2-D Shapes

An **angle** is a measure of turn.
Angles are measured in **degrees**.

## Types and names of angles

| **Acute angle** | **Right angle** | **Obtuse angle** | **Reflex angle** |
|---|---|---|---|

| $0° < a < 90°$ | $a = 90°$ | $90° < a < 180°$ | $180° < a < 360°$ |
|---|---|---|---|

## Angle properties

| **Angles at a point** | **Complementary angles** | **Supplementary angles** | **Vertically opposite angles** |
|---|---|---|---|

| $a + b + c = 360°$ | $x + y = 90°$ | $a + b = 180°$ | $a = c$ and $b = d$ |
|---|---|---|---|

## Lines

A straight line joining two points is called a **line segment**.

### Perpendicular lines
Lines which meet at right angles are **perpendicular** to each other.

### Parallel lines
**Parallel** lines are lines which never meet.

> Arrowheads are used to show that lines are parallel.

## Parallel lines and angles

Each diagram shows two parallel lines crossed by another straight line called a **transversal**.

| **Corresponding angles** | **Alternate angles** | **Allied angles** |
|---|---|---|

| $a = c$ | $b = c$ | $b + d = 180°$ |
|---|---|---|

> Corresponding angles are always on the same side of the transversal.

> Alternate angles are always on opposite sides of the transversal.

> Allied angles are always between parallels on the same side of the transversal.

## Naming angles

Angles can be identified by using small letters to mark the angle or by using three capital letters to show the sides that form the angle.

For example.

angle $a$

angle $ABD$
$\angle ABD$

∠ means 'angle'.

$\angle CBA$ is the same as $\angle ABC$.

Notice that the middle letter is where the angle is made.

### EXAMPLES

Without measuring, work out the size of the angles marked with letters.

**1**

Angles at a point add up to 360°.
$a + 95° + 120° = 360°$
$\qquad a = 360° - 95° - 120°$
$\qquad a = 145°$

**2**

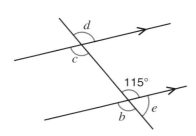

$b = 115°$ (vertically opposite angles)

$c = 115°$ (alternate angles)

$d = 115°$ (corresponding angles)

$e + 115° = 180°$ (supplementary angles)
$\qquad e = 180° - 115°$
$\qquad e = 65°$

$b = 115°, \quad c = 115°, \quad d = 115°, \quad e = 65°$

### Exercise 23.1

The diagrams in this exercise are not drawn accurately.

**1** Work out the size of the angles marked with letters. Give a reason for each answer.

(a)

(b)

(c)

**2** Work out the size of the angles marked with letters. Give a reason for each answer.

(a)

(b)

(c)

(d)

**3** Calculate the size of the angles marked with letters.

(a)

(b)

(c)

**4** Work out the size of the required angles.

(a) Find ∠ABC.

(b) Find ∠QRS.

(c) Find ∠ZYV.

(d) Find ∠AOB and ∠COD.

(e) Find ∠QTU and ∠QTS.

(f) Find reflex angle TUV.

## Triangles

A **triangle** is a shape made by three straight lines.
The sum of the three angles in a triangle is 180°.

$$a + b + c = 180°$$

## Types of triangle

**acute angled**
Triangles with three acute angles.

**obtuse angled**
Triangles with an obtuse angle.

**right angled**
Triangles with a right angle.

## Special triangles

**scalene triangle**
Sides have different lengths.
Angles are all different.

**isosceles triangle**
Two equal sides.
Two angles equal.

**equilateral triangle**
Three equal sides.
All angles are 60°.

## Exterior angle of a triangle

When one side of a triangle is extended, as shown, the angle formed is called an **exterior angle**.

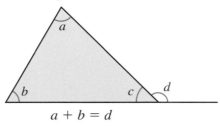

$$a + b = d$$

In any triangle the exterior angle is always equal to the
sum of the two opposite interior angles.
Check this by measuring the angles *a*, *b* and *d* in the diagram.

This result can easily be proved.

$a + b + c = 180°$
(sum of angles in a triangle)
$c + d = 180°$
(supplementary angles)
$a + b + c = c + d$
$a + b = d$

EXAMPLE

Find the sizes of the angles marked $a$ and $b$.

$a = 84° + 43°$  (ext. $\angle$ of a $\Delta$)
$a = 127°$

$b + 127° = 180°$  (supp. $\angle$'s)
$\phantom{b + 127°}b = 180° - 127°$
$\phantom{b + 127°}b = 53°$

○○○○○○○○○○○○○○○○○○○○○

**Short but accurate:**
In Geometry we often abbreviate words and use symbols to provide the reader with full details using the minimum amount of writing.

$\Delta$ is short for triangle.
ext. $\angle$ of a $\Delta$ means exterior angle of a triangle.
supp. $\angle$'s means supplementary angles.

---

**Exercise 23.2**   The diagrams in this exercise have not been drawn accurately.

**1** Is it possible to draw triangles with the following types of angles?
Give a reason for each of your answers.
(a)  three acute angles,
(b)  one obtuse angle and two acute angles,
(c)  two obtuse angles and one acute angle,
(d)  three obtuse angles,
(e)  one right angle and two acute angles,
(f)  two right angles and one acute angle.

**2** Is it possible to draw a triangle with these angles?
If a triangle can be drawn, what type of triangle is it?
Give a reason for each of your answers.
(a)  95°,  78°,  7°     (b)  48°,  62°,  90°     (c)  48°,  62°,  70°
(d)  90°,  38°,  52°    (e)  130°,  35°,  15°

**3** Work out the size of the marked angles.

(a)        (b)        (c)        (d)

**4** Work out the size of the angles marked with letters.

(a)                                          (b)

**5** In the diagram   $AB = BD = DA$   and   $BC = CD$.   $CD$ is extended to $E$.

(a)  What type of triangle is $BCD$?
(b)  What is the size of angle $BDC$?
(c)  Work out the size of angle $ADE$.

231

**6** Work out the size of the required angles.

(a)

Find ∠BCD.

(b)

Find ∠PRQ and ∠QRS.

(c)

ONX is a straight line.
Find ∠MNX.

## Quadrilaterals

A **quadrilateral** is a shape made by four straight lines.
The sum of the four angles of a quadrilateral is 360°.

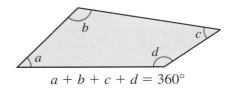

$$a + b + c + d = 360°$$

## Special quadrilaterals

### Square

Four equal sides.
Opposite sides parallel.
Angles of 90°.
Diagonals bisect each other at 90°.

### Rectangle

Opposite sides equal and parallel.
Angles of 90°.
Diagonals bisect each other.

### Parallelogram

Opposite sides equal and parallel.
Opposite angles equal.
Diagonals bisect each other.

### Rhombus

Four equal sides.
Opposite sides parallel.
Opposite angles equal.
Diagonals bisect each other at 90°.

### Trapezium

One pair of parallel sides.

### Kite

Two pairs of adjacent sides equal.
One pair of opposite angles equal.
One diagonal bisects the other at 90°.

**EXAMPLE**

*PQRS* is a parallelogram. Work out the size of the angle marked *x*.

The opposite angles of a parallelogram are equal.

$$55° + 55° + x + x = 360°$$
$$110° + 2x = 360°$$
$$2x = 360° - 110°$$
$$2x = 250°$$
$$x = 125°$$

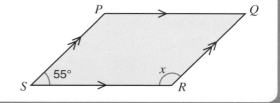

**Exercise 23.3**   Use squared paper to answer questions 1 to 4.

1   *PQRS* is a rectangle. *P* is the point (1, 3), *Q*(4, 6), *R*(6, 4).
   Find the coordinates of *S*.

2   *WXYZ* is a parallelogram. *W* is the point (1, 0), *X*(4, 1), *Z*(3, 3).
   Find the coordinates of *Y*.

3   *OABC* is a kite. *O* is the point (0, 0), *B*(5, 5), *C*(3, 1).
   Find the coordinates of *A*.

4   *STUV* is a square with *S* at (1, 3) and *U* at (5, 3).
   Find the coordinates of *T* and *V*.

5   The following diagrams have not been drawn accurately.
   Work out the size of the angles marked with letters.

**6**

PQRS is a rhombus. PUST is a rhombus.
Angle PTS = 80°.
Calculate angle SQR.

**7** WXYZ is a square.
Find the size of the marked angles.

## Polygons

A **polygon** is a shape made by straight lines.
A three-sided polygon is a **triangle**.
A four-sided polygon is called a **quadrilateral**.

A polygon is a many-sided shape.
Look at these polygons.

**Pentagon**   **Hexagon**   **Octagon**
5 sides       6 sides       8 sides

## Interior and exterior angles of a polygon

Angles formed by sides inside a polygon are called **interior angles**.

When a side of a polygon is extended, as shown, the angle formed
is called an **exterior angle**.

At each vertex of the polygon:
    interior angle + exterior angle = 180°

## Sum of the interior angles of a polygon

The diagram shows a polygon with the diagonals from one vertex drawn.

The polygon has 5 sides and is divided into 3 triangles.
So, the sum of the interior angles is   $3 \times 180° = 540°$.

In general, for any $n$-sided polygon, the sum of the interior angles is   $(n - 2) \times 180°$.

## Sum of the exterior angles of a polygon

The sum of the exterior angles of **any** polygon is 360°.

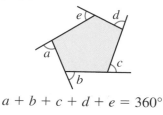

$$a + b + c + d + e = 360°$$

**EXAMPLES**

**1** Find the size of angle $x$.

The sum of the exterior angles is 360°.
$x + 100° + 45° + 150° = 360°$
$x + 295° = 360°$
$\qquad x = 360° - 295°$
$\qquad x = 65°$

**2** Find the sum of the interior angles of a pentagon.

To find the sum of the interior angles of a pentagon substitute $n = 5$ into $(n - 2) \times 180°$.
$(5 - 2) \times 180°$
$= 3 \times 180°$
$= 540°$

**3** Find the size of the angles marked $a$ and $b$.

$155° + a = 180°$
(int. angle + ext. angle = 180°)
$a = 180° - 155°$
$a = 25°$

The sum of the interior angles of a pentagon is 540°.
$b + 140° + 155° + 125° + 65° = 540°$
$b + 485° = 540°$
$\qquad b = 540° - 485°$
$\qquad b = 55°$

---

**Exercise 23.4**    The diagrams in this exercise have not been drawn accurately.

**1** In the diagram, $ABC$ is a straight line.
(a) Explain why angle $x = 50°$.
(b) Show that angle $y = 60°$.

**2** Work out the size of the angles marked with letters.

(a)

(b)

(c)

**3** Work out the sum of the interior angles of these polygons.

(a)

(b)

(c)

**4** Work out the size of the angles marked with letters.

(a)

(b)

(c)

**5** The figure is made up of straight lines.
Find the sum of the angles $a, b, c, d, e, f, g, h$.

## Regular polygons

A polygon with all sides equal and all angles equal is called a **regular polygon**.

Regular hexagon    Regular octagon

A regular triangle is usually called an **equilateral triangle**.
A regular quadrilateral is usually called a **square**.

## Exterior angles of regular polygons

In general, for any regular $n$-sided polygon:   exterior angle $= \frac{360°}{n}$

By rearranging the formula we can find the number of sides, $n$, of a regular polygon when we know the exterior angle.

$$n = \frac{360°}{\text{exterior angle}}$$

### EXAMPLE

A regular polygon has an exterior angle of 30°.
(a) How many sides has the polygon?
(b) What is the size of an interior angle of the polygon?

(a)  $n = \dfrac{360°}{\text{exterior angle}}$

$n = \frac{360°}{30°} = 12$

The polygon has 12 sides.

(b)  interior angle + exterior angle $= 180°$
int. $\angle + 30° = 180°$
int. $\angle = 180° - 30°$
interior angle $= 150°$

**Remember:**
It is a good idea to write down the formula you are using.

236

23

## Tessellations

Covering a surface with identical shapes produces a pattern called a **tessellation**.

To tessellate the shape must not overlap and there must be no gaps.

### Regular tessellations

This pattern shows a tessellation of regular hexagons.

This pattern is called a **regular tessellation** because it is made by using a single regular polygon.

## Exercise 23.5

**1** Calculate (a) the exterior angle and (b) the interior angle of these regular polygons.

(i)        (ii)        (iii)        (iv)

**2** A regular polygon has an exterior angle of 18°.
How many sides has the polygon?

**3** A regular polygon has an interior angle of 135°.
How many sides has the polygon?

**4** (a) Calculate the size of an exterior angle of a regular pentagon.
    (b) What is the size of an interior angle of a regular pentagon?
    (c) What is the sum of the interior angles of a pentagon?

**5** The following diagrams are drawn using regular polygons.
Work out the values of the marked angles.

(a)        (b)        (c)        (d)

**6** $AB$ and $BC$ are two sides of a regular octagon.
$PAB$ is an isosceles triangle with $AP = PB$.
Angle $APB = 36°$.
Calculate angle $PBC$.

**7** A regular polygon has 12 sides.
Calculate the size of an interior angle.

**8** Explain why regular pentagons will not tessellate.

**9** Any triangle can be used to make a tessellation.
Draw a triangle of your own, make copies, and show that it will tessellate.

## Lines of symmetry

These shapes are **symmetrical**.

When each shape is folded along the dashed line one side will fit exactly over the other side. The dashed line is called a **line of symmetry**.

Some shapes have more than one line of symmetry.

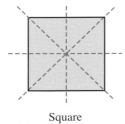

Square
4 lines of symmetry.

Circle
Infinite number of
lines of symmetry.

Shape with no lines of
symmetry.

## Rotational symmetry

*Is this shape symmetrical?*

The shape does not have line symmetry.

*Try placing a copy of the shape over the original
and rotating it about the centre of the circle.*

After 180° (a half-turn) the shape fits into its own outline.
The shape has **rotational symmetry**.
The point about which the shape is rotated is called the **centre of rotation**.
The **order of rotational symmetry** is 2.
When rotating the shape through 360° it fits into its own outline twice (once after a half-turn and again after a full-turn).
A shape is only described as having rotational symmetry if the order of rotational symmetry is 2 or more.

A shape can have both line symmetry and rotational symmetry.

For example, the shape on the right has:
order of rotational symmetry 4, and 4 lines of symmetry.

## Exercise 23.6

**1** These shapes have **line symmetry**.
Copy each shape and draw the line of symmetry.

(a)　　　　　(b)　　　　　(c)　　　　　(d)

**2** Find the number of lines of symmetry and the order of rotational symmetry for
(a)　a regular pentagon,　　(b)　a regular hexagon,　　(c)　a regular octagon.

**3** Look at these triangles.

Scalene triangle       Isosceles triangle       Equilateral triangle

What is the order of rotational symmetry of each triangle?

**4** Copy each of these diagrams.

     A              B              C

(a) Add **one** more flag to each of your diagrams so that the final diagrams have rotational symmetry.

(b) What is the order of rotational symmetry for each of your diagrams?

**5** These quadrilaterals have been drawn on squared paper.

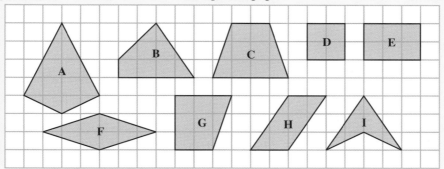

Copy and complete the table for each shape.

| Shape | A | B | C | D | E | F | G | H | I |
|---|---|---|---|---|---|---|---|---|---|
| Number of lines of symmetry | | | | | | | | | |
| Order of rotational symmetry | | | | | | | | | |

**6** Make a copy of this shape.

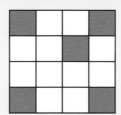

(a) How many lines of symmetry does the shape have?

(b) (i) Colour one more square so that your shape has rotational symmetry of order 2.

     (ii) Mark the centre of rotational symmetry on your shape.

**7** Make a copy of this shape.

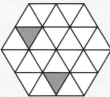

(a) How many lines of symmetry does the shape have?

(b) (i) Colour one more triangle so that your shape has rotational symmetry of order 3.

     (ii) How many lines of symmetry does your shape have?

# What you need to know

- An angle of 90° is called a **right angle**.
  An angle less than 90° is called an **acute angle**.
  An angle between 90° and 180° is called an **obtuse angle**.
  An angle greater than 180° is called a **reflex angle**.

- The sum of the angles at a point is 360°.

- Angles on a straight line add up to 180°.
  Angles which add up to 180° are called **supplementary angles**.
  Angles which add up to 90° are called **complementary angles**.

- When two lines cross, the opposite angles formed are equal and are called **vertically opposite angles**.

- A straight line joining two points is called a **line segment**.

- Lines which meet at right angles are **perpendicular** to each other.

- Lines which never meet and are always the same distance apart are **parallel**.

- When two parallel lines are crossed by a transversal the following pairs of angles are formed.

| Corresponding angles | Alternate angles | Allied angles |
|:---:|:---:|:---:|
|  |  |  |
| | | $a + b = 180°$ |

- Types of triangle:

| Scalene triangle | Isosceles triangle | Equilateral triangle |
|:---:|:---:|:---:|
|  |  |  |
| Sides have different lengths. Angles are all different. | Two equal sides. Two equal angles. | Three equal sides. Three equal angles, 60°. |

- The sum of the angles in a triangle is 180°.
  $$a + b + c = 180°$$

- The exterior angle is equal to the sum of the two opposite interior angles.
  $$a + b = d$$

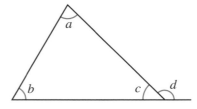

- A two-dimensional shape has **line symmetry** if the line divides the shape so that one side fits exactly over the other.

- A two-dimensional shape has **rotational symmetry** if it fits into a copy of its outline as it is rotated through 360°.

- A shape is only described as having rotational symmetry if the order of rotational symmetry is 2 or more.

- The number of times a shape fits into its outline in a single turn is the **order of rotational symmetry**.

Order of rotational symmetry 5

- The sum of the angles in a quadrilateral is 360°.
- Facts about these special quadrilaterals:

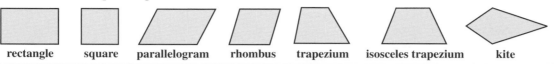

rectangle    square    parallelogram    rhombus    trapezium    isosceles trapezium    kite

| Quadrilateral | Sides | Angles | Diagonals | Lines of symmetry | Order of rotational symmetry |
|---|---|---|---|---|---|
| **Rectangle** | Opposite sides equal and parallel | All 90° | Bisect each other | 2 | 2 |
| **Square** | 4 equal sides, opposite sides parallel | All 90° | Bisect each other at 90° | 4 | 4 |
| **Parallelogram** | Opposite sides equal and parallel | Opposite angles equal | Bisect each other | 0 | 2 |
| **Rhombus** | 4 equal sides, opposite sides parallel | Opposite angles equal | Bisect each other at 90° | 2 | 2 |
| **Trapezium** | 1 pair of parallel sides | | | | |
| **Isosceles trapezium** | 1 pair of parallel sides, non-parallel sides equal | 2 pairs of equal angles | Equal in length | 1 | 1* |
| **Kite** | 2 pairs of adjacent sides equal | 1 pair of opposite angles equal | One bisects the other at 90° | 1 | 1* |

*A shape is only described as having rotational symmetry if the order of rotational symmetry is 2 or more.

- A **polygon** is a many-sided shape made by straight lines.
- A polygon with all sides equal and all angles equal is called a **regular polygon**.
- Shapes you need to know:    A 5-sided polygon is called a **pentagon**.
  A 6-sided polygon is called a **hexagon**.
  An 8-sided polygon is called an **octagon**.
- The sum of the exterior angles of any polygon is 360°.
- At each vertex of a polygon: interior angle + exterior angle = 180°
- The sum of the interior angles of an $n$-sided polygon is given by:
  $(n - 2) \times 180°$
- For a regular $n$-sided polygon: exterior angle $= \dfrac{360°}{n}$
- A shape will **tessellate** if it covers a surface without overlapping and leaves no gaps.
- All triangles tessellate.
- All quadrilaterals tessellate.

interior angle    exterior angle

## Review Exercise 23

**1**    In the diagram *AOB* and *POQ* are straight lines.
Angle *ROB* = 90°.    Angle *AOP* = 27°.

     (a)   (i)   Work out the size of angle *AOQ*.
          (ii)   Work out the size of angle *POR*.
     (b)   What angle is the same size as angle *AOP*?

**2** Work out the size of angle *a*. Give a reason for your answer.

OCR

**3**

In the diagram the lines *AB* and *CD* are parallel.
They are crossed by two straight lines.
Find angles *x* and *y*, giving reasons for your answer.

OCR

**4** In the diagram the lengths of *AB*, *BE*, *EC* and *CD* are equal. Angle *EBC* = 64°.

(a) Find the value of  (i) *x*,  (ii) *y*.

(b) Quadrilateral *AEDF* is symmetrical about the line *AD*.
What special name is given to this quadrilateral?

OCR

**5**

(a) How many lines of symmetry has a kite?
(b) Find the size of the angles marked with letters in each of these kites.

**6** The figure *PQRS* is a rhombus. Find *y* if *x* = 27°.

**7**

The diagram shows a trapezium.
Find the size of angle *a* and angle *b*.

**8** The diagram shows part of a regular polygon.
How many sides does the polygon have?

OCR

**9**

The diagram shows a regular decagon which has been divided into three parts.
(a) What is the order of rotational symmetry of a decagon?
(b) How many lines of symmetry has the quadrilateral *AEIJ*?
(c) Work out the size of angle *AED*?
(d) What is the size of angle *AEI*?
(e) Show that angle *EAJ* = 90°.

# Circle Properties

## Circles

A **circle** is the shape drawn by keeping a pencil the same distance from a fixed point on a piece of paper. Compasses can be used to draw circles accurately.

It is important that you understand the meaning of the following words:

**Circumference** – special name used for the perimeter of a circle.

**Radius** – distance from the centre of the circle to any point on the circumference.

**Diameter** – distance right across the circle, passing through the centre point.
Notice that the diameter is twice as long as the radius.

**Chord** – a line joining two points on the circumference. The longest chord of a circle is the diameter.

**Tangent** – a line which touches the circumference of a circle at one point only.

**Arc** – part of the circumference of a circle.

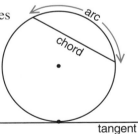

**Segment** – a chord divides a circle into two segments.

**Sector** – two radii divide a circle into two sectors.

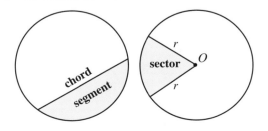

## Activity

Measure the marked angles in these diagrams. *What do you notice?*

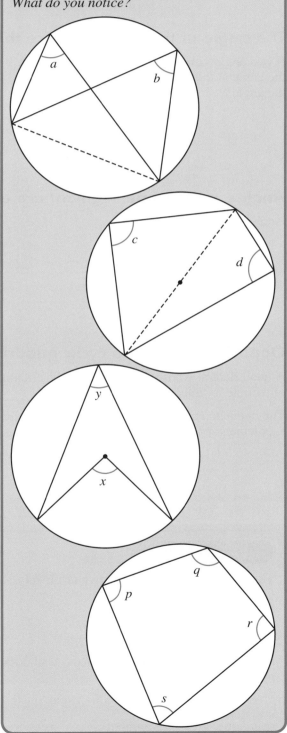

### The angle in a semi-circle is a right angle

Angles which are:
    at the circumference,
    standing on a diameter,
are equal to 90°.

$$c = d = 90°$$

### The angle at the centre is twice the angle at the circumference

If two angles are standing on the same chord, the angle at the centre of the circle is twice the angle at the circumference.

$$x = 2y$$

### Angles in the same segment are equal

Angles which are:
    at the circumference,
    standing on the same chord,
    in the same segment,
are equal.

$$a = b$$

### Opposite angles of a cyclic quadrilateral are supplementary

A quadrilateral whose vertices lie on the circumference of a circle is called a **cyclic quadrilateral**.

The opposite angles of a cyclic quadrilateral are supplementary (add up to 180°).

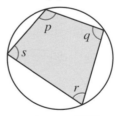

$$p + r = 180°$$
and
$$q + s = 180°$$

---

#### EXAMPLE

The diagram has not been drawn accurately.
$O$ is the centre of the circle.
Find the marked angles.

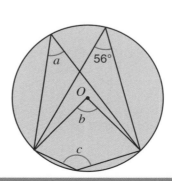

$a = 56°$   (angles in the same segment)

$b = 2 \times 56°$   ($\angle$ at centre = twice $\angle$ at circum.)
$b = 112°$

$c = 180° - 56°$   (opp. $\angle$'s of a cyclic quad.)
$c = 124°$

① The following diagrams show triangles drawn in semi-circles.
Work out the size of the marked angles.

(a)

(b)

(c)

(d)

② *O* is the centre of the circle.
Work out the size of the marked angles.

(a)

(b)

(c)

(d)

(e)

(f)

(g)

(h)

③ *O* is the centre of the circle.
Work out the size of the marked angles.

(a)

(b)

(c)

(d)

(e)

(f)

(g)

(h)

④ In the diagram *BD* is a diameter.
Angle *ACD* = 43°.
Calculate angle *x*.

**5** *ABCD* is a cyclic quadrilateral, with *BA* produced (extended) to *E*.
Angle *EAD* = 70° and angle *CDB* = 34°.
Calculate angles *BCD* and *CAD*.

**6**

*PQ* is a diameter.
Angle *RPQ* = 29°.
Calculate angle *PSR*.

**7** In the diagram, *O* is the centre of the circle.
Angle *PSQ* = 28° and angle *QSR* = 47°.
Calculate angle *PQR* and angle *QRS*.

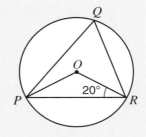

**8**

*P*, *Q*, *R*, *S* and *T* are points on a circle.
∠*QRS* = 105°, ∠*PTS* = 140°, ∠*PQR* = 135° and *PT* = *TS*.
Calculate ∠*PSR* and ∠*TPQ*.

**9** In the figure, *O* is the centre of the circle.
Angle *ORP* = 20°.
Calculate  (a) angle *POR*,  (b) angle *PQR*.

**10**

In the figure, *O* is the centre of the circle.
*AC* = *CB*.
Calculate the angles  (a) *DOE*,  (b) *ABD*,  (c) *DBE*.

**11** The centre of the circle is *O*.
Calculate the value of *x*.

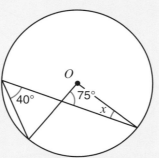

**12**

In the circle, centre *O*, *QR* is a diameter.
The line *QS* is a common chord of the two circles.
*TR* is a straight line.
Find angle *QPT*.

## Tangents

The diagram shows a tangent drawn from a point *P* to touch the circle, centre *O*, at *T*.

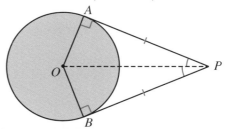

A tangent to a circle is a straight line which touches the circumference at one point only.

A tangent is perpendicular to the radius at the point of contact.

This diagram shows two tangents drawn from a point *P* to touch the circle, centre *O*, at points *A* and *B*.

Tangents drawn to a circle from the same point are equal,   *PA* = *PB*.
*OP* bisects angle *APB*.

*What is the name given to the shape OAPB?*

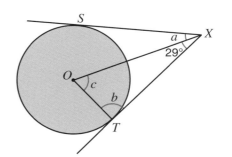

### EXAMPLE

The diagram has not been drawn accurately.
*O* is the centre of the circle. Find the marked angles.

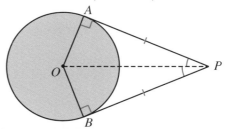

*a* = 29°   (*SX* and *TX* are tangents from *X*,
            so, ∠*TXO* = ∠*SXO*.)

*b* = 90°   (Tangent perpendicular to radius at *T*.)

*c* = 180° − 90° − 29°
*c* = 61°

## Activity

Measure the marked angles in these diagrams.
*What do you notice?*

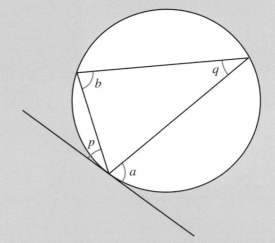

## Alternate segment theorem

You should find that in each diagram, angle $a$ = angle $b$ and angle $p$ = angle $q$.

The angle between a tangent and a chord is equal to any angle in the alternate segment, standing on the same chord.
This is known as the **alternate segment theorem**.

In each of these diagrams the shaded area shows the alternate (opposite) segment to the angle between the tangent and the chord.

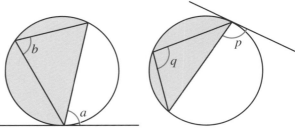

---

### Exercise 24.2

The diagrams in this exercise have not been drawn accurately.

**1** $O$ is the centre of the circle.
Work out the size of the marked angles.

(a)

(b)

(c)

(d)

(e)

(f)

(g)

(h)

**2** $O$ is the centre of the circle.
Work out the size of the marked angles.

(a)

(b)

(c)

(d)

(e)

(f)

**3**

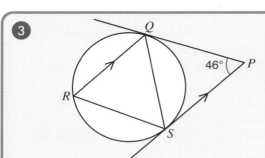

In the diagram, PQ and PS are tangents.
RQ is parallel to SP.
Angle SPQ = 46°.
Calculate (a) angle QRS,
(b) angle RSQ.

**4** In the diagram, PQ and PS are tangents to the circle centre O.
POR is a straight line.
Angle SRQ = 50°.
Calculate (a) ∠SOQ,
(b) ∠SPO,
(c) ∠RSO.

**5**

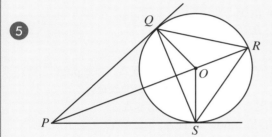

PQ and PS are tangents to the circle centre O.
POR is a straight line.
Angle SPO = 18°.
Calculate (a) ∠POS,
(b) ∠OSR,
(c) ∠SQR.

**6** In the diagram, PT is the tangent at T to the circle.
Find the sizes of the angles marked x, y and z.

**7**

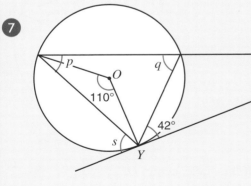

The line XY is a tangent to the circle and
O is the centre of the circle.
Find the sizes of the angles marked p, q, r and s.

**8** In the figure, AB touches the circle at T and CD is a diameter.
Write down the value of x + 2y.

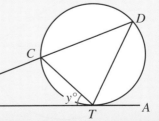

## Geometric proofs

Earlier in the chapter you used the properties of circles to find the numerical values of required angles. In this section we will prove that these properties, or **facts**, can be applied to all situations and not just to particular situations.

**To prove a geometrical fact involves:**
- starting with basic facts that can be assumed to be true,
- using these facts to deduce other facts, eventually leading to the proof of the required fact.

**Geometrical facts** are sometimes called **theorems**.
For example, Pythagoras' Theorem.

Once a geometrical fact has been proved it can be stated and used, without proof, in proving other required facts.

The angle at the centre is twice the angle at the circumference.

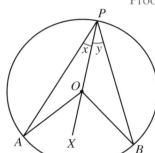

Prove that: $\angle AOB = 2 \times \angle APB$
Draw: Line from $P$, through $O$, to $X$.
Proof: Let $\angle APO = x$ and $\angle BPO = y$.

$\angle OAP = \angle APO = x$       ($\triangle AOP$ is isosceles)
$\angle AOX = \angle OAP + \angle APO = 2x$    (Ext. $\angle$ of a $\triangle$ – see page 230)
$\angle OBP = \angle BPO = y$       ($\triangle BOP$ is isosceles)
$\angle BOX = \angle OBP + \angle BPO = 2y$    (Ext. $\angle$ of a $\triangle$)
$\angle AOB = \angle AOX + \angle BOX$ and $\angle APB = \angle APO + \angle BPO$
$\qquad\qquad = 2x + 2y \qquad\qquad\qquad\qquad\qquad = x + y$
$\qquad\qquad = 2(x + y)$
$\qquad\qquad = 2 \times \angle APB$

So, $\angle AOB = 2 \times \angle APB$

## Exercise 24.3

**1** In the diagram:
$O$ is the centre of the circle.
$A$, $P$ and $B$ are points on the circumference.
The line $PX$ has been drawn.

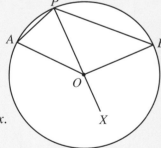

(a) If $\angle OPA = x$, show that $\triangle OAP$ is isosceles.
(b) If $\angle OPB = y$, show that $\triangle OBP$ is isosceles.
(c) Using the exterior angle of a triangle, show that $\angle AOX = 2x$.
(d) Find, in terms of $x$ and $y$, the size of the reflex angle $AOB$.
(e) Show that reflex $\angle AOB = 2 \times \angle APB$.

**2**

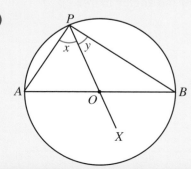

In the diagram:
$AB$ is a diameter of the circle, centre $O$.
$\angle APO = x$ and $\angle BPO = y$.

(a) Show that $\angle AOB = 2 \times \angle APB$.
(b) Hence, prove that the angle in a semi-circle is a right angle.

250

**3** (a) If ∠*APB* = *x*, write, in terms of *x*, the size of ∠*AOB*.
Give a reason for your answer.
(b) Write, in terms of *x*, the size of ∠*AQB*.
Give a reason for your answer.
(c) Hence, prove that angles in the same segment,
standing on the same chord, are equal.

**4**

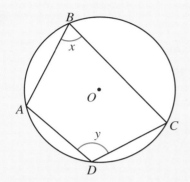

In the diagram:
∠*ABC* = *x* and ∠*ADC* = *y*.

(a) Copy the diagram.
Draw the lines *AO* and *CO*.
(b) Write, in terms of *x* and *y*, the size of
(i) ∠*AOC*, (ii) reflex ∠*AOC*.
Give reasons for your answers.
(c) ∠*AOC* + reflex ∠*AOC* = 360°.
Show that *x* + *y* = 180° and that opposite angles
of a cyclic quadrilateral are supplementary.

**5** In the diagram:
The line *PQ* is a tangent to the circle at *T*.
The line *TX* is a diameter of the circle, centre *O*.
∠*BTQ* = *x* and ∠*BTO* = *y*.

(a) Copy the diagram and draw the line *BX*.
(b) Explain why *x* + *y* = 90°.
(c) What is the size of ∠*BXT*?
(d) Explain why ∠*BXT* = ∠*BAT*.
(e) Show that ∠*BTQ* = ∠*BAT* and hence,
prove the alternate segment theorem.

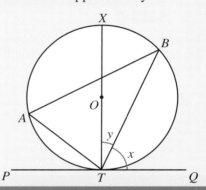

## What you need to know

● A **circle** is the shape drawn by keeping a pencil the same distance from a fixed point on a piece of paper.
● The meaning of the following words:

**Circumference** – special name used for the perimeter of a circle.

**Radius** – distance from the centre of the circle to any point on the circumference.
The plural of radius is **radii**.

**Diameter** – distance right across the circle, passing through the centre point.
The diameter is twice as long as the radius.

**Chord** – a line joining two points on the circumference.
The longest chord is the diameter.

**Tangent** – a line which touches the circumference of a circle at one point only.

**Arc** – part of the circumference of a circle.

**Segment** – a chord divides a circle into two segments.

**Sector** – two radii divide a circle into two sectors.

- **Circle properties**

The angle in a semi-circle is a right angle.

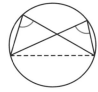

Angles in the same segment are equal.

$x = 2y$
The angle at the centre is twice the angle at the circumference.

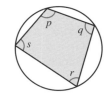

$p + r = 180°$ and $q + s = 180°$
Opposite angles of a cyclic quadrilateral are supplementary.

- The vertices of a **cyclic quadrilateral** lie on the circumference of a circle.

- A tangent is perpendicular to the radius at the point of contact.

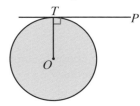

- **Alternate segment theorem**.
  The angle between a tangent and a chord is equal to any angle in the alternate (opposite) segment.

- Tangents drawn to a circle from the same point are equal in length.

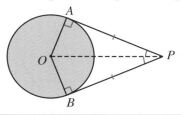

**You should be able to prove that:**
- the angle at the centre is twice the angle at the circumference,
- the angle in a semi-circle is a right angle,
- angles in the same segment are equal,
- opposite angles of a cyclic quadrilateral are supplementary,
- the angle between a tangent and a chord is equal to any angle in the alternate segment.

## Review Exercise 24

The diagrams in this exercise have not been drawn accurately.

**1** *O* is the centre of the circle.
Work out the size of the marked angles.

(a)

(b)

(c)

(d)

**2** In the diagram, *PT* is a tangent to the circle, centre *O*.
*RP* is a diameter.
Angle *ROQ* = 70°.

Work out *x*.
Show your method clearly.
Give a reason for each step of your work.

OCR

252

**3**

$W$, $X$, $Y$ and $Z$ are points on the circumference of a circle. The line $WY$ passes through $O$, the centre of the circle. Angle $YWX = 49°$.

Find the following angles, giving a reason for each answer.
(a)  Angle $WXY$.
(b)  Angle $YZX$.
(c)  Angle $YOX$.

OCR

**4**  $TA$ and $TB$ are tangents to the circle, centre $O$. $C$ is a point on the circle such that angle $ACB = 83°$. Work out the size of angle $x$. Give a reason for each step of your calculation.

OCR

**5**

$O$ is the centre of the circle. Tangents are drawn from $T$ to touch the circle at $A$ and $B$. Angle $OBA = 35°$. Explain why angle $ATB = 70°$.

**6**  $O$ is the centre of the circle. $ABC$ is a tangent to the circle at $B$. Work out the size of angles $x$, $y$ and $z$.

**7**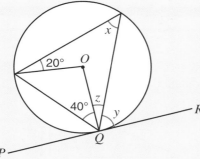

In the diagram, $O$ is the centre of the circle and $PQR$ is a tangent to the circle. Find the values of the angles marked $x$, $y$ and $z$.

**8**  $A$, $B$, $C$ and $D$ are points on a circle. $AB$ is equal in length and parallel to $CD$. Lines $AD$ and $BC$ intersect at $E$. Angle $EDC = 35°$.

(a)  Find the size of angle $AEC$. Show all your working.
(b)  What does this tell you about point $E$?
Give a reason for your answer.

OCR

**9**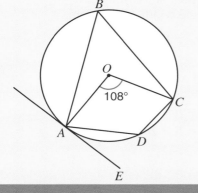

The diagram shows a circle with centre $O$. $ABCD$ is a cyclic quadrilateral. Angle $AOC = 108°$.

(a)  Prove that angle $ADC$ is $126°$.
(b)  $AE$ is the tangent at $A$.
Find angle $CAE$, giving your reasons.

OCR

# Perimeters and Areas

## Perimeter

The **perimeter** is the distance round the outside of a shape.
The perimeter of a rectangle (or square) is the sum of the lengths of its four sides.

## Area

**Area** is the amount of surface covered by a shape.
The standard unit for measuring area is the square centimetre, cm².
Small areas are measured using square millimetres, mm².
Large areas are measured using square metres, m², or square kilometres, km².

1 cm

1 cm² 1 cm

## Area formulae

| **Triangle** | **Rectangle** | **Parallelogram** | **Trapezium** |
|---|---|---|---|
| $A = \frac{1}{2} \times b \times h$ | $A = lb$ | $A = bh$ | $A = \frac{1}{2}(a + b)h$ |

## EXAMPLES

**1** Find the perimeter and area of this rectangle.

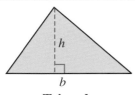

2.4 cm

1.5 cm

$$\text{Perimeter} = 1.5 + 2.4 + 1.5 + 2.4$$
$$= 7.8 \, \text{cm}$$
$$\text{Area} = \text{length} \times \text{breadth}$$
$$= 2.4 \times 1.5$$
$$= 3.6 \, \text{cm}^2$$

**3** Find the area of this trapezium.

5 cm

6 cm

9 cm

$$A = \frac{1}{2}(a + b)h$$
$$= \frac{1}{2}(5 + 9)6$$
$$= \frac{1}{2} \times 14 \times 6$$
$$= 42 \, \text{cm}^2$$

**2** Calculate the area of this triangle.

7 cm

12 cm

$$A = \frac{1}{2} \times b \times h$$
$$= \frac{1}{2} \times 12 \times 7$$
$$= 42 \, \text{cm}^2$$

**4** The area of a rectangular room is 17.5 m².
The room is 5 m long.
Find the width of the room.

Area = 17.5 m² $b$

5 m

$$A = lb$$
$$17.5 = 5 \times b$$
$$b = \frac{17.5}{5}$$
$$b = 3.5 \, \text{m}$$

1 Calculate the perimeters and areas of these rectangles and squares.

(a)

2.5 cm
1.5 cm

(b)

3 cm
1.8 cm

(c)

7 cm
7 cm

2 Calculate the areas of these triangles.

(a)

3 cm
6 cm

(b)

2.6 cm
3.2 cm

(c)

5 cm
3.2 cm

3 Calculate the areas of these shapes.

(a)

3 cm
4.5 cm

(b)

3 cm
4 cm
7 cm

(c)

2 cm
1.5 cm
3.8 cm

4 These shapes each have an area of 36 cm².
Calculate the lengths of the marked sides.

(a)

12 cm
*a*

(b)

6 cm
*b*

(c)

8 cm
*c*

5 A carpet measuring 4 m by 4 m is placed on a rectangular floor measuring 5 m by 6 m.
What area of floor is not carpeted?

6 A square has a perimeter of 20 cm.
Calculate the area of the square.

7 The diagram shows a picture in a rectangular frame.
The outer dimensions of the frame are 18 cm by 10 cm.
The frame is 2 cm wide.
What is the area of the picture?

2 cm
2 cm
10 cm
18 cm

8 A trapezium has an area of 30 cm².
The two parallel sides are 7 cm and 8 cm.
What is the perpendicular distance between these sides?

9 This triangle has an area of 150 cm².
Calculate the perimeter of the triangle.

20 cm
25 cm

### The Greek letter $\pi$

The circumference of any circle is just a bit bigger than three times the diameter of the circle.

The Greek letter $\pi$ is used to represent this number.

We use an approximate value for $\pi$, such as 3, $3\frac{1}{7}$, 3.14, or the $\pi$ key on a calculator, depending on the accuracy we require.

## Circumference of a circle

The diagram shows a circle with radius $r$ and diameter $d$.

The **circumference**, $C$, of a circle can be found using the formulae:

$$C = \pi \times d \quad \text{or} \quad C = 2 \times \pi \times r$$

### EXAMPLES

**1** Find the circumference of a circle with diameter 80 cm. Take $\pi$ to be 3.14.
Give your answer to the nearest centimetre.

$C = \pi \times d$
$\phantom{C} = 3.14 \times 80 \, \text{cm}$
$\phantom{C} = 251.2 \, \text{cm}$        Circumference is 251 cm to the nearest centimetre.

**2** A circle has circumference 37.2 cm.
Find the radius of the circle, giving your answer to the nearest millimetre. Take $\pi = 3.14$.

$C = 2 \times \pi \times r$
$37.2 = 2 \times 3.14 \times r$
$37.2 = 6.28 \times r$
$\phantom{37.2} r = \frac{37.2}{6.28}$
$\phantom{37.2} r = 5.923\ldots$        $r = 5.9 \, \text{cm}$, to the nearest millimetre.

## Exercise 25.2     Take $\pi$ to be 3.14 or use the $\pi$ key on your calculator.

**1** Calculate the circumference of these brackets.

(a)
4 cm

(b)
2.5 cm

(c)
7 cm

(d)
4.5 cm

**2** A circular biscuit tin has a diameter of 24 cm. What is the circumference of the tin?

**3** A circle has a radius of 6.5 cm. Calculate the circumference of the circle.
Give your answer correct to one decimal place.

**4** The circumference of a copper pipe is 94 mm.
Find, to the nearest millimetre, the diameter of the pipe.

**5** The circumference of a bicycle wheel is 190 cm.
Find the diameter of the wheel,
giving your answer to the nearest centimetre.

**6** The circumference of the London Eye is approximately 420 metres.
What is the radius? Give your answer correct to the nearest metre.

## Area of a circle

The area of a circle can be found using the formula: $A = \pi \times r^2$

### EXAMPLES

**1** Estimate the area of a circle with radius of 6 cm.
Take $\pi$ to be 3.

$A = \pi \times r \times r$
$= 3 \times 6 \times 6$
$= 108 \text{ cm}^2$

Area is approximately 108 cm².

**2** Calculate the area of a circle with diameter 10 cm.
Give your answer in terms of $\pi$.

> **Remember:** $r = \frac{d}{2}$

$A = \pi \times r \times r$
$= \pi \times 5 \times 5$
$= 25\pi \text{ cm}^2$

The area of the circle is $25\pi \text{ cm}^2$.

**3** The top of a tin of cat food has an area of 78.5 cm².
What is the radius of the tin?
Take $\pi = 3.14$.

$A = \pi \times r^2$

Substitute values for $A$ and $\pi$.

$78.5 = 3.14 \times r^2$

Solve this equation to find $r$.

Divide both sides of the equation by 3.14.

$\frac{78.5}{3.14} = r^2$

$r^2 = 25$

Take the square root of both sides.

$r = 5$

The radius of the tin is 5 cm.

---

### Exercise 25.3

Take $\pi$ to be 3.14 or use the $\pi$ key on your calculator.

**1** Calculate the areas of these circles. Give your answers correct to one decimal place.

(a)
4 cm

(b)
6 cm

(c)
7.5 cm

(d)
26 cm

**2** Calculate the shaded area in each of these diagrams.

(a)
3 cm   3 cm
6 cm

(b)
1.5 cm
4.6 cm

(c)
2.3 cm
6.8 cm

**3** A circle has an area of 50 cm².
Calculate the radius of the circle.

**4** A circular flower bed has an area of 40 m².
Calculate the diameter of the flower bed.
Give your answer to a suitable degree of accuracy.

**Perimeters and Areas**

# Mixed questions involving circumferences and areas of circles

Some questions will involve finding the area and some the circumference of a circle.

**Remember:** Choose the correct formula for area or circumference.

You need to think about whether to use the radius or the diameter.

In this exercise take $\pi$ to be 3.14 or use the $\pi$ key on your calculator.

**1**   Thirty students join hands to form a circle.
The diameter of the circle is 8.5 m.
  (a)   Find the circumference of the circle.
        Give your answer to the nearest metre.
  (b)   What area is enclosed by the circle?

**2**   A semi-circle has a radius of 6 cm.
Find the perimeter of a semi-circle with radius 6 cm.
Give your answer to the nearest whole number.

**3**   Which has the greater area:
        **a circle with radius 4 cm, or a semi-circle with diameter 11 cm?**
You must show all your working.

**4**   The radius of a circular plate is 15 cm.
  (a)   What is its area?
  (b)   What is its circumference?
Give your answers in terms of $\pi$.

**5**   The wheel of a wheelbarrow rotates 60 times
when it is pushed a distance of 50 m.
Calculate the radius of the wheel.

**6**   Calculate the area of a semi-circle with a diameter of 6.8 cm.

**7**   Calculate the perimeter of a semi-circle with a radius of 7.5 cm.

**8**   A pastry cutter is in the shape of a semi-circle.
The straight side of the semi-circle is 12 cm long.
How long is the curved side?

**9**   A circle has a circumference of 64 cm. Calculate the area of the circle.

**10**   A circle has an area of 128 cm². Calculate the circumference of the circle.

**11**   A circle has a circumference of $14\pi$ cm. Calculate the area of the circle in terms of $\pi$.

**12**   A circle has an area of $144\pi$ cm². Calculate the circumference of the circle in terms of $\pi$.

**13**   The diagram shows a small circle drawn inside a larger circle.
The shaded area is $55\pi$ cm².
The small circle has a radius of 3 cm.
Calculate the radius of the larger circle.

**14**   The diagram shows a small circle drawn inside a larger circle.
The small circle has an area of $16\pi$ cm².
The larger circle has a circumference of $18\pi$ cm.
Calculate the shaded area.
Give your answer in terms of $\pi$.

## Compound shapes

Shapes formed by joining different shapes together are called **compound shapes**.
To find the area of a compound shape we must first divide the shape up into rectangles, triangles, circles, etc, and then find the area of each part.
Shapes can be divided in different ways, but they should all give the same answer.

### EXAMPLE

Calculate the area of this shape.
Give the answer correct to three significant figures.

The shape can be split into: a rectangle $ABCD$,
a trapezium $BXYC$ and
a semi-circle $XYZ$.

Area $ABCD = 4.8 \times 3.2$ $= 15.36\,cm^2$

Area $BXYC = 0.5(4.8 + 2.6) \times 2.5$ $= 9.25\,cm^2$

Area $XZY = 0.5 \times \pi \times 1.3^2$ $= 2.65...\,cm^2$

Total area $= 15.36 + 9.25 + 2.65... = 27.26...$
$= 27.3\,cm^2$, to 3 s.f.

## Exercise 25.5

**1** Find the areas of these shapes which are made up of rectangles.

(a)

(b)

**2** Find the areas of these shapes.

(a)

(b)

(c)

**3** Calculate the shaded areas in each of these shapes.

(a)

(b)

(c)

A circle can be divided up in different ways.

**Segment** – a chord divides a circle into two segments.

**Sector** – two radii divide a circle into two sectors.

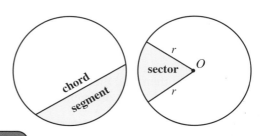

## Lengths of arcs and areas of sectors

The lengths of arcs and the areas of sectors of circles are in proportion to the angle at the centre of the circle.

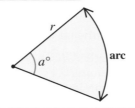

For a sector with angle $a°$    Length of arc $= \frac{a}{360} \times \pi d$    Area of sector $= \frac{a}{360} \times \pi r^2$

### EXAMPLE

This shape is a sector of a circle with radius 9 cm and angle 80°.
Calculate   (a)   the length of arc $AB$,
                  (b)   the area of sector $OAB$.

(a)   Length $AB = \frac{a}{360} \times \pi d$

$= \frac{80}{360} \times \pi \times 18$

$= 12.56...$

$= 12.6$ cm, to 3 s.f.

(b)   Area $OAB = \frac{a}{360} \times \pi r^2$

$= \frac{80}{360} \times \pi \times 9^2$

$= 56.54...$

$= 56.5$ cm², to 3 s.f.

## Exercise 25.6

Take $\pi$ to be 3.14 or use the $\pi$ key on your calculator.
Give answers correct to three significant figures.

**1**   Calculate (a) the length of the arc of each sector and (b) the area of each sector.

(i)

90°
2 cm

(ii)

40°
3 cm

(iii)

80°
4.5 cm

(iv)

125°
4.8 cm

(v)

160°
5.6 cm

(vi)

210°
7.2 cm

**2** $OPQ$ is a sector of a circle with radius 20 cm.
$X$ is the midpoint of $OP$ and $Y$ is the midpoint of $OQ$.
Angle $POQ = 65°$.

Calculate
(a)  the area of $XPQY$,
(b)  the perimeter of $XPQY$.

**3**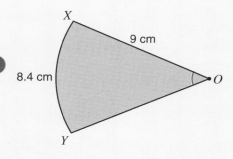

$OXY$ is a sector of a circle, centre $O$, with radius 9 cm.
The arc length of the sector is 8.4 cm.

Calculate the size of angle $XOY$.

**4** $OPQ$ is a sector of a circle, centre $O$.
The arc length of the sector is 15.6 cm.
Angle $POQ = 135°$.

Calculate the radius of the circle.

**5**

$AB$ and $DC$ are arcs of a circle, centre $O$.
$OA = 15$ cm   and   angle $AOB = 85°$.
The area of $ABCD$ is 100 cm².

Calculate
(a)  the length of $OD$,
(b)  the length of the arc $DC$.

**6** The diagram shows a quadrant of a circle, centre $O$.
Calculate the area of the shaded segment.

**7**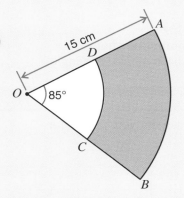

$OAB$ is a sector of a circle, centre $O$, with radius 9 cm.
The sector has an area of 13.5 cm².

Calculate the size of angle $a$.

**8** A sector of a circle has an area of 30 cm².
Angle $a = 72°$.

Calculate the radius of the circle.

Perimeters and Areas

# What you need to know

- **Perimeter** is the distance round the outside of a shape.
- **Area** is the amount of surface covered by a shape.
- **Area formulae**

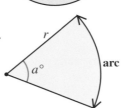

**Triangle**
$A = \frac{1}{2} \times b \times h$

**Rectangle**
$A = lb$

**Parallelogram**
$A = bh$

**Trapezium**
$A = \frac{1}{2}(a + b)h$

- The **circumference** of a circle is given by:
  $C = \pi \times d$ or $C = 2 \times \pi \times r$
- The **area** of a circle is given by: $A = \pi r^2$
- A **chord** divides a circle into two **segments**.
  **Two radii** divide a circle into two **sectors**.
- The **lengths of arcs** and the **areas of sectors** are proportional to the angle at the centre of the circle.
  For a sector with angle $a°$

  Length of arc $= \frac{a}{360} \times \pi d$

  Area of sector $= \frac{a}{360} \times \pi r^2$

- Shapes formed by joining different shapes together are called **compound shapes**.
  To find the area of a compound shape we must first divide the shape up into rectangles, triangles, circles, etc, and then find the area of each part.

## Review Exercise 25

Take $\pi$ to be 3.14 or use the $\pi$ key on your calculator.

**1** A house has a back garden with dimensions, as shown.
Calculate the area of the garden.

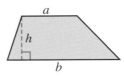

20 m
15 m
28 m

OCR

**2**

9 cm
8 cm

The diagram shows a square drawn inside a rectangle.
The shaded area is $47 \text{ cm}^2$.
What is the perimeter of the square?

**3**  The diagram shows two pulleys.
The larger pulley has radius 5 cm. The smaller pulley has diameter 8 cm.
(a) What is the area of the larger pulley?
(b) What is the circumference of the smaller pulley?

**4**

Michael's bicycle wheels each have a radius of 28 cm.
He cycles to work each day.
The length of the journey is 4.4 km.
How many times does each wheel go round on one journey?

OCR

262

**5** Boats are not allowed within 35 m of lighthouse L.
The diagram shows this region.
Calculate the shaded semi-circular area.

OCR

**6**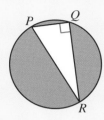

P, Q and R are points on the circumference of a circle, as shown.
The triangle PQR is right angled.
PQ = 5 cm, QR = 12 cm and PR = 13 cm.
Work out the area of the shaded part of the circle.

**7** A trapezium, ABCD, has an area of 48.1 cm².
The parallel sides, BC and AD, are 7.4 cm apart.
BC = 4.3 cm.
Calculate the length of AD.

**8** A circle has a circumference of 42 cm.
Calculate the area of the circle.
Give your answer correct to two significant figures.

**9**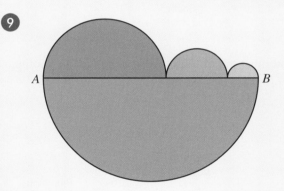

Four semi-circles are drawn on the line AB, as shown.
AB = 14 cm.

(a) Work out the perimeter of the shape.
Give your answer in terms of π.
Explain how you worked out your answer.

(b) The radii of the semi-circles are in the ratio 7 : 4 : 2 : 1.
Calculate the area of the shape.
Give your answer in terms of π.

**10** OXYZ is a sector of a circle, centre O, radius 4 cm.
Angle XOZ is 50°.
(a) Calculate the length of the arc XYZ.
(b) Calculate the area of the sector.

**11**

OABC is a sector of a circle, centre O.
OA = 6 cm, angle AOC = 210°.
The sector is folded to make a cone, as shown.
Calculate the radius of the cone.

**12** The diagram shows two sectors.
Paul says the areas and perimeters of these sectors are the same.
Is he right?
Show working to explain your answer.

**13** The area of a sector of a circle is 25 cm².
The radius of the sector is 6 cm.
Calculate the perimeter of the sector.

# Maps, Loci and Constructions

## Maps

When planning journeys we often use **maps**.
To interpret maps we need to understand:
    **angles** in order to describe **direction**   and   **scales** in order to find **distances**.
**Compass points** and **three-figure bearings** are used to describe direction.

## Compass points

The diagram shows the points of the compass.

The angle between North and East is 90°.

The angle between North and North-East is 45°.

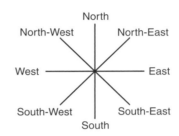

## Three-figure bearings

**Bearings** are used to describe the direction in which you must travel to get from one place to another.

A bearing is an angle measured from the North line in a clockwise direction.

The angle, which can be from 0° to 360°, is written as a three-figure number.

Bearings which are less than 100° include noughts to make up the three figures, e.g. 005°, 087°.

This diagram shows the positions of Bath and Poole.
The bearing of Poole from Bath is 162°.

If you are at Bath, facing North, and turn through 162° in a clockwise direction you will be facing in the direction of Poole.

## Back bearings

The return bearing of Bath from Poole is called a **back bearing**.
Back bearings can be found by using parallel lines and alternate angles.

The bearing of Poole from Bath is 162°.

$a = 162°$ (alternate angles)

Required angle = 180° + 162° = 342°.
The bearing of Bath from Poole (the back bearing) is 342°.

## Scale drawing

Maps and plans are scaled down representations of real-life situations.
The **scale** used in drawing a map or plan determines the amount of detail that can be shown.

The distances between different points on a map are all drawn to the same scale.
There are two ways to describe a scale.

**1** A scale of 1 cm to 10 km means that a distance of 1 cm on the map represents an actual distance of 10 km.

**2** A scale of 1 : 10 000 means that all distances measured on the map have to be multiplied by 10 000 to find the real distance.

### EXAMPLES

**1** A road is 3.7 cm long on a map.
The scale given on the map is '1 cm represents 10 km'.
What is the actual length of the road?

1 cm represents 10 km.
Scale up, so multiply.
3.7 cm represents 3.7 × 10 km = 37 km
The road is 37 km long.

**2** A plan of a field is to be drawn using a scale of 1 : 500.
Two trees in the field are 350 metres apart.
How far apart will they be on the plan?

Scale down, so divide.
Distance on plan = 350 m ÷ 500
Change 350 m to centimetres.
$\qquad$ = 35 000 cm ÷ 500 = 70 cm
The trees will be 70 cm apart on the plan.

## Exercise 26.1

**1** (a) Claire is facing South.
In which direction will she face after turning clockwise through an angle of 135°?
(b) Kevin turned anticlockwise through an angle of 270°.
He is now facing South-East.
In which direction was he facing?

**2** Here is a map of an island.
(a) Use your protractor to find:
(i) the bearing of $Q$ from $P$,
(ii) the bearing of $P$ from $Q$.

(b) (i) Measure the distance between $P$ and $Q$ on the map.
(ii) What is the actual distance between $P$ and $Q$?

Scale: 1 cm to 10 km

**3** The scale of a map is 1 : 200.
(a) On the map a house is 3.5 cm long. How long is the actual house?
(b) A field is 60 m wide. How wide is the field on the map?

**4** Helen drew a plan of her classroom using a scale of 5 cm to represent 1 m.
   (a) Write the scale Helen used in the form 1 : $n$.
   (b) On the plan, the length of the classroom is 29 cm.
       What is the actual length of the classroom?
   (c) The actual width of the classroom is 4.5 m.
       What is the width of the classroom on the plan?

**5** The diagram shows the plan of a cross-country course.
Runners have to go round markers at $A$, $B$ and $C$.

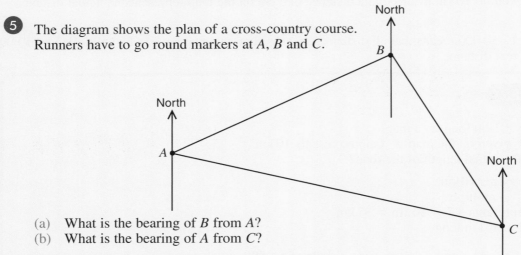

   (a) What is the bearing of $B$ from $A$?
   (b) What is the bearing of $A$ from $C$?

The plan has been drawn to a scale of 1 : 20 000.
   (c) What is the distance from $A$ to $C$ in metres?

**6** A building plot is a triangle with sides of length 60 m, 90 m and 100 m.
Construct an accurate scale drawing of the building plot.
Use a scale of 1 cm to 20 m.

**7** A boat leaves port and sails on a bearing of 144° for 4 km.
It then changes course and sails due East for 5 km to reach an island.
Find by scale drawing:
   (a) the distance of the island from the port,
   (b) the bearing of the island from the port,
   (c) the bearing on which the boat must sail to return directly to the port.

**8** A yacht sails on a bearing of 040° for 5000 m and then a further 3000 m on a bearing of 120°.
Find by scale drawing:
   (a) the distance of the yacht from its starting position,
   (b) the bearing on which it must sail to return directly to its starting position.

**9** An aircraft leaves an airport, at $A$, and flies on a bearing of 035° for 50 km and then on a
bearing of 280° for a further 40 km before landing at an airport, at $B$.
Find by scale drawing:
   (a) the distance between the airports,
   (b) the bearing of $B$ from $A$,
   (c) the bearing of $A$ from $B$.

## Locus

The path of a point which moves according to a rule is called a **locus**.
If we talk about more than one locus we call them **loci**.

For example:
John walks so that he is always 2 metres from a lamp post.

The locus of his path is a circle, radius 2 metres.

1   Adam goes down this slide. Make a sketch of the slide as viewed from the side and show the locus of Adam's head as he goes down the slide.

2   The diagram shows part of a rectangular lawn.
Starting from the wall, Sally walks across the lawn so that she is always the same distance from both hedges. Draw a sketch to show the locus of Sally's path.

3   *PQRS* is a square of side 8 cm.
A point *X* is inside the square.
*X* is less than 8 cm from *P*.
*X* is nearer to *PQ* than to *SR*.
Make a sketch showing where *X* could be.

4   A ball is rolled down a step.
Copy the diagram, and sketch the locus of *P*, the centre of the ball, as it rolls from *X* to *Y*.

5   A wire is stretched between two posts.
A ring slides along the wire and a dog is attached to the ring by a rope.
Make a sketch to show where the dog can go.

6   A point *P* is 1 cm from this shape.
Copy the diagram, and draw an accurate locus of **all** the positions of *P*.

Sometimes it is necessary to construct loci accurately.
You are expected to use only a ruler and compasses.
Here are the methods for two constructions.

### To draw the perpendicular bisector of a line

This means to draw a line at right angles to a given line dividing it into two equal parts.

**1** Draw line *AB*.

**2** Open your compasses to just over half the distance *AB*. Mark two arcs which cross at *C* and *D*.

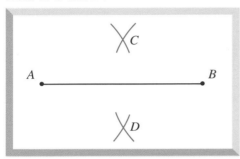

**3** Draw a line which passes through the points *C* and *D*.

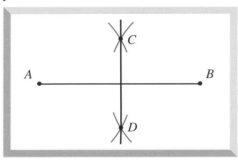

This line is the locus of a point which is the same distance from *A* and *B*.
Points on the line *CD* are **equidistant** (the same distance) from points *A* and *B*.
The line *CD* is at right angles to *AB*.
*CD* is sometimes called the **perpendicular bisector** of *AB*.

### To draw the bisector of an angle

This means to draw a line which divides an angle into two equal parts.

**1** Draw the angle *A*.
Use your compasses, centre *A*, to mark points *B* and *C* which are the same distance from *A*.

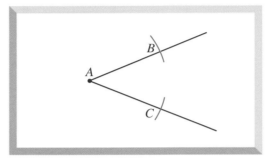

**2** Use points *B* and *C* to draw equal arcs which cross at *D*.

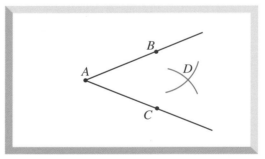

**3** Draw a line which passes through the points *A* and *D*.

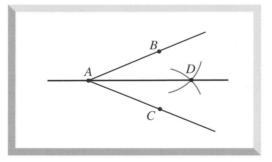

This line is the locus of a point which is the same distance from *AB* and *AC*.
Points on the line *AD* are **equidistant** from the lines through *AB* and *AC*.
The line *AD* cuts angle *BAC* in half.
*AD* is sometimes called the **bisector** of angle *BAC*.

1. Mark two points, *A* and *B*, 10 cm apart. Construct the perpendicular bisector of *AB*.

2. Use a protractor to draw an angle of 60°. Construct the bisector of the angle.
   Check that both angles are 30°.

3. Draw a triangle in the middle of a new page.
   Construct the perpendicular bisectors of all three sides. They should meet at a point, *Y*.

   Put the point of your compasses on *Y* and draw the circle which goes through all three vertices of the triangle. This construction is sometimes called the **circumscribed circle of a triangle**.

4. Draw another triangle on a new page. Bisect each angle of the triangle.
   The bisectors should meet at a point, *X*.

   Put the point of your compasses on point *X* and draw the circle which just touches each side of the triangle. This construction is sometimes called the **inscribed circle of a triangle**.

5.

   Using a circle of radius 4 cm, copy the diagram.
   Draw the perpendicular bisectors of the chords *WX* and *YZ*.
   What do you notice about the perpendicular bisectors?

   > The perpendicular bisector of a chord always passes through the centre of a circle.

6. Two trees are 6 metres apart.
   Alan walks so that he is always an equal distance from each tree.
   Draw a scale diagram to show his path.

7. *ABC* is an equilateral triangle with sides 4 cm.

   A point *X* is inside the triangle.
   It is nearer to *AB* than to *BC*.
   It is less than 3 cm from *A*.
   It is less than 2 cm from *BC*.
   Shade the region in which *X* could lie.

8. Draw a rectangle *ABCD* with  *AB* = 6 cm  and  *AD* = 4 cm.
   (a) Mark, with a thin line, the locus of a point which is 1 cm from *AB*.
   (b) Mark, with a dotted line, the locus of a point which is the same distance from *A* and *B*.
   (c) Mark, with a dashed line, the locus of a point which is 3 cm from *A*.

**9** Draw a right-angled triangle with sides of 6 cm, 8 cm and 10 cm.

A point *X* is in the triangle.
It is 4 cm from *B*.
It is the same distance from *A* and *B*.

Mark accurately, the position of *X*.

**10** Copy the diagram and draw the locus of a point which is the same distance from *PQ* and *RS*.

**11** Triangle *ABC* is isosceles with $AB = BC = 7$ cm and $AC = 6$ cm.
(a) Construct triangle *ABC*.
(b) Point *X* is equidistant from *A*, *B* and *C*. Mark accurately the position of *X*.

**12** (a) The diagram shows the sketch of a field.
Make a scale drawing of the field using 1 cm to represent 100 m.

(b) A tree is 400 m from corner *D* and 350 m from corner *C*.
Mark the position of the tree on your drawing.
(c) John walks across the field from corner *D*, keeping the same distance from *AD* and *CD*.
Show his path on your diagram.
(d) Does John walk within 100 m of the tree in crossing the field?

**13** Part of a coastline is shown.

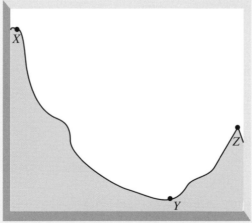

A boat is: (i) equidistant from *X* and *Z*, and (ii) equidistant from *XY* and *YZ*.
Copy the diagram and mark the position of the boat.

### To draw the perpendicular from a point to a line

This means to draw a line at right angles to a given line, from a point that **is not on the line**.

**1** Open your compasses so that from point *A* you can mark two arcs on the line *PQ*.

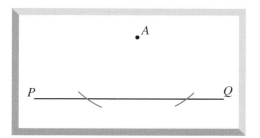

**2** Use points *B* and *C* to draw equal arcs which cross at *D*.

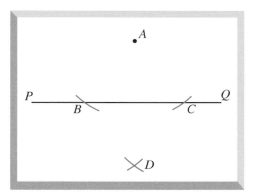

**3** Draw a line from *A* to *D*.

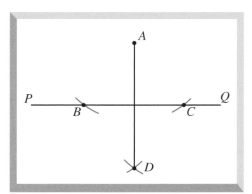

The line *AD* is perpendicular (at right angles) to the line *PQ*.

### To draw the perpendicular from a point on a line

This means to draw a line at right angles to a given line, from a point that **is on the line**.

Keep your compasses at the same setting whilst doing this construction.

**1** From *A*, draw an arc which cuts the line *PQ*.

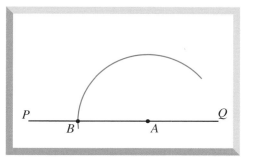

**2** From *B*, draw an arc to cut the first arc at *C*. Then from *C*, draw an arc to cut the first arc at *D*.

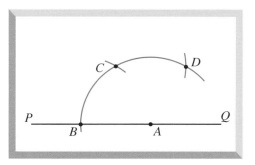

**3** From *C* and *D*, draw arcs to meet at *E*. Draw the line *AE*.

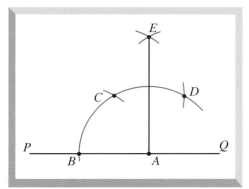

The line *AE* is perpendicular (at right angles) to the line *PQ*.

**Maps, Loci and Constructions**

271

**1** Draw a line *PQ*, 8 cm long.
Mark a point *A*, about 5 cm above the line.
Draw the line which passes through *A* and is perpendicular to line *PQ*.

**2** Draw a line *PQ*, 8 cm long. Mark a point *A*, somewhere on the line.

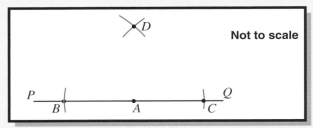

(a) Using your compasses, mark points *B* and *C*, which are 3 cm from *A* on the line *PQ*.
(b) Set your compasses to 5 cm.
Draw arcs from *B* and *C* which intersect at *D*.
(c) Draw the line *AD*.

**3** Using ruler and compasses only, make an accurate drawing
of the triangle shown in this sketch.

**4**

(a) Make an accurate drawing of this triangle.
(b) The **altitude** of the triangle is a line
perpendicular to a side which passes
through the opposite corner of the triangle.
Draw the altitude of the triangle *ABC* which
passes through point *B*.

**5** (a) Copy the diagram.
(b) Mark all points inside the rectangle that are
less than 2 cm from the line *AB*.

**6**

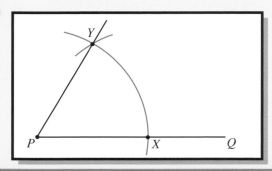

Draw a line *PQ*, 5 cm long.
Using compasses, draw an arc centre *P*
to cut *PQ* at *X*.
With your compasses at the same setting draw
another arc, centre *X*, to cut the first arc at *Y*.
Draw a line through *PY*.
Measure angle *XPY*.
What do you find?
Show how you can use this construction to
draw angles of 30° and 120°.

- **Compass points** and **three-figure bearings** are used to describe direction.
- A **bearing** is an angle measured from the North line in a clockwise direction.
- A bearing can be any angle from 0° to 360° and is written as a three-figure number.
- To find a bearing:
    measure angle $a$ to find the bearing of $Y$ from $X$,
    measure angle $b$ to find the bearing of $X$ from $Y$.

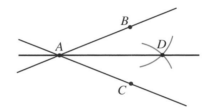

- **Scales**
  The distances between points on a map are all drawn to the same scale.
  There are two ways to describe a scale.
  1. A scale of 1 cm to 10 km means that a distance of 1 cm on the map represents an actual distance of 10 km.
  2. A scale of 1 : 10 000 means that all distances measured on the map have to be multiplied by 10 000 to find the real distance.
- The path of a point which moves according to a rule is called a **locus**.
- The word **loci** is used when we talk about more than one locus.

**Using a ruler and compasses you should be able to:**
- Construct the **perpendicular from a point to a line**.
- Construct the **perpendicular from a point on a line**.
- Construct the **perpendicular bisector of a line**.
- Construct the **bisector of an angle**.

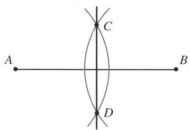

Points on the line $CD$ are **equidistant** from the points $A$ and $B$.

Points on the line $AD$ are **equidistant** from the lines $AB$ and $AC$.

1. A coin is rolled along a line.
   Sketch the locus of a point which starts off at the bottom.

   What is the locus of the point if the coin rolls around another coin, or if the coins are not round, or … ?

   Investigate.

2. **3-dimensional coordinates**
   One coordinate identifies a point on a line.
   Two coordinates identify a point on a plane.
   Three coordinates identify a point in space.

   The diagram shows a cuboid drawn in 3-dimensions.

   Using the axes $x$, $y$ and $z$ shown:
   Point $A$ is given as (0, 2, 0).
   Point $B$ is given as (2, 2, 0).
   Point $C$ is given as (2, 2, 3).

   Give the 3-dimensional coordinates of points $D$, $E$, $F$, and $G$.

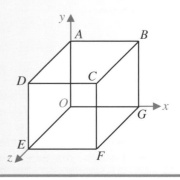

**Maps, Loci and Constructions**

**1**  The diagram shows the plan of a sailboard race.
The sailboards have to go round buoys at *A*, *B* and *C*.
Buoy *B* is on a bearing of 050° from buoy *A*.
Angle *ABC* is 90°.
  (a)  What is the bearing of *A* from *B*?
  (b)  What is the bearing of *C* from *B*?

The plan has been drawn to a scale of 1 : 20 000.
  (c)  (i)   Measure *AB*.
       (ii)  What is the distance from *A* to *B* in metres?

**2**  Buxbourne is 40 km from Ashwell.
The bearing of Buxbourne from Ashwell is 115°.
Chris is house hunting. He has decided he would like to live closer to Buxbourne than
Ashwell but no further than 30 km from Ashwell.
By using a scale of 1 cm to 5 km, draw a plan to show the positions of Ashwell and
Buxbourne and shade the area in which Chris should look for a house.                     OCR

**3**  (a)  Use ruler and compasses only to construct an equilateral triangle of side 4 cm.
     (b)  A point, *P*, is 1 cm from the edge of the triangle.
          Draw an accurate locus of **all** the possible positions of *P*.

**4**  (a)  Use ruler and compasses only to construct a parallelogram, *ABCD*, with
          *AB* = 5 cm,  *AD* = 7 cm  and  angle *BAD* = 60°.
     (b)  The bisector of angle *ADC* meets *BC* at *E*.
          Construct the bisector of angle *ADC* and measure *BE*.

**5**  In this question, use ruler and compasses only.
Triangle *LRB* is the plan of a garden.
A lime tree (*L*), a rowan tree (*R*) and a beech tree (*B*)
are at the corners of the garden.

  (a)  Use a scale of 1 cm to 1 m to construct an
       accurate plan of the garden.
  (b)  Construct the perpendicular bisector of *LR* on your plan.
       Show your construction lines clearly.
  (c)  Diana wants to put a bird table in the garden.
       The bird table must be nearer the rowan tree than the lime tree.
       It must also be within 4 metres of the beech tree.
       Shade the region on your plan where the bird table may be placed.            OCR

**6**  *PQRS* shows a sketch of a park.
  (a)  Use ruler and compasses only to construct a plan of the park using a scale of 1 cm to
       represent 100 m.

A fountain is:
       (i)   equidistant from *P* and *Q*,
       (ii)  equidistant from *PS* and *SR*.
  (b)  Draw the locus for (i) and (ii) on your plan and, hence, find the position of the fountain.
       Label it with the letter *F*.
  (c)  Find the distance, in metres, of the fountain from *R*.

**CHAPTER** **27**  **Transformations** ● ● ● ● ● ● ● ● ●

The movement of a shape from one position to another is called a **transformation**.
The change in position of the shape can be described in terms of a **reflection**, a **rotation** or a **translation**.
Later in the chapter you will meet another transformation, called an **enlargement**.

## Reflection

Look at this diagram.
It shows the reflection of shape $P$ in the line $x = 4$.

Shape $P_1$ is the **image** of $P$.
We also say that $P$ is **mapped** onto $P_1$.

When a shape is reflected it stays the same shape and size.

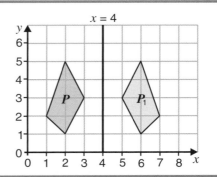

### EXAMPLE

Copy the shape below onto squared paper.
Draw the reflection of triangle $ABC$ in the line $y = x$.
Label the image $A_1 B_1 C_1$.

 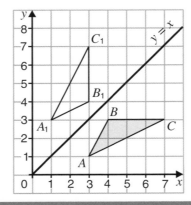

Notice that:
$A(3, 1) \rightarrow A_1(1, 3)$
$B(4, 3) \rightarrow B_1(3, 4)$
$C(7, 3) \rightarrow C_1(3, 7)$
*Can you see a pattern?*

## Exercise 27.1

① In the diagram $P$ is the point $(2, 1)$.

Find the coordinates of the image of $P$ under a reflection in
(a) the $x$ axis,
(b) the $y$ axis,
(c) the line $x = 1$,
(d) the line $y = -1$,
(e) the line $y = x$.

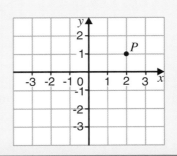

275

**2** Copy each of the following diagrams onto squared paper and draw the reflection of each shape in the line given.

(a)

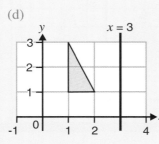

Reflect in the *y* axis.

(b)

Reflect in the *x* axis.

(c)

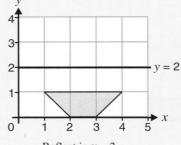

Reflect in *y* = 2.

(d)

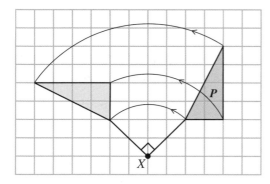

Reflect in *x* = 3.

(e)

Reflect in *y* = −1.

(f)

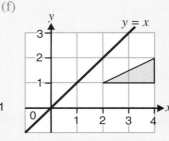

Reflect in *y* = *x*.

**3** The diagram shows a quadrilateral *ABCD*.
Give the coordinates of *B* after:
(a)   a reflection in the *x* axis,
(b)   a reflection in the *y* axis,
(c)   a reflection in the line   *x* = 3,
(d)   a reflection in the line   *x* = −1,
(e)   a reflection in the line   *y* = *x*.

## Rotation

Look at this diagram.
It shows the **rotation** of a shape *P* through $\frac{1}{4}$ turn anticlockwise about centre *X*.

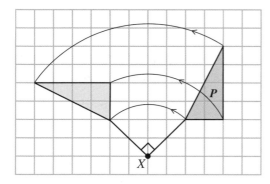

When describing rotations the direction of turn can be **clockwise** or **anticlockwise**.

Remember:

clockwise          anticlockwise

All points on shape *P* are turned through the same angle about the same point.
This point is called the **centre of rotation**.

When a shape is rotated it stays the same shape and size but its **position** on the page changes.

For a rotation we need: a centre of rotation, an amount of turn, a direction of turn.

## EXAMPLE

Copy triangle *ABC* onto squared paper.
Draw the image of triangle *ABC* after it has been rotated through 90° clockwise about the point *P* (1, 1).
Label the image $A_1B_1C_1$.

## Exercise **27.2**

**1**  Copy each of these shapes onto squared paper.
Draw the new position of each shape after the rotation given.

(a)

(b)

(c)

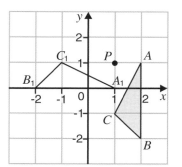

$\frac{1}{4}$ **turn clockwise about centre *X*.**     $\frac{1}{2}$ **turn about centre *X*.**     $\frac{3}{4}$ **turn anticlockwise about centre *X*.**

**2**  Copy each of these shapes onto squared paper.
Draw the new position of each shape after the rotation given.

(a)

(b)

(c)

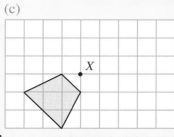

**90° clockwork about (0, 0).**     **90° anticlockwise about (0, 0).**     **180° about (0, 0).**

**3**  The diagram shows a quadrilateral *ABCD*.

Give the coordinates of *B* after:
(a)  a rotation through 90°, clockwise about (0, 0),
(b)  a rotation through 90°, anticlockwise about (0, 0),
(c)  a rotation through 180°, about (0, 0),
(d)  a rotation through 90°, clockwise about (2, 1),
(e)  a rotation through 90°, anticlockwise about (2, 1),
(f)  a rotation through 180°, about (2, 1).

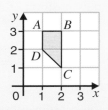

## Translation

Look at this diagram. It shows a **translation** of a shape $P$.

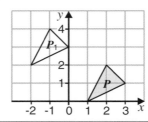

$P$ is mapped onto $P_1$.
All points on the shape $P$ are moved the same distance in the same direction without turning.
A translation can be given:

- in terms of a **distance** and a **direction**, e.g. 2 units to the right and 1 unit down.
- with a vector, e.g. $\left(\begin{smallmatrix} 2 \\ -1 \end{smallmatrix}\right)$.

When a **vector** is used to describe a translation:
the top number describes the **horizontal** part of the movement:
  $+$ = to the right, $\qquad$ $-$ = to the left
the bottom number describes the **vertical** part of the movement:
  $+$ = upwards, $\qquad$ $-$ = downwards

When a shape is translated it stays the same shape and size and has the same orientation.

### EXAMPLE

Copy triangle $P$ onto squared paper.

The translation $\left(\begin{smallmatrix} -3 \\ 2 \end{smallmatrix}\right)$ maps $P$ onto $P_1$.

Draw and label $P_1$.

**Vector notation:**
$\left(\begin{smallmatrix} -3 \\ 2 \end{smallmatrix}\right)$ means move triangle $P$
3 units to the left and 2 units up.

## Exercise 27.3

**1** Copy the shape onto squared paper.
Draw the new position of the shape after each of the following translations:
  (a) 2 units to the right and 3 units up,
  (b) 1 unit to the right and 2 units down,
  (c) 3 units to the left and 2 units up,
  (d) 1 unit to the left and 3 units down.

**2** Copy the shape onto squared paper.
Draw the new position of the shape after each of the following translations.

  (a) $\left(\begin{smallmatrix} 3 \\ 2 \end{smallmatrix}\right)$ $\qquad$ (b) $\left(\begin{smallmatrix} 2 \\ -3 \end{smallmatrix}\right)$ $\qquad$ (c) $\left(\begin{smallmatrix} -2 \\ 3 \end{smallmatrix}\right)$ $\qquad$ (d) $\left(\begin{smallmatrix} -2 \\ -3 \end{smallmatrix}\right)$

**3** The translation $\left(\begin{smallmatrix} 2 \\ -1 \end{smallmatrix}\right)$ maps $S\,(5,\ 3)$ onto $T$.

What are the coordinates of $T$?

**4** Write down the translation which maps:
  (a) $X(1, 1)$ onto $P(3, 2)$,
  (b) $X(1, 1)$ onto $Q(2, -1)$,
  (c) $X(1, 1)$ onto $R(-2, 2)$,
  (d) $X(1, 1)$ onto $S(-2, -1)$.

**5** The diagram shows quadrilateral $S$.
  Copy $S$ onto squared paper.

  (a) The translation $\begin{pmatrix} 3 \\ 2 \end{pmatrix}$ maps $S$ onto $T$.
    Draw and label $T$.

  (b) Write down the translation which maps $T$ onto $S$.

**6** The translation $\begin{pmatrix} -2 \\ -3 \end{pmatrix}$ maps $A$ onto $B$ and the translation $\begin{pmatrix} -1 \\ 2 \end{pmatrix}$ maps $C$ onto $B$.

  (a) $B$ has coordinates $(-1, 2)$.
    What are the coordinates of $A$?

  (b) Write down the translation which maps $A$ onto $C$.

## Enlargement

This diagram shows another transformation, called an **enlargement**.
It shows an enlargement of a shape $P$ with scale factor 2 and centre $O$.

$P$ is mapped onto $P_1$.

When a shape is enlarged:
  **angles** remain unchanged,
  all **lengths** are multiplied by a **scale factor**.

**Scale factor** $= \dfrac{\text{new length}}{\text{original length}}$

For an enlargement we need:
  a centre of enlargement,
  a scale factor.

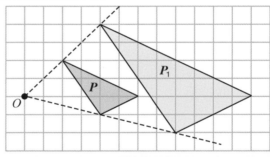

## Using a centre of enlargement

Draw a line from the centre of enlargement, $P$, to one corner, $A$.
Extend this line to $A'$ so that the length of $PA'$ = the scale factor $\times$ the length of $PA$.
Do the same for other corners of the shape.
Join up the corners to make the enlarged shape. Label the diagram.

### EXAMPLES

**1** Draw an enlargement of triangle $ABC$, centre $P(0, 1)$ and scale factor 3.

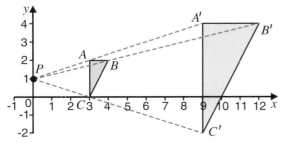

**2** Use centre $P(3, 2)$ and a scale factor of 2 to enlarge triangle $ABC$.

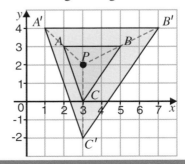

## Using a scale factor which is a fraction

When the scale factor is a value between 0 and 1, such as 0.5 or $\frac{1}{3}$, the new shape is smaller than the original shape.

Even though the shape gets smaller it is still called an enlargement.

**EXAMPLE**

Draw an enlargement of this shape with centre (0, 1) and scale factor $\frac{1}{3}$.

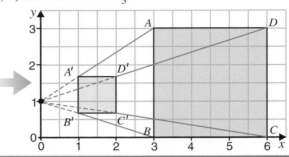

## Exercise 27.4

**1**   Copy this shape onto squared paper.
Enlarge the shape with scale factor 2, centre *X*.

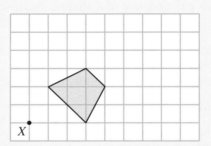

**2**   Copy each diagram onto squared paper and enlarge it using the centre and scale factor given.
You will need longer axes than those shown below.

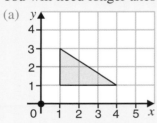

Centre (0, 0), scale factor 2.

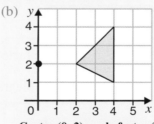

Centre (0, 2), scale factor 3.

Centre (3, 2), scale factor 2.

**3**   Copy the following shapes onto squared paper and draw the enlargement given.

(a)   Scale factor $\frac{1}{2}$, centre (1, 2).

(b)   Scale factor $\frac{1}{3}$, centre (0, 0).

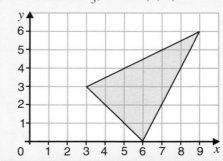

**4** The diagram shows a quadrilateral *ABCD*.
Give the coordinates of *B* after an enlargement:

  (a) scale factor 2, centre (0, 0),
  (b) scale factor 3, centre (0, 0),
  (c) scale factor 2, centre (0, 2),
  (d) scale factor 3, centre *C* (2, 1),
  (e) scale factor 2, centre *D* (1, 2),
  (f) scale factor 2, centre *A* (1, 3).

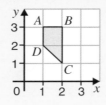

**5** For each of the following, give the coordinates of *B* after the enlargement given.

  (a) Scale factor $\frac{1}{3}$, centre (0, 1).

  (b) Scale factor $\frac{1}{2}$, centre (4, 3).

 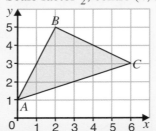

## Enlargement with a negative scale factor

Draw a line from one corner, *A*, to the centre of enlargement, *P*.
Extend this line to *A′* so that:
  the length of *PA′* = the scale factor × the length of *PA*.
Do the same for other corners of the shape.
Join up the corners to make the enlarged shape.
Label the diagram.

**EXAMPLE**

Draw an enlargement of triangle *ABC*, centre *P* (−2, −1) and scale factor −2.

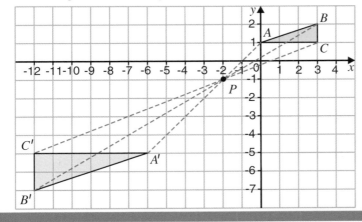

When a negative scale factor is used the image of the shape is **inverted**. *What does this mean?*

**Exercise 27.5**

**1** Copy this shape onto squared paper.
Enlarge the shape with scale factor −2, centre *X*.

**2** Copy the following shapes onto squared paper and draw the enlargement given.

(a) Scale factor $-1$, centre $(0, 0)$.

(b) Scale factor $-2$, centre $(-1, 0)$.

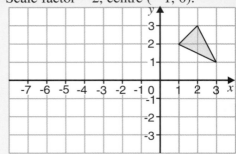

**3** Copy each diagram onto squared paper and enlarge it using the centre and scale factor given. You will need longer axes than those shown below.

(a)

Centre $(0, 0)$, scale factor $-2$.

(b)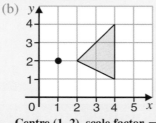

Centre $(1, 2)$, scale factor $-3$.

(c)

Centre $(2, 0)$, scale factor $-1$.

**4** Copy this shape onto squared paper.
Enlarge the shape with scale factor $-\frac{1}{2}$, centre $X$.

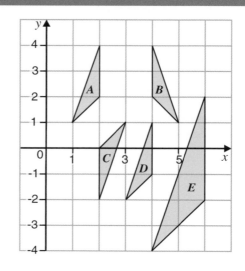

**5** Describe the images of shapes which have been enlarged using:

(a) $-1 <$ scale factor $< 0$,

(b) scale factor $= -1$,

(c) scale factor $< -1$.

**6** The diagram shows triangle $ABC$. Give the coordinates of $B$ after an enlargement:

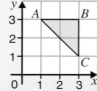

(a) scale factor $-2$, centre $(0, 0)$,

(b) scale factor $-2$, centre $A(1, 3)$,

(c) scale factor $-\frac{1}{2}$, centre $A(1, 3)$,

(d) scale factor $-\frac{1}{3}$, centre $(0, 0)$.

## Describing transformations

Look at the shapes in this diagram.

We can describe the single transformation which maps $A$ onto $B$ as a **reflection** in the line $x = 3$.

We can describe the single transformation which maps $A$ onto $C$ as a **rotation** of $180°$ about $(2, 1)$.

We can describe the single transformation which maps $A$ onto $D$ as a **translation** with vector $\begin{pmatrix} 2 \\ -3 \end{pmatrix}$.

We can describe the single transformation which maps $D$ onto $E$ as an **enlargement**, scale factor 2, centre $(2, 0)$.

The flow chart below can be used to decide what type of transformation has taken place. The details required to fully describe each type of transformation are also given.

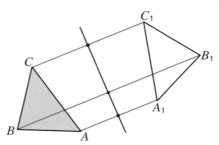

*Use the flow chart to check the transformations described at the bottom of page 282.*

## To find a line of reflection

1 Join each point to its image point.
2 Put a mark halfway along each line.
3 Use a ruler to join the marks.

## To find the centre and angle of rotation

1 Join each point to its image point.
2 Put a mark halfway along each line.
3 Use a set-square to draw a line at right angles to each line. The point where the lines cross is the centre of rotation, $R$.
4 Join one point and its image to the centre of rotation.
5 The angle of rotation is given by the size of the angle $ARA_1$.

## To find the centre and scale factor of an enlargement

1 Join each point to its image point.
2 Extend these lines until they meet. This point is the centre of enlargement.
3 Measure a pair of corresponding lengths.

$$\text{Scale factor} = \frac{\text{new length}}{\text{original length}}$$

### EXAMPLE

① Find the centre of enlargement and the scale factor when triangle $XYZ$ is mapped onto triangle $X'Y'Z'$.

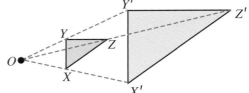

Scale factor $= \frac{X'Y'}{XY} = \frac{2.0}{0.8} = 2.5$

The centre of enlargement is the point $O$.

Transformations · · · Transformations · · ·

**EXAMPLE**

2 Find the centre of enlargement and the scale factor when triangle *XYZ* is mapped onto triangle *X'Y'Z'*.

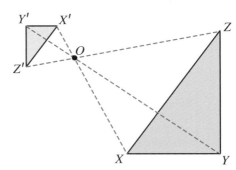

Scale factor $= \dfrac{X'Y'}{XY} = -\dfrac{0.7}{2.1} = -\dfrac{1}{3}$

The scale factor is negative because the image is inverted.
The centre of enlargement is the point *O*.

**Exercise 27.6**

1 Describe fully the single transformation which takes $\mathbf{L}_1$ onto $\mathbf{L}_2$, $\mathbf{L}_3$, $\mathbf{L}_4$, $\mathbf{L}_5$ and $\mathbf{L}_6$.

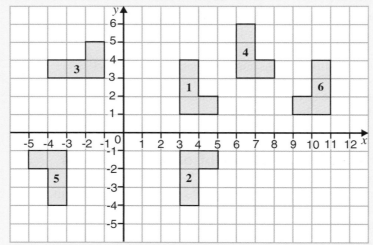

2 Describe fully the single transformation which maps
(a) *T* onto *U*,
(b) *T* onto *V*,
(c) *T* onto *W*.

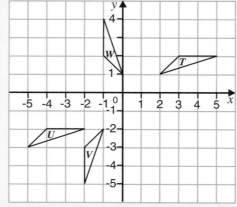

**3** Describe fully the single transformation which maps

   (a)   $A$ onto $B$,

   (b)   $A$ onto $C$,

   (c)   $A$ onto $D$.

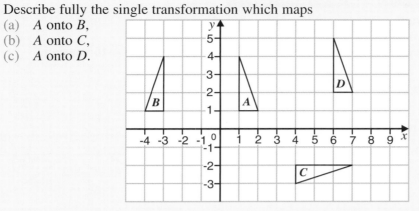

**4** For each of the following diagrams, describe fully the single transformation which maps $A$ onto $B$.

   (a)

   (b)

   (c)

   (d)

   (e)

   (f)

**5** For each of the following diagrams, describe fully the single transformation which maps $A$ onto $B$.

   (a)

   (b)

## Combinations of transformations

So far we have looked at **single** transformations only.
There is no reason why the image of a transformation cannot be transformed.
The result of applying more than one transformation is called a **combined transformation**.

For example, in the diagram $P$ has been mapped onto $P_1$
by a reflection in the $x$ axis.

Then $P_1$ has been mapped onto $P_2$ by a reflection in the $y$ axis.

The result of mapping $P$ onto $P_1$ and then $P_1$ onto $P_2$ is a
combined transformation.

### EXAMPLE

Copy triangle $Q$ onto squared paper.

(a)  $Q$ is mapped onto $Q_1$ by a rotation through $90°$, clockwise about $(0, 0)$.
     Draw and label $Q_1$.

(b)  $Q_1$ is mapped onto $Q_2$ by a reflection in the line   $y = 0$.
     Draw and label $Q_2$.

(c)  Describe the single transformation which maps $Q$ onto $Q_2$.

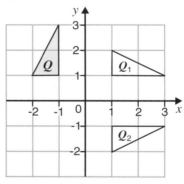

(c)  The single transformation which maps $Q$ onto $Q_2$ is a reflection in the line   $y = x$.

## Exercise 27.7

**1**  The diagram shows a quadrilateral labelled $A$. Copy the diagram onto squared paper.

(a)  $A$ is mapped onto $A_1$ by a reflection in the line   $x = 0$.
     Draw and label $A_1$.

(b)  $A_1$ is mapped onto $A_2$ by a reflection in the line   $x = 4$.
     Draw and label $A_2$.

(c)  Describe fully the single transformation which maps $A$ onto $A_2$.

**2** The diagram shows a triangle labelled *P*. Copy the diagram onto squared paper.

(a) *P* is mapped onto $P_1$ by a reflection in the line $y = x$.
Draw and label $P_1$.

(b) $P_1$ is mapped onto $P_2$ by a reflection in the line $x = 5$.
Draw and label $P_2$.

(c) Describe fully the single transformation which maps *P* onto $P_2$.

**3** The diagram shows a triangle labelled *T*. Copy the diagram.

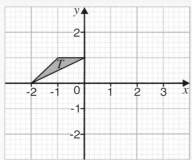

(a) Rotate *T* through 90° clockwise about (0, 0) to $T_1$.
Draw and label $T_1$.

(b) Reflect $T_1$ in the line $y = 0$ to $T_2$.
Draw and label $T_2$.

(c) Reflect $T_2$ in the line $x = 0$ to $T_3$.
Draw and label $T_3$.

(d) Describe fully the single transformation which maps *T* onto $T_3$.

**4** The diagram shows a quadrilateral labelled *Q*. Copy the diagram.

(a) *Q* is mapped onto $Q_1$ by a rotation through 90°, anticlockwise about (0, 0).
Draw and label $Q_1$.

(b) $Q_1$ is mapped onto $Q_2$ by a rotation through 90°, anticlockwise about (2, 0).
Draw and label $Q_2$.

(c) Describe fully the single transformation which maps *Q* onto $Q_2$.

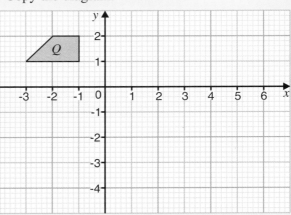

**5** The diagram shows a shape labelled *S*. Copy the diagram.

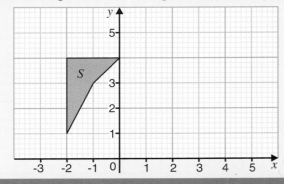

(a) The translation $\begin{pmatrix} 4 \\ 2 \end{pmatrix}$ maps *S* onto $S_1$.
Draw and label $S_1$.

(b) The translation $\begin{pmatrix} -8 \\ 1 \end{pmatrix}$ maps $S_1$ onto $S_2$.
Draw and label $S_2$.

(c) Describe fully the single transformation which maps *S* onto $S_2$.

**6** The diagram shows a triangle labelled $R$. Copy the diagram.

(a) $R$ is mapped onto $R_1$ by a rotation through 90°, anticlockwise about (0, 0). Draw and label $R_1$.

(b) $R_1$ is mapped onto $R_2$ by a reflection in the line $y = -x$. Draw and label $R_2$.

(c) $R_2$ is mapped onto $R_3$ by a reflection in the line $x = 3$. Draw and label $R_3$.

(d) Describe fully the single transformation which maps $R$ onto $R_3$.

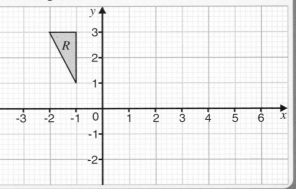

## What you need to know

- The movement of a shape from one position to another is called a **transformation**.
- **Single transformations** can be described in terms of a reflection, a rotation, a translation or an enlargement.
- **Reflection**: The image of the shape is the same distance from the mirror line as the original.
- **Rotation**: All points are turned through the same angle about the same point, called a centre of rotation.
- **Translation**: All points are moved the same distance in the same direction without turning.
- **Enlargement**: All lengths are multiplied by a scale factor.

  Scale factor $= \dfrac{\text{new length}}{\text{original length}}$       New length $=$ scale factor $\times$ original length

  The size of the original shape is:
  **increased** by using a scale factor greater than 1,
  **reduced** by using a scale factor which is a fraction, i.e. between 0 and 1.
- When a shape is enlarged using a **negative scale factor** the image is **inverted**.
- How to fully describe a transformation.

| Transformation | Image same shape and size? | Details needed to describe the transformation |
|---|---|---|
| Reflection | Yes | Mirror line, sometimes given as an equation. |
| Rotation | Yes | Centre of rotation, amount of turn, direction of turn. |
| Translation | Yes | Horizontal movement and vertical movement. Vector: top number = horizontal movement, bottom number = vertical movement. |
| Enlargement | No | Centre of enlargement, scale factor. |

## Review Exercise 27

 (a) Give the letter of the finishing position after:

(i) the shaded shape is reflected in the $y$ axis,

(ii) the shaded shape is rotated $\frac{1}{2}$ turn about (0, 0),

(iii) the shaded shape is translated 4 units left and 2 units up.

(b) Describe fully the single transformation which will map the shaded shape onto **E**.

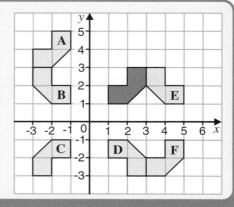

**2** The diagram shows triangles *P*, *Q*, *R*, *S* and *T*.
Describe fully the single transformation which maps

(a) *P* onto *Q*,
(b) *T* onto *Q*,
(c) *R* onto *S*,
(d) *S* onto *R*,
(e) *R* onto *T*,
(f) *T* onto *R*.

**3**

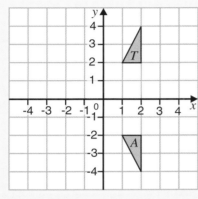

(a) Describe fully the transformation that maps triangle *T* onto triangle *A*.

Copy the diagram.
(b) Reflect triangle *T* in the line *y* = *x*.
Label the image *B*.
(c) Rotate triangle *T* through 90° anticlockwise, about (0, 1).
Label the image *C*.

OCR

**4** (a) A translation moves (3, 4) to (7, −2). The same translation moves (2, 1) to point *P*.
(i) Write down the coordinates of point *P*.
(ii) Write down the column vector which describes this translation.
(b) A reflection moves (9, 1) to (9, 5). The same reflection moves (11, 7) to point *Q*.
(i) Write down the coordinates of point *Q*.
(ii) Write down the equation of the mirror line of this reflection.

OCR

**5** (a)

For these triangles, describe fully the single transformation that maps **A** onto **B**.

(b) For these quadrilaterals, describe fully the single transformation that maps **Q** onto **R**.
(c) **Q** is reflected in *x* = 4, and then in *y* = 1.
Describe fully the single transformation that is equivalent to these two transformations.

OCR

**6**

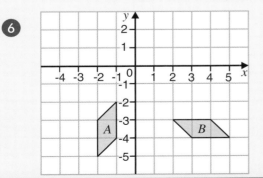

(a) Describe fully the single transformation which maps *A* onto *B*.

(b) Copy shape *A* onto squared paper.

(i) The translation, with vector $\begin{pmatrix} -2 \\ 3 \end{pmatrix}$, maps shape *A* onto *C*.
Draw and label *C*.
(ii) Describe the transformation which maps *C* onto *A*.

**7** Copy the diagram.

   (a) Reflect flag **A** in the line $y = x$.
Label the image **B**.

   (b) Enlarge flag **A** with scale factor $\frac{1}{2}$ and centre $(-3, 2)$.
Label the image **C**.

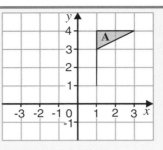

**8** The diagram shows a trapezium labelled **Q**.
Copy the diagram onto squared paper, drawing both $x$ and $y$ axes from $-2$ to $9$.

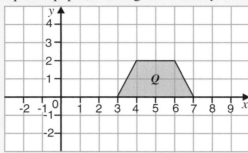

   (a) **Q** is mapped onto $\mathbf{Q}_1$ by a reflection in the $x$ axis. Draw and label $\mathbf{Q}_1$.

   (b) $\mathbf{Q}_1$ is mapped onto $\mathbf{Q}_2$ by a translation with vector $\begin{pmatrix} 2 \\ 4 \end{pmatrix}$. Draw and label $\mathbf{Q}_2$.

   (c) $\mathbf{Q}_2$ is mapped onto $\mathbf{Q}_3$ by a reflection in the line $y = x$. Draw and label $\mathbf{Q}_3$.

   (d) Describe fully the single transformation which maps **Q** onto $\mathbf{Q}_3$.

**9** Triangle $T$ has vertices $(1, 1)$, $(3, 2)$ and $(2, 4)$.

   (a) Draw triangle $T$ on squared paper.

   (b) Triangle $T$ is enlarged by scale factor $-2$, from centre of enlargement $(0, 1)$.
Draw the new triangle.

**10** The diagram shows the positions of shapes **R**, **S** and **T**.

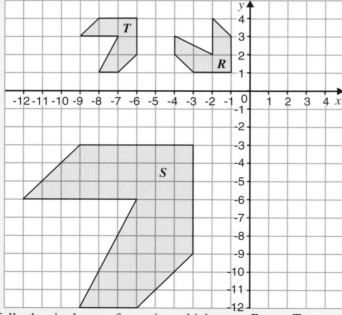

   (a) Describe fully the single transformation which maps **R** onto **T**.

   (b) Copy shape **S** onto squared paper.

      (i) **S** is mapped onto $\mathbf{S}_1$ by an enlargement, scale factor $\frac{1}{3}$, centre $(0, 0)$. Draw and label $\mathbf{S}_1$.

      (ii) $\mathbf{S}_1$ is mapped onto $\mathbf{S}_2$ by a rotation through $180°$ about $(0, 0)$. Draw and label $\mathbf{S}_2$.

      (iii) Describe fully the single transformation which maps $\mathbf{S}_2$ onto **S**.

# Pythagoras' Theorem

The longest side in a right-angled triangle is called the **hypotenuse**.

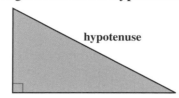

hypotenuse

In any right-angled triangle it can be proved that:

"The square on the hypotenuse is equal to the sum of the squares on the other two sides."

This is known as the **Theorem of Pythagoras**, or **Pythagoras' Theorem**.

## Checking the Theorem of Pythagoras

Look at this triangle.

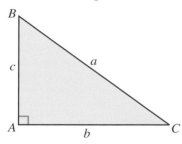

Notice that: the side opposite angle $A$ is labelled $a$,
the side opposite angle $B$ is labelled $b$,
the side opposite angle $C$ is labelled $c$.

$ABC$ is a right-angled triangle because $\angle BAC = 90°$.
$a = 5\,\text{cm}$, so, $a^2 = 25\,\text{cm}^2$.
$b = 4\,\text{cm}$, so, $b^2 = 16\,\text{cm}^2$.
$c = 3\,\text{cm}$, so, $c^2 = 9\,\text{cm}^2$.

$a^2 = b^2 + c^2$

## Activity

Use a ruler and a pair of compasses to draw the following triangles accurately.

(a)

(b)

(c)

(d)

(e)

(f)

For each triangle: Measure angle $BAC$.
Is angle $BAC = 90°$?
Does $a^2 = b^2 + c^2$?
Explain your answers.

When we know the lengths of two sides of a right-angled triangle, we can use the Theorem of Pythagoras to find the length of the third side.

## Finding the hypotenuse

### EXAMPLE

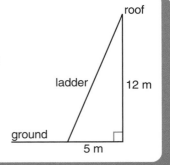

The roof of a house is 12 m above the ground.
What length of ladder is needed to reach the roof, if the foot of the ladder has to be placed 5 m away from the wall of the house?

Using Pythagoras' Theorem.
$$l^2 = 5^2 + 12^2$$
$$l^2 = 25 + 144$$
$$l^2 = 169$$

Take the square root of both sides.
$$l = \sqrt{169}$$
$$l = 13\,\text{m}$$

The ladder needs to be 13 m long.

## Exercise 28.1

**1** These triangles are right-angled. Calculate the length of the hypotenuse.

(a)

(b)

(c)

**2** These triangles are right-angled. Calculate the length of side $a$ to one decimal place.

(a)

(b)

(c)

**3** $AB$ and $CD$ are line segments, drawn on a centimetre-squared grid.
Calculate the exact length of
(a) $AB$,    (b) $CD$.

**4** Calculate the distance between the following points.
(a) $A(2, 0)$ and $B(6, 3)$.
(b) $C(6, 3)$ and $D(0, 10)$.
(c) $E(2, 2)$ and $F(-3, -10)$.
(d) $G(-2, -2)$ and $H(-6, 5)$.
(e) $I(3, -1)$ and $J(-3, -5)$.

**5** The coordinates of the vertices of a parallelogram are $P(1, 1)$, $Q(3, 5)$, $R(x, y)$ and $S(7, 3)$.
(a) Find the coordinates of $R$.
(b) $X$ is the midpoint of $PQ$. Find the coordinates of $X$.
(c) $Y$ is the midpoint of $PS$. Find the coordinates of $Y$.
(d) Calculate the distance $XY$.

## Finding one of the shorter sides

To find one of the shorter sides we can rearrange the Theorem of Pythagoras.

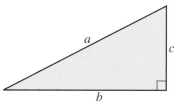

To find $b$ we use:     To find $c$ we use:
$b^2 = a^2 - c^2$        $c^2 = a^2 - b^2$

To find the length of a shorter side of a right-angled triangle:
Subtract the square of the known short side from the square on the hypotenuse.
Take the square root of the result.

### EXAMPLE

A wire used to keep a radio aerial steady is 9 metres long.
The wire is fixed to the ground 4.6 metres from the base of the aerial.
Find the height of the aerial, giving your answer correct to one decimal place.

Using Pythagoras' Theorem.   $9^2 = h^2 + 4.6^2$

Rearranging this we get:   $h^2 = 9^2 - 4.6^2$
$h^2 = 81 - 21.16$
$h^2 = 59.84$

Take the square root of both sides.   $h = \sqrt{59.84}$
$h = 7.735\ldots$
$h = 7.7\,\text{m}$, correct to 1 d.p.

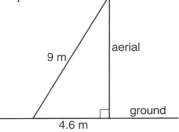

The height of the aerial is 7.7 m, correct to 1 d.p.

## Exercise 28.2

**1** Work out the length of side $b$.

(a)

10 cm, 6 cm, $b$

(b)

6.5 cm, $b$, 2.5 cm

(c)

2.5 cm, 1.5 cm, $b$

**2** Work out the length of side $c$, correct to one decimal place.

(a)

8 cm, 4 cm, $c$

(b)

5 cm, 12 cm, $c$

(c)

10 cm, 3 cm, $c$

**3** Two boats $A$ and $B$ are 360 m apart.
Boat $A$ is 120 m due east of a buoy.
Boat $B$ is due north of the buoy.
How far is boat $B$ from the buoy?

**4** The diagram shows a right-angled triangle, *ABC*, and a square, *ACDE*.

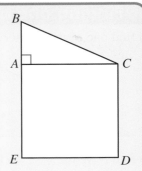

$AB = 2.5\,\text{cm}$ and $BC = 6.5\,\text{cm}$.
Calculate the area of the square *ACDE*.

**5**

The diagram shows a right-angled triangle, *ABC*, and a square, *XYBA*.

$BC = 6\,\text{cm}$.
The square *XYBA* has an area of $23.04\,\text{cm}^2$.
Calculate the length of *AC*.

## Problems involving the use of Pythagoras' Theorem

Questions leading to the use of Pythagoras' Theorem often involve:

**Understanding the problem.**
> What information is given?
> What are you required to find?

**Drawing diagrams.**
> In some questions a diagram is not given.
> Drawing a diagram may help you to understand the problem.

**Selecting a suitable right-angled triangle.**
> In more complex problems you will have to select a right-angled triangle which can be used to answer the question. It is a good idea to draw this triangle on its own, especially if it has been taken from a three-dimensional drawing.

### EXAMPLE

The diagram shows the side view of a swimming pool.
It slopes steadily from a depth of 1 m to 3.6 m.
The pool is 20 m long.
Find the length of the sloping bottom of the pool,
giving the answer correct to three significant figures.

$\Delta CDE$ is a suitable right-angled triangle.
$CD = 3.6 - 1 = 2.6\,\text{m}$

Using Pythagoras' Theorem in $\Delta CDE$.

$DE^2 = CD^2 + CE^2$

$DE^2 = 2.6^2 + 20^2$

$DE^2 = 6.76 + 400$

$DE^2 = 406.76$

$DE = \sqrt{406.76}\,\text{m}$

$DE = 20.1682\ldots\,\text{m}$

The length of the sloping bottom of the pool is 20.2 m, correct to 3 sig. figs.

**1** In each of the following, work out the length of the side marked *x*.

(a)

*x*

2.4 cm

1.7 cm

(b) 4 cm

7 cm

*x*

(c) 3.6 cm

*x*

2.9 cm

(d)

*x*          *x*

2.8 cm

**2** A rectangle is 8 cm wide and 15 cm long.
Work out the length of its diagonals.

**3** The length of a rectangle is 24 cm. The diagonals of the rectangle are 26 cm.
Work out the width of the rectangle.

**4** A square has sides of length 6 cm.
Work out the length of its diagonals.

**5** The diagonals of a square are 15 cm.
Work out the length of its sides.

**6** The height of an isosceles triangle is 12 cm. The base of the triangle is 18 cm.
Work out the length of the equal sides.

**7** An equilateral triangle has sides of length 8 cm.
Work out the height of the triangle.

**8** The diagram shows the side view of a car ramp.
The ramp is 110 cm long and 25 cm high.
The top part of the ramp is 40 cm long.
Calculate the length of the sloping part of the ramp.

40 cm

25 cm

110 cm

**9**

12 cm    *l*

The top of a lampshade has a diameter of 10 cm.
The bottom of the lampshade has a diameter of 20 cm.
The height of the lampshade is 12 cm.
Calculate the length, *l*, of the sloping sides.

**10** The top of a bucket has a diameter of 30 cm.
The bottom of the bucket has a diameter of 16 cm.
The sloping sides are 25 cm long.
How deep is the bucket?

*h*    25 cm

**11**

*B*

*A*          *C*

*D*

*ABCD* is a kite.
*AB* = 8.5 cm,   *BC* = 5.4 cm   and   *BD* = 7.6 cm.
(a)   Calculate the length of *AC*.
(b)   Calculate the area of the kite.

When we solve problems in three dimensions we often need to use more than one triangle to solve the problem.

**EXAMPLE**

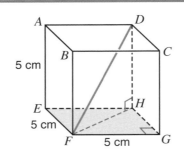

This cube has sides of length 5 cm.
What is the distance from $D$ to $F$?
Give the answer correct to 1 decimal place.

$\Delta DFH$ is a suitable right-angled triangle,
but we only know the length of the side $DH$.
The length of $FH$ can be found by using $\Delta FGH$.

Using Pythagoras' Theorem in $\Delta FGH$.

$FH^2 = FG^2 + GH^2$
$FH^2 = 5^2 + 5^2$
$FH^2 = 25 + 25$
$FH^2 = 50$
$FH = \sqrt{50}$ cm

Using Pythagoras' Theorem in $\Delta DFH$.

$DF^2 = DH^2 + FH^2$
$DF^2 = 5^2 + (\sqrt{50})^2$
$DF^2 = 25 + 50$
$DF^2 = 75$
$DF = \sqrt{75}$ cm
$DF = 8.66\ldots$ cm
$DF = 8.7$ cm, correct to 1 d.p.

For accuracy, the exact value of $FH$, $(\sqrt{50})$, should be used.

---

## Exercise 28.4

**1** The cube has sides of length 6 cm.
Calculate the length of the diagonal $PQ$.

**2**

The diagram shows a wedge $ABCDEF$.
$AD = 13$ cm, $DE = 15$ cm and $EC = 6$ cm.
Calculate the length of the line $AC$.

**3** $ABCDEFGH$ is a cuboid.
$AE = 5$ cm, $EH = 9$ cm and $HG = 6$ cm.
Calculate the length of the line $AG$.

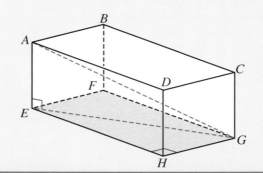

**4** The diagram shows a pyramid *PABCD*.
*X* is at the centre of the base.
The base *ABCD* is a rectangle with
$AB = CD = 12$ cm  and  $BC = DA = 9$ cm.
The height of the pyramid, *PX*, is 18 cm.
Calculate the length of the edge *PA*.

**5**

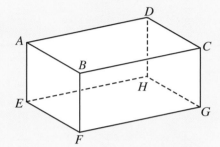

The diagram of a cuboid is shown.
(a)  Calculate the length of *EC*, when
     $EF = 6$ cm,  $FG = 8$ cm  and  $CG = 5$ cm.
(b)  Calculate the length of *AG*, when
     $AD = 10$ cm,  $DC = 8$ cm  and  $CG = 6$ cm.
(c)  Calculate the length of *FD*, when
     $FG = 7$ cm,  $GH = 5$ cm  and  $HD = 4$ cm.

**6** The diagram shows a square based pyramid.
All edges are 7 cm in length.
Calculate the height of the pyramid, *PX*.

**7**

The diagram shows a cuboid drawn in 3-dimensions.
Using the *x*, *y* and *z* axes shown:
     Point *A* has coordinates (0, 3, 0).
     Point *B* has coordinates (2, 3, 0).
     Point *C* has coordinates (2, 3, 4).

Find the lengths of the following.
(a)  *AB*       (b)  *BC*       (c)  *AC*
(d)  *DF*       (e)  *AE*       (f)  *OF*
Give your answers correct to one decimal place.

## What you need to know

- The longest side in a right-angled triangle is called the **hypotenuse**.
- The **Theorem of Pythagoras** states:
  "In any right-angled triangle the square on the hypotenuse is
  equal to the sum of the squares on the other two sides."
       $a^2 = b^2 + c^2$
       Rearranging gives:
       $b^2 = a^2 - c^2$
       $c^2 = a^2 - b^2$

- When we know the lengths of two sides of a right-angled triangle, we can use the
  Theorem of Pythagoras to find the length of the third side.

Pythagoras' Theorem

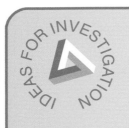

Investigate the relationship between
the areas of the semi-circles *A, B* and *C*.

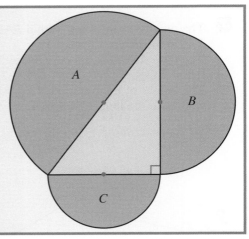

---

## Review Exercise 28

Do not use a calculator for questions 1 to 3.

**1** The diagram shows a right-angled triangle *PQR*.
*PR* = 12 cm   and   *QR* = 9 cm
Calculate the length of *PQ*.

**2** The coordinates of the points *A* and *B* are (4, 5) and (1, 1).
Work out the length of *AB*.

**3** A sketch of a right-angled triangle is shown.
Calculate the perimeter of the triangle.

**4** The sensor for a security light is fixed to a
house wall 2.5 m above the ground.
It can detect movement on the ground up to
12.0 m away from the house.
*P* is the furthest point where the sensor, *S*,
can detect movement.
Calculate the distance, *SP*.                          OCR

**5** The diagram shows a sketch of triangle *PQR*.
Show that *PQR* is a right-angled triangle.

**6** The diagram shows the end, *ABCD*, of a storage container.
Calculate the length of *CD*.

OCR

298

**7** Mike is standing 200 m due west of a power station and 300 m due north of a pylon. Calculate the distance of the power station from the pylon.

**8** A ladder, 6.4 metres long, is placed against a vertical wall. The foot of the ladder is on horizontal ground, 1.8 metres from the wall. Calculate the height of the top of the ladder above the ground.

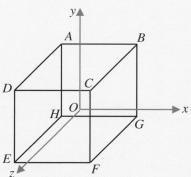

6.4 m

1.8 m

OCR

**9**

The diagram consists of two right-angled triangles. $AB = 9.5$ cm, $BC = 4.3$ cm and $AD = 8.7$ cm.

Calculate the length of $CD$.
Give your answer to an appropriate degree of accuracy.

**10** A helicopter flies from its base on a bearing of 045° for 20 km before landing. How far east of its base is the helicopter when it lands?

**11** The diagram shows a cuboid drawn in 3 dimensions.
Using the axes $x$, $y$ and $z$ shown:
Point $A$ is given as $(-2, 4, 1)$.
Point $B$ is given as $(4, 4, 1)$.
Point $C$ is given as $(4, 4, 9)$.
The length of $AB$ is 6 units.
Find the exact lengths of the lines $AC$, $AE$ and $AF$.

**12**

3 cm

6.5 cm

8 cm

Calculate the length of the longest, thin, straight rod that will fit inside this cuboid.

OCR

**13** The diagram shows a wedge $ABCDEF$.
$AC = 13$ cm, $DE = 7$ cm and $EC = 5$ cm.
Calculate the length of the line $AD$.

13 cm

5 cm

7 cm

**14**

8 cm

8 cm

8 cm

$X$

$P$

The diagram shows a square based pyramid.
All edges are 8 cm in length.
Calculate the height of the pyramid, $PX$.

**15** The 3-dimensional coordinates of $M$ and $N$ are $(2, 0, -1)$ and $(-1, 2, 3)$. Calculate the length of $MN$, correct to one decimal place.

# Trigonometry ● ● ● ● ● ● ● ● ●

We use **trigonometry** to find the lengths of sides and the sizes of angles in right-angled triangles.

We already know that the longest side of a right-angled triangle is called the **hypotenuse**.

In order to understand the relationships between sides and angles the other sides of the triangle also need to be named.

The **opposite** side is the side directly opposite the angle being used and the **adjacent** side is the side next to the angle.

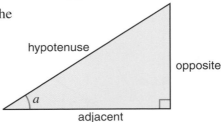

Look at this diagram.
It shows how the height of a kite changes as more and more string is let out.

When the kite is at $A$, the string is 5 m long and the kite is 3 m high.

At $A$, the ratio $\dfrac{\text{height of kite}}{\text{length of string}}$, is therefore $\frac{3}{5} = 0.6$.

Calculate the value of the same ratio at $B$ and $C$.

*What do you notice?*

When the kite is flying at angle $a$, the ratio $\dfrac{\text{height of kite}}{\text{length of string}}$ will always be the same whatever the length of the kite string and is called the **sine** of angle $a$.

### The sine ratio

For any right-angled triangle: $\quad \sin a = \dfrac{\text{opposite}}{\text{hypotenuse}}$

The sine ratio links three pieces of information:

the size of an **angle**,
the length of the side **opposite** the angle,
the length of the **hypotenuse**.

If we are given the values for two of these we can find the value of the third.

# Finding the length of the opposite side

### EXAMPLE

Find the height of a kite when it is flying at an angle of 40° and the kite string is 12 m long.
Give the answer correct to 3 significant figures.

$$\sin a = \frac{\text{opp}}{\text{hyp}}$$

Substitute known values.

$$\sin 40° = \frac{h}{12}$$

Multiply both sides by 12.

$$h = 12 \times \sin 40°$$

12 m (hyp)

height (opp)

40°

| Mathematical shorthand: | |
|---|---|
| **Word** | **Abbreviation** |
| sine | sin |
| opposite | opp |
| hypotenuse | hyp |

Using your calculator, press: 1  2  ×  sin  4  0  =

$$h = 7.713...$$
$$h = 7.71 \text{ m, correct to 3 s.f.}$$

The height of the kite is 7.71 m, correct to 3 s.f.

## Exercise 29.1

**1** Find the height, $h$, of these kites.
Give your answers correct to 3 significant figures.

(a)

5 m, 27°, $h$

(b)

7 m, 35°, $h$

(c)

9 m, 63°, $h$

**2** Calculate the lengths marked $x$.
Give your answers correct to 3 significant figures.

(a)

4.6 cm, $x$, 19°

(b)

3.7 cm, 54°, $x$

(c)

37°, 9.6 cm, $x$

**3** In $\triangle ABC$, angle $ACB = 90°$.

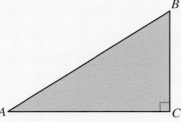

$B$

$A$     $C$

(a) If $\angle BAC = 47.5°$ and $AB = 4.6$ m     find $BC$.
(b) If $\angle ABC = 67.4°$ and $AB = 12.4$ m     find $AC$.
(c) If $\angle BAC = 15.8°$ and $AB = 17.4$ cm     find $BC$.
(d) If $\angle BAC = 35°$     and $AB = 8.5$ cm     find the size of $\angle ABC$ and then find $AC$.
Give your answers correct to 3 significant figures.

Trigonometry . . . . Trigonometry . . . .

## Finding an angle

If you are given the sine of an angle and asked to find the angle, use the inverse sine function, $\sin^{-1}$, on your calculator.

Using your calculator, press: [sin] [3] [0]
The display should read 0.5.

Clear the display and press: [$\sin^{-1}$] [0] [.] [5] [=]

*What do you notice?*

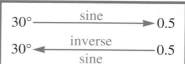

30° $\xrightarrow{\text{sine}}$ 0.5

30° $\xleftarrow[\text{sine}]{\text{inverse}}$ 0.5

---

**EXAMPLE**

Find the size of angle $a$ when the kite string is 12 m long and the kite is flying 7 m above the ground.
Give the answer correct to one decimal place.

$$\sin a = \frac{\text{opp}}{\text{hyp}}$$

Substitute known values.

$$\sin a° = \frac{7}{12}$$

$$a = \sin^{-1} \frac{7}{12}$$

12 m (hyp)

7 m (opp)

$a$

Using your calculator, press: [$\sin^{-1}$] [(] [7] [÷] [1] [2] [)] [=]

$a = 35.685...$

$a = 35.7°$, correct to 1 d.p.

---

## Exercise **29.2**

**1** Find the size of angle $a$ for each of these kites.
Give your answers correct to one decimal place.

(a)

4.3 m    3.8 m

$a$

(b)

6.4 m

2.7 m

$a$

(c)

5.8 m    4.5 m

$a$

**2** Find the size of angle $x$ in each of these triangles.
Give your answers correct to one decimal place.

(a)
7.2 cm
$x$
5.7 cm

(b)
$x$
5.4 cm
4.7 cm

(c)
4.1 cm
$x$
3.6 cm

**3** In $\triangle PQR$ angle $PQR = 90°$.
  (a) If $QR = 4$ m    and $PR = 10$ m    find the size of $\angle QPR$.
  (b) If $PQ = 4.7$ cm and $PR = 5.2$ cm find the size of $\angle PRQ$.
  (c) If $QR = 7.2$ m    and $PR = 19.4$ m find the size of $\angle QPR$.
  (d) If $PQ = 3.7$ cm and $PR = 9.1$ cm find the size of $\angle QRP$
     and then find the size of $\angle QPR$.
  Give your answers correct to one decimal place.

R

P    Q

# Finding the hypotenuse

### EXAMPLE

Find the length of the string, $l$, when a kite is 6 m high and the string makes an angle of 50° with the ground.
Give the answer correct to 3 significant figures.

$$\sin a = \frac{\text{opp}}{\text{hyp}}$$

Substitute known values.

$$\sin 50° = \frac{6}{l}$$

Multiply both sides by $l$.

$$l \times \sin 50° = 6$$

Divide both sides by $\sin 50°$.

$$l = \frac{6}{\sin 50°}$$

Using your calculator, press: [ 6 ] [ ÷ ] [ sin ] [ 5 ] [ 0 ] [ = ]
$$l = 7.832…$$
$$l = 7.83 \text{ m, correct to 3 s.f.}$$

The length of the string is 7.83 m, correct to 3 s.f.

## Exercise 29.3

**1** Find the lengths, $l$, of these kite strings.
Give your answers correct to 3 significant figures.

(a)

5.2 m
48°

(b)

3.4 m
27°

(c)
2.9 m
36°

**2** Calculate the length of side $x$ in each of these triangles.
Give your answers correct to two decimal places.

(a)

23.6°
2.6 cm
$x$

(b)

$x$
47.3°
3.9 cm

(c)

4.7 cm
63.7°
$x$

**3** In $\triangle ABC$ angle $ACB = 90°$.
(a) If $\angle BAC = 36.2°$ and $BC = 4.5$ m find $AB$.
(b) If $\angle ABC = 64.7°$ and $AC = 15.8$ cm find $AB$.
(c) If $\angle BAC = 12.7°$ and $BC = 14.7$ cm find $AB$.
(d) If $\angle BAC = 72.8°$ and $AC = 7.6$ m find the size of $\angle ABC$ and then find $AB$.
Give your answers correct to 3 significant figures.

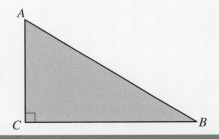

## The cosine and tangent ratios

We have found that **sine** is the ratio $\dfrac{\text{opposite}}{\text{hypotenuse}}$.

In a similar way we can find two other ratios, the **cosine** of angle $a$ and the **tangent** of angle $a$.

### The cosine ratio

For any right-angled triangle:

$$\cos a = \frac{\text{adjacent}}{\text{hypotenuse}}$$

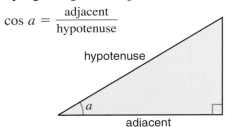

The cosine ratio links three pieces of information:
  the size of an **angle**,
  the length of the side **adjacent** to the angle,
  the length of the **hypotenuse**.
If we are given the values of two of these we can find the value of the third.

### The tangent ratio

For any right-angled triangle:

$$\tan a = \frac{\text{opposite}}{\text{adjacent}}$$

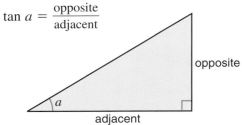

The tangent ratio links three pieces of information:
  the size of an **angle**,
  the length of the side **opposite** to the angle,
  the length of the side **adjacent** to the angle.
If we are given the values of two of these we can find the value of the third.

---

### EXAMPLE

 Write down the sin, cos and tan ratios for angle $a$ in the triangle.

$$\sin a = \frac{\text{opp}}{\text{hyp}} = \frac{8}{17}$$

$$\cos a = \frac{\text{adj}}{\text{hyp}} = \frac{15}{17}$$

$$\tan a = \frac{\text{opp}}{\text{adj}} = \frac{8}{15}$$

**Mathematical shorthand:**

| Word | Abbreviation |
|------|--------------|
| adjacent | adj |
| opposite | opp |
| hypotenuse | hyp |
| sine | sin |
| cosine | cos |
| tangent | tan |

---

## How to select and use the correct ratio

There are only 3 different types of question for each of the ratios.
Selecting the correct ratio is most important.
To do this:

1. Go to the angle you know (or want to find).
2. Name sides (opp, adj, hyp).
   If you are trying to find the length of a side, name that side first together with one other side of known length.
   If you are trying to find the size of an angle, name two sides of known length.
3. Select the correct ratio and write it down.

$$\sin a = \frac{\text{opp}}{\text{hyp}} \qquad \cos a = \frac{\text{adj}}{\text{hyp}} \qquad \tan a = \frac{\text{opp}}{\text{adj}}$$

   One way to remember the ratios is to use the initial letters, SOHCAHTOA.
   You may know another method.

4. Substitute known values from the question.
5. Rearrange to isolate the angle, or side, you are trying to find.
6. Use your calculator to find the size of the angle, or side, writing down more figures than you need for the final answer.
7. Correct to the required degree of accuracy.
8. Give the answer, stating the degree of approximation and giving the correct units. When giving the answer to a problem you should use a short sentence.

## EXAMPLES

**2** Find the length, $h$, giving the answer to 3 significant figures

$$\tan a = \frac{\text{opp}}{\text{adj}}$$

Substitute known values.

$$\tan 28° = \frac{h}{12.4}$$

Multiply both sides by 12.4.

$$h = 12.4 \times \tan 28°$$

Using your calculator, press: ⬚1 ⬚2 ⬚. ⬚4 ⬚× ⬚tan ⬚2 ⬚8 ⬚=

$$h = 6.593…$$
$$h = 6.59 \text{ m, correct to 3 s.f.}$$

$h$ (opp)

28°

12.4 m (adj)

**3** Find the size of angle $a$, correct to one decimal place.

$$\cos a = \frac{\text{adj}}{\text{hyp}}$$

Substitute known values.

$$\cos a° = \frac{11}{16}$$

$$a = \cos^{-1}\frac{11}{16}$$

Using your calculator, press: ⬚cos⁻¹ ⬚( ⬚1 ⬚1 ⬚÷ ⬚1 ⬚6 ⬚) ⬚=

$$a = 46.56…$$
$$a = 46.6°, \text{ correct to 1 d.p.}$$

$a$

16 cm (hyp)

11 cm (adj)

## Exercise 29.4

**1** Write down the sin, cos and tan ratios for angle $p$ in each of the following triangles.

(a)

13

5

12

$p$

(b)

24

$p$

25

7

(c)

5

4

3

$p$

**2** By choosing the correct ratio, calculate angle $p$ in each of the following triangles.
Give your answers correct to one decimal place.

(a)

3.2 cm

$p$

3.7 cm

(b)

8.6 cm

$p$

5.3 cm

(c)

4.6 cm

$p$

5.9 cm

(d)

6.7 cm

$p$

4 cm

(e)

4.7 cm

$p$

3 cm

(f)

4.9 cm

3.5 cm

$p$

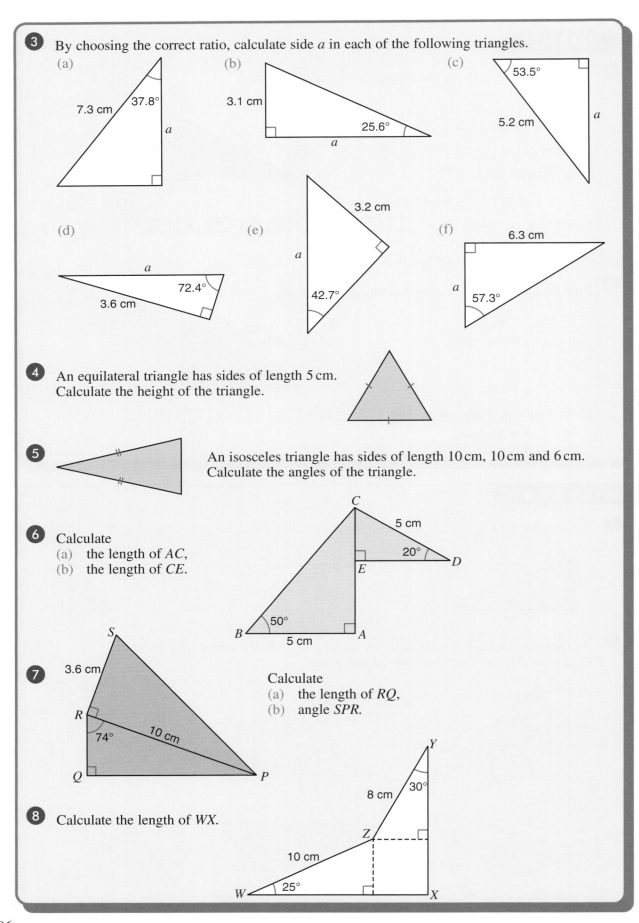

**3** By choosing the correct ratio, calculate side $a$ in each of the following triangles.

(a) 7.3 cm, 37.8°, $a$

(b) 3.1 cm, 25.6°, $a$

(c) 53.5°, 5.2 cm, $a$

(d) $a$, 72.4°, 3.6 cm

(e) 3.2 cm, $a$, 42.7°

(f) 6.3 cm, $a$, 57.3°

**4** An equilateral triangle has sides of length 5 cm. Calculate the height of the triangle.

**5** An isosceles triangle has sides of length 10 cm, 10 cm and 6 cm. Calculate the angles of the triangle.

**6** Calculate
(a) the length of $AC$,
(b) the length of $CE$.

$C$, 5 cm, 20°, $D$, $E$, 50°, $B$, 5 cm, $A$

**7** Calculate
(a) the length of $RQ$,
(b) angle $SPR$.

$S$, 3.6 cm, $R$, 74°, 10 cm, $Q$, $P$

**8** Calculate the length of $WX$.

$Y$, 30°, 8 cm, $Z$, 10 cm, $W$, 25°, $X$

**9** Calculate the length of *PQ*.

**10** Calculate the length of *CD*.

## Angles of elevation and depression

When we look **up** from the horizontal the angle we turn through is called an **angle of elevation**.

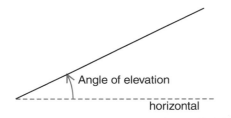

When we look **down** from the horizontal the angle we turn through is called an **angle of depression**.

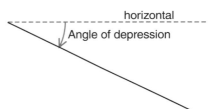

### EXAMPLES

**1** From a point on the ground, 30 m from the base of a pylon, the angle of elevation to the top of the pylon is 50°.

Find the height of the pylon.

$$\tan a = \frac{\text{opp}}{\text{adj}}$$

$$\tan 50° = \frac{h}{30}$$

$$h = 30 \times \tan 50°$$
$$h = 35.75\ldots$$
$$h = 35.8 \text{ m, correct to 3 s.f.}$$

The height of the pylon is 35.8 m, correct to 3 s.f.

**2** Staten Island Ferry is 270 m away from the base of the Statue of Liberty.
The ferry can be seen from a viewing point in the lantern, 85 m above the ground.

What is the angle of depression to the ferry from the viewing point?

$$\tan a = \frac{\text{opp}}{\text{adj}}$$

$$\tan d° = \frac{85}{270}$$

$$d = \tan^{-1} \frac{85}{270}$$
$$d = 17.47\ldots$$
$$d = 17.5°, \text{ correct to 1 d.p.}$$

The angle of depression to the ferry from the viewing point is 17.5°, correct to 1 d.p.

**1** From a point on the ground 20 m from the base of a tree, the angle of elevation to the top of the tree is 47°. Calculate the height of the tree.

47°

20 m

**2** From a point on the ground 10 m from a block of flats, the angle of elevation to the top of the block is 76°. Calculate the height of the block of flats.

**3** A fishing boat is 200 m from the bottom of a vertical cliff. From the top of the cliff the angle of depression to the fishing boat is 34°.
 (a) Calculate the height of the cliff.
 (b) A buoy is 100 m from the bottom of the cliff. Calculate the angle of depression to the buoy from the top of the cliff.

34°

200 m

**4** A yacht is 20 m from the bottom of a lighthouse. From the top of the lighthouse the angle of depression to the yacht is 48°. Calculate the height of the lighthouse.

**5** A cat is on the ground 25 m from the foot of a house. A bird is perched on the gutter of the house 15 m from the ground. Calculate the angle of elevation from the cat to the bird.

**6** A tree, 6 m high, casts a shadow of 4.8 m on horizontal ground. Calculate the angle of elevation to the sun.

**7** From a point, $A$, on the ground, the angle of elevation to a hot air balloon is 9°. The balloon is 150 m above the ground. Calculate the distance from $A$ to the balloon.

**8** From the top of a cliff, 36 m high, the angles of depression of two boats at sea are 17° and 25°. The boats are in a straight line from the foot of the cliff. Calculate the distance between the two boats.

## Bearings

Bearings are used to describe the direction in which you must travel to get from one place to another. They are measured from the North line in a clockwise direction.
A bearing can be any angle from 0° to 360° and is written as a three-figure number.

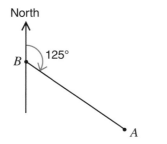

$A$ is on a bearing of 125° from $B$.

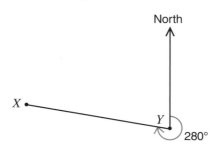

$X$ is on a bearing of 280° from $Y$.

**EXAMPLE**

A plane flies 300 km on a bearing of 132° from an airport.
How far South and East is it from the airport?
Give the answers correct to 3 significant figures.

$x$ is the distance South.
$y$ is the distance East.
Using supplementary angles:
$\angle PAB = 180° - 132° = 48°$.

**To find $x$**

$$\cos a = \frac{\text{adj}}{\text{hyp}}$$

$$\cos 48° = \frac{x}{300}$$

$x = 300 \times \cos 48°$
$x = 200.73\ldots$ km
$x = 201$ km, correct to 3 s.f.

**To find $y$**

$$\sin a = \frac{\text{opp}}{\text{hyp}}$$

$$\sin 48° = \frac{y}{300}$$

$y = 300 \times \sin 48°$
$y = 222.94\ldots$ km
$y = 223$ km, correct to 3 s.f.

**Sketch diagrams:**
Drawing a sketch diagram may help you to understand the question.
More information can be added to the diagram as you answer the question.

The plane is 201 km South and 223 km East of the airport, correct to 3 s.f.

*How can you use Pythagoras' Theorem to check the answer?*

## Exercise **29.6**

**1** A plane flies 250 km on a bearing of 050°.
(a) How far north is it from its original position?
(b) How far east is it from its original position?

**2** A helicopter leaves its base and flies 23 km on a bearing of 285°.
How far west is it from its base?

**3** A ship at $A$ is 3.8 km due north of a lighthouse.
A ship at $B$ is 2.7 km due east of the same lighthouse.
What is the bearing of the ship at $B$ from the ship at $A$?

**4** A helicopter has flown from its base on a bearing of 153°. Its distance east of base is 19 km.
How far has the helicopter flown?

**5** A fishing boat leaves port and sails on a straight course.
After 2 hours its distance south of port is 24 km and its distance east of port is 7 km.
On what bearing did it sail?

**6** A yacht sails 15 km on a bearing of 053°, then 7 km on a bearing of 112°.
How far north is the yacht from its starting position?

**7** A plane flies 307 km on a bearing of 234°, then 23 km on a bearing of 286°.
How far south is the plane from its starting position?

**8** Jayne sails 1.5 km on a bearing of 050°.
She then changes course and sails 2 km on a bearing of 140°.
On what bearing must she sail to return to her starting position?

# Solving problems in three-dimensions

When we solve problems in three-dimensions the first task is to identify the length, or angle, we are asked to calculate.

This length, or angle, will always form part of a triangle. Having identified a suitable triangle it is a good idea to draw it in two dimensions, so that lengths of sides and sizes of angles can clearly be seen.

Most problems in three-dimensions involve:
 finding lengths,
 finding the size of an angle between a line and a plane.

A suitable triangle includes the side, or angle, you are trying to calculate **and** either:
 two other sides of known length,
 or one side of known length and an angle of known size.
Sometimes we need to use more than one triangle to solve a problem.

## The angle between a line and a plane

A straight line meets a plane at a **point**, $P$.

**To find the angle between a line and a plane:**
 Take a point, $X$, on the line.
 From $X$, draw a line, $XT$, which is at right angles to the plane.
The angle $XPT$ is the angle between the line and the plane.

---

$PQRST$ is a pyramid. The perpendicular height, $PX$, is 10 cm.
The base is a square of side 8 cm and $X$ is at the centre of the square.

Calculate the angle between the line $PQ$ and the base $QRST$.

The angle between the line $PQ$ and the base $QRST$ is $\angle PQX$.

$\triangle PQX$ is a suitable triangle, but we only know the length of the side $PX$.

To find $QX$ we use $\triangle QMX$, where $M$ is the midpoint of $QT$.
Using Pythagoras' Theorem in $\triangle QMX$.
$$QX^2 = MQ^2 + MX^2$$
$$= 4^2 + 4^2$$
$$= 16 + 16$$
$$= 32$$
$$QX = \sqrt{32}$$
Mark this length on your diagram.

Using the tangent ratio in $\triangle PQX$.
$$\tan a = \frac{\text{opp}}{\text{adj}}$$
$$\tan \angle PQX = \frac{PX}{QX} = \frac{10}{\sqrt{32}}$$
$$\angle PQX = \tan^{-1} \frac{10}{\sqrt{32}}$$
$$= 60.503\ldots$$
$$\angle PQX = 60.5°$$
The angle between the line $PQ$ and the base $QRST$ is 60.5°, correct to 1 decimal place.

**1** The diagram shows a wedge *ABCDXY*.
The base *ABCD* and the face *CBXY* are rectangles.
Angle *XAB* = 90°.
*BC* = 9 cm, *BA* = 18 cm and *AX* = 15 cm.

Calculate
(a) angle *XBA*,
(b) the angle between the line *XC* and the base *ABCD*.

**2**

The diagram shows a ramp.
The ramp, *PQRS*, is 8 m wide and 10 m long.
The ramp slopes at 24° to the horizontal.
Find the slope of the diagonal *QS* to the horizontal.

**3** The diagram shows a cube *ABCDEFGH*.
*AB* = 6 cm.

Calculate
(a) angle *DCE*,
(b) the angle between the line *AH* and the base *EFGH*.

**4**

*PQRSTUVW* is a cuboid.
*PQ* = 8 cm, *QR* = 6 cm and *RW* = 4 cm.

Calculate
(a) angle *PVU*,
(b) the angle between the line *PW* and the base *UVWT*.

**5** *PLMNO* is a pyramid of height 8 cm.
The base of the pyramid is a square.
*OL* = *LM* = *MN* = *NO* = 10 cm.
*P* is directly above the centre of the base.

Calculate the angle between the line *PN* and the base *LMNO*.

**6**

*VABCD* is a square based pyramid.
The perpendicular height, *VX*, is 8 cm.
*AB* = *BC* = *CD* = *DA* = 6 cm.
*V* is directly above the centre of the base.
*P* is the midpoint of the line *BC*.

Calculate
(a) the length *VP*,
(b) the angle *XPV*,
(c) the angle between the line *VA* and the base *ABCD*.

# What you need to know

- **Trigonometry** is used to find the lengths of sides and the sizes of angles in right-angled triangles.

- You must learn the **sine**, **cosine** and **tangent** ratios.

  $$\sin a = \frac{\text{opposite}}{\text{hypotenuse}} \qquad \cos a = \frac{\text{adjacent}}{\text{hypotenuse}} \qquad \tan a = \frac{\text{opposite}}{\text{adjacent}}$$

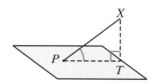

- Each ratio links the size of an angle with the lengths of two sides. If we are given the values for two of these we can find the value of the third.

- When we look **up** from the horizontal the angle we turn through is called the **angle of elevation**.

- When we look **down** from the horizontal the angle we turn through is called the **angle of depression**.

- **Bearings** are used to describe the direction in which you must travel to get from one place to another.
  They are measured from the North line in a clockwise direction.
  A bearing can be any angle from 0° to 360° and is written as a three-figure number.

- When working in three-dimensions the first task is to identify the length, or angle, that you are trying to find. The length, or angle, will always form part of a triangle together with either:
  two other sides of known length, or
  one side of known length and an angle of known size.
  Sometimes, more than one triangle is needed to solve a problem.

- A straight line meets a plane at a **point**.
  The angle *XPT* is the **angle between the line and the plane**.
  The line *XT* is perpendicular to the plane.

## Review Exercise 29

**1**

When Colin is 10 m from a haystack, the angle of elevation to the top of the haystack is 18°.

Calculate *h*, the height of the haystack.

**2** The sensor for a security light is fixed to a house wall 2.5 m above the ground.
It can detect movement on the ground up to 12.0 m away from the house.
*P* is the furthest point where the sensor, *S*, can detect movement.

Calculate the size of angle *b*.

OCR

**3**

In the diagram, *CB* is perpendicular to *AD*.
*CB* = 4.9 cm and *AC* = 5.6 cm.
(a) Calculate angle *A*.

Angle *ACD* is 100°.
(b) Calculate *BD*.

OCR

312

**4**

Maria, *M*, is 55 m from a tower.
She measures the angle of elevation of the top of the tower, *T*, as 15°.
There is a flagpole, *TF*, 3 m high on top of the tower.

Calculate the angle of elevation of *F* from *M*.

OCR

**5** The diagram shows a cross-section of a suspended road bridge, *AB*.
All measurements are in metres.

(a) Calculate angle *x*.
(b) The total distance of *AB* is 22.5 m.
Calculate the length of *CB*.

OCR

**6**

The diagram shows the route, *LAB*, taken by a
ship leaving Liverpool, *L*.
*A* is 14 km North of *L* on a bearing of 335°.
*B* is 12 km West of *A*.

(a) Calculate the distance *A* is West of *L*.
(b) Calculate the bearing of *L* from *B*.

OCR

**7** Cos $PQR = \frac{12}{13}$

(a) Find  (i) tan *PQR*,  (ii) sin *PQR*.

(b) *PQ* = 6 cm.
What are the lengths of *QR* and *PR*?

**8**

The diagram shows a cuboid with length 9 cm,
width 4 cm and height 5 cm.

(a) Show that the length of the diagonal *AB* is
11.05 cm, correct to 2 decimal places.
(b) Calculate the angle between the diagonal *AB*
and the base.

OCR

**9** The diagram shows a square based pyramid.
*P* is directly above the centre of the base.
*PA* = 6 cm  and  *AD* = 4 cm.

(a) Calculate
  (i)  the height of the pyramid,
  (ii) the angle between the line *PA* and the base *ABCD*.

*X* is the midpoint of the line *DC*.

(b) Calculate the angle between *PX* and the base *ABCD*.

# 3-D Shapes

## 3-D shapes (or solids)

These are all examples of 3-dimensional shapes.

**Cuboid**   **Cylinder**   **Sphere**   **Pyramid with square base**   **Cone**

*What other 3-dimensional shapes do you know?*

## Making and drawing 3-D shapes

### Nets
3-dimensional shapes can be made using **nets**. This is the net of a cube.

### 2-D drawings of 3-D shapes
**Isometric drawings** are used to draw 3-dimensional shapes. Here is an isometric drawing of a cube.

## Naming parts of a 3-D shape

Each flat surface is called a **face**. Two faces meet at an **edge**. Edges of a shape meet at a corner, or point, called a **vertex**. The plural of vertex is **vertices**.

← vertex
← edge
← face

## Exercise 30.1

**1** (a) Draw an accurate net for each of these 3-D shapes.

(i)
2 cm   3 cm   1 cm

(ii)
4 cm   4 cm   4 cm   6 cm

(iii)
4 cm   3 cm   3 cm

(b) How many edges does the pyramid have?

**2** Draw these 3-D shapes on isometric paper.
(a) A cube of side 3 cm.
(b) A cuboid measuring 3 cm by 2 cm by 1 cm.

## Symmetry in three-dimensions

### Planes of symmetry

Two-dimensional shapes can have line symmetry.
Three-dimensional objects can have **plane symmetry**.
A **plane of symmetry** slices through an object so that one half is the mirror image of the other half.

A cuboid has three planes of symmetry as shown.

### Axes of symmetry

A wall is built using cuboids.

*In how many different ways can the next cuboid be placed in position?*

If the cuboid can be placed in more than one way, it must have rotational symmetry about one or more **axes**.

A cuboid has three axes of symmetry.
The diagram shows one **axis of symmetry**.
The order of rotational symmetry about this axis is two.

### Exercise **30.2**

1 How many planes of symmetry has a cube?

2 State the order of rotational symmetry about the axis shown in each of the following.
  (a) Cube            (b) Square-based pyramid        (c) Cylinder            (d) Cone

3
Each end of this cuboid is a square.
The axes of symmetry are labelled *a*, *b* and *c*.
What is the order of rotational symmetry about:
  (a) axis *a*,
  (b) axis *b*,
  (c) axis *c*?

4 The diagram shows a cuboid, with a square base.
On top of the cuboid is a square-based pyramid with vertex *A* above the centre of the top of the cuboid.
  (a) How many planes of symmetry has the figure?
  (b) How many axes of symmetry has the figure?
      Give the order of rotational symmetry about each axis.

## Plans and Elevations

When an architect designs a building he has to draw diagrams to show what the building will look like from different directions.
These diagrams are called **plans and elevations**.

The view of a building looking from above is called the **plan**.
The views of a building from the front or sides are called **elevations**.

To show all the information about a 3-dimensional shape we often need to draw several diagrams.

### EXAMPLE

The diagram shows a 3-dimensional shape.
Draw the plan and the elevations **A**, **B** and **C**.

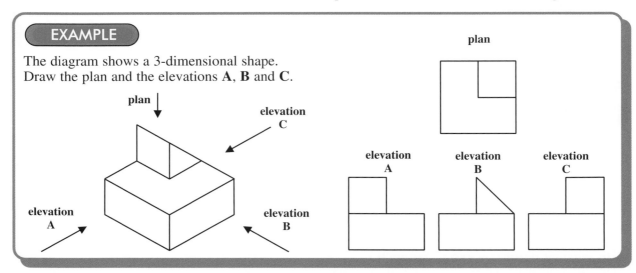

### Exercise **30.3**

1. Draw a sketch to show the plan view of each of these 3-dimensional shapes.
   (a) **a staircase**
   (b) **a pyramid**
   (c) **a cup**

2. Each of these 3-D shapes has been made using 5 linking cubes of side 1 cm.
   On squared paper, draw diagrams to show the plan and the elevations **A**, **B** and **C** of each shape.
   (a)
   (b)
   (c)

3. The diagram shows a plastic cylinder of height 3 cm and radius 2 cm with a hole of radius 1 cm drilled through the centre.

3 cm

Draw the plan and a side elevation of the cylinder.

**4** The plans and elevations of two 3-D shapes made from linking cubes of side 1 cm are shown.
Draw both of these 3-D shapes on isometric paper.

(a) | **Plan** | **Left - side elevation** | **Front elevation** | **Right - side elevation**

(b) | **Plan** | **Left - side elevation** | **Front elevation** | **Right - side elevation**

## Surface area of a cuboid

Opposite faces of a cuboid are the same shape and size.

To find the surface area of a cuboid find the areas
of the six rectangular faces and add the answers.

The surface area of a cuboid can also be found by finding the area of its net.

## Volume

**Volume** is the amount of space occupied by a three-dimensional shape.

This **cube** is 1 cm long, 1 cm wide and 1 cm high.
It has a volume of **1 cubic centimetre**.
The volume of this cube can be written as 1 cm³.

Small volumes can be measured using cubic millimetres (mm³).
Large volumes can be measured using cubic metres (m³).

**Volume = 1 cm³**

## Volume of a cuboid

○ ○ ○ ○ ○ ○ ○ ○ ○ ○ ○ ○ ○ ○ ○ ○ ○ ○ ○ ○ ○ ○ ○ ○ ○

**Volume of a cube:**
A cube is a special cuboid in which the length,
breadth and height all have the same measurement.
Volume = length × length × length
$V = l^3$

The formula for the volume of a cuboid is:   Volume = length × breadth × height
This formula can be written using letters as:       $V = lbh$

317

---

**EXAMPLE**

Find the volume and surface area of a cuboid
measuring 30 cm by 15 cm by 12 cm.

$$\begin{aligned}
\text{Volume} &= lbh \\
&= 30\,\text{cm} \times 15\,\text{cm} \times 12\,\text{cm} \\
&= 5400\,\text{cm}^3 \\
\text{Surface area} &= (2 \times 30 \times 15) + (2 \times 15 \times 12) + (2 \times 30 \times 12) \\
&= 900 + 360 + 720 \\
&= 1980\,\text{cm}^2
\end{aligned}$$

## Exercise 30.4

You should be able to do questions 1 to 3 without using a calculator.

**1** A cuboid measures 2 cm by 4 cm by 3 cm.
   (a) Draw a net of the cuboid on one-centimetre squared paper.
   (b) Find the surface area of the cuboid.

**2** Calculate the volumes and surface areas of these cubes and cuboids.

   (a)

   (b)

   (c)

**3** Shapes are made using one-centimetre cubes.
   Find the volume and surface area of each shape.

   (a)   (b)   (c)   (d)   (e)   (f) 

**4** A cuboid measures 3.2 cm by 4.8 cm by 6.3 cm.
   Calculate the volume and surface area of the cuboid.

**5** A cuboid has a volume of 76.8 cm³.
   The length of the cuboid is 3.2 cm. The breadth of the cuboid is 2.4 cm.
   What is the height of the cuboid?

**6** A cuboid has a volume of 2250 cm³.
   The length of the cuboid is 25 cm. The height of the cuboid is 12 cm.
   Calculate the surface area of the cuboid.

**7** The surface area of a cuboid is 294 cm².
   Calculate the volume of a cube with the same surface area.

## Prisms

These shapes are all **prisms**.

*What do these 3-dimensional shapes have in common?*
*Draw a different 3-dimensional shape which is a prism.*

## Volume of a prism

The formula for the volume of a prism is:

  Volume = area of cross-section × length.

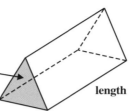

cross-section

length

## Volume of a cylinder

A **cylinder** is a prism.

The **volume of a cylinder** can be written as:

  Volume = area of cross-section × height

  $V = \pi r^2 h$

Notice that length has been replaced by height.

### EXAMPLES

Find the volumes of these prisms.

(a)

Area 18 cm²

10 cm

Volume = area of cross-section × length
= 18 × 10
= 180 cm³

(b)

3 cm

8 cm   A

2 cm

B

5 cm

6 cm

Area A = 8 × 3 = 24 cm²
Area B = 3 × 2 = 6 cm²
Total area = 30 cm²
Volume = 30 × 5 = 150 cm³

(c)

5 cm

6 cm

$V = \pi r^2 h$
$= \pi \times 5^2 \times 6$
$= 471.238...$
= 471 cm³, correct to 3 s.f.

## Exercise **30.5**

**1** Find the volumes of these prisms.

(a)

Area = 20 cm²

2 cm

(b)

Area 28 cm²

5 cm

(c)

Area 9.6 cm²

10 cm

**2** Calculate the shaded areas and the volumes of these prisms.

(a)

1.5 cm

2 cm

4 cm

1.4 cm

4 cm

(b)

4 cm

3 cm

2.5 cm

(c)

10 cm

20 cm

Take π to be 3.14

(d)

5 cm

2 cm

Take π to be 3.14

**3** Find the volumes of these prisms.
Where necessary take $\pi$ to be 3.14 or use the $\pi$ key on your calculator.

**4** Sylvia says, "A cylinder with a radius of 5 cm and a height of 10 cm has the same volume as a cylinder with a radius of 10 cm and a height of 5 cm."
Is she right? Explain your answer.

**5** The radius of a cylinder is 5 cm. It has a volume of 900 cm³.
Calculate the height of the cylinder, giving your answer correct to 1 decimal place.

**6** A cylinder is 8 cm high. It has a volume of 183 cm³.
Calculate the radius of the cylinder correct to 1 decimal place.

**7** A cylinder has a diameter of 10.6 cm. The volume of the cylinder is 1060 cm³.
Calculate the height of the cylinder. Give your answer to an appropriate degree of accuracy.

**8** A cylinder with a radius of 3 cm and a height of 8 cm is full of water.
The water is poured into another cylinder with a diameter of 8 cm.
Calculate the height of the water.

## Surface area of a cylinder

The top and bottom of a cylinder are circles. The curved surface of a cylinder is a rectangle.

The rectangle has the same height, $h$, as the cylinder.
The length of the rectangle must be just long
enough to "wrap around" the circle.
The lid of the cylinder has radius $r$ and
circumference $2\pi r$.
So, the length of the rectangle is
also $2\pi r$.

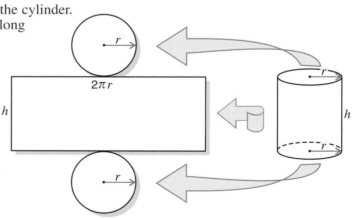

$$\text{Area of lid} = \pi r^2$$
$$\text{Area of base} = \pi r^2$$
$$\text{Area of lid and base} = 2\pi r^2$$
$$\text{Area of rectangle} = \text{length} \times \text{breadth}$$
$$= 2\pi r \times h$$
$$= 2\pi rh$$

If a cylinder has radius, $r$, and height, $h$,
then the formula for the surface area is:

$$\text{Surface area} = 2\pi r^2 + 2\pi rh$$

↗ Area of the top and bottom      ↖ Area of the rectangle

The formula for the surface area
is sometimes given as:
Surface area $= 2\pi r(r + h)$

**EXAMPLE**

Find the surface area of a cylinder with radius 4 cm and height 6 cm.
Use the $\pi$ key on your calculator.

Area $= 2\pi rh + 2\pi r^2$
$= 2 \times \pi \times 4 \times 6 + 2 \times \pi \times 4^2$
$= 150.796 \ldots + 100.530 \ldots$
$= 251.327 \ldots$
$= 251.3 \text{ cm}^2$, correct to 1 d.p.

**Exercise 30.6**     Take $\pi$ to be 3.14 or use the $\pi$ key on your calculator.

**1** Find the surface areas of these cylinders.

(a)

(b)

(c)

**2** Show that the curved surface area
of this can is approximately 75 cm².

**3**

A bucket is in the shape of a cylinder.
(a) Calculate the area of the bottom of the bucket.
(b) Calculate the curved surface area of the bucket.

**4** A cylinder has a radius of 3.6 cm. The length of the cylinder is 8.5 cm.
Calculate the total surface area of the cylinder.
Give your answer to an appropriate degree of accuracy.

**5** A concrete pipe is 150 cm long.
It has an internal radius of 15 cm and an external radius of 20 cm.
Calculate, giving your answers to 3 significant figures,
(a) the area of the curved surface inside of the pipe,
(b) the curved surface area of the outside of the pipe.

**6** A cylinder is 15 cm high.
The curved surface area of the cylinder is 377 cm².
Calculate the radius of the cylinder.

## Cones

The diagram shows a cone with: circular base, radius $r$, slant height $l$, perpendicular height $h$.

Using Pythagoras' Theorem, $l^2 = r^2 + h^2$.

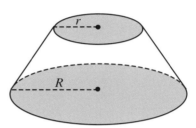

Volume of a cone $= \frac{1}{3} \times$ base area $\times$ perpendicular height
The area of the circular base $= \pi r^2$.
$V = \frac{1}{3} \pi r^2 h$
Curved surface area $= \pi r l$

A **frustum of a cone** is formed by removing the top of a cone with a cut parallel to its circular base.

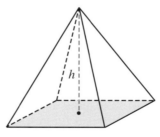

Frustum of a cone

The **volume of a frustum** = Volume of complete cone − Volume of cone removed

$$= \frac{1}{3} \pi R^2 H - \frac{1}{3} \pi r^2 h$$

where  $R$  is the base radius of the complete cone,
   $r$  is the base radius of the cone removed,
   $H$  is the height of the complete cone,
   $h$  is the height of the cone removed.

The **curved surface area** of a frustum is given by:

Curved surface area of complete cone − Curved surface area of cone removed

*How could you find the total surface area of a solid frustum of a cone?*

## Pyramids

The volume of a pyramid is given by:  $V = \frac{1}{3} \times$ base area $\times$ perpendicular height

## Spheres

Volume $= \frac{4}{3} \pi r^3$    Surface area $= 4 \pi r^2$

EXAMPLE

A child's toy is made from a cone with base 3 cm and height 4 cm joined to a hemisphere with radius 3 cm.

(a) Calculate the volume of the toy.
(b) Calculate the total surface area.

(a) Volume of hemisphere
$$= \frac{1}{2} \times \frac{4}{3} \pi r^3$$
$$= \frac{1}{2} \times \frac{4}{3} \times \pi \times 3^3$$
$$= 56.548... \text{ cm}^3$$

Volume of cone
$$= \frac{1}{3} \pi r^2 h$$
$$= \frac{1}{3} \times \pi \times 3^2 \times 4$$
$$= 37.699... \text{ cm}^3$$

Total volume
$$= 56.548... + 37.699...$$
$$= 94.247... \text{ cm}^3$$
$$= 94.2 \text{ cm}^3, \text{ correct to 3 s.f.}$$

(b) Surface area of hemisphere
$$= \frac{1}{2} \times 4 \pi r^2$$
$$= \frac{1}{2} \times 4 \times \pi \times 3^2$$
$$= 56.548... \text{ cm}^2$$

Curved surface area of cone $= \pi r l$
By Pythagoras: $l^2 = r^2 + h^2$
$$l^2 = 3^2 + 4^2$$
$$l^2 = 25$$
$$l = \sqrt{25} = 5 \text{ cm}$$

Curved surface area of cone
$$= \pi \times 3 \times 5$$
$$= 47.123... \text{ cm}^2$$

Total surface area
$$= 56.548... + 47.123...$$
$$= 103.672...$$
$$= 104 \text{ cm}^2, \text{ correct to 3 s.f.}$$

## Exercise 30.7

Use the $\pi$ key on your calculator and give answers correct to 3 significant figures where appropriate.

**1** Find the volumes of these solids.

(a)

(b)

**Sphere, radius 8 cm**

(c)

**2** Find the areas of the curved surfaces for these cones.

(a)

(b)

(c)

**3** Which of these containers has the greater volume?
Show all your working.

A cone 15 cm high with radius 5 cm

A hemispherical bowl of radius 6 cm

**4** A pyramid with base area 20 cm² has volume 250 cm³.
What is the height of the pyramid?

**5** Find the surface areas of these solids.

(a)

Sphere, radius 5 cm

(b)

7 cm
10 cm

(c)

15 cm

Hemisphere, radius 15 cm

**6** For each of these solids, find,
(i)   the total volume,        (ii)   the total surface area.

(a)

4 cm
6 cm

(b)

2 cm
4 cm

(c)

5 cm
8 cm    6 cm

**7** A cone is 6.4 cm high. It has a volume of 150 cm³.
Calculate the radius of the cone.

**8** A sphere has a volume of 58 cm³.
Calculate the radius of the sphere.

**9** Rubber bungs are made by removing the tops of cones.
Starting with a cone of radius 10 cm and height 16 cm,
a rubber bung is made by cutting a cone of radius 5 cm
and height 8 cm from the top.
Find the volume and total surface area of the rubber bung.

8 cm
5 cm
16 cm
10 cm

**10**

X
12 cm
B
A
18 cm    10 cm
C
D

*ABCDX* is a pyramid.
The base *ABCD* is a rectangle measuring 18 cm by 10 cm
and *X* is 12 cm vertically above the midpoint of the base.

Calculate
(a)   the volume of the pyramid,
(b)   the total surface area of the pyramid.

- **Faces**, **vertices** (corners) and **edges**.
  For example, a cube has 6 faces, 8 vertices and 12 edges.

- A **net** can be used to make a solid shape.

- 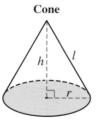 **Isometric paper** is used to make 2-D drawings of 3-D shapes.

- A **plane of symmetry** slices through a 3-D shape
  so that one half is the mirror image of the other half.

- Three-dimensional shapes can have **axes of symmetry**.

- **Plans and Elevations.**
  The view of a 3-D shape looking from above is called a **plan**.
  The view of a 3-D shape from the front or sides is called an **elevation**.

- **Volume** is the amount of space occupied by a 3-D shape.

- The formula for the volume of a **cuboid** is:
  Volume = length × breadth × height
  $V = l \times b \times h$

- To find the **surface area** of a cuboid find the area of
  the six rectangular faces and add the answers together.

- Volume of a **cube** is:   Volume = (length)³
  $V = l^3$

- A prism is a 3-D shape with the same
  cross-section throughout its length.

- Volume of a prism = area of cross-section × length

Triangular prism

-  A **cylinder** is a prism.
  Volume of a cylinder is:   $V = \pi \times r^2 \times h$
  Surface area of a cylinder is:   Surface area = $2\pi r^2 + 2\pi rh$

- These formulae are used in calculations involving **cones, pyramids,** and **spheres.**

**Cone**

$V = \frac{1}{3} \times$ base area × height
$V = \frac{1}{3} \pi r^2 h$
Curved surface area = $\pi rl$

**Pyramid**

$V = \frac{1}{3} \times$ base area × height

**Sphere**

Volume = $\frac{4}{3} \pi r^3$
Surface area = $4 \pi r^2$

- A **frustum of a cone** is formed by removing the
  top of a cone with a cut parallel to its circular base.

**1** This 3-D shape has been made using 4 linking cubes of side 1 cm.
Draw this shape on isometric paper.

**2**

A box contains 2 balls of radius 2 cm, as shown.

(a) Draw a plan of the box.
(b) Draw an elevation of the box from the direction marked **X**.

**3** The diagram shows a triangular prism.
The ends of the prism are equilateral triangles.
(a) How many axes of symmetry has the prism?
(b) How many planes of symmetry has the prism?

**4** Matt has two pieces of wood.
A cuboid which measures 6 cm by 5 cm by 4 cm. A cube of edge 5 cm.
(a) Which piece of wood has the larger volume?
(b) Which piece of wood has the larger surface area?
Show working for each of your answers.

**5** The volume of the cuboid shown is 120 cm³.
Work out the height.

OCR

**6** A cylinder has a diameter of 10 cm and a height of 10 cm.
Calculate the **total** surface area of the cylinder.
Give your answer in terms of $\pi$.

**7** This container is a prism of length 5 m.
The cross-section of the container is a trapezium.
Calculate the volume of the container.

OCR

**8**

The surface area of this cuboid is 197 cm².
Calculate the volume of the cuboid.

**9** The diagram shows a block of wood.
The block is a cuboid with edges 18 cm, 25 cm and 32 cm.
A cylindrical hole with radius 12 cm and depth 15 cm
is made in the wood.
Find the volume of wood remaining.
Give your answer to a sensible degree of accuracy.

OCR

**10** A solid bar has length 2.5 m.
The cross-section of the bar is a sector of a circle with sector angle 80° and radius 35 cm.

Calculate the total surface area of the bar.

OCR

**11**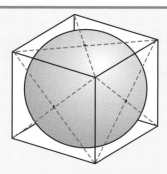

This diagram shows a sphere of radius 4.5 cm fitting tightly inside a box.
The box is a cube.

Calculate the volume of the space around the sphere, inside the cube.

**12** A hemispherical bowl has a radius of 30 cm.

(a) (i) Calculate the volume of the bowl.
Leave your answer as a multiple of $\pi$.

(ii) A cylinder of radius 20 cm and height $h$ cm has the same volume as the bowl.
Calculate the value of $h$.

Water is poured into the bowl to a depth of 12 cm.
(b) Calculate the radius of the surface of the water.

OCR

**13**

The diagram shows the net of a cone.
Calculate the volume of the cone.

315°

8 cm

OCR

**14** A solid clay object is a cylinder together with a cone.
The dimensions are shown in the diagram.
The clay is reshaped into a sphere.
Find the radius of the sphere.

6 cm

2 cm

7 cm

OCR

**15**

9 cm

15 cm

Eddie cuts a large wooden cone into a smaller cone and a frustum.
The smaller cone has a diameter of 6 cm and a height of 10 cm.

(a) Calculate the volume of the frustum.
(b) Calculate the curved surface area of the frustum.

327

# Understanding and Using Measures

## Units of measurement

Different units can be used to measure the same quantity.
For example:

The same **length** can be measured using centimetres, kilometres, inches, miles, …
The same **mass** can be measured using grams, kilograms, pounds, ounces, …
The same **capacity** can be measured using litres, millilitres, gallons, pints, …

There are two sorts of units in common use − **metric** units and **imperial** units.

## Metric units

The common metric units used to measure length, mass (weight) and capacity (volume) are shown below.

| **Length** | **Mass** | **Capacity and volume** |
|---|---|---|
| 1 kilometre (km) = 1000 metres (m) | 1 tonne (t) = 1000 kilograms (kg) | 1 litre = 1000 millilitres (ml) |
| 1 m = 100 centimetres (cm) | 1 kg = 1000 grams (g) | 1 cm³ = 1 ml |
| 1 cm = 10 millimetres (mm) | | |

**Kilo** means thousand, 1000.   So, a **kilo**gram is one thousand grams.

For example: 3 kilograms = 3000 grams.

**Centi** means hundredth, $\frac{1}{100}$.   So, a **centi**metre is one hundredth of a metre.

For example: 2 centimetres = $\frac{2}{100}$ metre = 0.02 metres.

**Milli** means thousandth, $\frac{1}{1000}$.   So, a **milli**litre is one thousandth of a litre.

For example: 5 millilitres = $\frac{5}{1000}$ litre = 0.005 litres.

## Changing from one metric unit to another

Changing from one metric unit to another involves multiplying, or dividing,
by a power of 10 (10, 100 or 1000).

### EXAMPLES

**1** Change 6.3 cm into millimetres.

| 1 cm = 10 mm |
|---|

To change centimetres into millimetres,
multiply by 10.
6.3 × 10 = 63
6.3 cm = 63 mm

**2** Change 245 g into kilograms.

| 1 kg = 1000 g |
|---|

To change grams into kilograms,
divide by 1000.
245 ÷ 1000 = 0.245
245 g = 0.245 kg

## Changing units - areas and volumes

$$1\,m = 100\,cm$$
$$1\,m^2 = 100 \times 100\,cm^2 = 10\,000\,cm^2$$
$$1\,m^3 = 100 \times 100 \times 100\,cm^3 = 1\,000\,000\,cm^3$$

*How many mm equal 1 cm?*

*How many mm² equal 1 cm²?*

*How many mm³ equal 1 cm³?*

Do not use a calculator.

**1** Copy and complete each of the following.
  (a)  320 000 ml = ...... $l$
  (b)  0.32 t  = ...... kg = ...... g
  (c)  320 mm = ...... cm = ...... m
  (d)  32 000 cm² = ...... m²

**2** Find the number of kilograms in    9300 g.

**3** Find the number of metres in    8000 mm.

**4** Find the number of millilitres in    0.03 litres.

**5** Which two lengths are the same?    2000 m    20 km    200 m    2 km    0.02 km

**6** Which two weights are the same?    8 g    8 kg    8000 g    0.8 kg    80 kg

**7** Which length is longest?    0.5 km    50 m    5000 mm    500 cm

**8** Which weight is heaviest?    0.3 t    3000 g    3 kg    30 kg

**9** Which length is the shortest?    0.02 km    200 mm    2 cm    20 m

**10** How many:
  (a)  metres are there in 3123 mm,
  (b)  centimetres are there in 4.5 m,
  (c)  metres are there in 3.24 km,
  (d)  grams are there in 1 tonne,
  (e)  litres are there in 400 ml?

**11** Which area is larger?    0.5 m²    or    500 cm²    Give a reason for your answer.

**12** Which volume is larger?  0.08 m³  or  800 000 cm³  Give a reason for your answer.

**13** A can of coke contains 330 ml. How many litres of coke are there in 6 cans?

**14** One lap of a running track is 400 m. How many laps are run in an 8 km race?

**15** Twenty children at a party share equally 1 kg of fruit pastilles.
How many grams of pastilles does each child receive?

**16** A recipe for a dozen biscuits uses 240 g of flour. James has 1.2 kg of flour.
How many biscuits can he make?

**17** Ben takes two 5 ml doses of medicine four times a day for 5 days.
Originally, there was $\frac{1}{4}$ of a litre of medicine.
How much medicine is left?

**18** A table mat has an area of 360 cm². What area does it cover in square metres?

**19** The floor of a corridor is a rectangle, 5.6 m long and 120 cm wide.
Calculate the area of the floor in:  (a)  square centimetres,    (b)  square metres.

**20** A box has a volume of 0.6 m³. What is the volume of the box in cubic centimetres?

## Estimating with sensible units using suitable degrees of accuracy

It is a useful skill to be able to estimate length, mass and capacity. These facts might help you.

**Length**
Most adults are between 1.5 m and 1.8 m tall. The door to your classroom is about 2 m high.
*Find some more facts which will help you to estimate length and distance.*

**Mass**
A biro weighs about 5 g. A standard bag of sugar weighs 1 kg.
*Find some more facts which will help you to estimate weight or mass.*

**Capacity**
A teaspoon holds about 5 ml. A can of pop holds about 330 ml.
*Find some more facts which will help you to estimate volume and capacity.*

**1** The Great Wall of China, the longest man-made structure in the world, is about 2350 km long.
Degree of accuracy: nearest 50 km.

**2** Earthquake shock waves travel through rock at a speed of approximately 25 000 km/hour.
Degree of accuracy: nearest 1000 km/hour.

**3** The smallest mammal is the Kitti's hog-nosed bat. It weighs about 1.5 g.
Degree of accuracy: nearest 0.1 g.

**4** The current Olympic record for the men's 100 m is 9.92 seconds.
Degree of accuracy: nearest 0.01 seconds.

## Exercise 31.2

**1** Give the most appropriate metric unit that you would use to measure the following.
  (a) The distance from London to York.     (b) The distance across a road.
  (c) The length of your foot.               (d) The length of your little finger nail.
  (e) The weight of a bag of potatoes.       (f) The weight of an egg.
  (g) The capacity of a bucket.              (h) The capacity of a medicine bottle.

**2** Which of the following is the best estimate for the mass of a banana?
  1 kg          5 g          250 g          30 g          3 kg          750 g

**3** Which of the following is the best estimate for the diameter of a football?
  2 m          50 mm          30 cm          1.5 m          0.6 m          800 mm

**4** Which of the following would be the best estimate for the capacity of a mug?
  15 m          1200 ml          2 l          0.5 l          200 ml          800 ml

**5** Give a sensible estimate using an appropriate unit for the following measures:
  (a) the length of a matchstick,           (b) the length of a football pitch,
  (c) the weight of a 30 cm ruler,          (d) the weight of a double decker bus,
  (e) the volume of drink in a glass.
  In each case state the degree of accuracy you have chosen for your estimate.

**6**

> **"My teacher's height is about 1.7 mm."**
> **This statement is incorrect.**

It can be corrected by changing the unit:          "My teacher's height is about 1.7 m."
It can also be corrected by changing the quantity:   "My teacher's height is about 1700 mm."

Each of these statements is also incorrect.
"Tyrannosaurus, a large meat-eating dinosaur, is estimated to have been about 12 cm long."
"The tallest mammal is the giraffe which grows up to about 5.9 mm tall."
"My car used 5 ml of petrol on a journey of 35 miles."
"The area of the school hall is about 500 mm²."

Correct each statement:
  (a) by changing the unit,     (b) by changing the quantity.

## Imperial units

The following imperial units of measurement are in everyday use.

| Length | Mass | Capacity and volume |
|---|---|---|
| 1 foot = 12 inches | 1 pound = 16 ounces | 1 gallon = 8 pints |
| 1 yard = 3 feet | 14 pounds = 1 stone | |

## Metric and imperial conversions

In order to convert to and from metric and imperial units you need to know these facts.

| Length | Mass | Capacity and volume |
|---|---|---|
| 5 miles is about 8 km | 1 kg is about 2.2 pounds | 1 litre is about 1.75 pints |
| 1 inch is about 2.5 cm | | 1 gallon is about 4.5 litres |
| 1 foot is about 30 cm | | |

### EXAMPLES

**1** Convert 40 cm to inches.

1 inch is about 2.5 cm.
40 cm is about 40 ÷ 2.5 inches.
40 cm is about 16 inches.

**2** Tim is 6 feet 2 inches tall.
Estimate Tim's height in centimetres.

6 feet 2 inches = 6 × 12 + 2 = 74 inches.
74 inches is about 74 × 2.5 cm.
6 feet 2 inches is about 185 cm.

## Exercise 31.3

**1** Convert each quantity to the units given.
  (a) 15 kg to pounds.　　(b) 20 litres to pints.　　(c) 5 metres to inches.
  (d) 6 inches to millimetres.　(e) 50 cm to inches.　　(f) 6 feet to centimetres.

**2** How far is 32 km in miles?

**3** How many pints are there in a 4-litre carton of milk?

**4** Kelvin is 5 feet 8 inches tall. Estimate Kelvin's height in centimetres.

**5** Paddy weighs 9 stones 12 pounds. Estimate Paddy's weight in kilograms.

**6** Estimate the number of:
  (a) metres in 2000 feet,　　(b) kilometres in 3 miles,　　(c) feet in 150 centimetres,
  (d) pounds in 1250 grams,　　(e) litres in 10 gallons.

**7** The capacity of a car's petrol tank is 54 litres. How much does the petrol tank hold in gallons?

**8** A box contains 200 balls. Each ball weighs 50 g.
Estimate the total weight of the balls in pounds.

**9** Jemma has a 4-litre carton of milk and 20 glasses. Each glass holds one third of a pint.
Can Jemma fill all the glasses with milk? Show your working.

**10** Lauren says 10 kg of potatoes weighs the same as 20 lb of sugar.
Is she correct? Show all your working.

**11** Alfie cycles 6 miles. Jacob cycles 10 kilometres.
Alfie claims that he has cycled further than Jacob. Is he correct? Show all your working.

**12** One litre of water weighs 1 kg. Estimate the weight of one gallon of water in pounds.

**13** A sheet of card measures 12 inches by 20 inches.
What is the area of the card in square centimetres?

**14** Convert the following speeds to kilometres per hour.
  (a) 30 miles per hour.　　(b) 50 miles per hour.　　(c) 30 metres per second.

**15** Convert the following speeds to miles per hour.
  (a) 60 km per hour.　　(b) 40 metres per second.

Understanding and Using Measures

**16** Convert a speed of 60 miles per hour to metres per second.
Give your answer to a suitable degree of accuracy.

**17** (a) A car does 40 miles to the gallon. How many kilometres does it do per litre?
(b) A car does 9.6 kilometres to the litre. How many miles does it do per gallon?

**18** 30 g of grass seed is needed to sow 1 m² of lawn.
What weight of grass seed is needed to sow a rectangular lawn measuring 40 foot by 30 foot?

**19** Concrete is sold by the cubic metre.
A path, 31 feet long, 5 feet wide and 1 foot 6 inches deep, is to be made of concrete.
How many cubic metres of concrete are needed?

## Discrete and continuous measures

### Discrete measures

**Discrete measures** can only take particular values.

For example: The number of people on a bus is 42.
Two ice skating judges give scores of 5.1 and 5.2.

The number of people on a bus must be a whole number.
The ice skating scores show that a discrete measure does not need to be a whole number.
They are discrete because scores are not given between numbers like 5.1 and 5.2.

> Accuracy in data and measurement, lower and upper bounds (limits) were first covered in Chapter 3.

### Continuous measures

James was 14 on the day of his 14th birthday.
He will still be called 14 years old right up to the day before his 15th birthday.
So, although James is 14, his actual age is any age within a range of 1 year.

> I am 14.

> I am 14 years and 3 months.

Jenny is **not** exactly 14 years and 3 months old.
However, Jenny's age is given to a greater degree of accuracy than James' age because the range of possible ages in her case is smaller.
*What is the range of possible ages in Jenny's measurement of her age?*

Measures which can lie within a range of possible values are called **continuous measures**.
The value of a continuous measure depends on the accuracy of whatever is making the measurement.

> If a **continuous measure**, $c$, is recorded to the nearest $x$, then:
> the **limits** of the possible values of $c$ can be written as: $c \pm \frac{1}{2}x$.

### EXAMPLES

**1** The number of words on a page of a book is 400 to the nearest 100.
What is the smallest and largest possible number of words on the page?

The smallest whole number that rounds to 400 is 350.
The largest whole number that rounds to 400 is 449.
The smallest number of words on the page is 350 and the largest number of words is 449.

**2** The length of this page is 26 cm to the nearest centimetre.
What are the limits between which the true length of the page must lie?

Length of page = 2 cm ± 0.5 cm       25.5 cm ≤ length of page < 26.5 cm.

**1** State whether each of the following are discrete or continuous measures.
    (a)    The volume of wine in a wine glass.
    (b)    The votes cast for the Independent Party candidate in a local election.
    (c)    The number of pages in a newspaper.
    (d)    The time it takes to walk to school.

**2** For each of the following measures state whether the value given is an exact value or give the limits within which it could lie.
    (a)    A book has 224 pages.    (b)    A bus was 5 minutes late.    (c)    I weigh 63 kg.

**3** What are the slowest and fastest possible times:
    (a)    of Derek who runs exactly 100 metres in 13 seconds measured to the nearest second,
    (b)    of Jan who swims exactly 100 metres in 82.6 seconds measured to the nearest tenth of a second?

**4** Fifty flowers, to the nearest 10, each grow to a height of 50 cm, to the nearest 10 cm.

    (a)    Show on one copy of the number line the possible numbers of flowers.
    (b)    Show on another copy of the number line the possible heights of the flowers.

**5** Tina is 1.53 m tall.
    (a)    To what degree of accuracy is Tina's height given?
    (b)    What are the limits between which her true height lies?

**6** (a)    What is the minimum weight of a 62 kg parcel measured to the nearest kilogram?
    (b)    What is the minimum length of a 2.3 m shelf measured to the nearest 0.1 m?
    (c)    What is the minimum time for a race timed at 12.63 seconds measured to the nearest one hundredth of a second?

**7** What degree of accuracy has been used to make these estimates of the length of a corridor:
    (a)    About 120 m. The smallest possible length is 115 m.
    (b)    About 100 m. The smallest possible length is 75 m.
    (c)    About 200 m. The smallest possible length is 150 m.

**8** Write down the largest and smallest values of the following discrete measures.
    (a)    10 000 measured to the nearest 1000.    (b)    10 000 measured to the nearest 100.
    (c)    10 000 measured to the nearest 50.    (d)    500 measured to 3 significant figures.
    (e)    500 measured to 2 significant figures.

## Calculations involving continuous measures

### EXAMPLE

Gail's best time for running 100 metres is 12.7 seconds.
The length is accurate to the nearest metre. The time is accurate to the nearest tenth of a second.
Calculate her maximum possible average speed.

Time
Upper bound $= 12.7\,s + 0.05\,s = 12.75\,s$
Lower bound $= 12.7\,s - 0.05\,s = 12.65\,s$

Distance
Upper bound $= 100\,m + 0.5\,m = 100.5\,m$
Lower bound $= 100\,m - 0.5\,m = 99.5\,m$

Gail's maximum possible average speed $= \dfrac{\text{greatest distance}}{\text{shortest time}} = \dfrac{100.5 \text{ metres}}{12.65 \text{ seconds}} = 7.944\ldots \text{ m/s}$

Gail's maximum possible average speed $= 7.94$ m/s, correct to 3 significant figures.
*What bounds should be used to calculate Gail's minimum possible average speed?*

**1** In the diagram, all angles are measured to the nearest degree.
Find the maximum possible size of angle $a$.

**2**
9.4 cm

5.2 cm

A cylinder has radius 5.2 cm and height 9.4 cm.
Both measurements are given to the nearest 0.1 cm.
Find the difference between the minimum and maximum
possible volumes of the cylinder.

**3** A water tank, in the shape of a cuboid, is full of water.
Water is drained from the tank at a rate of 8 litres per minute.
The dimensions of the tank are given to the nearest 10 cm.
The rate at which the water is drained from the tank is
given to the nearest 0.5 litres per minute.

(a) Calculate the smallest possible time to drain the tank.
(b) Calculate the greatest possible time to drain the tank.

0.8 m    1.6 m

1.2 m

**4** 12.6 cm

Area = 93.20 cm²

A rectangle has length 12.6 cm and area 93.20 cm².
The length is given to the nearest millimetre.
The area is given to the nearest 0.05 cm².
Calculate the upper bound of the width of the rectangle.

**5** The diameter of a concrete sphere is given as 20 cm,
to the nearest centimetre.
The density of concrete is 2.2 g/cm³.
Calculate the minimum mass of the sphere.

20 cm

**6** The distance between $A$ and $B$ is 12.2 km to the nearest 100 m.
The distance between $B$ and $C$ is 14.34 km to the nearest 10 m.
Trevor walks from $A$ to $B$ and then from $B$ to $C$.
He takes 8.5 hours to the nearest half an hour.

(a) Calculate the upper and lower bounds of the total distance that Trevor walks.
(b) Calculate the lower bound of Trevor's average speed on the walk.

**7** The diagram shows a rectangular flag, $ABCD$.
The flag is blue with a central white circle.
$AB = 3.2$ m and $BC = 2.1$ m,
both accurate to the nearest 10 cm.
The diameter of the circle is 0.95 m
to the nearest centimetre.
Calculate the lower bound of the area
coloured blue on the flag.

A    3.2 m    B

0.95 m

2.1 m

D    C

## Dimensions and formulae

**Formulae** can be used to calculate perimeters, areas and volumes of various shapes.
By analysing the **dimensions** involved it is possible to decide whether a given formula represents a perimeter, an area or a volume.

**Length** (L) has **dimension 1.**
Length (L) × Length (L) = **Area** ($L^2$) has **dimension 2.**
Length (L) × Length (L) × Length (L) = **Volume** ($L^3$) has **dimension 3.**

The size of this square based cuboid depends on:
    $x$, the length of the side of the square base,    $y$, the height of the cuboid.

The total **length** of the edges of the cuboid is given by the formula:   $E = 8x + 4y$
This formula involves:   Numbers: 8 and 4
                             Lengths (L): $x$ and $y$
                             The formula has **dimension 1**.

The total **surface area** of the cuboid is given by the formula:   $S = 2x^2 + 4xy$
This formula involves:   Numbers: 2 and 4
                             Areas ($L^2$): $x \times x$ and $x \times y$
                             The formula has **dimension 2**.

The **volume** of the cuboid is given by the formula:   $V = x^2y$
This formula involves:   Volume ($L^3$): $x \times x \times y$
                             This formula has **dimension 3**.

---

### EXAMPLE

In each of these expressions the letters $a$, $b$ and $c$ represent lengths.
Use dimensions to check whether the expressions
could represent a perimeter, an area or a volume.

(a)   $2a + 3b + 4c$      (b)   $3a^2 + 2b(a + c)$
(c)   $2a^2b + abc$        (d)   $3a + 2ab + c^3$

> **Note:**
> When checking formulae and expressions,
> numbers can be ignored because they have
> no dimension.
> ≡ means 'is equivalent to'.

(a)   $2a + 3b + 4c$
     Write this using dimensions.
     $L + L + L \equiv 3L \equiv L$
     $2a + 3b + 4c$   has dimension 1 and could represent a perimeter.

(b)   $3a^2 + 2b(a + c)$
     Write this using dimensions.
     $L^2 + L(L + L)$
     $\equiv L^2 + L(2L)$
     $\equiv L^2 + 2L^2$
     $\equiv 3L^2$
     $\equiv L^2$
     $3a^2 + 2b(a + c)$   has dimension 2 and could represent an area.

(c)   $2a^2b + abc$
     Write this using dimensions.
     $L^2 \times L + L \times L \times L$
     $\equiv L^3 + L^3$
     $\equiv 2L^3$
     $\equiv L^3$
     $2a^2b + abc$   has dimension 3 and could represent a volume.

(d)   $3a + 2ab + c^3$
     Write this using dimensions.
     $L + L \times L + L^3$
     $\equiv L + L^2 + L^3$
     The dimensions are **inconsistent**.
     $3a + 2ab + c^3$   does not represent a perimeter, an area or a volume.

Understanding and Using Measures

**1** $p$, $q$, $r$ and $x$, $y$, $z$ represent lengths.
For each formula state whether it represents
a length, an area or a volume.
  (a) $pq$  (b) $2\pi x$   (c) $p + q + r$  (d) $\pi z$
  (e) $pqr$  (f) $2(pq + qr + pr)$  (g) $\pi x^2 y$   (h) $2\pi x(x + y)$

**2** In each of the expressions below, $x$, $y$ and $z$ represent lengths.
By using dimensions decide whether each expression could represent a perimeter, an area,
a volume or none of these. Explain your answer in each case.
  (a) $x + y + z$   (b) $xy + xz$    (c) $xyz$    (d) $x^2(y^2 + z^2)$
  (e) $x(y + z)$    (f) $\dfrac{x^2}{y}$      (g) $\dfrac{xz}{y}$      (h) $x + y^2 + z^3$
  (i) $xy(y + z)$    (j) $x^3 + x^2(y + z)$    (k) $xy(y^2 + z)$    (l) $x(y + z) + z^2$

**3** The diagram shows a discus. $x$ and $y$ are the lengths shown on the diagram.
These expressions could represent certain quantities relating to the discus.

   $\pi(x^2 + y^2)$    $\pi x^2 y^2$    $\pi xy$    $2\pi(x + y)$

  (a) Which of them could be an expression for:
    (i) the longest possible distance around the discus,
    (ii) the surface area of the discus?
  (b) Use dimensions to explain your answers to part (a).

**4** $x$, $y$ and $z$ represent lengths.
  (a) $A = xyz + z(x - y) + 2y$
    This is not a formula for perimeter, area or volume. Use dimensions to explain why.
  (b) $P = 3z(x + y)$
    This could be a formula for area. Use dimensions to explain why.
  (c) $V = x^2 y + z^2(2x - y) + 2y^3$
    This could be a formula for volume. Use dimensions to explain why.

**5** $p$, $q$, $r$ and $s$ represent the lengths of the edges of this triangular prism.
Match the formulas to the measurements.

**Formulas**  $\frac{1}{2}pqs$   $2\left(p + q + r + \dfrac{3s}{2}\right)$   $s(p + q + r) + pq$

**Measurements**  Edge length   Surface area   Volume

**6** These arrows are similar.

$w$ represents the width of any arrow.
k and c are numbers.
$H$ represents the height of the arrow and $A$ its area.
Which of the following statements could be correct and which **must** be wrong?
  (a) $H = kw$      (b) $H = ckw$      (c) $H = kw + c$
  (d) $A = cw$      (e) $A = kw^2$      (f) $A = kw^3$
Give a reason for each of your answers and where you think the formula **must** be wrong
suggest what it might be for.

**7** In these formulae $a$, $b$ and $c$ represent lengths and $A$ represents an area.
  (a) $a = b + c$       (b) $a^2 = bc$       (c) $A = a^2 + bc$
  (d) $c = A + ab$      (e) $Ab = a^3$       (f) $A = \dfrac{a^2}{c} + b^2$
Which of the formulae have consistent dimensions?

- The common units – both **metric** and **imperial** – used to measure **length**, **mass** and **capacity**.
- How to convert from one unit to another. This includes knowing the connection between one metric unit and another and the approximate equivalents between metric and imperial units.

| Metric Units | Imperial Units | Conversions |
|---|---|---|
| **Length** <br> 1 kilometre (km) = 1000 metres (m) <br> 1 m = 100 centimetres (cm) <br> 1 cm = 10 millimetres (mm) | **Length** <br> 1 foot = 12 inches <br> 1 yard = 3 feet | **Length** <br> 5 miles is about 8 km <br> 1 inch is about 2.5 cm <br> 1 foot is about 30 cm |
| **Mass** <br> 1 tonne (t) = 1000 kilograms (kg) <br> 1 kg = 1000 grams (g) | **Mass** <br> 1 pound = 16 ounces <br> 14 pounds = 1 stone | **Mass** <br> 1 kg is about 2.2 pounds |
| **Capacity and volume** <br> 1 litre = 1000 millilitres (ml) <br> $1 \, cm^3 = 1 \, ml$ | **Capacity and volume** <br> 1 gallon = 8 pints | **Capacity and volume** <br> 1 litre is about 1.75 pints <br> 1 gallon is about 4.5 litres |

- How to change between units of area. For example $1 \, m^2 = 10\,000 \, cm^2$.
- How to change between units of volume. For example $1 \, m^3 = 1\,000\,000 \, cm^3$.
- Be able to recognise limitations on the accuracy of measurements.
  A **discrete measure** can only take a particular value and a **continuous measure** lies within a range of possible values which depends upon the degree of accuracy of the measurement.

  > If a **continuous measure**, $c$, is recorded to the nearest $x$, then:
  > the **limits** of the possible values of $c$ can be written as: $c \pm \frac{1}{2} x$.

- By analysing the **dimensions** of a formula it is possible to decide whether a given formula represents a **length** (dimension 1), an **area** (dimension 2) or a **volume** (dimension 3).

## Review Exercise 31

**1**
  (a)   How many metres are there in 2.65 kilometres?
  (b)   The distance from Calais to Paris is 280 km.
        What is this distance in miles?

**2**
  (a)   Fiona weighs 10 stones 3 pounds.
        Estimate her weight in kilograms.
  (b)   Fiona is 5 feet 2 inches tall.
        Work out her height in metres.

                              OCR

**3**
The diagram shows the petrol gauge on a car.
The car's petrol tank holds 60 litres when full.
Estimate how many gallons are in the petrol tank.

**4**
Change   $1.5 \, m^2$ to $cm^2$.

**5**
A rectangular strip of card measures 0.8 metres by 5 cm.

                       0.8 m

                                     5 cm

Calculate the area of the card in:
  (a)   square metres,         (b)   square centimetres.

**6**
What is 48 kilometres per hour in   (a)   miles per hour,        (b)   metres per second?

**7** James runs at an average speed of 12 miles/hour.
Tim runs at an average speed of 320 m/minute.
Who runs the fastest?

**8** According to the instructions Vinyl Matt paint covers about 13 m²/litre.
Estimate how many litres of paint is needed to cover a wall which measures 18 feet by 10 feet.

**9** A blue whale weighs 140 tonnes, to the nearest 10 tonnes.
What is the smallest possible weight of a blue whale?

**10** Bob weighs 76.9 kg, to the nearest 100 g.
What is Bob's maximum weight?

**11** $r$, $a$ and $b$ are all lengths.
Which of the following expressions could be a volume?

$$\frac{ar}{2}(4b + \pi r) \qquad 2(ab)^2 + \pi r^2 b \qquad 4a^2 b + rb^3 \qquad 2abr + \frac{\pi ar^2}{2}$$

OCR

**12** What is the greatest possible difference between the times of two runners who both run a race in 12.2 seconds timed to the nearest tenth of a second?

**13** A cable is 50 m long, correct to the nearest metre.
Barrie cuts off a piece which is 15 m long, correct to the nearest 10 cm.
Calculate the maximum length of the remaining cable.

OCR

**14** A lorry is 3.8 m high, to the nearest 0.1 m.
It is driven under a bridge 4.28 m high, to the nearest cm.
(a) What is the least possible clearance of the lorry as it travels under the bridge?

The lorry tail lift can carry a safe working load of 1200 kg, to the nearest 50 kg.
It is used to load boxes that weigh 36 kg, to the nearest kg.
(b) What is the maximum number of boxes it can be sure to lift safely?

OCR

**15** When a ball is thrown upwards, the maximum height, $h$, it reaches is

given by the formula $h = \dfrac{U^2}{2g}$.

It is given that $U = 4.2$ and $g = 9.8$, both correct to 2 significant figures.
Calculate the upper and lower bounds of $h$.

OCR

**16** The length of the base of a triangle is 12 cm, correct to the nearest cm.
The area of this triangle is 80 cm², correct to the nearest 10 cm².
Calculate the smallest and the largest possible values of the height of the triangle.

OCR

**17** Tommy the tortoise was weighed in April and again in October.
In April he weighed 1.42 kg and in October 1.78 kg.
Each of the weights is given correct to the nearest 20 g.
Calculate his maximum percentage weight gain.

OCR

**18** A decorative candle has a cross-section which is a square of side 5.5 cm,
correct to one decimal place.
(a) Calculate the maximum possible length of the diagonal of the square.

A candle holder is a shallow glass cylinder with internal radius of 3.92 cm,
correct to three significant figures.
(b) Is it certain that the candle will fit into the holder?
Justify your answer.

OCR

# Congruent Triangles and Similar Figures

## Congruent shapes

When two shapes are the same shape and size they are said to be **congruent**.
A copy of one shape would fit exactly over the second shape.
Sometimes it is necessary to turn the copy over to get an exact fit.
These shapes are all congruent.

## Congruent triangles

There are four ways to show that a pair of triangles are congruent.

**1** Three sides.
SSS

**2** Two sides and the included angle.
SAS

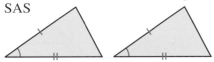

The included angle is the angle between the two sides.

**3** Two angles and a corresponding side.
ASA

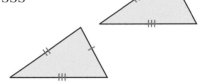

This can be written as AAS if the corresponding side is not between the angles.

**4** Right angle, hypotenuse and one side.
RHS

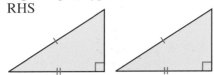

The hypotenuse is the side opposite the right angle and is the longest side in a right-angled triangle.

To show that two triangles are congruent you will need to state which pairs of sides and/or angles are equal, to match one of the four conditions for congruency given above.

### EXAMPLE

Show that triangles $ABC$ and $PQR$ are congruent.

$AB = PQ$   (equal lengths, given)
$AC = PR$   (equal lengths, given)
$\angle BAC = \angle QPR$   (equal angles, given)

So, triangles $ABC$ and $PQR$ are congruent.
Reason: SAS   (Two sides and the included angle.)

Since the triangles are congruent we also know that
$BC = QR$,   $\angle ABC = \angle PQR$   and   $\angle ACB = \angle PRQ$.

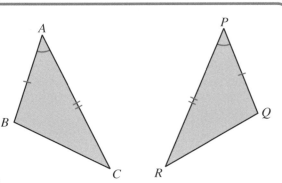

**1** Which of these shapes are congruent to each other?

A  B  C  D  E  F

**2** The diagram shows a rectangle that has been divided into five triangles.

(a) Which triangle is congruent to triangle *AFG*?
(b) Which quadrilateral is congruent to quadrilateral *ABEF*?

**3** Triangle *ABC* has been divided into four smaller triangles as shown.
Name two pairs of congruent triangles.

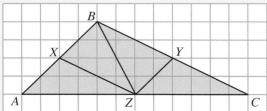

**4** The following triangles have not been drawn accurately.
Which two of these triangles are congruent to each other?
Give a reason for your answer.

**5** The following triangles have not been drawn accurately.
Which two of these triangles are congruent to each other?
Give a reason for your answer.

**6** The following triangles have not been drawn accurately.
State whether each pair of triangles is congruent or not.
Where triangles are congruent give the reason.

(a)    (b)    (c)

**7** The following triangles have not been drawn accurately.
State whether each pair of triangles is congruent or not.
Where triangles are congruent give the reason.

(a)

(b)

(c)

(d)

(e)

(f)

**8** For each of the following, is it possible to draw a congruent triangle without taking any other measurements from the original triangle?
If a triangle can be drawn give the reason for congruence which applies.

(a)
30° 115° 35°

(b)
5 cm 9 cm

(c)
6 cm 3 cm

(d)
105° 37°

(e)
85° 4 cm 55°

(f)
35° 45° 3 cm

(g)
4 cm 3 cm 6 cm

(h)
70° 5 cm 4 cm

(i)
27° 3 cm

**9** Triangle $ABC$ has angles 90°, 50° and 40°.
Triangle $XYZ$ also has angles 90°, 50° and 40°.
The triangles are not congruent.
Can you explain why?

**10** Show that triangles $DEF$ and $PQR$ are congruent.

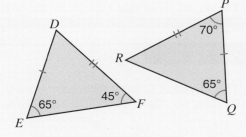

**11**

In the diagram $AB$ is parallel to $CD$.
$AB = CD = 7$ cm   and   $\angle ABD = 25°$.
(a) What is the size of $\angle BDC$?
(b) Show that triangles $ABD$ and $BCD$ are congruent.
(c) Name an angle which is the same size as $\angle CBD$.

## Similar figures

When one figure is an enlargement of another, the two figures are **similar**.

Sometimes one of the figures is rotated or reflected.

For example:
> Figures **C** and **E** are enlargements of figure **A**.
> Figures **A**, **C** and **E** are similar.

|  |  |  |  |  |
|---|---|---|---|---|
| **A** | **B** | **C** | **D** | **E** |

When two figures are **similar**:
> their **shapes** are the same,
> their **angles** are the same,
> corresponding **lengths** are in the same ratio,
> this ratio is the **scale factor** of the enlargement.

$$\text{Scale factor} = \frac{\text{new length}}{\text{original length}}$$

This can be rearranged to give
new length = original length × scale factor.

### EXAMPLES

**1**  A photo has width 6 cm and height 9 cm.
An enlargement is made, which has width 8 cm.
Calculate the height of the enlargement.

Scale factor $= \frac{8}{6}$
$h = 9 \times \frac{8}{6}$
$h = 12$ cm

9 cm

$h$

6 cm          8 cm

**2**  These two figures are similar.
Calculate the lengths of $x$ and $y$.
Write down the size of the angle marked $a$.
The scale factor $= \frac{4.5}{3} = 1.5$

1.4 cm   62°   $y$   3 cm          $x$   2.7 cm   $a$   4.5 cm

Lengths in the large figure are given by:   length in small figure × scale factor
$x = 1.4 \times 1.5$
$x = 2.1$ cm

Lengths in the small figure are given by:   length in large figure ÷ scale factor
$y = 2.7 \div 1.5$
$y = 1.8$ cm

The angles in similar figures are the same, so,   $a = 62°$.

## Exercise 32.2

**1**  The shapes in this question have been drawn accurately.
Explain why these two shapes are not similar to each other.

**2**  Which of the following must be similar to each other?
(a)  Two circles.          (b)  Two kites.          (c)  Two parallelograms.
(d)  Two squares.          (e)  Two rectangles.

**3** These rectangles are all similar. The diagrams have not been drawn accurately.
Work out the lengths of the sides marked *a* and *b*.

**4** These two kites are similar.
   (a)   What is the scale factor of their lengths?
   (b)   Find the length of the side marked *x*.
   (c)   What is the size of angle *a*?

**5** A shape has width 8 cm and length 24 cm.
It is enlarged to give a new shape with width 10 cm.
Calculate the length of the new shape.

**6** In each part, the two figures are similar. Lengths are in centimetres.
Calculate the lengths and angles marked with letters.

(a)

(b)

(c)

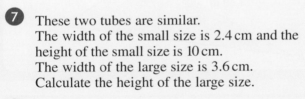

**7** These two tubes are similar.
The width of the small size is 2.4 cm and the
height of the small size is 10 cm.
The width of the large size is 3.6 cm.
Calculate the height of the large size.

**8** A motor car is 4.2 m long and 1.4 m high.
A scale model of the car is 8.4 cm long.
What is the height of the model?

**9** The smallest angle in triangle *T* is 18°.
Triangle *T* is enlarged by a scale factor of 2.
How big is the smallest angle in the enlarged triangle?

**10** A castle has height 30 m.
The height of the castle wall is 6 m.
A scale model of the castle has height 25 cm.
Calculate the height of the castle wall in the scale model.

**11** The dimensions of three sizes of paper are given.

| Length (cm) | 24 | 30 | *y* |
|---|---|---|---|
| Width (cm) | *x* | 20 | 32 |

All the sizes are similar.
Calculate the values of *x* and *y*.

Congruent Triangles and Similar Figures

## Similar triangles

For any pair of similar triangles:
corresponding lengths are opposite equal angles,
the scale factor is the ratio of corresponding sides.

$$\frac{AB}{PQ} = \frac{BC}{QR} = \frac{CA}{RP} = \text{scale factor}$$

### EXAMPLES

**1** These two triangles are similar, with the equal angles marked.
Calculate the lengths $x$ and $y$.
Scale factor $= \frac{6}{5} = 1.2$

$x = 2 \times 1.2$

$x = 2.4\,\text{cm}$

$y = 4.8 \div 1.2$

$y = 4\,\text{cm}$

**2** Triangles $ABC$ and $PQR$ are similar.
Calculate the lengths of $AC$ and $PQ$.
$BC$ and $PR$ are corresponding sides.
Scale factor $= \frac{4.48}{3.20} = 1.4$

$AC = 6.04 \div 1.4$

$AC = 4.31\,\text{m}$, correct to 2 d.p.

$PQ = 1.70 \times 1.4$

$PQ = 2.38\,\text{m}$

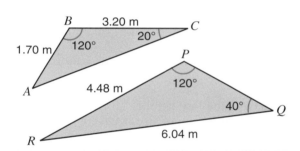

## Exercise 32.3    Question 1 should be done without a calculator.

**1** In each part, the triangles are similar, with equal angles marked.
Lengths are in centimetres.
Calculate lengths $x$ and $y$.

(a)

(b)

(c)

(d)

**2** Triangles *ABC* and *ADE* are similar.
Lengths are in centimetres.
∠*AED* = ∠*ACB*.

Calculate the lengths of *AB* and *AE*.

**3** In each part the triangles are similar.
Calculate the unknown lengths in both triangles.

(a)

(b)

(c)

(d)

**4** Triangles *PST* and *PQR* are similar.
Lengths are in centimetres.
∠*PTS* = ∠*PRQ*.

(a) Write down the length of *PR*.
(b) Calculate *QR*, *PQ* and *QS*.

**5**

Triangles *ABC* and *ADE* are similar.
∠*ADE* = ∠*ABC*.

(a) Write down the length of *AB*.
(b) Calculate the lengths of *BC* and *AC*.
(c) What is the length of *EC*?

**6** Triangles *DEF* and *DGH* are similar.
∠*DGH* = ∠*DEF*.

Calculate *GH* and *FH*.

## Showing that two triangles are similar

To show that two triangles are similar you have to show that:

**either** they have equal angles **or** corresponding lengths are all in the same ratio.

If you can show that one of these conditions is true then the other one is also true.

### EXAMPLES

**1** *AB* and *CD* are parallel lines. *AD* and *BC* meet at *X*.

(a) Prove that triangles *ABX* and *DCX* are similar.

(b) Which side in triangle *DCX* corresponds to *AX* in triangle *ABX*?

(c) Calculate the length of *AX*.

(a) $\angle BAX = \angle CDX$ (alternate angles)
$\angle AXB = \angle DXC$ (vertically opposite angles)
Triangles *ABX* and *DCX* contain two pairs of equal angles and so they are similar.
*If two pairs of angles are equal then the third pair must be equal. Why?*

(b) $\angle ABX = \angle DCX$.
Sides *AX* and *DX* are opposite these equal angles.
So, *DX* corresponds to *AX*.

(c) $\frac{AX}{3} = \frac{5}{4}$ (or scale factor $= \frac{5}{4}$)
$AX = \frac{5}{4} \times 3$
$AX = 3.75 \text{ cm}$

> You **must** give reasons for any statements you make.

**2** Show that these two triangles are similar.

$\frac{5}{2} = 2.5$
$\frac{3.75}{1.5} = 2.5$
$\frac{2.5}{1} = 2.5$

All three pairs of corresponding sides are in the same ratio, so, the triangles are similar.

## Exercise 32.4

**1** *BC* is parallel to *PQ*.
Show that triangles *ABC* and *APQ* are similar and calculate the required lengths.

(a)

Calculate *AC* and *AP*.

(b)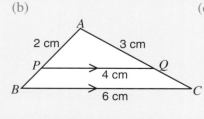

Calculate *AC* and *BP*.

(c)

Calculate *BC* and *BP*.

**2** *BC* is parallel to *PQ*.
Show that triangles *ABC* and *APQ* are similar and calculate the required lengths.

(a)

Calculate *AQ* and *BC*.

(b)

Calculate *AQ* and *BP*.

**3** Show that these pairs of triangles are similar and find angle *x*.

(a)

(b)

**4** All marked lengths are in centimetres.

(a) In each part show that triangles *ABC* and *APQ* are similar and find angle *x*.

(i)

(ii)

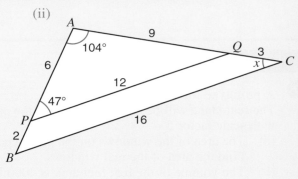

(b) In each part find the perimeters of triangles *ABC* and *APQ*.
What do you notice about the ratio of the perimeters of the triangles and the ratio of the lengths of corresponding sides?

**5** (a) Explain why triangles *ABC* and *PQR* are similar.
(b) Calculate the length of *AB*.
(c) The perimeter of triangle *ABC* is 7.5 cm.
Find the perimeter of triangle *PQR*.

**6**

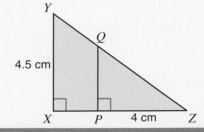

Triangles *XYZ* and *PQZ* are similar.
∠*ZXY* = ∠*ZPQ* = 90°.
*PZ* = 4 cm and *XY* = 4.5 cm.
The ratio *QZ* : *YZ* is 2 : 3.
Calculate the area of triangle *XYZ*.

## Lengths, areas and volumes of similar figures

### Activity

Some cubes have side 2 cm.
They are built together to make a larger cube with side 6 cm.
This represents an enlargement with scale factor 3.

Copy and complete the table.

| | Length of side (cm) | Area of face (cm²) | Volume of cube (cm³) |
|---|---|---|---|
| Small cube | 2 | | 8 |
| Large cube | 6 | 36 | |
| Scale factor | $\frac{6}{2} = 3$ | $\frac{36}{\phantom{0}} =$ | $\frac{\phantom{0}}{8} =$ |

*What do you notice about the three scale factors?*

Repeat this activity with a scale factor of 4.
Now repeat it with a scale factor of $k$.

**Spheres**

Three spheres have radii $r$ cm, $2r$ cm and $3r$ cm.
Compare the surface areas and volumes of the three spheres.

### Scale factors for length, area and volume

When the length scale factor $= k$
    the area scale factor $= k^2$
    the volume scale factor $= k^3$

For solids made of the same material, **mass is proportional to volume**.
So, the mass scale factor is $k^3$.

### EXAMPLES

**1** A prototype for a new plane is made.
The real plane will be an enlargement of the prototype with scale factor 5.
(a) The area of the windows on the prototype is 0.18 m². Find the area of the real windows.
(b) The volume of the real fuel tank is 4000 litres. Find the volume of the fuel tank on the prototype.

It can be assumed that "scale factor" refers to the length scale factor, unless specified differently in a question.

(a) Area scale factor $= 5^2 = 25$.
Real area $= 0.18 \times 25 = 4.5$ m²

(b) Volume scale factor $= 5^3 = 125$.
Prototype volume $= \frac{4000}{125} = 32$ litres.

**Corresponding lengths, areas and volumes:**

| Prototype plane | multiply by scale factor → | Real plane |
|---|---|---|
| Prototype plane | ← divide by scale factor | Real plane |

**2** A metal ingot has volume 20 000 cm³.
It is melted down and made into identical smaller ingots.
Each small ingot is similar to the original ingot and has volume 25 cm³.
The length of the large ingot is 50 cm.
Calculate the length of the small ingots.

Volume scale factor $= \frac{20\,000}{25} = 800$      Length scale factor $= \sqrt[3]{800} = 9.28\ldots$

Length of small ingot $= \frac{25}{\sqrt[3]{800}} = 2.693\ldots = 2.69$ cm, correct to 3 s.f.

1   A model of a train is 60 cm long. It is made on a scale of 1 to 50.
    What is the length of the actual train in metres?

2   A rectangle has length 8 cm and width 6 cm. A similar rectangle has length 12 cm.
    (a)   What is the scale factor of their lengths?
    (b)   What is the width of the larger rectangle?

3   A motor car is 4.2 m long and 1.4 m high. A scale model of the car is 8.4 cm long.
    (a)   What is the scale of the model?
    (b)   What is the height of the model?

4   The lengths of the sides of a kite are doubled. What happens to its area?

5   A rectangular vegetable plot needs 10 kg of fertiliser.
    How much fertiliser is needed for a plot with double the dimensions?

6   Circle $P$ has a radius of 3.5 cm. Circle $Q$ has a radius of 35 cm.
    How many times larger than the area of circle $P$ is the area of circle $Q$?

7   A company logo is printed on all its stationery.
    On small sheets of paper the logo is 1.2 cm high and covers an area of 3.5 cm².
    On large sheets of paper the logo covers an area of 14 cm².
    What is the height of the logo on large sheets of paper?

8   The lengths of the sides of a square are halved. What happens to its area?

9   A picture is 30 cm high and has an area of 360 cm².
    Another print of the same picture is 15 cm high.
    What is its area?

10  A king-size photograph is 18 cm long and 12 cm wide.
    A standard size photograph is 12 cm long.
    (a)   What is the width of a standard size photograph?
    (b)   What is the area of a standard size photograph?

11  Two rugs are similar. The larger rug is 3.6 m in length and has an area of 9 m².
    The smaller rug has an area of 4 m². What is the length of the smaller rug?

12  The scale of a map is 1 to 50 000.
    (a)   The distance between two junctions on the map is 3 cm.
          What is the actual distance between the junctions, in kilometres?
    (b)   A lake covers 20 cm² on the map.
          How many square kilometres does the lake actually cover?

13  A map has a scale of 1 : 25 000.
    (a)   The length of a road is 3.5 km. Calculate its length, in centimetres, on the map.
    (b)   The area of a field on the map is 12 cm². Calculate the true area in square metres.
    (c)   A park has an area of 120 000 m². Calculate the area of the park on the map.

14  The measurements of a rabbit hutch are all doubled.
    How many times bigger is its volume?

15  A teapot has a volume of 500 ml.
    A similar teapot is double the height.
    What is the volume of this teapot?

16  A box of height 4 cm has a surface area of 220 cm² and a volume of 200 cm³.
    (a)   What is the surface area and volume of a similar box of height 8 cm?
    (b)   What is the surface area and volume of a similar box of height 2 cm?

**17** Two garden ponds are similar.
The dimensions of the larger pond are three times as big as the smaller pond.
The smaller pond holds 20 litres of water.
How many litres of water does the larger pond hold?

**18** Two solid spheres are made of the same material.
The smaller sphere has a radius of 4 cm and weighs 1.5 kg.
The larger sphere has a radius of 8 cm. How much does it weigh?

**19** The measurements of a box are each halved. What happens to its volume?

**20** A cylinder with a height of 6 cm has a volume of 200 cm³.
What is the volume of a similar cylinder with a height of 3 cm?

**21** A box with a height of 4 cm has a volume of 120 cm³.
What is the volume of a similar box with a height of 6 cm?

**22** The volumes of two similar statues are 64 cm³ and 125 cm³.
The height of the smaller statue is 8 cm.
  (a)   What is the height of the larger statue?
  (b)   What is the ratio of their surface areas?

**23** Two fish tanks are similar. The smaller tank is 12 cm high and has a volume of 3.6 litres.
The larger tank has a volume of 97.2 litres. What is the height of the larger tank?

**24** Pop and Fizzo come in similar cans. Cans of Pop are 8 cm tall and cans of Fizzo are 10 cm tall.
A can of Pop holds 200 ml. How much does a can of Fizzo hold?

**25**  (a)   A scale model of a house is made using a scale of 1 : 200.
           The roof area on the model is 82 cm². Find the real roof area, in square metres.
      (b)   The volume of the real roof space is 360 m³.
           Find the volume of the roof space in the model, in cubic centimetres.

**26** Jane makes a scale model of her village.
A fence of length 12 m is represented by a length of 4 cm on her model.
  (a)   Calculate the scale which Jane is using.
  (b)   Calculate, in cubic centimetres, the volume on the model of a pool which has a
        volume of 20 m³.
  (c)   Calculate the actual area of a playground which has an area of 320 cm² on the model.

**27** Joe wants to enlarge a picture so that its area is doubled.
What length scale factor should he use?

**28** Two balls have radii of 2 cm and 5 cm.
  (a)   Calculate the volumes of the two balls and
        show that the ratio of the volumes is 8 : 125.
  (b)   Show that the surface area of the smaller ball
        is 16% of the surface area of the larger ball.

**29** Coffee filters are paper cones.
The cones are made in these similar sizes; small, medium and large.
The slant height of a small cone is 5 cm and the surface area is $15\pi$ cm².
  (a)   A large cone has a surface area of $135\pi$ cm².
        Calculate the length of its slant height.
  (b)   A medium cone has a volume of $\frac{81\pi}{2}$ cm³.
        Calculate the surface area of a medium cone.

**30** A bronze statue is made in two sizes.
The taller statue is 15 cm high and the shorter one is 9 cm high.
The taller statue weighs 3.75 kg.
What is the weight of the shorter statue?

- When two shapes are the same shape and size they are said to be **congruent**.
- There are four ways to show that a pair of triangles are congruent:
  - SSS    Three equal sides.
  - SAS    Two sides and the included angle.
  - ASA    Two angles and a corresponding side.
  - RHS    Right angle, hypotenuse and one other side.
- When two figures are **similar**:
  - their **shapes** are the same,
  - their **angles** are the same,

$$\text{Scale factor} = \frac{\text{new length}}{\text{original length}}$$

  corresponding **lengths** are in the same ratio, this ratio is the **scale factor** of the enlargement.
- All circles are similar to each other.
- All squares are similar to each other.
- For **similar triangles**:
  corresponding lengths are opposite equal angles, the
  scale factor is the ratio of the corresponding sides.
- For **similar areas and volumes**:
  when the **length** scale factor $= k$
  the **area** scale factor $= k^2$
  the **volume** scale factor $= k^3$

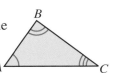

$$\frac{AB}{PQ} = \frac{BC}{QR} = \frac{CA}{RP} = \text{scale factor}$$

## Review Exercise 32

**1** These triangles have not been drawn accurately.

Which two of these triangles are congruent?
Give a reason for your answer.

**2** $A$, $B$, $C$ and $D$ lie on the circumference of a circle.
$AB$ is parallel to $CD$.
$BC$ is a diameter.
Prove that the triangles $ABC$ and $DCB$ are congruent.

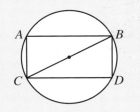

OCR

**3** This big logo shown is an enlargement of the small one.
All the lengths marked are in centimetres.

(a) What is the scale factor of this enlargement?
(b) Calculate the length, $x$, on the big logo.
(c) What is the size of angle $y$ on the big logo?

OCR

**4** *ABC* and *PQR* are similar triangles.

(a) Find the length marked
   (i) *x*,
   (ii) *y*.

(b) (Area of triangle *PQR*) = *n* × (Area of triangle *ABC*)
   Find the value of *n*.

OCR

**5** (a)

These tins are similar shapes.
The diameter and height of the small tin are 10 cm and 16 cm respectively.
The diameter of the large tin is 15 cm.

Work out the height, *h*, of the large tin.

(b) Here are the labels for the tins.
   They are also similar shapes.

   Calculate *d*.

(c) The tins are filled with baked beans.
   The mass of the beans in the small tin is 1000 grams.

   Calculate the mass of the beans in the large tin.

OCR

**6** These candles are similar.
**P** has a surface area of 24 cm².
**Q** has a surface area of 54 cm².
**P** is 4 cm high.
(a) How high is **Q**?
(b) What is the ratio of their volumes?

**7** A scale model of a ship is made, using a scale of 1 : 40.
(a) The area of the real deck is 500 m².
   Find, in square centimetres, the area of the deck on the model.
(b) The volume of the hold on the model is 187 500 cm³.
   Find, in cubic metres, the volume of the real hold.

**8** The ratio of the volumes of two similar objects is 1 : 64.
What is the ratio of their surface areas?

OCR

**9** Spinning tops A and B are similar.

(a) The surface area of top B is 54 cm².
   Calculate the surface area of top A.

Spinning tops C and D are similar.

(b) The volume of top D is 432 cm³.
   The volumes of tops A and C are equal.
   Calculate the volume of top B.

# Vectors ●●●●●●●●●●●●●●●●●●

## Vectors and scalars

Quantities which have both **size** and **direction** are called **vectors**.
Examples of vector quantities are:

| **Displacement** |
|:---:|
| A combination of distance and direction |

| **Velocity** |
|:---:|
| A combination of speed and direction |

**Quantities** which have size only are called **scalars**.
Examples of scalar quantities are: distance, area, speed, mass, volume, temperature, etc.

## Vector notation

### Column vectors

The diagram shows the translation of a triangle by the vector $\begin{pmatrix} 3 \\ 2 \end{pmatrix}$.

The triangle has been displaced 3 units to the right and 2 units up.

$\begin{pmatrix} 3 \\ 2 \end{pmatrix}$ gives information about the size and direction of the displacement.

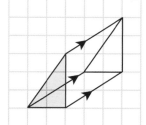

The vector $\begin{pmatrix} 3 \\ 2 \end{pmatrix}$ is sometimes called a **column vector**, because it consists of one column of numbers.

### Directed line segments
Vectors can be represented in diagrams using **line segments**.
The **length** of a line represents the **size of the vector**.
The **direction of the vector** is shown by an **arrow**.

### Labelling vectors
The notation $\overrightarrow{AB}, \overrightarrow{CD}, \overrightarrow{OX}, \ldots$ is often used.

$\overrightarrow{AB}$ indicates the displacement from $A$ to $B$.

$\overrightarrow{AB}$ should be read as "vector $AB$".

Bold lower case letters such as **a**, **b**, **c**, … are also used.
In hand-written work **a** should be written as a̲.
**a** and a̲ should both be read as "vector **a**".

---

### EXAMPLE

Draw and label the following vectors.

(a) $\mathbf{a} = \begin{pmatrix} -2 \\ 3 \end{pmatrix}$     (b) $\mathbf{b} = \begin{pmatrix} 3 \\ -2 \end{pmatrix}$     (c) $\overrightarrow{AB} = \begin{pmatrix} -4 \\ -2 \end{pmatrix}$

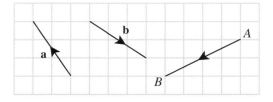

**Remember:**
The top number describes the
**horizontal** part of the movement:
$+$ = to the right    $-$ = to the left

The bottom number describes the
**vertical** part of the movement:
$+$ = upwards    $-$ = downwards

1. On squared paper, draw and label the following vectors.

   (a) $\mathbf{a} = \begin{pmatrix} -5 \\ 2 \end{pmatrix}$
   (b) $\mathbf{b} = \begin{pmatrix} 5 \\ -2 \end{pmatrix}$
   (c) $\mathbf{c} = \begin{pmatrix} -5 \\ -2 \end{pmatrix}$
   (d) $\mathbf{d} = \begin{pmatrix} 5 \\ 2 \end{pmatrix}$

2. Mark the point $O$ on squared paper.
   Draw and label the following vectors.

   (a) $\overrightarrow{OA} = \begin{pmatrix} 2 \\ 4 \end{pmatrix}$
   (b) $\overrightarrow{OB} = \begin{pmatrix} 4 \\ 2 \end{pmatrix}$
   (c) $\overrightarrow{OC} = \begin{pmatrix} 4 \\ -2 \end{pmatrix}$
   (d) $\overrightarrow{OD} = \begin{pmatrix} 2 \\ -4 \end{pmatrix}$

   (e) $\overrightarrow{OE} = \begin{pmatrix} -2 \\ -4 \end{pmatrix}$
   (f) $\overrightarrow{OF} = \begin{pmatrix} -4 \\ -2 \end{pmatrix}$
   (g) $\overrightarrow{OG} = \begin{pmatrix} -4 \\ 2 \end{pmatrix}$
   (h) $\overrightarrow{OH} = \begin{pmatrix} -2 \\ 4 \end{pmatrix}$

3. Write each of these vectors as column vectors.

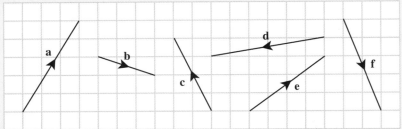

## Equal vectors

The diagram shows three vectors, $\overrightarrow{AB}$, $\overrightarrow{PQ}$ and $\overrightarrow{XY}$.

$\overrightarrow{AB} = \begin{pmatrix} 5 \\ 2 \end{pmatrix}$    $\overrightarrow{PQ} = \begin{pmatrix} 5 \\ 2 \end{pmatrix}$    $\overrightarrow{XY} = \begin{pmatrix} 5 \\ 2 \end{pmatrix}$

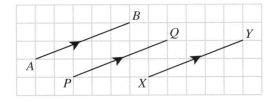

The column vectors are equal, so, $\overrightarrow{AB} = \overrightarrow{PQ} = \overrightarrow{XY}$.

> Vectors are **equal** if:   they have the same length,   **and**   they are in the same direction.

## Multiplying a vector by a scalar

The diagram shows three vectors, $\mathbf{a}$, $\mathbf{b}$ and $\mathbf{c}$.

$\mathbf{a} = \begin{pmatrix} 4 \\ -2 \end{pmatrix}$    $\mathbf{b} = \begin{pmatrix} 8 \\ -4 \end{pmatrix}$    $\mathbf{c} = \begin{pmatrix} 2 \\ -1 \end{pmatrix}$

$\mathbf{a}$ and $\mathbf{b}$ are in the same direction.

$\mathbf{b} = \begin{pmatrix} 8 \\ -4 \end{pmatrix} = \begin{pmatrix} 2 \times 4 \\ 2 \times -2 \end{pmatrix}$

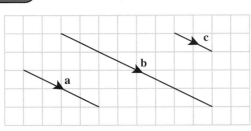

This can be written as   $\mathbf{b} = 2 \times \begin{pmatrix} 4 \\ -2 \end{pmatrix}$

So, $\mathbf{b} = 2\mathbf{a}$.
This means that $\mathbf{b}$ is twice the length of $\mathbf{a}$.

$\mathbf{b}$ and $\mathbf{c}$ are in the same direction.

$\mathbf{b} = \begin{pmatrix} 8 \\ -4 \end{pmatrix} = 4 \times \begin{pmatrix} 2 \\ -1 \end{pmatrix} = 4\mathbf{c}$

This means that $\mathbf{b}$ is 4 times as long as $\mathbf{c}$.

$\mathbf{a}$ and $\mathbf{c}$ are in the same direction.

$\mathbf{c} = \frac{1}{2}\mathbf{a}$.

This means that $\mathbf{c}$ is half the length of $\mathbf{a}$.

> $\mathbf{a}$ and $n\mathbf{a}$ are vectors in the same direction.
> The length of vector $n\mathbf{a} = n \times$ the length of vector $\mathbf{a}$.

## Vectors in opposite directions

The diagram shows two vectors, **a** and **b**.
The vectors are equal in length, **but** are in opposite directions.

$$\mathbf{a} = \begin{pmatrix} 5 \\ 2 \end{pmatrix} \qquad \mathbf{b} = \begin{pmatrix} -5 \\ -2 \end{pmatrix} \qquad \text{So, } \mathbf{b} = -\mathbf{a}$$

> Vectors **a** and −**a** have the same length, **but** are in opposite directions.

### EXAMPLE

The diagram shows three vectors: **a**, **b** and **c**.
(a)   Write each of **a**, **b** and **c** as column vectors.
(b)   Express **b** and **c** in terms of **a**.

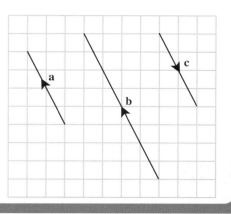

(a)   $\mathbf{a} = \begin{pmatrix} -2 \\ 4 \end{pmatrix} \qquad \mathbf{b} = \begin{pmatrix} -4 \\ 8 \end{pmatrix} \qquad \mathbf{c} = \begin{pmatrix} 2 \\ -4 \end{pmatrix}$

(b)   **b** is twice the length of **a** and in the same direction.
$\mathbf{b} = 2\mathbf{a}$

**c** is the same length as **a** but in the opposite direction.
$\mathbf{c} = -\mathbf{a}$

## Exercise 33.2

**1**   The points $X$ and $Y$ are marked on the grid.
On squared paper, draw each of the vectors **a** to **d**, where

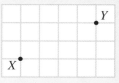

$\mathbf{a} = 2\overrightarrow{XY}, \qquad \mathbf{b} = -\overrightarrow{XY}, \qquad \mathbf{c} = \tfrac{1}{2}\overrightarrow{XY}, \qquad \mathbf{d} = \overrightarrow{YX}.$

**2**   This diagram shows three vectors, labelled **p**, **q** and **r**.

In the diagram below, which vectors can be expressed in the form:
(i)    $n\mathbf{p}$,          (ii)   $n\mathbf{q}$,          (iii)  $n\mathbf{r}$?
For each vector give the value of $n$.

**3**   $\mathbf{a} = \begin{pmatrix} 2 \\ -1 \end{pmatrix} \qquad \mathbf{b} = \begin{pmatrix} -1 \\ 4 \end{pmatrix} \qquad \mathbf{c} = \begin{pmatrix} -3 \\ -1 \end{pmatrix} \qquad \mathbf{d} = \begin{pmatrix} -1 \\ 2 \end{pmatrix}$

On squared paper draw vectors to represent the following.
(a)   2**a**                      (b)   2**b**                      (c)   3**a**                      (d)   −**a**
(e)   2**c**                      (f)   −2**d**                     (g)   −4**b**                     (h)   5**d**

Vectors . . . Vectors . . . Vectors . . . Vectors . . .

## Vector addition

The diagram shows the points $A$, $B$ and $C$.
Start at $A$ and move to $B$.
Then move from $B$ to $C$.

The combination of these two displacements is
equivalent to a total displacement from $A$ to $C$.
This can be written using vectors as:

$$\overrightarrow{AB} + \overrightarrow{BC} = \overrightarrow{AC}$$

$\overrightarrow{AC}$ is called the **resultant vector**.

Using column vectors: $\overrightarrow{AB} = \begin{pmatrix} 5 \\ 3 \end{pmatrix}$, $\overrightarrow{BC} = \begin{pmatrix} 3 \\ -4 \end{pmatrix}$ and $\overrightarrow{AC} = \begin{pmatrix} 8 \\ -1 \end{pmatrix}$

The resultant vector, $\overrightarrow{AC}$, is a combination of: $\begin{pmatrix} 5 \text{ units right followed by 3 units right} \\ 3 \text{ units up followed by 4 units down} \end{pmatrix} = \begin{pmatrix} 8 \text{ units right} \\ 1 \text{ unit down} \end{pmatrix}$

$$\overrightarrow{AB} + \overrightarrow{BC} = \overrightarrow{AC}$$

$$\begin{pmatrix} 5 \\ 3 \end{pmatrix} + \begin{pmatrix} 3 \\ -4 \end{pmatrix} = \begin{pmatrix} 5 + 3 \\ 3 + -4 \end{pmatrix} = \begin{pmatrix} 8 \\ -1 \end{pmatrix}$$

*Use vector addition to show that:* $\overrightarrow{AB} + \overrightarrow{BC} = \overrightarrow{BC} + \overrightarrow{AB} = \overrightarrow{AC}$.

## Vector diagrams

Diagrams can be drawn to show the combination of
any number of vectors.
To combine vectors when the vectors are not joined,
draw equal vectors so that the second vector joins
the end of the first vector.

**Note:**
**With** the arrow $= +$
**Against** the arrow $= -$

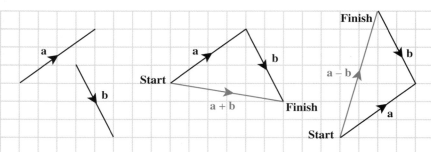

With the arrow, $+\mathbf{a}$
With the arrow, $+\mathbf{b}$
Resultant vector, $\mathbf{a} + \mathbf{b}$

With the arrow, $+\mathbf{a}$
Against the arrow, $-\mathbf{b}$
Resultant vector, $\mathbf{a} - \mathbf{b}$

### EXAMPLE

$\mathbf{a}$, $\mathbf{b}$ and $\mathbf{c}$ are three vectors as shown in the diagram.

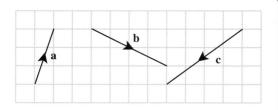

Draw diagrams to show:

(a) $\mathbf{a} + 2\mathbf{b}$

(b) $\mathbf{a} - \mathbf{c}$

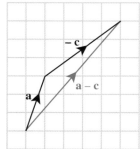

*Draw a vector diagram to show that:* $\mathbf{a} + \mathbf{b} = \mathbf{b} + \mathbf{a}$

356

1. $\overrightarrow{OA} = \begin{pmatrix} -1 \\ 4 \end{pmatrix}$, $\quad \overrightarrow{OB} = \begin{pmatrix} 4 \\ 3 \end{pmatrix}$, $\quad \overrightarrow{OC} = \begin{pmatrix} 5 \\ 1 \end{pmatrix}$.

   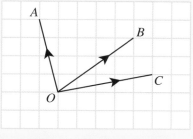

   (a) (i) Draw $\overrightarrow{OD}$ where $\overrightarrow{OD} = \overrightarrow{OA} + \overrightarrow{OB}$.

   (ii) Draw $\overrightarrow{OE}$ where $\overrightarrow{OE} = 2\overrightarrow{OA} + \overrightarrow{OC}$.

   (iii) Draw $\overrightarrow{OF}$ where $\overrightarrow{OF} = 2\overrightarrow{OB} - \overrightarrow{OC}$.

   (iv) Draw $\overrightarrow{OG}$ where $\overrightarrow{OG} = 2\overrightarrow{BO} + 3\overrightarrow{OA}$.

   (b) Draw a vector diagram to show the resultant vector of $\overrightarrow{OC} - \overrightarrow{OB}$.

2. The diagram below shows vectors **a**, **b** and **c**.

   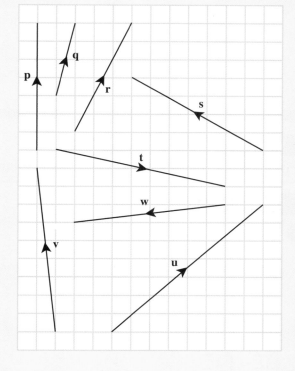

   Match the following vectors to those in the diagram opposite.

   (a) **a** + **b**

   (b) **a** − **b**

   (c) **b** + **c**

   (d) **b** − **c**

   (e) **a** + **b** − **c**

   (f) **a** + 2**b**

   (g) −2**a** − 3**c**

   (h) 2**a** + **c**

3. This is a grid of congruent parallelograms.

   $\overrightarrow{OA} = \mathbf{x}$ and $\overrightarrow{OB} = \mathbf{y}$.

   (a) On a copy of the grid mark each of the points *C* to *H* where:

   (i) $\overrightarrow{OC} = 3\mathbf{y}$

   (ii) $\overrightarrow{OD} = \mathbf{x} + 2\mathbf{y}$

   (iii) $\overrightarrow{OE} = 4\mathbf{x} + 3\mathbf{y}$

   (iv) $\overrightarrow{EF} = -2\mathbf{x} + \mathbf{y}$

   (v) $\overrightarrow{FG} = -2\mathbf{x} - 2\mathbf{y}$

   (vi) $\overrightarrow{GH} = 4\mathbf{x} + 2\mathbf{y}$

   (b) Using vectors, explain why *OBHE* is a parallelogram.

**4** In the diagram *ABCD* is a parallelogram and *C* is the midpoint of *BE*.
*P*, *Q*, *R* and *S* are the midpoints of *AB*, *BC*, *CD* and *DA* respectively.

(a) Draw vector diagrams to show the resultant vectors for:

 (i) $\overrightarrow{AQ} + \overrightarrow{QR}$  (ii) $\overrightarrow{AQ} - \overrightarrow{QR}$  (iii) $\overrightarrow{PR} - \overrightarrow{RA}$  (iv) $\overrightarrow{AP} + \overrightarrow{PQ} + \overrightarrow{QR}$

$\overrightarrow{AB} = \mathbf{a}$  and  $\overrightarrow{AD} = \mathbf{b}$.

(b) Write each of the following vectors in terms of **a** and **b**.

 (i) $\overrightarrow{PC}$  (ii) $\overrightarrow{AR}$  (iii) $\overrightarrow{AE}$

(c) What do your answers to (b) tell you about the lines:

 (i) *PC* and *AR*,  (ii) *PC* and *AE*?

## Vectors and geometry

The relationships between vectors can be used to solve geometrical problems.

### EXAMPLE

**1** *ABCD* is a parallelogram.
*E* is the midpoint of the diagonal *AC*.
Show that *E* is also the midpoint of the diagonal *BD*.

Let $\overrightarrow{AB} = \mathbf{x}$  and  $\overrightarrow{AD} = \mathbf{y}$.

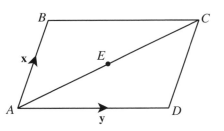

$\overrightarrow{AC} = \overrightarrow{AB} + \overrightarrow{BC}$

$\quad = \mathbf{x} + \mathbf{y}$

$\overrightarrow{AE} = \tfrac{1}{2} \overrightarrow{AC}$

$\quad = \tfrac{1}{2} (\mathbf{x} + \mathbf{y})$

$\overrightarrow{BD} = \overrightarrow{BA} + \overrightarrow{AD}$

$\quad = -\mathbf{x} + \mathbf{y}$

$\overrightarrow{BE} = \overrightarrow{BA} + \overrightarrow{AE}$

$\quad = -\mathbf{x} + \tfrac{1}{2} (\mathbf{x} + \mathbf{y})$

Multiply out brackets and simplify.

$\quad = -\tfrac{1}{2} \mathbf{x} + \tfrac{1}{2} \mathbf{y}$

$\qquad (-\mathbf{x} + \mathbf{y})$

$\qquad \tfrac{1}{2} \overrightarrow{BD}.$

same direction as *BD* and is half its length.

common to both *BE* and *BD*, *BED* must be a straight line.

midpoint of *BD*.

Remember:
**With** the arrow  $= +$
**Against** the arrow  $= -$

## EXAMPLE

**2** $\overrightarrow{AB} = 2\mathbf{a} + n\mathbf{b}$    $\overrightarrow{PQ} = 5\mathbf{a} - 10\mathbf{b}$

Calculate $n$ if $AB$ and $PQ$ are parallel.

The number of $\mathbf{a}$'s and the number of $\mathbf{b}$'s in $\overrightarrow{AB}$ and $\overrightarrow{PQ}$ are in the same ratio.

$\frac{5}{2} = -\frac{10}{n}$

$5n = -20$

$n = -4$

> $\overrightarrow{AB}$ and $\overrightarrow{PQ}$ are parallel.
> So, $\overrightarrow{PQ}$ must be a multiple of $\overrightarrow{AB}$.
> *Why?*

---

### Exercise **33.4**

The diagrams in this exercise have not been drawn accurately.

**1** In the diagram, $\overrightarrow{OA} = \mathbf{a}$ and $\overrightarrow{OB} = \mathbf{b}$.

$M$ is the midpoint of $AB$.

Express in terms of $\mathbf{a}$ and $\mathbf{b}$ in its simplest form,

(a) $\overrightarrow{AO}$,    (b) $\overrightarrow{AB}$,    (c) $\overrightarrow{MB}$,    (d) $\overrightarrow{MO}$.

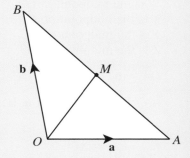

**2** $OXYZ$ is a parallelogram.
$P$ is the midpoint of $OX$ and $Q$ is the midpoint of $OZ$.

$\overrightarrow{OP} = \mathbf{p}$ and $\overrightarrow{OQ} = \mathbf{q}$

(a) Express in terms of $\mathbf{p}$ and $\mathbf{q}$ in its simplest form,

   (i) $\overrightarrow{PQ}$,    (ii) $\overrightarrow{OX}$,

   (iii) $\overrightarrow{OY}$,    (iv) $\overrightarrow{XZ}$.

(b) What can you say about the lines $PQ$ and $XZ$?

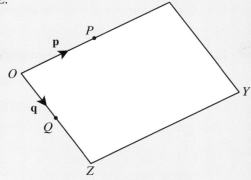

**3** $OABC$ is a square.
$X$ is the midpoint of $BC$.

$Y$ is a point on $XA$ such that $\overrightarrow{XA} = 3\overrightarrow{XY}$.

$\overrightarrow{OA} = \mathbf{a}$ and $\overrightarrow{OC} = \mathbf{b}$.

(a) Express in terms of $\mathbf{a}$ and $\mathbf{b}$:

   (i) $\overrightarrow{CX}$    (ii) $\overrightarrow{OX}$

   (iii) $\overrightarrow{XA}$    (iv) $\overrightarrow{XY}$

   (v) $\overrightarrow{OY}$    (vi) $\overrightarrow{OB}$

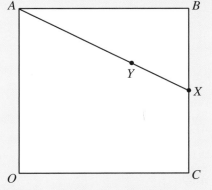

(b) What do $\overrightarrow{OY}$ and $\overrightarrow{OB}$ tell you about the points $O$, $Y$ and $B$?

**4** *OXY* is a triangle.

*P, Q* and *R* are the midpoints of the sides *YO, OX* and *XY* respectively.

$\overrightarrow{OP} = \mathbf{p}$ and $\overrightarrow{OQ} = \mathbf{q}$.

(a) Express in terms of **p** and **q** in its simplest form:

(i) $\overrightarrow{OX}$     (ii) $\overrightarrow{OY}$

(iii) $\overrightarrow{PQ}$     (iv) $\overrightarrow{XY}$

(v) $\overrightarrow{PR}$     (vi) $\overrightarrow{RQ}$

(b) What can you say about the triangles *OXY* and *PQR*?

**5** *OABC* is an irregular quadrilateral.

*W* is the midpoint of *OA*.
*X* is the midpoint of *AB*.
*Y* is the midpoint of *BC*.
*Z* is the midpoint of *CO*.

$\overrightarrow{OA} = \mathbf{a}$,   $\overrightarrow{OB} = \mathbf{b}$,   $\overrightarrow{OC} = \mathbf{c}$.

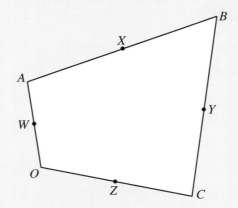

(a) Find in terms of **a**, **b** and **c**:

(i) $\overrightarrow{CB}$     (ii) $\overrightarrow{YZ}$

(iii) $\overrightarrow{CX}$     (iv) $\overrightarrow{YX}$

(v) $\overrightarrow{ZW}$

(b) Use your answers to (a) to show that *WXYZ* is a parallelogram.

**6** In the trapezium *OABC*, *AB* is parallel to *OC*.

$\overrightarrow{OA} = -\mathbf{a} + 2\mathbf{b}$ and $\overrightarrow{OB} = 3\mathbf{a} + 4\mathbf{b}$.

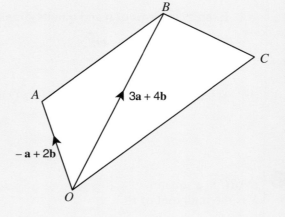

(a) Calculate $\overrightarrow{AB}$ in terms of **a** and **b**.

$\overrightarrow{BC} = 3\mathbf{a} + n\mathbf{b}$.

(b) Calculate $\overrightarrow{OC}$ in terms of **a**, **b** and *n*, and hence, calculate the value of *n*.

**7** $\overrightarrow{OA} = -2\mathbf{a} + 4\mathbf{b}$    $\overrightarrow{OB} = -\mathbf{a} + 6\mathbf{b}$

$\overrightarrow{OD} = \mathbf{a} + 2\mathbf{b}$    $\overrightarrow{OC} = 5\mathbf{a} + 2\mathbf{b}$

(a) Find, in terms of **a** and **b**,

$\overrightarrow{AD}$ and $\overrightarrow{BC}$.

(b) What do $\overrightarrow{AD}$ and $\overrightarrow{BC}$ tell you about quadrilateral *ABCD*?

- **Vector quantities**

  Quantities which have both **size** and **direction** are called **vectors**.
  Examples of vector quantities are:

  | **Displacement** |
  |---|
  | A combination of distance and direction |

  | **Velocity** |
  |---|
  | A combination of speed and direction |

- **Vector notation**

  Vectors can be represented by **column vectors** or by **directed line segments**.
  Vectors can be labelled using:

  capital letters to indicate the start and finish of a vector,
  bold lower case letters.

  In a **column vector:**

  The top number describes the **horizontal**
  part of the movement:
  $+$ = to the right        $-$ = to the left
  The bottom number describes the **vertical**
  part of the movement:
  $+$ = upwards        $-$ = downwards

  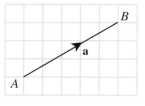

  $$\overrightarrow{AB} = \mathbf{a} = \begin{pmatrix} 5 \\ 3 \end{pmatrix}$$

- Vectors are **equal** if they have the same length **and** they are in the same direction.
  Vectors $\mathbf{a}$ and $-\mathbf{a}$ have the same length **but** are in **opposite directions**.
  The vector $n\mathbf{a}$ is parallel to the vector $\mathbf{a}$.
  The length of vector $n\mathbf{a} = n \times$ the length of vector $\mathbf{a}$.

- **Vector addition**

  The combination of the displacement from $A$ to $B$ followed by the displacement from $B$ to $C$ is
  equivalent to a total displacement from $A$ to $C$.

  This can be written using vectors as     $\overrightarrow{AB} + \overrightarrow{BC} = \overrightarrow{AC}$

  $\overrightarrow{AC}$ is called the **resultant vector**.

- Combinations of vectors can be shown on **vector diagrams**.

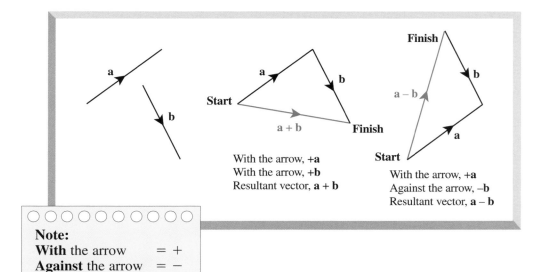

With the arrow, +**a**
With the arrow, +**b**
Resultant vector, **a** + **b**

With the arrow, +**a**
Against the arrow, –**b**
Resultant vector, **a** – **b**

**Note:**
**With** the arrow    = +
**Against** the arrow    = –

- **Vector geometry** uses vectors to solve simple geometrical problems, which often involve
  parallel lines.

The diagrams in this exercise have not been drawn accurately.

**1** *OAB* is a triangle. *E* is the midpoint of *AB*.

$\overrightarrow{OA} = \mathbf{a}$  and  $\overrightarrow{OB} = \mathbf{b}$.

Find in terms of **a** and **b**:

(a)  $\overrightarrow{AB}$

(b)  $\overrightarrow{AE}$

(c)  $\overrightarrow{OE}$

**2**

In the diagram, *A* and *C* are the points with coordinates $(-2, 1)$ and $(2, -2)$.
*M* is the midpoint of *AB* and *N* is the midpoint of *AC*.

The vector  $\overrightarrow{AB} = \begin{pmatrix} 6 \\ 5 \end{pmatrix}$.

(a)  Write down the coordinates of
(i)  *B*,      (ii)  *M*,      (iii)  *N*.

(b)  Calculate the vectors  (i)  $\overrightarrow{BC}$,     (ii)  $\overrightarrow{MN}$.

(c)  State the relationship between *BC* and *MN*.     OCR

**3**  In the diagram,  $\overrightarrow{OA} = \mathbf{a}$  and  $\overrightarrow{OB} = \mathbf{b}$.
*M* is the midpoint of *AC* and *B* is the midpoint of *OC*.

(a)  Find in terms of **a** and **b**,

(i)  $\overrightarrow{OC}$      (ii)  $\overrightarrow{BA}$      (iii)  $\overrightarrow{OM}$

(b)  *H* is a point on *BA* and  $\overrightarrow{BH} = \frac{1}{3}\overrightarrow{BA}$.

Find the vector  $\overrightarrow{OH}$  in terms of **a** and **b**.

(c)  What do your results tell you about the points *O*, *H* and *M* ?     OCR

**4**

The position of vectors *A*, *B* and *C* are **a**, **b** and $4\mathbf{b} - 3\mathbf{a}$ respectively.

(a)  (i)  Find $\overrightarrow{AB}$ in terms of **a** and **b**.
(ii)  Show clearly that *A*, *B* and *C* lie on a straight line.

(b)  Find the ratio of the lengths *BC* : *AC*.     OCR

**5**  In the diagram,  $\overrightarrow{OA} = \mathbf{a}$,  $\overrightarrow{OB} = \mathbf{b}$  and  *APB* is a straight line.

(a)  Write down $\overrightarrow{AB}$ in terms of **a** and **b**.

*P* divides *AB* in the ratio 1 : 2.

(b)  Find $\overrightarrow{OP}$ in terms of **a** and **b**.
Write your answer in its simplest form.

*OPQ* is also a straight line and  $\overrightarrow{OQ} = \frac{3}{2}\overrightarrow{OP}$.

(c)  Find $\overrightarrow{AQ}$ in terms of **a** and **b**.
Write your answer in its simplest form.

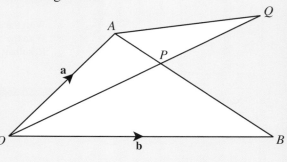

(d)  What conclusions can you make about the line segments *AQ* and *OB*?     OCR

# Further Trigonometry

So far we have found sines, cosines and tangents of angles between 0° and 90°, but it is possible to find the sine, cosine and tangent of any angle.

## Trigonometric functions and their graphs

### Activity

**The sine function**
Copy and complete this table.
Use your calculator to find the value of $\sin x°$, correct to two decimal places, where necessary.

| $x°$ | 0 | 30 | 60 | 90 | 120 | 150 | 180 | 210 | 240 | 270 | 300 | 330 | 360 |
|------|---|----|----|----|-----|-----|-----|-----|-----|-----|-----|-----|-----|
| $\sin x°$ | 0 | 0.5 | 0.87 | | | | | | | | | | |

Plot these values on graph paper.
Draw the graph of the sine function by joining the points with a smooth curve.

What is the maximum value of $\sin x°$?
What is the minimum value of $\sin x°$?

Describe what happens to the sine function when $x > 360°$.
Describe what happens to the sine function when $x < 0°$.

You might also try this activity using a graphical calculator, or a computer and suitable software.

In a similar way, draw the graphs of the **cosine function** and the **tangent function**.
What do you notice about the graphs of each of these functions?

$y = \sin x°$

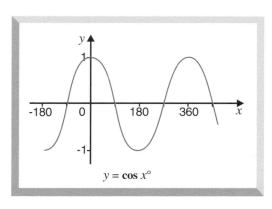

$y = \cos x°$

For every angle $x°$, the signs of $\sin x°$, $\cos x°$ and $\tan x°$ can be summarised as follows:

$y = \tan x°$

|  | 90° |  |
|---|---|---|
| **2nd quadrant** | | **1st quadrant** |
| sin + | | sin + |
| cos − | | cos + |
| tan − | | tan + |
| 180° | | 0° 360° |
| sin − | | sin − |
| cos − | | cos + |
| tan + | | tan − |
| **3rd quadrant** | 270° | **4th quadrant** |

Consider a point $P$. Line $OP$ makes an angle $x°$ with line $OX$.
If $OP = 1$ unit, then in triangle $OMP$:

**Positive** angles are measured **anticlockwise** from the axis $OX$.

$\sin x° = \dfrac{\text{opp}}{\text{hyp}}$

$\cos x° = \dfrac{\text{adj}}{\text{hyp}}$

$\tan x° = \dfrac{\text{opp}}{\text{adj}}$

$\sin x° = \dfrac{PM}{OP}$

$\cos x° = \dfrac{OM}{OP}$

$\tan x° = \dfrac{PM}{OM}$

$\sin x° = \dfrac{PM}{1}$

$\cos x° = \dfrac{OM}{1}$

$\tan x° = \dfrac{\sin x°}{\cos x°}$

$PM = \sin x°$

$OM = \cos x°$

*Explain why.*

| 2nd quadrant | 3rd quadrant | 4th quadrant |
|---|---|---|
|  |  |  |
| $\angle POM = (180 - x)°$ | $\angle POM = (x - 180)°$ | $\angle POM = (360 - x)°$ |

When $90° < x < 180°$, $\sin x$ is positive.

When $180° < x < 270°$, $\sin x$ is negative.

When $270° < x < 360°$, $\sin x$ is negative.

We can write:
$\sin x° = \sin (180 - x)°$

We can write:
$\sin x° = -\sin (x - 180)°$

We can write:
$\sin x° = -\sin (360 - x)°$

**Example**
$\begin{aligned} \sin 150° &= \sin (180 - 150)° \\ &= \sin 30° \\ &= 0.5 \end{aligned}$

**Example**
$\begin{aligned} \sin 210° &= -\sin (210 - 180)° \\ &= -\sin 30° \\ &= -0.5 \end{aligned}$

**Example**
$\begin{aligned} \sin 330° &= -\sin (360 - 330)° \\ &= -\sin 30° \\ &= -0.5 \end{aligned}$

## Activity

In a similar way investigate the values of $\cos x$ and $\tan x$ for values of $x$ between 0° and 360°.

---

**EXAMPLE**   Express the following in terms of the sin, cos or tan of an acute angle.
(a)  $\tan 100°$    (b)  $\sin 200°$   (c)  $\cos 300°$   (d)  $\sin (-10)°$
(e)  $\cos (-20)°$   (f)  $\tan 400°$   (g)  $\sin 500°$

(a)  $\tan 100°$  $= -\tan (180 - 100)° = -\tan 80°$
(b)  $\sin 200°$  $= -\sin (200 - 180)° = -\sin 20°$
(c)  $\cos 300°$  $=\ \ \cos (360 - 300)° =\ \ \cos 60°$

(d)  $\sin (-10)° = -\sin 10°$
(e)  $\cos (-20)° =\ \ \cos 20°$

**Negative** angles are measured **clockwise** from the axis $OX$.

(f)  $\tan 400°$  $= \tan (400 - 360)° = \tan 40°$
(g)  $\sin 500°$  $= \sin (500 - 360)° = \sin 140°$
$= \sin (180 - 140)° = \sin 40°$

**Angles greater than 360°**
Subtract 360°, or multiples of 360°, to get the equivalent angle between 0° and 360°.

Do not use a calculator for this exercise.

**1** State whether the following are positive or negative.

| | | | |
|---|---|---|---|
| (a) sin 50° | (b) cos 50° | (c) tan 50° | (d) sin 100° |
| (e) cos 100° | (f) tan 100° | (g) cos 150° | (h) sin 200° |
| (i) tan 250° | (j) cos 300° | (k) sin 350° | (l) tan 87° |
| (m) cos 143° | (n) sin 117° | (o) tan 162° | (p) cos 296° |
| (q) tan 321° | (r) cos 196° | (s) sin 218° | (t) cos 400° |
| (u) tan 500° | (v) sin 500° | (w) cos (−30)° | (x) sin (−100)° |
| (y) cos (−100)° | (z) tan (−100)° | | |

**2** Express each of the following in terms of the sin, cos or tan of an acute angle.

| | | | |
|---|---|---|---|
| (a) tan 100° | (b) cos 150° | (c) sin 200° | (d) tan 250° |
| (e) cos 300° | (f) sin 120° | (g) tan 170° | (h) cos 210° |
| (i) sin 290° | (j) tan 330° | (k) cos 370° | (l) sin 260° |
| (m) tan 370° | (n) sin 480° | (o) cos 600° | (p) sin (−50)° |
| (q) cos (−100)° | (r) tan (−150)° | | |

**3** The exact values of sin 45°, cos 45° and tan 45° can be found by using this triangle.

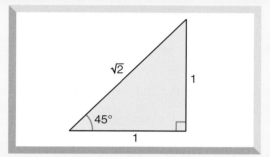

E.g. $\sin 45° = \dfrac{1}{\sqrt{2}}$

(a) Write down the exact value of
   (i) cos 45°,   (ii) tan 45°.
(b) Hence, write down the exact values of
   (i) cos 135°,   (ii) tan 225°,   (iii) sin 315°,
   (iv) sin 135°,   (v) cos 225°,   (vi) tan 315°.

**4** The exact values of sin 30°, cos 30°, tan 30° and sin 60°, cos 60°, tan 60° can be found by using this triangle.

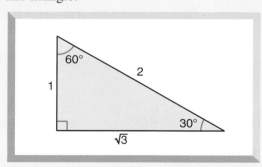

(a) Write down the exact values of sin 30°, cos 30°, tan 30° and hence, give the exact values of
   (i) sin 150°,   (ii) cos 210°,   (iii) tan 330°,   (iv) cos 330°.

(b) Write down the exact values of sin 60°, cos 60°, tan 60° and hence, give the exact values of
   (i) cos 120°,   (ii) tan 240°,   (iii) cos 240°,   (iv) sin 300°.

## Finding angles

For which angles, between $0°$ and $360°$, is $\cos p = 0.412$?

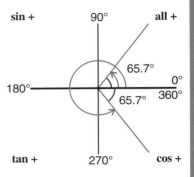

$\cos p = 0.412$
$\cos p$ is positive, so, possible angles are in the 1st and 4th quadrants.
This can be shown on a diagram.
Because of the symmetries of the graphs of trigonometric functions,
angles formed between the lines and the horizontal axis are
always **equal**.
$p = \cos^{-1}(0.412)$

Using a calculator.
$p = 65.669...$
$p = 65.7°$ to 1 d.p.

Positive angles are measured anticlockwise.
$p = 65.7°$ and $p = 360° - 65.7° = 294.3°$

So, $p = 65.7°$ and $294.3°$, correct to 1 d.p.

### EXAMPLE

For which angles, between $0°$ and $360°$, is $\tan p = -1.5$?

$\tan p = -1.5$
$\tan p$ is negative, so, possible angles are in the 2nd and 4th quadrants.
$p = \tan^{-1}(-1.5)$
$p = -56.309...$
$p = -56.3°$, to 1 d.p.

$p = 180° - 56.3° = 123.7°$, and $p = 360° - 56.3° = 303.7°$

So, $p = 123.7°$ and $303.7°$, correct to 1 d.p.

### Exercise 34.2    Use a calculator for this exercise.

**1** Find the values of the following. Give your answers to three decimal places.
    (a) $\sin 100°$      (b) $\cos 150°$      (c) $\tan 200°$      (d) $\sin 250°$
    (e) $\cos 300°$      (f) $\tan 350°$      (g) $\tan 187°$      (h) $\cos 187°$
    (i) $\cos 143°$      (j) $\sin 117°$      (k) $\tan 162°$      (l) $\cos 296°$
    (m) $\tan 321°$      (n) $\cos 196°$      (o) $\sin 218°$      (p) $\cos 400°$
    (q) $\tan 500°$      (r) $\sin 500°$      (s) $\cos (-30)°$      (t) $\sin (-100)°$

**2** For each of the following, find all the values of $p$ between $0°$ and $360°$.
    (a) $\cos p = 0.5$      (b) $\sin p = -0.5$      (c) $\tan p = 1$      (d) $\sin p = 0.5$
    (e) $\tan p = -1$      (f) $\cos p = -0.5$      (g) $\sin p = -0.766$      (h) $\cos p = 0.766$
    (i) $\sin p = 0.866$      (j) $\tan p = -2.050$      (k) $\tan p = 0.193$      (l) $\cos p = 0.565$
    (m) $\sin p = 0.342$      (n) $\cos p = -0.866$      (o) $\tan p = 0.700$

**3** Find the values of $x$, between $0°$ and $720°$, where $\sin x = -0.75$.
    Give your answers to one decimal place.

**4** One solution of the equation $\cos x = -0.42$ is $x = 115°$, to the nearest degree.
    Find **all** the other solutions to the equation $\cos x = -0.42$
    for values of the $x$ between $-360°$ and $360°$.

**5** Solve the equation $\sin x = 0.8$ for $-360° \leqslant x \leqslant 360°$.
    Give your answers to the nearest degree.

# Another look at the graphs of trigonometric functions

At the beginning of the chapter we looked at the graphs of the sine, cosine and tangent functions. Each of the functions is called a **periodic function**.
After a **period** (distance along the $x$ axis) each graph repeats itself.

The **sine function** is a periodic function with period 360°.
$$-1 \leqslant \sin x \leqslant 1$$

The **cosine function** is a periodic function with period 360°.
$$-1 \leqslant \cos x \leqslant 1$$

The **tangent function** is a periodic function with period 180°.
Tan $x$ is undefined at 90°, 270°, ...

### EXAMPLE

Compare the following graphs: $y = \sin x$, $y = 2\sin x$, $y = \sin 2x$.

| $x$ | 0 | 45 | 90 | 135 | 180 | 225 | 270 | 315 | 360 |
|---|---|---|---|---|---|---|---|---|---|
| $y = \sin x$ | 0 | 0.71 | 1 | 0.71 | 0 | −0.71 | −1 | −0.71 | 0 |
| $y = 2\sin x$ | 0 | 1.41 | 2 | 1.41 | 0 | −1.41 | −2 | −1.41 | 0 |
| $y = \sin 2x$ | 0 | 1 | 0 | −1 | 0 | 1 | 0 | −1 | 0 |

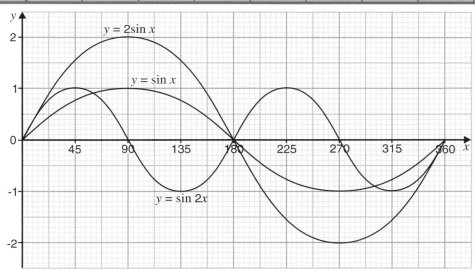

$y = \sin x$   Period: 360°   $-1 \leqslant \sin x \leqslant 1$
$y = 2\sin x$   Period: 360°   $-2 \leqslant 2\sin x \leqslant 2$
$y = \sin 2x$   Period: 180°   $-1 \leqslant \sin 2x \leqslant 1$

## Exercise 34.3

**1** Use the graphs of the sine function and the cosine function, to find the values of $x$, between 0° and 360°, when:

(a) (i) $\sin x = 1$  (ii) $\sin x = 0$  (iii) $\sin x = -1$
(b) (i) $\cos x = 1$  (ii) $\cos x = 0$  (iii) $\cos x = -1$

Further Trigonometry

**2** Given that $\tan 45° = 1$, use the graph of the tangent function to find all the values of $x$, between 0° and 360°, when

(a) $\tan x = 1$        (b) $\tan x = 0$        (c) $\tan x = -1$

**3** (a) Draw the graph of $y = 3\sin x$ for values of $x$ between 0° and 360°.
(b) Use your graph to find:
    (i) $x$ when $y = 1.50$        (ii) $y$ when $x = 240°$

**4** (a) Draw the graph of $y = 3\cos x$ for values of $x$ between 0° and 360°.
(b) Use your graph to solve the equation $3\cos x = 0.6$.

In questions 5 to 8, draw graphs for values of $x$ between 0° and 360°.

**5** Compare the graph of $y = 3\sin x$ with $y = \sin x$
and the graph of $y = 3\cos x$ with $y = \cos x$.
What do you notice?
Hence, sketch the graphs of:

(a) (i) $y = 2\sin x$        (ii) $y = 5\sin x$        (iii) $y = \frac{1}{2}\sin x$

(b) (i) $y = 2\cos x$        (ii) $y = 5\cos x$        (iii) $y = \frac{1}{2}\cos x$

**6** (a) Draw the graph of $y = \sin 2x$.
(b) Compare this graph with the graph of $y = \sin x$.
What do you notice?
(c) Hence, sketch the graph of $y = \sin 3x$.

**7** (a) Draw the graph of $y = \cos 2x$.
(b) Compare this graph with the graph of $y = \cos x$.
What do you notice?
(c) Hence, sketch the graph of $y = \cos 3x$.

**8** (a) Draw graphs of the following.
    (i) $y = \sin x + 1$        (ii) $y = \sin x - 2$
(b) Compare these graphs with the graph of $y = \sin x$.
What do you notice?
(c) Hence, sketch the graphs of:
    (i) $y = \cos x + 2$        (ii) $y = \cos x - 1$

## Triangles which are not right-angled

In Chapter 29 we used trigonometry to find sides and angles in right-angled triangles.
However, not all triangles are right-angled and to solve problems involving acute-angled and
obtuse-angled triangles we need to know further rules.

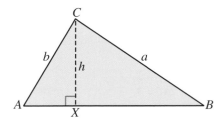

**Remember:**
**Angles** are labelled with **capital letters** and the **sides** opposite the angles with **lower case letters**.

The **altitude**, or height of the triangle, is shown by the line $CX$.
The line $CX$ divides triangle $ABC$ into two right-angled triangles.

In triangle $CAX$.

$\sin A = \frac{h}{b}$

This can be rearranged to give:
   $h = b \sin A$

In triangle $CBX$.

$\sin B = \frac{h}{a}$

This can be rearranged to give:
   $h = a \sin B$

$h = b \sin A$ and $h = a \sin B$,
so, $b \sin A = a \sin B$,
which can be rearranged as:

$$\frac{a}{\sin A} = \frac{b}{\sin B}$$

## Activity

Find rules to connect:
sin $A$  and  sin $C$,
sin $B$  and  sin $C$.

Can you find similar rules for
obtuse-angled triangles?

## The Sine Rule

In any triangle labelled $ABC$ it can be proved that:

$$\frac{a}{\sin A} = \frac{b}{\sin B} = \frac{c}{\sin C}$$

The Sine Rule can also be written as:

$$\frac{\sin A}{a} = \frac{\sin B}{b} = \frac{\sin C}{c}$$

## Finding sides

To find a side using the Sine Rule you need:
two angles of known size, **and**
the length of a side which is opposite one of the known angles.

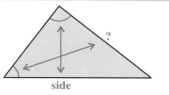

## EXAMPLE

In triangle $ABC$,   angle $A = 37°$,   angle $C = 72°$   and   $b = 12$ cm.
Calculate $a$, correct to 3 significant figures.

Using the Sine Rule:

$$\frac{a}{\sin A} = \frac{b}{\sin B} = \frac{c}{\sin C}$$

Substitute known values.

$$\frac{a}{\sin 37°} = \frac{12}{\sin 71°} = \frac{c}{\sin 72°}$$

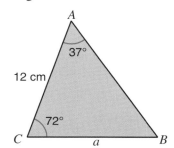

To find angle $B$:
$\angle A + \angle B + \angle C = 180°$
$37° + \angle B + 72° = 180°$
$\angle B = 71°$

Using:

$$\frac{a}{\sin 37°} = \frac{12}{\sin 71°}$$

Multiply both sides by sin 37°.

$$a = \frac{12 \times \sin 37°}{\sin 71°}$$

$$= 7.637...$$
$a = 7.64$ cm, correct to 3 s.f.

**Alternative method:**
First rearrange the equation, then substitute known values.

Use   $\dfrac{a}{\sin A} = \dfrac{b}{\sin B}$

Rearrange to give   $a = \dfrac{b \sin A}{\sin B}$

Substitute known values   $a = \dfrac{12 \times \sin 37°}{\sin 71°}$

**1** Find the side marked *a* in each of the following triangles.

(a)

(b)

(c)

**2** Find the marked side in each of these triangles.

(a)

(b)

(c)

(d)

(d)

(e)

(f)
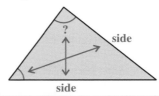

**3** Find the remaining angles and sides of these triangles.
   (a) $\triangle ABC$, when $\angle BAC = 57°$, $\angle ABC = 68°$ and $BC = 6.7\,\text{cm}$.
   (b) $\triangle LMN$, when $\angle LMN = 33.2°$, $\angle LNM = 75.6°$ and $LN = 3.3\,\text{cm}$.
   (c) $\triangle PQR$, when $\angle PQR = 62.8°$, $\angle PRQ = 47.4°$ and $PQ = 12.3\,\text{cm}$.
   (d) $\triangle STU$, when $\angle TSU = 94.9°$, $\angle STU = 53.3°$ and $SU = 19.4\,\text{cm}$.
   (e) $\triangle XYZ$, when $\angle XYZ = 108.6°$, $\angle YXZ = 40.2°$ and $XZ = 13.8\,\text{cm}$.

**4** In $\triangle PQR$, $\angle PQR = 110°$, $\angle QRP = 29°$ and $PQ = 5\,\text{cm}$.
Calculate
(a) the length of *PR*,
(b) the length of *QR*.
Give your answers correct to one decimal place.

## Finding angles

To find an angle using the Sine Rule you need:
   the length of the side opposite the angle you are trying to find, **and**
   the length of a side opposite an angle of known size.

## EXAMPLE

Angle $A = 42°$, $a = 6$ cm and $c = 4$ cm.
Calculate angle $C$, correct to one decimal place.

Using the Sine Rule:

$$\frac{\sin A}{a} = \frac{\sin B}{b} = \frac{\sin C}{c}$$

Substitute known values.

$$\frac{\sin 42°}{6} = \frac{\sin B}{b} = \frac{\sin C}{4}$$

Using:

$$\frac{\sin 42°}{6} = \frac{\sin C}{4}$$

Multiply both sides by 4.

$$\sin C = \frac{4 \times \sin 42°}{6}$$

$\sin C = 0.446...$
$C = \sin^{-1}(0.446...)$
$C = 26.49...$
$C = 26.5°$, correct to 1 d.p.

$C = \sin^{-1}(0.446...)$
gives possible angles of 26.5° and 153.5°.
$C \neq 153.5°$, since in an obtuse-angled triangle,
the obtuse angle is always opposite the longest
side of the triangle.

## The ambiguous case

There are two angles between 0° and 180° which have the same sine.
When we use the sine rule to find an angle we must therefore look at the information to see if there are
two possible values for the angle.

## EXAMPLE

In triangle $PQR$, $PQ = 8$ cm, $QR = 6$ cm and angle $QPR = 38°$.
Find the size of angle $QRP$.

Using this information **two** triangles can be drawn.
*Use a ruler and compasses to construct the triangles.*

Using the Sine Rule:

$$\frac{\sin P}{p} = \frac{\sin Q}{q} = \frac{\sin R}{r}$$

Substitute known values.

$$\frac{\sin 38°}{6} = \frac{\sin Q}{q} = \frac{\sin R}{8}$$

Using:

$$\frac{\sin 38°}{6} = \frac{\sin R}{8}$$

Multiply both sides by 8.

$$\sin R = \frac{8 \times \sin 38°}{6}$$

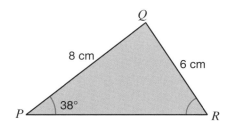

$\sin R = 0.820...$
$R = \sin^{-1}(0.820...)$
$R = 55.17...$
$R = 55.2°$
Also, $R = 180° - 55.2° = 124.8°$
$\angle QRP = 55.2°$ or $124.8°$, correct to 1 d.p.

**1** Find angle $A$ in each of these acute-angled triangles.

(a)

72°
5 cm
5.4 cm
$A$

(b)

13 cm
16 cm
83°
$A$

(c)

$A$
55°
6.2 cm
7.3 cm

**2** Find angle $A$ in each of these obtuse-angled triangles.

(a)

24°
15 cm
9 cm
$A$

(b)

$A$
20 cm
38°
25 cm

(c)

19.4 cm
10.7 cm
$A$
29°

**3** In triangle $ABC$, $AB = 6$ cm, $BC = 4$ cm and angle $BAC = 30°$.
There are two possible triangles that can be constructed.
Calculate the two possible values of angle $BCA$.

**4** In triangle $PQR$, $QR = 7.5$ cm, $RP = 7$ cm and angle $PQR = 60°$.
There are two possible triangles that can be constructed.
Find the missing angles and sides of both triangles.

**5** Find the missing angles and sides in each of the following triangles.
(a) $\triangle ABC$, when $AB = 8.3$ cm, $AC = 8.9$ cm and angle $ABC = 69.3°$.
(b) $\triangle DEF$, when $DE = 8.5$ cm, $DF = 16.34$ cm and angle $DEF = 125°$.

## Deriving the Cosine Rule

$AB = c$
Let $AX = x$
So, $BX = c - x$

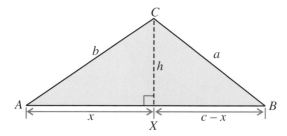

In triangle $ACX$.
Using Pythagoras' Theorem.

$b^2 = x^2 + h^2$

Using the cosine ratio.

$\cos A = \dfrac{\text{adj}}{\text{hyp}}$

$\cos A = \dfrac{x}{b}$

$x = b \cos A$

In triangle $BCX$.
Using Pythagoras' Theorem.

$a^2 = (c - x)^2 + h^2$

$a^2 = c^2 - 2cx + x^2 + h^2$

Replace: $x^2 + h^2$ by $b^2$ and $x$ by $b \cos A$.

$a^2 = c^2 - 2c(b \cos A) + b^2$

This can be rearranged as:

$a^2 = b^2 + c^2 - 2bc \cos A$, and is called the **Cosine Rule**.

## The Cosine Rule

In any triangle labelled *ABC* it can be proved that:

$$a^2 = b^2 + c^2 - 2bc \cos A$$

In a similar way, we can find the Cosine Rule for $b^2$ and $c^2$.

$$b^2 = a^2 + c^2 - 2ac \cos B$$
$$c^2 = a^2 + b^2 - 2ab \cos C$$

When using the Cosine Rule to find the size of an angle it is sometimes easier to rearrange the above formulae as:

$$\cos A = \frac{b^2 + c^2 - a^2}{2bc} \qquad \cos B = \frac{a^2 + c^2 - b^2}{2ac} \qquad \cos C = \frac{a^2 + b^2 - c^2}{2ab}$$

## Finding sides

To find a side using the Cosine Rule you need:
> two sides of known length, **and**
> the size of the angle between the known sides.

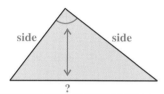

side    side

?

### EXAMPLE

Calculate the length of side *a*.

Using the Cosine Rule:
$$a^2 = b^2 + c^2 - 2bc \cos A$$
Substitute known values.
$$a^2 = 20^2 + 16^2 - 2 \times 20 \times 16 \times \cos 56°$$
$$= 400 + 256 - 357.88...$$
$$= 298.116...$$
Take the square root.
$$a = 17.266...$$
$$a = 17.3 \text{ cm, correct to 3 s.f.}$$

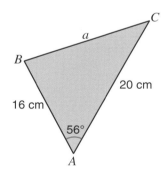

## Exercise 34.6

1. Calculate the lengths of the sides marked *a*.
   Give your answers correct to three significant figures.

   (a)

   (b)

   (c)

**2** Calculate the lengths of the sides marked with letters.
Give your answers correct to three significant figures.

(a)

(b)

(c)

**3** In triangle $ABC$, $AB = 8\,cm$, $AC = 13\,cm$ and $\angle BAC = 70°$.
Calculate $BC$.

**4** In triangle $LMN$, $LM = 16\,cm$, $MN = 9\,cm$ and $\angle LMN = 46.8°$.
Calculate $LN$.

**5** In triangle $PQR$, $PQ = 9\,cm$, $PR = 5.4\,cm$ and $\angle RPQ = 135°$.
Calculate $QR$.

**6** In triangle $XYZ$, $XY = 7.5\,cm$, $YZ = 13\,cm$ and $\angle XYZ = 120°$.
Calculate $XZ$.

**7** $L$ is 19 km from $K$ on a bearing of 068°.
$K$ is 13 km due north of $M$.
Calculate the distance of $L$ from $M$.

## Finding angles

To find an angle using the Cosine Rule you need:
   three sides of known length.

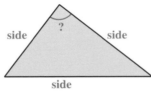

### EXAMPLE

Calculate the size of angle $A$.

Using the Cosine Rule:

$$\cos A = \frac{b^2 + c^2 - a^2}{2bc}$$

Substitute known values.

$$\cos A = \frac{5^2 + 4^2 - 6^2}{2 \times 5 \times 4}$$

$\cos A = 0.125$

$A = \cos^{-1}(0.125)$

$A = 82.819...$

$A = 82.8°$, correct to 1 d.p.

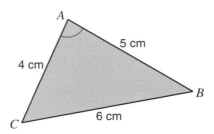

1. Calculate angle $A$ in each of the following.
   Give your answers correct to one decimal place.

   (a)

   (b)

   (c)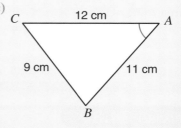

2. In this question give your answers correct to one decimal place.

   (a) Calculate $\angle B$.

   (b) Calculate $\angle C$.

   (c) Calculate $\angle P$.

3. In triangle $ABC$, $AB = 18\,\text{cm}$, $BC = 23\,\text{cm}$ and $CA = 24\,\text{cm}$.
   Calculate $\angle ACB$.

4. In triangle $PQR$, $PQ = 10\,\text{cm}$, $QR = 12\,\text{cm}$ and $RP = 20\,\text{cm}$.
   Calculate $\angle PQR$.

5. In triangle $LMN$, $LM = 8\,\text{cm}$, $MN = 6\,\text{cm}$ and $NL = 11\,\text{cm}$.
   Calculate $\angle LMN$.

6. In triangle $XYZ$, $XY = 9.6\,\text{cm}$, $YZ = 13.4\,\text{cm}$ and $XZ = 20\,\text{cm}$.
   Calculate $\angle XYZ$.

## Area of a triangle

Look at these triangles.
Both are labelled $ABC$.

 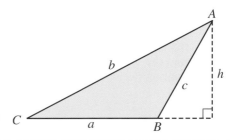

The height of each triangle is labelled $h$.
In both triangles $h = b \sin C$.

The area of triangle $ABC = \frac{1}{2} \times$ base $\times$ height

$$= \frac{1}{2} \times a \times b \sin C$$

$$= \frac{1}{2} ab \sin C$$

For any triangle $ABC$: Area $= \frac{1}{2} ab \sin C$

To use this formula to find the area of a
triangle we need:
   two sides of known length, **and** the size
   of the angle between
   the known sides.

side      side

*Can you find a rule which gives the area of a parallelogram?*

**EXAMPLE**

Calculate the area of triangle *PQR*.

Area $PQR = \frac{1}{2} \times p \times q \times \sin R$

$\quad\quad\quad = 0.5 \times 2.4 \times 4.5 \times \sin 67°$

$\quad\quad\quad = 4.9707...$

$\quad\quad\quad = 4.97 \text{ cm}^2$, correct to 3 s.f.

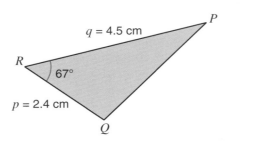

## Exercise **34.8**

**1** Calculate the areas of these triangles.
Give your answers correct to three significant figures.

(a)

(b)

(c)

(d)

**2** *PQRS* is a parallelogram. *PQ* = 9.2 cm, *PS* = 11.4 cm and angle *QPS* = 54°.
Calculate the area of the parallelogram.

**3** *ABCD* is a quadrilateral.

(a) Calculate the length of *BD*.
(b) Calculate the area of *ABCD*.

**4** A regular hexagon has sides of length 5 cm.
Calculate the area of the hexagon.

**5** The area of triangle *PQR* is 31.7 cm². *PQ* = 9.6 cm and angle *PQR* = 48°.
Calculate the length of *QR*.
Give your answer correct to one decimal place.

**6** *PQRS* is a kite.
*PQ* = *SP* = 35 cm.
*QR* = *RS* = 24 cm.
Angle *QPS* = 48°, angle *QRS* = 72°.
Calculate the area of the kite.

**7** Triangle *XYZ* is isosceles, with *XY* = *YZ*. Angle *XYZ* = 54°.
The area of triangle *XYZ* is 22 cm². Calculate the lengths of *XY* and *YZ*.

**8** The area of triangle *ABC* is 25.6 cm². *AB* = 6.7 cm, *AC* = 9.2 cm.
Calculate the two possible sizes of angle *A*.

## Solving problems involving triangles

**Right-angled triangles**
Use the **trigonometric ratios** (sin, cos and tan) or **Pythagoras' Theorem**.

**Triangles which are not right-angled**

**The Sine Rule**
To find a **side** you need:
two angles of known size, **and**
the length of a side which is opposite
one of the known angles.

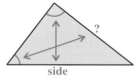

**The Sine Rule**
To find an **angle** you need:
the length of the side opposite the angle
you are trying to find, **and** the length of
a side opposite an angle of known size.

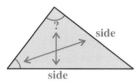

**The Cosine Rule**
To find a **side** you need:
two sides of known length, **and**
the size of the angle between the known sides.

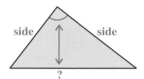

**The Cosine Rule**
To find an **angle** you need:
three sides of known length.

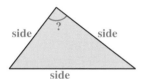

To find the **area of a triangle**, when you know two sides and the angle between the sides, use:

$$\text{Area of triangle} = \tfrac{1}{2}\, ab \sin C$$

---

**EXAMPLE**

Find the unknown sides and angles in this triangle.

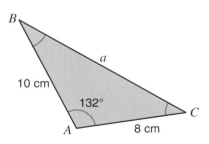

Using the Cosine Rule to find $a$.
$$a^2 = b^2 + c^2 - 2bc \cos A$$
$$a^2 = 8^2 + 10^2 - 2 \times 8 \times 10 \times \cos 132°$$
$$a^2 = 271.06...$$
$$a = 16.46...$$

Store this accurate value of $a$ in the memory of your calculator.

$$a = 16.5 \text{ cm, correct to 3 s.f.}$$

Now use the Sine Rule to find angle $C$.

$$\frac{\sin A}{a} = \frac{\sin B}{b} = \frac{\sin C}{c}$$

$$\frac{\sin 132°}{16.46...} = \frac{\sin B}{8} = \frac{\sin C}{10}$$

Using:
$$\frac{\sin 132°}{16.46...} = \frac{\sin C}{10}$$

$$\sin C = \frac{10 \times \sin 132°}{16.46...}$$

$$\sin C = 0.451...$$
$$C = \sin^{-1}(0.451...)$$
$$C = 26.83...$$
$$C = 26.8°, \text{ correct to 1 d.p.}$$

$$B = 180° - 26.8° - 132°$$
$$B = 21.2°$$

**1** (a) Find the unknown sides and angles in these triangles.
(b) Calculate the area of each triangle.

(i)

9 cm
60°
12 cm

(ii)

3.6 cm
110°
6.5 cm

**2** The diagram shows the positions of a tree, at *T*, and a pylon, at *P*, on opposite sides of a river. Two bridges cross the river at *X* and *Y*.

*T*
73 m          95 m
*X*
145 m          48°
*Y*
27 m
*P*

○○○○○○○○○○

**Remember:**

The **longest side** is opposite the **largest angle**.

The **shortest side** is opposite the **smallest angle**.

$XY = 145$ m,  $XT = 73$ m,  $TY = 95$ m,  $YP = 27$ m  and  $\angle XYP = 48°$.
(a) Calculate the angles of triangle *XTY*.
(b) Calculate *XP* and $\angle XPY$.

**3** Two ships, *P* and *Q*, leave port at 2 pm.
*P* travels at 24 km/h on a bearing of 085°.
*Q* travels at 32 km/h on a bearing of 120°.
Calculate the distance between the ships at 2.30 pm.

**4**

43°          74°
*A* |←  10 m  →| *B*

The diagram shows a tower.
At *A* the angle of elevation to the top of the tower is 43°.
At *B* the angle of elevation to the top of the tower is 74°.
The distance *AB* is 10 m.
Calculate the height of the tower.

**5** The diagram shows part of a steel framework, *ABC*.
*B* is on horizontal ground. *A* is 10 m vertically above *B*.
$BC = 16$ m.   Angle $ABC = 23°$.
(a) Calculate the length of *AC*.
(b) Calculate angle *BCA*.
(c) Calculate the vertical height of *C* above *B*.

*C*
*A*
16 m
10 m
23°
*B*

**6** In triangle *LMN*,  $MN = 7.5$ cm,
angle $MLN = 104°$  and  angle $LMN = 34°$.
(a) Calculate the length of *LM*.
(b) Calculate the area of the triangle.

**7** The diagram shows a quadrilateral $PQRS$.
$PQ = 4\,\text{cm}$, $QR = 5\,\text{cm}$, $RS = 7\,\text{cm}$,
$QS = 8\,\text{cm}$ and angle $SPQ = 110°$.
(a) Calculate angle $QSP$.
(b) Calculate angle $QSR$.
(c) Calculate the area of $PQRS$.

**8** An isosceles triangle has an area of $25.6\,\text{cm}^2$.
The two equal sides are $8.4\,\text{cm}$ long.
Calculate the two possible lengths of the third side.

## What you need to know

- The graphs of the trigonometric functions.

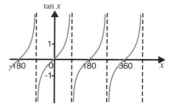

The **sine function** is a periodic function with period $360°$.
$-1 \leqslant \sin x \leqslant 1$

The **cosine function** is a periodic function with period $360°$.
$-1 \leqslant \cos x \leqslant 1$

The **tangent function** is a periodic function with period $180°$.
Tan $x$ is undefined at $90°$, $270°$, ...

- For every angle $x°$, the signs of $\sin x°$, $\cos x°$ and $\tan x°$ can be shown on a diagram.
  **Positive** angles are measured **anticlockwise**.
  **Negative** angles are measured **clockwise**.
  For angles greater than $360°$: subtract $360°$, or multiples of $360°$, to get the equivalent angle between $0°$ and $360°$.

- The **exact values** of the trigonometric ratios for the angles $30°$, $45°$ and $60°$ can be found from the triangles below.

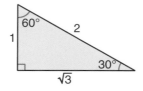

|  | $30°$ | $45°$ | $60°$ |
|---|---|---|---|
| sin | $\frac{1}{2}$ | $\frac{1}{\sqrt{2}}$ | $\frac{\sqrt{3}}{2}$ |
| cos | $\frac{\sqrt{3}}{2}$ | $\frac{1}{\sqrt{2}}$ | $\frac{1}{2}$ |
| tan | $\frac{1}{\sqrt{3}}$ | $1$ | $\sqrt{3}$ |

- **The Sine Rule**

$$\frac{a}{\sin A} = \frac{b}{\sin B} = \frac{c}{\sin C}$$

This can be also written as: $\dfrac{\sin A}{a} = \dfrac{\sin B}{b} = \dfrac{\sin C}{c}$

- **The Cosine Rule**

$$a^2 = b^2 + c^2 - 2bc \cos A$$
$$b^2 = a^2 + c^2 - 2ac \cos B$$
$$c^2 = a^2 + b^2 - 2ab \cos C$$

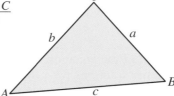

When using the Cosine Rule to find the size of an angle it is sometimes easier to rearrange the above formulae as:

$$\cos A = \frac{b^2 + c^2 - a^2}{2bc} \qquad \cos B = \frac{a^2 + c^2 - b^2}{2ac} \qquad \cos C = \frac{a^2 + b^2 - c^2}{2ab}$$

- To find the **area of a triangle** when you know two sides and the angle between the two sides use:
    Area of triangle $= \frac{1}{2}\, ab \sin C$

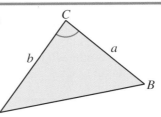

- Solving problems involving triangles.
  **Right-angled triangles**
  Use the **trigonometric ratios** (sin, cos and tan) or **Pythagoras' Theorem.**

  **Triangles which are not right-angled**
  **The Sine Rule**

  To find a **side** you need:
    two angles of known size, **and** the length of a side which is opposite one of the known angles.

  To find an **angle** you need:
    the length of the side opposite the angle you are trying to find, **and** the length of a side opposite an angle of known size.

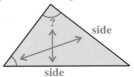

  **The Cosine Rule**
  To find a **side** you need:
    two sides of known length, **and** the size of the angle between the known sides.

  To find an **angle** you need:
    three sides of known length.

IDEAS FOR INVESTIGATION

Investigate graphs of the form $y = a \sin bx$ and $y = a \cos bx$.

What can you say about the values of $a$ and $b$ and the graphs of the functions?

## Review Exercise 34

**1** Here is the graph of $y = \sin x°$ for values of $x$ between $-360$ and $360$.

(a) One solution of the equation $\sin x° = 0.766$ is $x = -230$.
Find the other solutions for $x$ in the range $-360$ to $360$.

(b) Draw the graph of  (i) $y = \sin (2x)°$,  (ii) $y = \sin (x + 90)°$.  OCR

**2** Sin $30° = \cos x°$. Find the two values for $x$, given that $0 < x < 360$.

**3** (a) Draw a sketch of $y = \cos x°$ for $0 \leqslant x \leqslant 360$.
(b) Calculate the values of $x$ when $\cos x° = -0.5$ and $0 \leqslant x \leqslant 360$.  OCR

**4** The distance, $AC$, is 10.3 m.
The distance, $CD$, is 16.0 m.
Angle $BAC = 47°$, angle $ACD = 69°$
and angle $ABC$ is a right angle.

(a) Calculate the distance $BC$.
(b) Calculate the distance $AD$.
(c) Calculate the area of triangle $ACD$.

OCR

**5**

In the diagram, calculate

(a) the angle $DBC$,
(b) the side $AD$.

OCR

**6** Ship $A$ is 3.4 km from port $P$ on a bearing of 040°.
Ship $B$ is 15 km from port $P$ on a bearing of 155°.

(a) Calculate the distance between the two ships.
(b) Calculate the bearing of ship $A$ from ship $B$.

OCR

**7**

In the diagram, $ABCD$ is a kite.

(a) Prove that triangles $ABC$ and $ADC$ are congruent.
(b) $AB = 5.7$ cm, $BC = 7.6$ cm and $AC = 10.7$ cm.
   (i) Calculate angle $ABC$.
   (ii) Calculate the area of the kite $ABCD$.

OCR

**8** Billy and Colin are standing on the straight platform of a railway station when a
train, $FE$, arrives.

$E$ is due East of $F$. Colin is standing due East of Billy.
The bearing of $F$ from Billy is 228°.
The bearing of $F$ from Colin is 253°.

(a) Colin is 16 m from $F$. Calculate the distance that Billy is from $F$.
(b) $FE$ is 40 m long. How far is Colin from $E$?

OCR

**9** The diagram represents a level triangular piece of land.
$AB = 61$ metres, $AC = 76$ metres,
and the area of the land is 2300 m². Angle $BAC$ is acute.
Calculate the length of $BC$.
Give your answer to an appropriate degree of accuracy.

OCR

Do not use a calculator for this exercise.

**1** This triangle is isosceles.

Calculate the size of the lettered angles, giving your reasons. OCR

**2** A cuboid has a volume of 540 cm³. The base of the cuboid measures 5 cm by 9 cm.
Find the height of the cuboid.

**3**

The diagram shows triangles **P**, **Q** and **R**.
(a) Describe the single transformation which takes **P** onto **Q**.
(b) Describe the single transformation which takes **P** onto **R**.

Copy triangle **P** onto squared paper.
(c) Draw an enlargement of triangle **P** with scale factor 2, centre (0, 0).

**4** In the diagram, lines *PQ* and *RS* are parallel.
They are crossed by two other straight lines.
Find the size of the angle marked *y*.

**5**

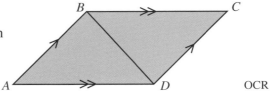

James has drawn this plan of his classroom.
What is the area of his classroom floor?

OCR

**6** Convert an area of 2.5 m² to cm².

**7** *ABCD* is a parallelogram. *BD* is a diagonal.
(a) Describe fully a single transformation which maps triangle *ABD* onto triangle *CDB*.
(b) What does this tell you about the triangles *ABD* and *CDB*?

OCR

**8** A table top is a circle of radius 50 cm.
(a) Calculate the circumference of the table top.
(b) Calculate the area of the table top.
Give your answers in terms of π.

**9** Jean gives her height as 166 cm, to the nearest centimetre.
What are the limits between which her actual height lies?

**10** *Y* is 50 m from *X* on a bearing of 080°.
*Z* is 70 m from *Y* on a bearing of 110°.
(a) Make a scale drawing to show the positions of *X*, *Y* and *Z*.
Use a scale of 1 cm to 10 m.
(b) Find by measurement the distance and bearing of *X* from *Z*.

**11** (a) Find the centre of the rotation which maps triangle *A* onto triangle *B*.

(b) Describe the single transformation which maps triangle *B* onto triangle *C*.

OCR

**12** (a)  The exterior angle of a regular polygon is 30°.
How many sides does the polygon have?

(b) *AB* is one side of another polygon.
Calculate the length of *AB*.

OCR

**13**  The roof of a barn is a triangular prism, as shown.
The dimensions, in metres, are given on the diagram.
The volume of the roof space is 48 m³.
Work out the length of the roof, *y* metres.

OCR

**14** The diagram shows a sketch of triangle *ABC*.
For this question leave in all construction lines.
  (a) Using ruler and compasses only:
    (i) make an accurate drawing of the triangle *ABC*,
    (ii) bisect angle *BAC*,
    (iii) draw the locus of the points that are equidistant from *A* and *C*.
  (b) Shade the region within the triangle where all the points are nearer to *AC* than *AB*, **and** nearer to *C* than *A*.

OCR

**15** (a) Explain why these triangles are similar.
(b) Find the length of *PQ*.

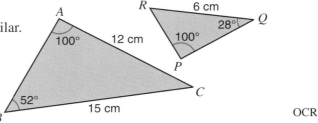

OCR

**16** Shape *P* is enlarged with scale factor 3 and centre (2, 1) onto shape *Q*.
(a) Describe the enlargement that would map shape *Q* onto shape *P*.

Shape *Q* has an area of 36 cm².
(b) What is the area of shape *P*?

OCR

**17** (a) Sketch the curve  $y = \cos x°$  for  $0 \leqslant x \leqslant 360$.
(b) Given that  $\cos 60° = 0.5$,  solve  $\cos x° = -0.5$  for  $0 \leqslant x \leqslant 360$.

OCR

**18** These boxes are similar.

(a) The volume of the smaller box is 240 cm³.
Work out the volume of the larger box.

(b) The surface area of the larger box is 558 cm².
Work out the surface area of the smaller box.

**19**

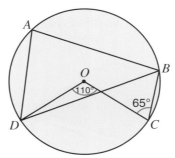

The diagram on the left shows a sector of a circle with radius 10 cm and angle 216°.
The sector is made into the cone with a slant height of 10 cm.

(a) Calculate the radius, $r$, of the base of the cone.

(b) (i) Calculate the height, $h$, of the cone.
(ii) Calculate the volume of the cone.
Leave your answer as a multiple of $\pi$.

OCR

**20** $O$ is the centre of a circle through $A$, $B$, $C$ and $D$.
Angle $DOC$ is 110° and angle $OCB$ is 65°.

Find
(a) angle $DBC$,
(b) angle $DCO$,
(c) angle $DAB$.

OCR

**21** A solid cylinder has diameter $d$ cm. The height of the cylinder is twice its diameter.
The total surface area of the cylinder is the same as the surface area of a sphere radius $r$ cm.
Prove that $r^2 = \frac{5}{8} d^2$.

OCR

**22** A metal sphere has a radius of 6 cm.
(a) Calculate the volume of the sphere.
Leave your answer as a multiple of $\pi$.

The diagram shows a cylinder of radius 10 cm.
It already contains water to a depth of 15 cm.
The metal sphere is placed in the water.
(b) Calculate the height, $h$ cm, that the water level rises.

OCR

**23**

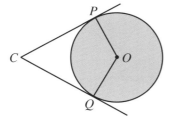

$CP$ and $CQ$ are tangents to the circle with centre $O$.
(a) Prove that triangles $CPO$ and $CQO$ are congruent.
(b) Given that angle $PCQ = 74°$, calculate the reflex angle $POQ$.

OCR

**24** In the triangle $OPQ$, $OA = \mathbf{a}$, $AP = 2\mathbf{a}$,
$OB = \mathbf{b}$, $BQ = 2\mathbf{b}$.

(a) Express $BP$ in terms of $\mathbf{a}$ and $\mathbf{b}$.

$X$ lies on $BP$ such that $BX : XP = 1 : 3$.

(b) Express $AX$ in terms of $\mathbf{a}$ and $\mathbf{b}$.
(c) Show that the ratio $AX : XQ = 1 : 3$.

OCR

# Shape, Space and Measures
# Calculator Paper

You may use a calculator for this exercise.

**1** (a) Work out the size of the angle marked $x$.
Give a reason for your answer.

(b)

(i) What special name is given to this shape?
Give a reason for your answer.
(ii) Find the value of $y$.

**2** The diagram shows a rectangular doormat.
What is the area of the doormat
(a) in cm²,
(b) in m²?

**3** The diagram shows three points, $A$, $B$ and $C$, on a map.
$B$ is 3 km due East of $A$.
(a) Work out the bearing of $C$ from $A$.
(b) (i) Make an accurate scale drawing of triangle $ABC$.
Use a scale of 2 cm to 1 km.
(ii) What is the distance, $AC$, on the ground,
in kilometres?
(c) Write the scale 2 cm to 1 km in the form $1 : n$.

OCR

**4** (a) Adrian is 6 feet 3 inches tall. Work out Adrian's height in centimetres.
(b) Adrian weighs 78 kg. Work out Adrian's weight in pounds.

**5** The diagram shows a cube. The surface area of the cube is 24 cm².
(a) What is the volume of the cube?
(b) How many of these cubes will fit into a cuboid which
measures 4 cm by 7 cm by 10 cm?

**6**

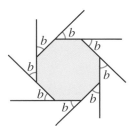

This diagram shows the cross-section of a
swimming pool.
Calculate the area of this cross-section.

OCR

**7** (a) The diagram shows two regular polygons.
Work out the size of angles $a$ and $b$.

(b) What is the sum of the interior angles
of a regular pentagon?

**8** (a) Construct parallelogram $PQRS$, with $PQ = 4$ cm, $SP = 3$ cm and angle $SPQ = 60°$.
(b) A point $X$ is 2 cm from the parallelogram and outside the parallelogram.
Draw the locus of all the possible positions of $X$.

**9** This is a parallelogram.
(a) Work out the area of the parallelogram.
(b) Work out the perimeter of the parallelogram.

4 cm

2 cm   5 cm

OCR

**10** (a) Describe the single transformation which maps:
(i) *A* onto *B*, (ii) *A* onto *C*.

Copy triangle *C* onto squared paper.
(b) Draw an enlargement of triangle *C*
with scale factor −2, centre (−1, 1).

**11** A solid plastic cylinder has a radius of 8 cm and a height of 15 cm.
Eighteen of these cylinders are put into a rectangular box measuring 48 cm by 48 cm by 30 cm.
The space around the cylinders is filled with packing.
Calculate the volume of packing required.
Give your answer to a sensible degree of accuracy.

OCR

**12** The diagram shows a plan of a rectangular garden.
There is a semi-circular paved area, then a lawn
leading to a rectangular vegetable plot.
(a) Find the area of the lawn.
(b) The gardener lays a pipe diagonally across
the vegetable plot, as shown in the diagram.
Calculate the length of the pipe.

24 m   Lawn   24 cm

28 m   22 m

OCR

**13** A sack of rice weighs 25 kg, measured to the nearest kg.
It is used to fill bags that contain 500 g of rice, measured to the nearest 10 g.
Find the maximum number of bags that could be filled.

OCR

**14** (a) The diagram shows a kite, *ABCD*, with measurements in metres.
*BD* bisects *AC* at right angles.
Calculate the size of angle *ABC*.

A

1.8   1.2
0.8

D   B

0.8

1.8   1.2

C

(b) *PQRS* is similar to *ABCD*.
*PR* is of length 1 metre.
Calculate the length of the side *PS*.

P

S   Q

R

OCR

**15** A circular hole has diameter 38 mm. A square peg will just fit into the hole.
Find the length of a side of the square.

OCR

**16**

Street level

32°

18.6 m

22.4 m

Platform   39°

The diagram shows the two escalators that carry passengers from a horizontal underground
platform up to street level.
Calculate the vertical height of the street level above the underground platform.

OCR

386

**17** (a) In the diagram, *AB* is a diameter of the circle, centre *O*.
*CD* is a tangent touching the circle at *C*.
Angle *BCD* = 53°.
Write down the size of each of the following angles,
giving your reasons.
(i)   Angle *ACB*.      (ii)   Angle *BAC*.

(b)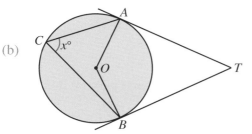

In the diagram, *TA* and *TB* are tangents to
the circle, centre *O*.
Angle *ACB* = *x*°.
Find the size of angle *ATB* in terms of *x*.

OCR

**18** The curved surface of this cone is formed from the sector of a
circle of radius 16.3 cm.
The angle of the sector is 126°.
Calculate the total surface area of the cone, including its base.

16.3 cm      16.3 cm

OCR

**19**

The diagram shows the positions of three ships, *A*, *B* and *C*.
(a)   Calculate the distance *BC*.
(b)   An air-sea rescue search has to be made
of the region inside triangle *ABC*.
Calculate the area to be searched.

OCR

**20** (a)   (i)   Sketch the graph of   *y* = sin *x*,   for values of *x* between 0° and 360°.
(ii)   State a value of *x* other than 30° for which   sin *x* = 0.5.
(b)   Find all the solutions between −360° and 360° for the equation   5 sin *x* = −2.      OCR

**21** A camping gas container is in the shape of a cylinder with a
hemispherical top.
The dimensions of the container are shown in the diagram.
It is decided to increase the volume of the container by 20%.
The new container is mathematically similar to the old one.
Calculate the base diameter of the new container.

8.5 cm

←8.5 cm→

OCR

**22**

A trapezium has area 610 mm² to 2 significant figures.
It has parallel sides 20 mm and 42 mm, each to the nearest millimetre.
Calculate the lower bound of the height, *h*, of the trapezium.

OCR

**23** A can of tinned fish is in the shape of a frustum of a right cone.
The diameter of the top is 7.6 cm.
The diameter of the base is 6.6 cm.
The vertical height is 10.8 cm.

Calculate the capacity of the can.

OCR

387

# Collection and Organisation of Data

To answer questions such as:   Which is the most popular colour of car?
Is it going to rain tomorrow?
Which team won the World Cup in 2002?

we need to collect data.

## Primary and secondary data

When data is collected by an individual or organisation to use for a particular purpose it is called **primary data**.
Primary data is obtained from experiments, investigations, surveys and by using questionnaires.

Data which is already available or has been collected by someone else for a different purpose is called **secondary data**.
Sources of secondary data include the Annual Abstract of Statistics, Social Trends and the Internet.

## Data

Data is made up of a collection of **variables**. Each variable can be described, numbered or measured.

Data which can only be **described** in words is **qualitative**.
Such data is often organised into categories, such as make of car, colour of hair, etc.

Data which is given **numerical** values, such as shoe size or height, is **quantitative**.
Quantitative data is either **discrete** or **continuous**.
  **Discrete** data can only take certain values, usually whole numbers, but may include fractions (e.g. shoe sizes).
  **Continuous** data can take any value within a range and is measurable
  (e.g. height, weight, temperature, etc.).

### EXAMPLES

The taste of an orange is a qualitative variable.
The number of pips in an orange is a discrete quantitative variable.
The surface area of an orange is a continuous quantitative variable.

## Exercise 35.1

State whether the following data is qualitative or quantitative.
If the data is quantitative state whether it is discrete or continuous.

1. The colours of cars in a car park.

2. The weights of eggs in a carton.

3. The numbers of desks in classrooms.

4. The names of students in a class.

5. The sizes of spanners in a toolbox.

6. The depths that fish swim in the sea.

7. The numbers of goals scored by football teams on a Saturday.

8. The brands of toothpaste on sale in supermarkets.

9. The sizes of ladies dresses in a store.

10. The heights of trees in a wood.

## Collection of data

Data can be collected in a variety of ways:

by observation, by interviewing people and by using questionnaires.

The method of collection will often depend on the type of data to be collected.

### Data collection sheets

**Data collection sheets** are used to record data.

To answer the question, "Which is the most popular colour of car?" we could draw up a simple data collection sheet and record the colours of passing cars by observation.

### EXAMPLE

A **data collection sheet** for colour of car is shown, with some cars recorded.

| Colour of car | Tally | Frequency |
|---|---|---|
| Black | \|\| | 2 |
| Blue | ЖЖ ЖЖ \|\|\| | 13 |
| Green | \|\|\|\| | 4 |
| Red | ЖЖ ЖЖ \| | |
| Silver | ЖЖ \|\| | |
| White | ЖЖ ЖЖ \|\|\|\| | |
| | Total | |

The colour of each car is recorded in the **tally** column by a single stroke.

To make counting easier, groups of 5 are recorded as ЖЖ.

*How many red cars are recorded?*
*How many cars are recorded altogether?*

The total number of times each colour appears is called its **frequency**.
A table for data with the totals included is called a **frequency distribution**.

For large amounts of discrete data, or for continuous data, we organise the data into **groups** or **classes**. When data is collected in groups it is called a **grouped frequency distribution** and the groups you put the data into are called **class intervals**.

### EXAMPLE

The weights of 20 boys are recorded in the grouped frequency table shown below.

| Weight $w$ kg | Tally | Frequency |
|---|---|---|
| $50 \leq w < 55$ | \| | 1 |
| $55 \leq w < 60$ | \|\|\| | 3 |
| $60 \leq w < 65$ | ЖЖ \|\|\|\| | 9 |
| $65 \leq w < 70$ | ЖЖ \| | 6 |
| $70 \leq w < 75$ | \| | 1 |
| | Total | 20 |

Weights are grouped into class intervals of equal width.

$55 \leq w < 60$

means 55 kg, or more, but less than 60 kg.

*John weighs 54.9 kg. In which class interval is he recorded?*
*David weighs 55.0 kg. In which class interval is he recorded?*

*What is the width of each class interval?*

Collection and Organisation of Data

389

## Databases

If we need to collect data for more than one type of information, for example: the make, colour, number of doors and mileage of cars, we will need to collect data in a different way.

We could create a **data collection card** for each car.

| Car | 1 |
|---|---|
| Make | Vauxhall |
| Colour | Grey |
| Number of doors | 3 |
| Mileage | 18 604 |

Alternatively, we could use a data collection sheet and record all the information about each car on a separate line.

This is an example of a simple **database**.

| Car | Make | Colour | Number of doors | Mileage |
|---|---|---|---|---|
| 1 | Vauxhall | Grey | 3 | 18 604 |
| 2 | Ford | Blue | 2 | 33 216 |
| 3 | Ford | White | 5 | 27 435 |
| 4 | Nissan | Red | 4 | 32 006 |

When all the data has been collected, separate frequency or grouped frequency tables can be drawn up.

## Exercise 35.2

1. The tally chart shows the number of glass bottles put into a bottle bank one day.

| Colour of glass | Tally |
|---|---|
| Clear | IIII IIII IIII II |
| Brown | IIII IIII IIII IIII I |
| Green | IIII IIII IIII |

How many **more** brown bottles than clear bottles were put into the bottle bank?

2. The heights, in centimetres, of 36 girls are recorded as follows.

| | | | | | | | | |
|---|---|---|---|---|---|---|---|---|
| 148 | 161 | 175 | 156 | 155 | 160 | 178 | 159 | 170 |
| 163 | 147 | 150 | 173 | 169 | 170 | 174 | 166 | 163 |
| 162 | 158 | 155 | 165 | 168 | 154 | 156 | 163 | 167 |
| 172 | 170 | 165 | 160 | 164 | 172 | 157 | 173 | 161 |

(a) Copy and complete the grouped frequency table for the data.

| Height $h$ cm | Tally | Frequency |
|---|---|---|
| $145 \leq h < 150$ | | |
| $150 \leq h < 155$ | | |

(b) What is the width of each class interval?
(c) How many girls are in the class interval $155 \leq h < 160$?
(d) How many girls are less than 160 cm?
(e) How many girls are 155 cm or taller?

**3** The database gives information about the babies born at a maternity hospital one day.

| Baby's name | Time of birth | Weight (kg) | Length (cm) |
|---|---|---|---|
| Alistair | 0348 | 3.2 | 44 |
| Francis | 0819 | 3.5 | 48 |
| Louisa | 1401 | 3.7 | 47 |

(a) Which baby was the longest?
(b) Which baby was the heaviest?
(c) Which baby was born first?

**4** A database of cars is shown.

| Car | Make | Colour | Number of doors | Mileage |
|---|---|---|---|---|
| 1 | Vauxhall | Grey | 3 | 18 604 |
| 2 | Ford | Blue | 2 | 33 216 |
| 3 | Ford | White | 5 | 27 435 |
| 4 | Nissan | Red | 4 | 32 006 |
| 5 | Vauxhall | Blue | 4 | 31 598 |
| 6 | Ford | Green | 3 | 37 685 |
| 7 | Vauxhall | Red | 3 | 21 640 |
| 8 | Nissan | White | 2 | 28 763 |
| 9 | Ford | White | 3 | 30 498 |
| 10 | Vauxhall | White | 5 | 9 865 |
| 11 | Nissan | Red | 3 | 7 520 |
| 12 | Vauxhall | Grey | 5 | 16 482 |

(a) (i) Draw up separate frequency tables for make, colour and number of doors.
　　(ii) Draw up a grouped frequency table for mileage.
　　　　Use class intervals of 5000 miles,
　　　　starting at $0 \leqslant m < 5000$, $5000 \leqslant m < 10\,000$, …
(b) (i) Which make of car is the most popular?
　　(ii) How many Ford cars are white?
　　(iii) How many cars have a mileage of 30 000 or more?
　　(iv) How many cars have exactly 3 doors?

**5** Use data collection cards to collect information about students in your class.
Include gender, height, shoe size and pulse rate.
(a) What is the smallest shoe size for students in your class?
(b) What is the gender of the student with the highest pulse rate?
(c) What is the difference between the highest pulse rate and the lowest pulse rate?
(d) What is the height of the tallest student?
(e) What differences are there in the data collected for male and female students?

**6** (a) Design a data collection card to collect information on the leisure time activities
　　　of students.
(b) Draw up frequency or grouped frequency tables for the data.
(c) Which leisure time activity is the most popular?
(d) What differences are there in the leisure time activities of male and female students?

**Collection and Organisation of Data**

## Questionnaires

**Questionnaires** are frequently used to collect data.
In business they are used to get information about products or services and in politics they are frequently used to test opinion on a range of issues and personalities.

When constructing questions for a questionnaire you should:

(1) use simple language, so that everyone can understand the question;

(2) ask short questions which can be answered precisely, with a "yes" or "no" answer, a number, or a response from a choice of answers;

(3) provide tick boxes, so that questions can be answered easily;

(4) avoid open-ended questions, like: "What do you think of education?" which might produce long rambling answers which would be difficult to collate or process;

(5) avoid leading questions, like: "Don't you agree that there is too much bad language on television?" and ask instead:
"Do you think that there is too much bad language on television?"     Yes ☐     No ☐

(6) ask questions in a logical order.

### Multiple-response questions

In many instances a choice of responses should be provided.

Instead of asking, "How old are you?" which does not indicate the degree of accuracy required and many people might consider personal, we could ask instead:

Which is your age group?

under 18 ☐     18 to 40 ☐     41 to 65 ☐     over 65 ☐

Notice there are no gaps and only **one** response applies to each person.

Sometimes we invite **multiple responses** by asking questions, such as:

Which of these soaps do you watch?

Coronation Street ☐     EastEnders ☐     Emmerdale ☐     Hollyoaks ☐
*Tick as many as you wish.*

## Hypothesis

A **hypothesis** is a statement that may or may not be true.
To test a hypothesis we can construct a questionnaire, carry out a survey and analyse the results.

### EXAMPLE

A questionnaire to test the hypothesis,
*"People think it is better to give than to receive,"*
could include questions like these.

1. **Gender:**     male ☐     female ☐

2. **Age (years):** 11 - 16 ☐     17 - 21 ☐     22 - 59 ☐     60 & over ☐

3. **Do you think it is better to give than to receive?**

   Yes ☐          No ☐

4. **To which of the following have you given in the last year?**

   School ☐          Charities ☐          Church ☐

   Hospital ☐     Special appeals ☐     Homeless ☐

   Other (please list) _____

*Suggest another question which could be included.*

**1** Susan wants to find out what people think about the Health Service.
Part of the questionnaire she has written is shown.

> Q4. What is your date of birth?
>
> Q5. Don't you agree that waiting lists for operations are too long?
>
> Q6. How many times did you visit your doctor last year?
>
> ☐ less than 5          ☐ 5 - 10          ☐ 10 or more

  (a)  Why should Q4 not be asked?
  (b)  Give a reason why Q5 is unsuitable.
  (c)  (i)   Explain why Q6 is unsuitable in its present form.
       (ii)  Rewrite the question so that it could be included in the questionnaire.

**2** In preparing questions for a survey on the use of a library the following questions were
considered. Explain why each question in its present form is unsuitable and rewrite the question.
  (a)  How old are you?
  (b)  How many times have you used the library?
  (c)  Which books do you read?
  (d)  How could the library be improved?

**3** A mobile phone company wants to carry out a survey.
It wants to find out the distribution of the age and sex of customers and the frequency with
which they use the phone. The company intends to use a questionnaire.
Write three questions and responses that will enable the company to carry out the survey.

**4** A survey of reading habits is to be conducted. Suggest five questions which could be included.

**5** Phil included this question in a questionnaire:
> ***Don't you agree that the radio gives the best news reports?***

Explain why this question is unsuitable.

**6** Design a questionnaire to test the hypothesis:
> ***"People think that everyone should take part in sport."***

**7** Design a questionnaire to test the hypothesis:
> ***"People think that animals should not be used to test drugs."***

**8** Design a questionnaire to test the hypothesis: ***"Children have too much homework."***

## Two-way tables

We have already seen that the results of a survey can be recorded on data collection sheets and then
collated using frequency or grouped frequency tables. We can also illustrate data using **two-way tables**.

A two-way table is used to illustrate the data for two different features (variables) in a survey.

### EXAMPLE

The two-way table shows the results of a survey.

  (a)  How many boys wear glasses?
  (b)  How many children wear glasses?
  (c)  Do the results prove or disprove the hypothesis:
> ***"More boys wear glasses than girls"***?

|  | Wear Glasses | |
|---|---|---|
|  | Yes | No |
| Boys | 4 | 14 |
| Girls | 3 | 9 |

  (a)  4      (b)  7      (c)  Disprove.  Boys: $\frac{4}{18} \times 100 = 22\%$  Girls: $\frac{3}{12} \times 100 = 25\%$

**1** The two-way table shows information about the ages of people in a retirement home.

Age (years)

|  | 60 - 64 | 65 - 69 | 70 - 74 | 75 - 79 | 80 and over |
|---|---|---|---|---|---|
| Men | 0 | 2 | 5 | 8 | 1 |
| Women | 2 | 5 | 6 | 5 | 6 |

(a) How many men are aged 75 - 79?
(b) How many men are included?
(c) How many people are aged 75 or more?
(d) How many people are included?
(e) What percentage of these people are aged 75 or more?

**2** The two-way table shows information about a class of pupils.

|  | Can swim | Cannot swim |
|---|---|---|
| Boys | 14 | 6 |
| Girls | 8 | 2 |

(a) How many boys can swim?
(b) How many boys are in the class?
(c) What percentage of the boys can swim?
(d) What percentage of the girls can swim?
(e) Do the results prove or disprove the hypothesis:

*"More boys can swim than girls"*?

Explain your answer.

**3** The two-way table shows the number of boys and girls in families taking part in a survey.

| | | | | | |
|---|---|---|---|---|---|
| 3 | 1 | | 2 | | |
| 2 | 1 | 2 | 3 | | |
| 1 | 5 | 9 | | 1 | 1 |
| 0 | | 3 | | 2 | |
| | 0 | 1 | 2 | 3 | 4 |

Number of girls (left label), Number of boys (bottom label)

(a) (i) How many families have two children?
    (ii) Does the data support the hypothesis:
    *"More families have less than 2 children than more than 2 children"*?
    Explain your answer.
(b) (i) How many girls are included in the survey?
    (ii) Does the data support the hypothesis:
    *"More boys are born than girls"*?
    Explain your answer.

**4** In a survey, 100 people were asked: "Would you like to be taller?"

58 of the people asked were men.
65 of the people asked said, "Yes."
24 of the women asked said, "No."

(a) Construct a two-way table to show the results of the survey.

(b) A newspaper headline stated:

> **Over 80% of men would like to be taller.**

Do the results of the survey support this headline?
Give a reason for your answer.

## Sampling

When information is required about a small group of people it is possible to survey everyone.
When information is required about a large group of people it is not always possible to survey everyone and only a **sample** may be asked.
The sample chosen should be large enough to make the results meaningful and representative of the whole group or the results may be **biased**.
For example, to test the hypothesis,

*"Girls are more intelligent than boys"*,

you would need to ask equal numbers of boys and girls from various age groups.
The results of a survey may also be biased if there is any form of deliberate selection or if the sample is incomplete.

## Sampling methods

In a **simple random sample** everyone has an equal chance of being selected.
For example, the names of the whole group could be written on identical pieces of paper and placed in a hat.
Names could then be taken from the hat, without looking, until the sample is complete.

> A **census** is when the whole of a population is surveyed.
> The only true sample is when 100% of the population is surveyed.
> A large sample allows more reliable inferences to be made about the whole population.

In a **systematic random sample** people are selected according to some rule.
For example, names could be listed in alphabetical order and every tenth person selected.

However, samples chosen using these methods may not be representative of the whole group.
For example, a sample taken from a school population may consist of girls only, or pupils from Year 10 only.

> **Quota samples** are often used in market research.
> The population is divided into groups (gender, age, etc).
> A given number (quota) is surveyed from each group.
> This type of sample is not random, but is cheap to carry out and can be done quickly.
> *How reliable are such samples?*

A **stratified random sample** is used to overcome the possible bias of random samples by taking into account the composition of all the people in the original group.
The original group is divided up into separate categories or strata, such as male/female, age group, etc, before a random sample is taken.
A simple random sample is then taken from each category in proportion to the size of the category.

### EXAMPLE

Jayne is investigating the spending habits of girls in her school.
The table shows the numbers of girls in each part of the school.

| Year Group | Lower School | Upper School | Sixth Form |
|---|---|---|---|
| Number of girls | 140 | 100 | 60 |

Jayne wants a stratified random sample of 30 girls.
How many girls should be chosen from each part of the school?

Sample size    Lower School:   $\frac{140}{300} \times 30 = 14$

                 Upper School:   $\frac{100}{300} \times 30 = 10$

                 Sixth Form:   $\frac{60}{300} \times 30 = 6$

Collection and Organisation of Data

**1** George is investigating the cost of return journeys by train.
He plans to ask ten passengers who are waiting at a station at midday the cost of their
return journeys. Give two reasons why he might get biased results.

**2** Judy is investigating shopping habits.
She plans to interview 50 women at her local supermarket on a Tuesday morning.
Give three reasons why she might get biased results.

**3** State one advantage and one disadvantage of a postal survey.

**4** The two-way table shows the age and gender of people taking part in a survey.

Age (years)

|        | Under 18 | 18 - 25 | 26 - 40 | 41 - 64 | 65 and over |
|--------|----------|---------|---------|---------|-------------|
| Female | 0        | 2       | 7       | 9       | 7           |
| Male   | 0        | 4       | 17      | 19      | 10          |

Give two reasons why the data collected may not be representative of the whole population.

**5** In a school there are 320 pupils in the lower school and 240 pupils in the upper school.
How many pupils from each part of the school should be included in a stratified random
sample of size 40?

**6** The number of pupils in each year group at a boys school is shown.

| Year Group     | 7  | 8   | 9   | 10  | 11 |
|----------------|----|-----|-----|-----|----|
| Number of boys | 90 | 110 | 110 | 100 | 90 |

The school carries out a homework survey.
(a) Explain why a simple random sample of pupils should not be used.
(b) Calculate how many pupils should be included from each year group in a stratified
random sample of size 50.

**7** The table shows the numbers of employees in each section of a company.

| Department          | Managerial | Clerical | Technical | Manual |
|---------------------|------------|----------|-----------|--------|
| Number of employees | 26         | 65       | 637       | 572    |

A survey on job satisfaction is to be carried out.
(a) Explain why a simple random sample of employees is unsuitable.
(b) A stratified random sample of size 100 is used.
How many employees from the technical department will be included?

**8** The table shows the age distribution of a club's membership.

| Age (years) | Under 21 | 21 to 65 | Over 65 |
|-------------|----------|----------|---------|
| Number      | 49       | 76       | 13      |

How many members should be included from each of these age groups in a stratified random
sample of 25?

**9** An industrial concern employs personnel as shown in the table.

| Management | Sales | Shop floor |
|------------|-------|------------|
| 48         | 261   | 2691       |

How many employees from each section should be included in a stratified random sample of
60 employees?

# What you need to know

- **Primary data** is data collected by an individual or organisation to use for a particular purpose. Primary data is obtained from experiments, investigations, surveys and by using questionnaires.
- **Secondary data** is data which is already available or has been collected by someone else for a different purpose. Sources of secondary data include the Annual Abstract of Statistics, Social Trends and the Internet.
- **Qualitative** data – Data which can only be described in words.
- **Quantitative** data – Data that has a numerical value.
  Quantitative data is either **discrete** or **continuous**.
  **Discrete** data can only take certain values.
  **Continuous** data has no exact value and is measurable.
- **Data Collection Sheets** – Used to record data during a survey.
- **Tally** – A way of recording each item of data on a data collection sheet.
  A group of five is recorded as ⊩⊩.
- **Frequency Table** – A way of collating the information recorded on a data collection sheet.
- **Grouped Frequency Table** – Used for continuous data or for discrete data when a lot of data has to be recorded.
- **Database** – A collection of data.
- **Class Interval** – The width of the groups used in a grouped frequency distribution.
- **Questionnaire** – A set of questions used to collect data for a survey.
  Questionnaires should:
  > (1) use simple language,
  > (2) ask short questions which can be answered precisely,
  > (3) provide tick boxes,
  > (4) avoid open-ended questions,
  > (5) avoid leading questions,
  > (6) ask questions in a logical order.
- **Hypothesis** – A hypothesis is a statement which may or may not be true.
- When information is required about a large group of people it is not always possible to survey everyone and only a **sample** may be asked.
  The sample chosen should be large enough to make the results meaningful and representative of the whole group (population) or the results may be **biased**.
- **Two-way Tables** – A way of illustrating two features of a survey.
- In a **simple random sample** everyone has an equal chance of being selected.
- In a **systematic random sample** people are selected according to some rule.
- In a **stratified random sample** the original group is divided up into separate categories or strata, such as male/female, age group, etc, before a random sample is taken.
  A simple random sample is then taken from each category in proportion to the size of the category.

## Review Exercise 35

**1** Paul is doing a survey to find if there should be an airport near his town.
This is one of his questions.

> *Do you agree that having an airport would make it easier to travel to your holiday destination and if we did have one would you use it?*

State **two** things wrong with this question.

OCR

**2** Terry is carrying out a survey on the shopping habits of people at a superstore.
He says,
"People who travel further to the store will come less often and spend more money per visit."
Write three questions which would help him test his statement.

**3** Rashid is writing a questionnaire about the rates of pay for various jobs.
One of his questions is, "What is your weekly pay?"
(a) Explain what is wrong with this question.
(b) Suggest a better question, which overcomes the problem involved. OCR

**4** The table shows the age and gender of people taking part in a survey to test the hypothesis:

### *"Children have too much homework."*

|  | Age (years) | | | | |
| --- | --- | --- | --- | --- | --- |
|  | Under 11 | 11 - 16 | 17 - 25 | 26 - 50 | Over 50 |
| Male | 0 | 4 | 6 | 5 | 5 |
| Female | 0 | 0 | 0 | 0 | 0 |

Give three reasons why this is not a suitable sample.

**5** A travel agent says, "More women prefer holidays abroad than men".
The table shows the results of a survey to test this statement.

|  | Men | Women |
| --- | --- | --- |
| Prefer holidays abroad | 18 | 21 |
| Prefer holidays in the UK | 6 | 7 |

Do these results support the statement made by the travel agent?
Explain your answer.

**6** A mixed 11 - 18 Comprehensive school has 1000 pupils.
The timing of the school day has been changed.
To judge how effective the new school day is, the governors are to give out 200 questionnaires.
Explain how they could obtain a stratified sample. OCR

**7** This table shows the number of students in Years 9 to 11 at Rivers School who have school lunches.

| Year | 9 | 10 | 11 |
| --- | --- | --- | --- |
| Number of students | 103 | 86 | 61 |

A catering researcher wants to do a survey about the choice of food available.
Suggest how he should construct a stratified sample of 50 students. OCR

**8** An 11 - 16 school has 1000 students.
An alphabetical list of all the students is produced.
Explain why taking every 10th person from this list may not produce a suitable sample
of the school's students. OCR

**9** Michael carried out a survey on the number of hours spent on homework in a week.
He asked 90 students in his school.
Michael used simple random sampling to choose the 90 students.
(a) Describe carefully a simple random sampling method he could have used.

Abigail also carried out a homework survey at her school.
She chose, at random, 10% of each year group.
(b) Name the type of sampling method that Abigail used.
(c) Give one advantage that Abigail's method has over Michael's method.
(d) Give one advantage that Michael's method has over Abigail's method. OCR

**10** At a tennis tournament there were 164 judges, 118 ball boys and 118 ball girls.
A representative sample is to be chosen.
Explain why it would be difficult to choose a stratified sample of 100. OCR

# Averages and Range

## Types of average

There are three types of **average**: the **mode**, the **median** and the **mean**.

The **mode** is the most common value.

The **median** is the middle value (or the mean of the two middle values) when the values are arranged in order of size.

$$\textbf{Mean} = \frac{\text{Total of all values}}{\text{Number of values}}$$

## Range

The **range** is a measure of **spread**, and is the difference between the highest and lowest values.

Range = highest value − lowest value.

---

### EXAMPLE

The price, in pence, of a can of cola in eight different shops is shown.

$$35, \quad 39, \quad 39, \quad 32, \quad 37, \quad 35, \quad 35, \quad 40.$$

Find   (a)   the mode,

       (b)   the median,

       (c)   the mean,

       (d)   the range of these prices.

(a)   The **mode** is the most common value.

     The most common price is 35.

     The mode is 35 pence.

     We sometimes say the modal price is 35p.

(b)   The **median** is found by arranging the values in order of size and taking the middle value.

     Arrange the prices in order of size.

     32,   35,   35,   35,   37,   39,   39,   40.

     The middle price is   $\frac{35 + 37}{2} = 36$

     The median is 36 pence.

Where there are an even number of values the median is the average of the middle two.

(c)   The **mean** is found by finding the total of all the values and dividing the total by the number of values.

     Add the prices.

     $35 + 39 + 39 + 32 + 37 + 35 + 35 + 40 = 292$

     The mean $= \frac{292}{8} = 36.5$

     The mean is 36.5 pence.

(d)   The **range** = highest value − lowest value.

     The highest price = 40p, the lowest price = 32p

     The range = 40 − 32 = 8 pence.

---

### Exercise 36.1

Do not use a calculator for questions 1 and 2.

**1**   Claire recorded the number of e-mail messages she received each day last week.

           5    2    1    7    4    1    1

Find the mode, median, mean and range of the number of messages received each day.

**2** Gail noted the number of stamps on parcels delivered to her office.

3   2   4   5   7   3   4   3   5   3

(a)   Write down the mode.
(b)   Find the range of the number of stamps on a parcel.
(c)   Find the median number of stamps on a parcel.
(d)   Calculate the mean number of stamps on a parcel.

**3** The boot sizes of players in a rugby team are:

9   8   10   11   9   8   10   9   10   9   10   10   8   9   10

(a)   Which boot size is the mode?
(b)   Find the median boot size.
(c)   Calculate the mean boot size. Give your answer correct to one decimal place.

**4** The weights of 8 men in a rowing team are:

86 kg   95 kg   89 kg   93 kg   84 kg   78 kg   91 kg   79 kg

Calculate the mean of their weights correct to one decimal place.

**5** The mean of six numbers is 5. Five of the numbers are:  2,  3,  7,  8  and  6.
What is the other number?

**6** The mean length of 8 rods is 75 cm. An extra rod is added.
The total length of the 9 rods is 729 cm.
What is the length of the extra rod?

**7** A group of 2 boys and 3 girls take a test.
The mean mark for the boys is 14.5
The mean mark for the girls is 16.
Calculate the mean mark for the whole group.

## Frequency distributions

After data is collected it is often presented using a **frequency distribution table**.
To find measures of average for a **frequency distribution** we have to take into account the frequency of each amount.

### EXAMPLE

The table shows the boot sizes of players in a rugby team.

| Boot size | 8 | 9 | 10 | 11 |
|-----------|---|---|----|----|
| Frequency | 3 | 5 | 6  | 1  |

Find  (a)  the mode,  (b)  the median,  (c)  the mean boot size.

(a)   The mode is the boot size with the largest frequency.
      The modal boot size is 10.

(b)   The median is the boot size of the middle player.
      There are 15 players altogether.
      The middle one is the 8th player.
      The first 3 players wear boot size 8,
      the next 5 wear boot size 9.
      So, the 8th player wears boot size 9.
      The median boot size is 9.

> **Mathematical shorthand:**
> $\Sigma$ is the Greek letter 'sigma'.
> $\Sigma f$ means the sum of frequencies.
> $\Sigma fx$ means the sum of the values of $fx$.
>
> Mean $= \dfrac{\Sigma fx}{\Sigma f}$

(c)   The mean $= \dfrac{\text{Total of all boot sizes}}{\text{Total number of players}} = \dfrac{8 \times 3 + 9 \times 5 + 10 \times 6 + 11 \times 1}{3 + 5 + 6 + 1} = \dfrac{140}{15} = 9.333...$

      The mean boot size is 9.3, correct to 1 d.p.

### EXAMPLE

Calculate the range, mode, median and mean of the ages for the data shown in the bar chart.

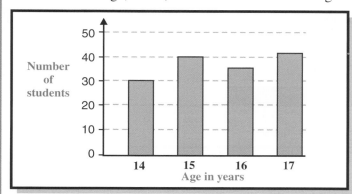

The range is the difference between the highest and lowest ages.
Range = 17 - 14
= 3 years

The most common age is shown by the tallest bar.
So, the modal age is 17 years.

Use a table to find the median and the mean.

| Age (years) $x$ | Frequency $f$ | Frequency × Age $f \times x$ |
|---|---|---|
| 14 | 30 | 420 |
| 15 | 40 | 600 |
| 16 | 36 | 576 |
| 17 | 41 | 697 |
| Totals | $\Sigma f = 147$ | $\Sigma fx = 2293$ |

The middle student is given by: $\frac{147 + 1}{2} = 74$

The 74th student in the list has the median age.
The first 70 students are aged 14 or 15 years.
The 74th student has age 16 years.
Median age is 16 years.

$$\text{Mean} = \frac{\text{Total of all ages}}{\text{Number of students}} = \frac{\Sigma fx}{\Sigma f}$$

Mean = $\frac{2293}{147}$ = 15.598...

Mean age is 15.6 years, correct to 1 d.p.

### Exercise 36.2

**1** Find the mode, median and mean for the following data.

| Number of letters delivered | 1 | 2 | 3 | 4 | 5 | 6 |
|---|---|---|---|---|---|---|
| Number of days taken to deliver | 6 | 9 | 6 | 6 | 2 | 1 |

**2** Hilary observed customers using the express checkout at a supermarket.

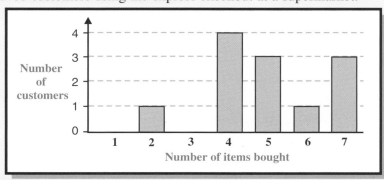

(a) Find the range of the number of items bought.
(b) What is the mode of the number of items bought?
(c) Work out the median number of items bought.
(d) Calculate the mean number of items bought.

**3** A group of students took part in a quiz on the Highway Code. The bar chart shows their scores.

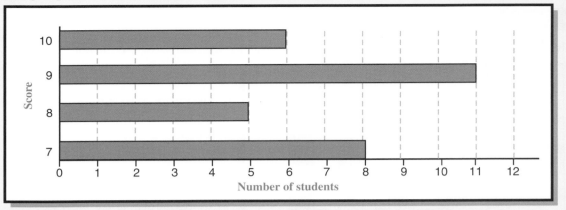

(a) Which score is the mode?
(b) What is the median score?
(c) How many students took part in the quiz?
(d) Calculate the mean score.

## Grouped frequency distributions

When there is a lot of data, or the data is continuous, **grouped frequency distributions** are used.

**Calculating the mean**

For a grouped frequency distribution the true value of the mean cannot be found as the actual values of the data are not known.

To **estimate the mean**, we assume that all the values in each class are equal to the midpoint of the class.

$$\text{Estimated mean} = \frac{\Sigma \text{ (frequency} \times \text{midpoint)}}{\text{Total frequency}} = \frac{\Sigma fx}{\Sigma f}$$

**Modal class**

For a grouped frequency distribution with equal class width intervals, the **modal class** is the class (or group) with the highest frequency.

---

### EXAMPLE

The table shows the masses of a group of children.
(a) Calculate an estimate of the mean mass.
(b) Find the modal class.

| Mass ($m$ kg) | Frequency |
|---|---|
| $40 \leqslant m < 50$ | 3 |
| $50 \leqslant m < 60$ | 10 |
| $60 \leqslant m < 70$ | 6 |
| $70 \leqslant m < 80$ | 12 |

(a)

| Mass ($m$ kg) | Midpoint $x$ | Frequency $f$ | Frequency $\times$ Midpoint $f \times x$ |
|---|---|---|---|
| $40 \leqslant m < 50$ | 45 | 3 | 135 |
| $50 \leqslant m < 60$ | 55 | 10 | 550 |
| $60 \leqslant m < 70$ | 65 | 6 | 390 |
| $70 \leqslant m < 80$ | 75 | 12 | 900 |
| | Totals | $\Sigma f = 31$ | $\Sigma fx = 1975$ |

Midpoint of the class
$40 \leqslant m < 50$
is given by:

$$\frac{40 + 50}{2} = \frac{90}{2} = 45$$

Estimate of mean $= \dfrac{\Sigma fx}{\Sigma f} = \dfrac{1975}{31} = 63.709\ldots$

Estimate of mean mass $= 63.7$ kg, correct to 3 sig. figs.

(b) The modal class is $70\,\text{kg} \leqslant m < 80\,\text{kg}$.

## Exercise 36.3

**1** Give the modal class and calculate an estimate of the mean for each of the following.

> ○○○○○○○○○○○○○○○○
> 0 - means 0 or more but less than 10.

(a)

| Salary (s) (£000's) | Number of employees |
|---|---|
| $10 \leqslant s < 20$ | 79 |
| $20 \leqslant s < 30$ | 32 |
| $30 \leqslant s < 40$ | 14 |
| $40 \leqslant s < 50$ | 0 |
| $50 \leqslant s < 60$ | 2 |

(b)

| Time spent watching TV per week (hours) | Number of students |
|---|---|
| 0 - | 2 |
| 10 - | 8 |
| 20 - | 5 |
| 30 - | 14 |
| 40 - 50 | 7 |

**2** The table shows the distribution of the weights of some turkeys.

| Weight (w kg) | $2 \leqslant w < 4$ | $4 \leqslant w < 6$ | $6 \leqslant w < 8$ | $8 \leqslant w < 10$ |
|---|---|---|---|---|
| Frequency | 7 | 9 | 5 | 3 |

Calculate an estimate of the mean weight of these turkeys.
Give your answer correct to one decimal place.

**3** The table shows the distribution of the prices of houses for sale in a particular neighbourhood.

| Price (p £000's) | $60 \leqslant p < 80$ | $80 \leqslant p < 100$ | $100 \leqslant p < 120$ | $120 \leqslant p < 140$ |
|---|---|---|---|---|
| Number of houses | 3 | 7 | 4 | 1 |

Calculate an estimate of the mean price of these houses.
Give your answer to an appropriate degree of accuracy.

**4** The table shows the distribution of marks in a test.

| Mark | 0 - 19 | 20 - 29 | 30 - 34 | 35 - 39 | 40 - 50 |
|---|---|---|---|---|---|
| Number of students | 12 | 23 | 25 | 14 | 3 |

Calculate an estimate of the mean mark. *Notice that the class intervals are not all equal.*

## Comparing distributions

The table shows the marks gained in a test. Compare the marks obtained by the boys and the girls.

| Mark (out of 10) | 7 | 8 | 9 | 10 |
|---|---|---|---|---|
| Number of boys | 2 | 5 | 3 | 0 |
| Number of girls | 4 | 0 | 2 | 1 |

To compare the marks we can use the range and the mean.

> Boys: Range = $9 - 7 = 2$
> Girls: Range = $10 - 7 = 3$

The girls had the higher range of marks.

> Boys: Mean = $\dfrac{2 \times 7 + 5 \times 8 + 3 \times 9 + 0 \times 10}{10} = \dfrac{81}{10} = 8.1$

> Girls: Mean = $\dfrac{4 \times 7 + 0 \times 8 + 2 \times 9 + 1 \times 10}{7} = \dfrac{56}{7} = 8$

The boys had the higher mean mark.

Overall the boys did better as:
> the girls' marks were more spread out with a lower average mark,
> the boys' marks were closer together with a higher average mark.

> ○○○○○○○○○
> **Note:**
> To compare the overall standard, the median could be used instead of the mean.

**1** The times, in minutes, taken by 8 boys to swim 50 metres are shown.

| 1.8 | 2.0 | 1.7 | 2.2 | 2.1 | 1.9 | 1.8 | 2.1 |
|-----|-----|-----|-----|-----|-----|-----|-----|

(a)  (i)   What is the range of these times?
     (ii)  Calculate the mean time.

The times, in minutes, taken by 8 girls to swim 50 metres are shown.

| 2.1 | 1.9 | 1.8 | 2.3 | 1.6 | 2.0 | 2.6 | 1.9 |
|-----|-----|-----|-----|-----|-----|-----|-----|

(b)  Comment on the times taken by these boys and girls to swim 50 m.

**2** Use the mean and the range to compare the number of visits to the cinema by these women and men.

| Number of visits to the cinema last month | 0 | 1 | 2 | 3 | 4 | 5 | 6 | More than 6 |
|---|---|---|---|---|---|---|---|---|
| Number of women | 8 | 9 | 7 | 3 | 2 | 1 | 1 | 0 |
| Number of men | 0 | 12 | 7 | 1 | 0 | 0 | 0 | 0 |

**3** Deepak thought that the girls in his class wore smaller shoes than the boys on average, but that the boys' shoe sizes were less varied than the girls'.
He did a survey to test his ideas.
The table shows his results. Was he correct?

| Shoe size | $4\frac{1}{2}$ | 5 | $5\frac{1}{2}$ | 6 | $6\frac{1}{2}$ | 7 | $7\frac{1}{2}$ | 8 | $8\frac{1}{2}$ | 9 | $9\frac{1}{2}$ |
|---|---|---|---|---|---|---|---|---|---|---|---|
| Number of boys | 1 | 0 | 5 | 4 | 4 | 2 | 1 | 0 | 1 | 0 | 0 |
| Number of girls | 0 | 2 | 0 | 2 | 3 | 0 | 2 | 0 | 3 | 1 | 1 |

**4** (a)  Find the modal class for the ages of customers in each of these two restaurants.
   (b)  Which restaurant attracts more younger people?
   (c)  Why is it only possible to find an approximate value for the age range of customers?

| Age (years) | 0 - 9 | 10 - 19 | 20 - 29 | 30 - 39 | 40 - 49 | 50 - 59 | 60 - 69 | 70 - 79 | 80 - 89 |
|---|---|---|---|---|---|---|---|---|---|
| MacQuick | 8 | 9 | 10 | 7 | 1 | 1 | 3 | 1 | 0 |
| Pizza Pit | 2 | 4 | 12 | 15 | 5 | 3 | 3 | 2 | 1 |

**5** The graphs show the monthly sales of bicycles before and after a marketing campaign.
Calculate the medians and the ranges.
Use your results to compare 'Before' with 'After'.

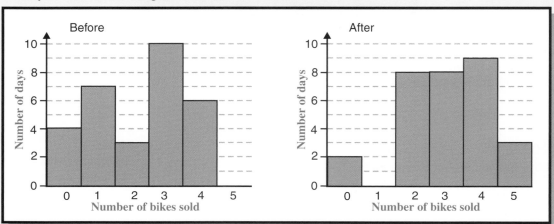

## Which is the best average to use?

Many questions in mathematics have definite answers. This one does not.
Sometimes the mean is best, sometimes the median and sometimes the mode.
It all depends on the situation and what you want to use the average for.

### EXAMPLE

A youth club leader gets a discount on cans of drinks if she buys all one size.
She took a vote on which size people wanted.
The results were as follows:

| Size of can (ml) | 100 | 200 | 330 | 500 |
|---|---|---|---|---|
| Number of votes | 9 | 12 | 19 | 1 |

Mode = 330 ml
Median = 200 ml
Mean = 245.6 ml, correct to one decimal place.

Which size should she buy?

The mean is no use at all because she can't buy cans of size 245.6 ml.
Even if the answer is rounded to the nearest whole number (246 ml), it's still no use.
The median is possible because there is an actual 200 ml can.
However, only 12 out of 41 people want this size.
In this case the **mode** is the best average to use, as it is the most popular size.

## Exercise 36.5

In questions 1 and 2 find all the averages possible.
State which is the most sensible and why.

**1** On a bus: 23 people are wearing trainers,
              10 people are wearing boots,
               8 people are wearing lace-up shoes.

**2** 20 people complete a simple jigsaw. Their times, in seconds, are recorded.

    5,     6,     8,     8,     9,     10,     11,     11,     12,     12,
    12,    15,    15,    15,    15,    18,    19,    20,    22,    200.

**3** The times for two swimmers to complete each of ten 25 m lengths are shown below.

| Swimmer A | 30.1 | 30.1 | 30.1 | 30.6 | 30.7 | 31.1 | 31.1 | 31.5 | 31.7 | 31.8 |
|---|---|---|---|---|---|---|---|---|---|---|
| Swimmer B | 29.6 | 29.7 | 29.7 | 29.9 | 30.0 | 30.0 | 30.1 | 30.1 | 30.1 | 44.6 |

Which is the better swimmer?
Explain why.

**4** A teacher sets a test.
He wants to choose a minimum mark for a distinction so that 50% of his students get this result.
Should he use the modal mark, the median mark or the mean mark?
Give a reason for your answer.

**5** The cost of Bed and Breakfast at 10 different hotels is given.
    £39.50    £55    £60    £50    £49    £42    £95    £59    £39.50    £45

(a) Wyn says, "The average cost of Bed and Breakfast is £39.50."
Which average is he using?
Give a reason why this is not a sensible average to use for this data.

(b) Which of the mode, median and mean best describes the average cost of
Bed and Breakfast?
Give a reason for your answer.

- There are three types of **average**: the **mode**, the **median** and the **mean**.
  The **mode** is the most common value.
  The **median** is the middle value (or the mean of the two middle values) when the values are arranged in order of size.

  $$\textbf{Mean} = \frac{\text{Total of all values}}{\text{Number of values}}$$

- The **range** is a measure of **spread**.
  Range = highest value − lowest value

- To find the mean of a **frequency distribution** use:

  $$\text{Mean} = \frac{\text{Total of all values}}{\text{Number of values}} = \frac{\Sigma fx}{\Sigma f}$$

- To find the mean of a **grouped frequency distribution**, first find the value of the midpoint of each class.
  Then use:   $\text{Estimated mean} = \dfrac{\text{Total of all values}}{\text{Number of values}} = \dfrac{\Sigma fx}{\Sigma f}$

- Choosing the best average to use:
  When the most **popular** value is wanted use the **mode**.
  When **half** of the values have to be above the average use the **median**.
  When a **typical** value is wanted use either the **mode** or the **median**.
  When all the **actual** values have to be taken into account use the **mean**.
  When the average should not be distorted by a few very small or very large values do **not** use the mean.

## Review Exercise 36

**1**  The cost of a DVD player at 11 different stores is given.

   £35   £26   £45   £20   £29   £28   £22   £27   £25   £22   £40

   (a)  Work out the median cost.
   (b)  Give a reason why the mode would not be a sensible average for these data.

**2**  Some students took part in a charity event.
   They each had to carry as many bags of potatoes as they could across the school field in 15 minutes.
   The results are shown in the bar chart below.

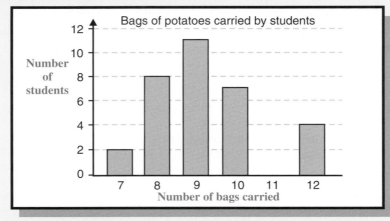

   (a)  How many students took part?
   (b)  What was the modal number of bags carried?
   (c)  What was the range of the number of bags carried?
   (d)  (i)   What was the total number of bags carried?
        (ii)  What was the mean number of bags carried?

OCR

**3** The weights, in kilograms, of the 11 boys in a class are:

| 58.3 | 48.1 | 60.3 | 55.4 | 61.7 | 72.5 | 48.6 | 51.4 | 50.6 | 57.9 | 54.7 |

The mean weight of the 13 girls in the class is 53.1 kg.
Calculate the mean weight of the 24 pupils in the class.                    OCR

**4** Holly wrote a story. She counted how many words she wrote on a line. Here are her results.

| Words on a line | 11 | 12 | 13 | 14 | 15 | 16 |
|-----------------|----|----|----|----|----|----|
| Frequency       | 1  | 4  | 8  | 7  | 11 | 4  |

Calculate the mean number of words Holly wrote on a line.                    OCR

**5** The graph shows the results of a survey of the number of faults in cars before and after servicing.

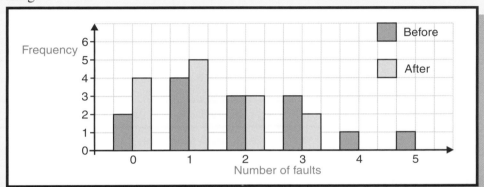

(a) A mechanic says, "The survey shows all cars have fewer faults after servicing."
    Is this true? Explain your answer.
(b) A customer says, "The survey shows the average number of faults in cars before and
    after servicing is the same." Which average is being used?
(c) A report on the survey says, "The average number of faults per car before servicing is 2."
    Which average is being used?
    Use the same average to find the average number of faults per car after servicing.

**6** One hundred batteries were tested to see how long they lasted.
The results are shown in the table below.

| Time ($t$ hours) | $0 \leqslant t < 4$ | $4 \leqslant t < 8$ | $8 \leqslant t < 12$ | $12 \leqslant t < 16$ | $16 \leqslant t < 20$ |
|------------------|---------------------|---------------------|----------------------|-----------------------|-----------------------|
| Frequency        | 12                  | 20                  | 34                   | 25                    | 9                     |

Use the midpoints of the intervals to calculate an estimate of the mean time that a battery lasted.
OCR

**7** The salaries of each of the 39 employees of a small company are summarised in the table.

| Salary (£$P$) | Number of workers |
|---------------|-------------------|
| $10\,000 \leqslant P < 12\,000$ | 4 |
| $12\,000 \leqslant P < 14\,000$ | 17 |
| $14\,000 \leqslant P < 16\,000$ | 11 |
| $16\,000 \leqslant P < 18\,000$ | 5 |
| $18\,000 \leqslant P < 20\,000$ | 2 |

(a) Calculate an estimate of the mean salary.

The managing director of the company has a salary of £50 000.
(b) If his salary is included in the figures, how would this affect the mode and the mean?
    Explain your answer.                    OCR

Most people find numerical information easier to understand if it is presented in pictorial form. For this reason, television reports, newspapers and advertisements frequently use graphs and diagrams to present and compare information.

The height of each bar gives the **frequency**.
The most frequently occurring variable is called the **mode** or **modal category**.

## Bar charts

**Bar charts** are a simple but effective way of displaying data.
Bars can be drawn either horizontally or vertically.
Bar charts can also be used to compare data.

> **EXAMPLE**
>
> The table shows how a class of children travelled to school one day.
>
> | Method of travel | Bus | Cycle | Car | Walk |
> |---|---|---|---|---|
> | Boys | 2 | 7 | 1 | 5 |
> | Girls | 3 | 1 | 5 | 6 |
>
> To make it easier to compare information for boys and girls we can draw both bars on the same diagram, as shown.
>
> Cycling it the most popular method of travelling to school for boys. Which method of travelling to school is the most popular for girls?
>
> *Compare and comment on the method of travel of these boys and girls.*
>
>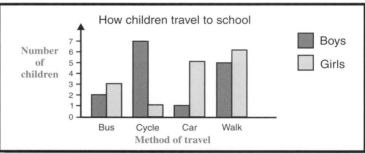

Instead of drawing bars to show frequency we could draw horizontal or vertical lines. Such graphs are called **bar-line graphs**.

## Pie charts

Pie charts are useful for showing and comparing proportions of data.
However, they do not show frequencies. Such information can be found by interpreting the pie chart. The whole circle represents the total frequency and each sector represents the frequency of one part (category) of the data.

> **EXAMPLE**
>
> The pie chart shows the makes of 120 cars.
>
> (a) Which make of car is the mode?
>
> (b) How many of the cars are Ford?
>
>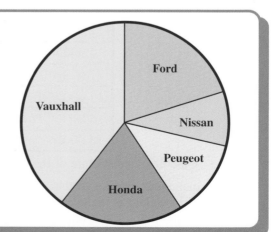
>
> (a) The sector representing Vauxhall is the largest. Therefore, Vauxhall is the mode.
>
> (b) The angle of the sector representing Ford is 72°.
>
> The number of Ford cars $= \frac{72}{360} \times 120 = 24$.

**1** The table shows the amount of pocket money given each week to a number of girls.

| Amount (£) | 1 | 2 | 3 | 4 | 5 | 6 | 7 | 8 | 9 | 10 |
|---|---|---|---|---|---|---|---|---|---|---|
| Number of girls | 0 | 0 | 1 | 5 | 10 | 4 | 0 | 3 | 0 | 7 |

(a)  Draw a bar-line graph of the data.
(b)  What is the range of the amount of pocket money given each week?
(c)  Calculate the mean amount of pocket money given each week.
(d)  What percentage of the girls got less than £5?

**2** The breakfast cereal preferred by some adults is shown.

| Breakfast cereal | Corn flakes | Muesli | Porridge | Bran flakes |
|---|---|---|---|---|
| Number of adults | 25 | 20 | 12 | 15 |

(a)  Show the information in a pie chart.
(b)  Which breakfast cereal is the mode?

**3** A group of children were asked how many hours they had spent watching television on a particular Sunday.
The bar chart shows the results.

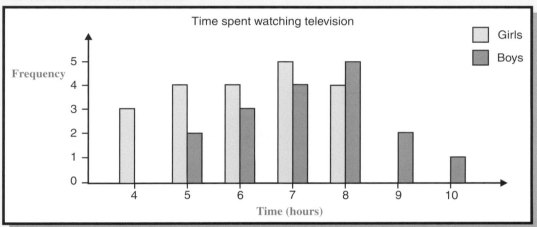

(a)  What was the modal time for the girls?
(b)  What was the range in time for the boys?
(c)  How many boys watched television for more than 8 hours?
(d)  (i)   How many girls were included in the survey?
      (ii)  What percentage of the girls watched television for 6 hours?
(e)  Compare and comment on the time spent watching television for these boys and girls.

**4** The pie chart shows the different types of tree in a forest.
There are 54 oak trees and these are represented by a sector with an angle of 27°.

(a)  The pine trees are represented by an angle of 144°.
     How many pine trees are there?

(b)  There are 348 silver birch trees.
     Calculate the angle of the sector representing
     silver birch trees.

(c)  Write, in its simplest form, the ratio of ash trees to
     oak trees in the forest.

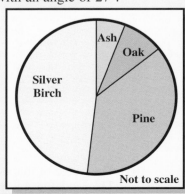

## Stem and leaf diagrams

Data can also be represented using a **stem and leaf diagram**.
**Back to back stem and leaf diagrams** can be used to compare two sets of data.

### EXAMPLES

**1** The times, in seconds, taken by 14 students to complete a puzzle are shown.

| 15 | 9 | 23 | 32 | 17 | 12 | 27 | 19 | 26 | 15 | 11 | 24 | 31 | 10 |

Construct a stem and leaf diagram to represent this information.

A stem and leaf diagram is made by splitting each number into two parts.
As the data uses 'tens' and 'units', the stem will represent the 'tens' and the leaf will
represent the 'units'.
To draw the stem and leaf diagram begin by drawing a vertical line.
The digits to the left of the line make the **stem**.
The digits to the right of the line are the **leaves**.

> The first number is 15.
> Next to the stem of 1 record 5.

9 is recorded as 0 9 ⟶

```
0 | 9
1 | 5  7  2  9  5  1  0
2 | 3  7  6  4
3 | 2  1
```

Once the data has been recorded, it is usual to redraw the diagram so that the leaves are in
numerical order.

```
            1 | 5   means 15 seconds
0 | 9
1 | 0  1  2  5  5  7  9
2 | 3  4  6  7
3 | 1  2
```

> Stem and leaf diagrams are often drawn
> without column headings, in which case a key
> is necessary.
> e.g.  1 | 5   means 15 seconds

**2** The results for examinations in Mathematics and English for a group of students are shown.
The marks are given as percentages.

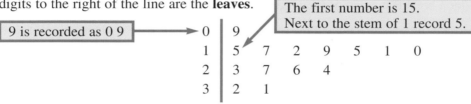

| **Mathematics:** | 91 | 27 | 55 | 69 | 83 | 25 | 45 | 53 | 67 | 71 |
| | 30 | 52 | 45 | 59 | 86 | 73 | 65 | 47 | 54 | 38 |
| **English:** | 45 | 40 | 48 | 65 | 75 | 55 | 36 | 85 | 76 | 69 |
| | 64 | 58 | 47 | 64 | 67 | 72 | 83 | 74 | 62 | 51 |

(a) Construct a back to back stem and leaf diagram for this data.
(b) Compare and comment on the results in Mathematics and English.

(a)

```
        Mathematics   |   |      English        3 | 6  means 36%
                7  5  | 2 |
                8  0  | 3 | 6
             7  5  5  | 4 | 0  5  7  8
       9  5  4  3  2  | 5 | 1  5  8
          9  7  5  | 6 | 2  4  4  5  7  9
                3  1  | 7 | 2  4  5  6
                6  3  | 8 | 3  5
                   1  | 9 |
```

> For Mathematics:
> 5 | 2 means 25%

(b) The range of marks in Mathematics is larger than in English.
The modal group in English is 60 to 69, in Mathematics it is 50 to 59.

**1** The amount of petrol, in litres, bought by 20 motorists is shown.

| 16 | 23 | 27 | 10 | 35 | 42 | 26 | 25 | 24 | 17 |
|----|----|----|----|----|----|----|----|----|----|
| 23 | 41 | 33 | 35 | 25 | 19 | 16 | 31 | 12 | 29 |

(a) Construct a stem and leaf diagram to represent this information.
(b) What is the range in the amount of petrol bought?

**2** The times, in seconds, taken to answer 24 telephone calls are shown.

| 3.2 | 5.6 | 2.4 | 3.5 | 4.3 | 3.6 | 2.8 | 5.8 | 3.3 | 2.6 | 3.2 | 2.8 |
|-----|-----|-----|-----|-----|-----|-----|-----|-----|-----|-----|-----|
| 5.6 | 3.5 | 4.2 | 1.5 | 2.7 | 2.5 | 3.7 | 3.1 | 2.9 | 4.2 | 2.4 | 3.0 |

(a) Copy and complete the stem and leaf diagram to represent this information.

$$3 \mid 2 \quad \text{means 3.2 seconds}$$

```
1
2
3 | 2
4
5
```

For this data:
the stem represents 'units',
the leaf represents 'tenths'.

(b) What is the median time taken to answer a telephone call?

**3** The heights, in centimetres, of the heels on 20 different pairs of shoes are shown.

| 2.7 | 3.4 | 2.0 | 6.0 | 4.5 | 3.6 | 3.1 | 2.4 | 4.2 | 1.8 |
|-----|-----|-----|-----|-----|-----|-----|-----|-----|-----|
| 3.5 | 2.5 | 2.6 | 2.1 | 4.0 | 3.5 | 4.2 | 2.6 | 3.9 | 5.4 |

Construct a stem and leaf diagram to represent this information.

**4** David did a survey to find the cost, in pence, of a loaf of bread.
The stem and leaf diagram shows the results of his survey.

$$2 \mid 7 \quad \text{means 27 pence}$$

```
2 | 7  9
3 | 1  1  2  9  9  9
4 | 2  5  5  9
5 | 0  4  5
6 | 0  5
```

(a) How many loaves of bread are included in the survey?
(b) What is the range of the prices?
(c) Which price is the mode?

**5** The time taken to complete a computer game is recorded to the nearest tenth of a minute.
The times for a group of 20 adults and 20 children are shown.

| Adults | | | | | | | | | |
|-----|-----|-----|-----|-----|------|-----|-----|-----|-----|
| 7.9 | 8.2 | 7.3 | 9.2 | 6.4 | 6.5  | 6.1 | 8.2 | 7.8 | 7.0 |
| 9.4 | 8.0 | 7.3 | 5.4 | 7.7 | 10.1 | 5.9 | 6.7 | 7.3 | 6.0 |

| Children | | | | | | | | | |
|-----|-----|-----|-----|-----|-----|-----|-----|-----|-----|
| 6.4 | 5.4 | 4.9 | 6.6 | 7.1 | 5.1 | 6.5 | 6.3 | 7.4 | 6.5 |
| 8.2 | 7.7 | 5.9 | 6.8 | 7.6 | 5.3 | 6.2 | 8.0 | 4.7 | 7.9 |

(a) Construct a back to back stem and leaf diagram for this data.
(b) Compare and comment on the times for adults and children.

## Scatter graphs

When we investigate statistical information we often find there are connections between sets of data, for example, height and weight.
In general taller people weigh more than shorter people.

To see if there is a connection between two sets of data we can plot a **scatter graph**.
The scatter graph below shows information about the heights and weights of ten boys.

Each cross plotted on the graph represents the weight and height of one boy.

The diagram shows that taller boys generally weigh more than shorter boys.

## Correlation

The relationship between two sets of data is called **correlation**.

In general the scatter graph of the heights and weights shows that as height increases, weight increases. This type of relationship shows there is a **positive correlation** between height and weight.

But if as the value of one variable increases the value of the other variable decreases, then there is a **negative correlation** between the variables.

When no linear relationship exists between two variables there is **zero correlation**. This does not necessarily imply "no relationship", but merely "no linear relationship".

The following graphs show types of correlation.

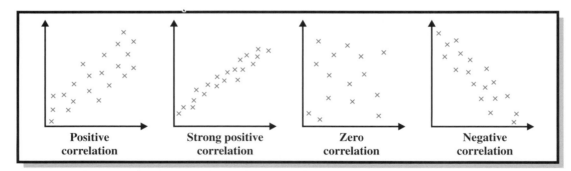

| Positive correlation | Strong positive correlation | Zero correlation | Negative correlation |

As points get closer to a straight line the stronger the correlation.
**Perfect correlation** is when all the points lie on a straight line.

## Exercise 37.3

1. Describe the type of correlation you would expect between:
   (a) the age of a car and its secondhand selling price,
   (b) the heights of children and their ages,
   (c) the shoe sizes of children and the distance they travel to school,
   (d) the number of cars on the road and the number of road accidents,
   (e) the engine size of a car and the number of kilometres it can travel on one litre of fuel.

2  (a)  Which of these graphs shows the strongest positive correlation?
   (b)  Which of these graphs shows perfect negative correlation?
   (c)  Which of these graphs shows the weakest correlation?

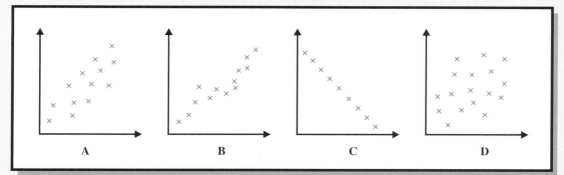

     A            B            C            D

3  The scatter graph shows the shoe sizes and heights of a group of girls.

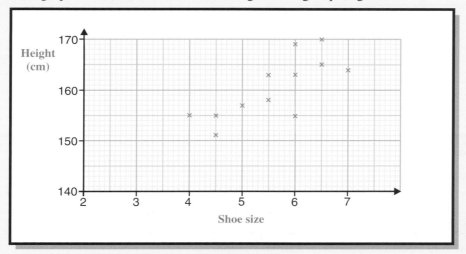

(a)  How many girls wear size $6\frac{1}{2}$ shoes?
(b)  How tall is the girl with the largest shoe size?
(c)  Does the shortest girl wear the smallest shoes?
(d)  What do you notice about the shoe sizes of taller girls compared to shorter girls?

4  The table shows the distance travelled and time taken by motorists on different journeys.

| Distance travelled (km) | 30 | 45 | 48 | 80 | 90 | 100 | 125 |
|---|---|---|---|---|---|---|---|
| Time taken (hours) | 0.6 | 0.9 | 1.2 | 1.2 | 1.3 | 2.0 | 1.5 |

(a)  Draw a scatter graph for the data.
(b)  What do you notice about distance travelled and time taken?
(c)  Give one reason why the distance travelled and the time taken are not perfectly correlated.

5  Tyres were collected from a number of different cars.
The table shows the distance travelled and depth of tread for each tyre.

| Distance travelled (1000 km) | 4 | 5 | 9 | 10 | 12 | 15 | 18 | 25 | 30 |
|---|---|---|---|---|---|---|---|---|---|
| Depth of tread (mm) | 9.2 | 8.4 | 7.6 | 8 | 6.5 | 7.4 | 7 | 6.2 | 5 |

(a)  Draw a scatter graph for the data.
(b)  What do you notice about the distance travelled and the depth of tread?
(c)  Explain how you can tell that the relationship is quite strong.

# Line of best fit

We have seen that **scatter graphs** can be used to illustrate two sets of data and, from the distribution of points plotted, an indication of the relationship which exists between the data can be seen.

The scatter graph of heights and weights has been redrawn below and a **line of best fit** has been drawn, by eye, to show the relationship between height and weight.

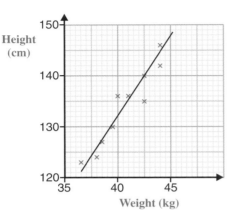

**Lines of best fit:**

- The slope of the line shows the trend of the points.

- A line is only drawn if the correlation (positive or negative) is strong.

- The line does not have to go through the origin of the graph.

Where there is a relationship between the two sets of data the line of best fit can be used to estimate other values.

A boy is 132 cm tall.
Using the line of best fit an estimate of his weight is 40 kg.

## Exercise 37.4

**1** The table shows the ages and weights of ten babies.

| Age (weeks) | 2 | 4 | 9 | 7 | 13 | 5 | 6 | 1 | 10 | 12 |
|---|---|---|---|---|---|---|---|---|---|---|
| Weight (kg) | 3.5 | 3.3 | 4.2 | 4.7 | 5 | 3.8 | 4 | 3 | 5 | 5.5 |

(a) Use this information to draw a scatter graph.
(b) What type of correlation is shown on the scatter graph?
(c) Draw a line of best fit.
(d) Mrs Wilson's baby is 11 weeks old.
    Use the graph to estimate the weight of her baby.

**2** The table shows the temperature of water as it cools in a freezer.

| Time (minutes) | 5 | 10 | 15 | 20 | 25 | 30 |
|---|---|---|---|---|---|---|
| Temperature (°C) | 36 | 29 | 25 | 20 | 15 | 8 |

(a) Use this information to draw a scatter graph.
(b) What type of correlation is shown?
(c) Draw a line of best fit.
(d) Use the graph to estimate the time when the temperature of the water reaches 0°C.

**3** The table shows the times taken by some boys to run 200 metres and their inside-leg measurements.

| Time (seconds) | 31 | 33 | 34 | 38 | 38 | 38 | 42 | 43 | 45 | 47 |
|---|---|---|---|---|---|---|---|---|---|---|
| Inside-leg (cm) | 69 | 65 | 72 | 63 | 69 | 75 | 70 | 65 | 74 | 69 |

(a) Plot a scatter graph of these data.
(b) Explain why a line of best fit for these data would not be useful in estimating the time for a different boy to run 200 metres by taking his inside-leg measurement.

**4** The table shows the weights and fitness factors for a number of women.
The higher the fitness factor the fitter a person is.

| Weight (kg) | 45 | 48 | 50 | 54 | 56 | 60 | 64 | 72 | 99 | 112 |
|---|---|---|---|---|---|---|---|---|---|---|
| Fitness Factor | 41 | 48 | 40 | 40 | 35 | 40 | 34 | 30 | 17 | 15 |

(a)  Use this information to draw a scatter graph.
(b)  What type of correlation is shown on the scatter graph?
(c)  Draw a line of best fit.
(d)  Use the graph to estimate:
    (i)   the fitness factor for a woman whose weight is 80 kg,
    (ii)  the weight of a woman whose fitness factor is 22.

**5** The following table gives the marks obtained by some candidates taking examinations in French and German.

| Mark in French | 53 | 35 | 39 | 53 | 50 | 59 | 36 | 43 |
|---|---|---|---|---|---|---|---|---|
| Mark in German | 64 | 32 | 44 | 70 | 56 | 68 | 40 | 48 |

(a)  (i)   Use this information to draw a scatter graph.
    (ii)  Draw the line of best fit by eye.
(b)  Use the graph to estimate:
    (i)   the mark in German for a candidate who got 70 in French,
    (ii)  the mark in French for a candidate who got 58 in German.
(c)  Which of the two estimates in (b) is likely to be more reliable?
Give a reason for your answer.

## What you need to know

- **Bar chart**. Used for data which can be counted.
  Often used to compare quantities of data in a distribution.
  Bars can be drawn horizontally or vertically.
  Bars are the same width and there are gaps between bars.
  The length of each bar represents frequency.
  The longest bar represents the **mode**.
  The difference between the largest and smallest variable is called the **range**.

- **Bar-line graph**. Instead of drawing bars, horizontal or vertical lines are drawn to show frequency.

- **Pie chart**. Used for data which can be counted.
  Often used to compare proportions of data, usually with the total.
  The whole circle represents all the data.
  The size of each sector represents the frequency of data in that sector.
  The largest sector represents the **mode**.

- **Stem and leaf diagrams**. Used to represent data in its original form.
  Data is split into two parts.
  The part with the higher place value is the stem,
  e.g.   15   stem 1 leaf 5.

  The data is shown in numerical order on the diagram.

  e.g.  2 | 3  5  9   represents 23, 25, 29.

  A key is given to show the value of the data.

  e.g.  3 | 4   means 34 cm   or   3 | 4   means 3.4 cm, etc.

  **Back to back stem and leaf diagrams** can be used to compare two sets of data.

Presentation of Data 1

- A **scatter graph** can be used to show the relationship between two sets of data.

- The relationship between two sets of data is referred to as **correlation**.

- You should be able to recognise **positive** and **negative** correlation.

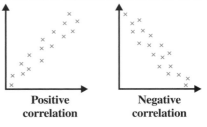

Positive correlation    Negative correlation

- When there is a relationship between two sets of data a **line of best fit** can be drawn on the scatter graph.
The correlation is stronger as points get closer to a straight line.
**Perfect correlation** is when all the points lie on a straight line.

- The line of best fit can be used to **estimate** the value from one set of the data when the corresponding value of the other set is known.

## Review Exercise 37

**1** The weights, in grams, of 20 cherry tomatoes are shown.

| 5.4 | 4.6 | 6.7 | 3.9 | 4.2 | 5.0 | 6.3 | 5.4 | 4.8 | 3.5 |
| 4.6 | 5.6 | 5.8 | 6.0 | 2.8 | 4.4 | 4.7 | 5.6 | 5.1 | 4.8 |

Draw a stem and leaf diagram to represent this information.

**2** Paul asked 50 boys what was their favourite fruit. Here are his results.

| Fruit | Apple | Orange | Banana | Grapes | Other |
|---|---|---|---|---|---|
| Number of boys | 8 | 6 | 20 | 9 | 7 |

Draw a pie chart to show these results.

OCR

**3** The data from a survey of cars was used to plot several scatter graphs.

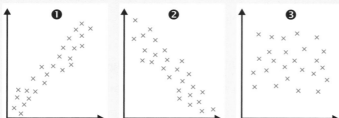

A  Age of car against height of car
B  Age of car against mileage
C  Age of car against value of car

Match each scatter graph to the correct description.

**4** The stem and leaf diagram shows the distribution of marks for a test marked out of 50.

| Boys | | | | | Girls | | | | | 1 | 7 | means 17 marks |
|---|---|---|---|---|---|---|---|---|---|---|---|---|
| | | | | 0 | 9 | | | | | | | |
| | | 6 | 2 | 1 | 0 | 1 | 2 | 7 | | | | |
| | 7 | 6 | 4 | 3 | 2 | 1 | 3 | 5 | 5 | 6 | 7 | 8 |
| 9 | 5 | 3 | 2 | 0 | 3 | 2 | 5 | 9 | | | | |
| | | 5 | 1 | 4 | 1 | | | | | | | |
| | | | 0 | 5 | | | | | | | | |

(a)  What is the lowest mark for the girls?
(b)  What is the highest mark for the boys?
(c)  How many of these boys and girls scored more than 25 marks?
(d)  Compare and comment on the marks for boys and girls.

**5** The frequency diagram shows the distribution of marks for a class of 30 pupils in a mental arithmetic test.

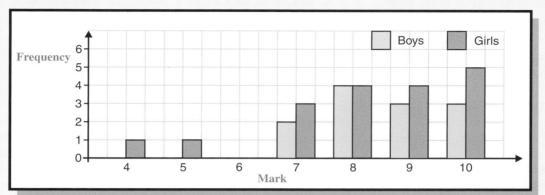

(a) What is the ratio of boys to girls in the class?

(b) The test is marked out of 10.
What percentage of the class scored full marks?

(c) By comparing the mode and range for the girls with the mode and range for the boys, comment on the marks scored.

**6** Nicky compared the scores awarded by two judges in a gymnastics competition.
Here are their scores for 10 competitors.

| Judge 1 | 2.3 | 7.3 | 7.7 | 4.4 | 8.5 | 7.7 | 1.8 | 8.1 | 4.9 | 7.0 |
|---------|-----|-----|-----|-----|-----|-----|-----|-----|-----|-----|
| Judge 2 | 2.4 | 7.5 | 6.9 | 4.7 | 8.7 | 7.9 | 2.3 | 7.8 | 5.1 | 6.5 |

(a) Draw a scatter graph for these data.

(b) Describe fully the correlation between the two sets of scores.

(c) (i) Draw the line of best fit on the graph.
(ii) Estimate the score from Judge 2 for a competitor given 5.6 by Judge 1.          OCR

**7** The table below shows the heights of a group of Year 7 pupils together with the height of each of their fathers.
All measurements are in centimetres.

| Height of pupil | 138 | 141 | 145 | 148 | 149 | 154 | 155 | 161 | 162 |
|-----------------|-----|-----|-----|-----|-----|-----|-----|-----|-----|
| Height of father | 151 | 155 | 153 | 170 | 161 | 176 | 185 | 186 | 192 |

(a) Draw a scatter graph to show this information.

(b) Describe the correlation between the two sets of heights.

(c) Draw a line of best fit on your scatter diagram.

(d) A new pupil joins the group. His height is 151 cm.
Use your line of best fit to estimate the height of his father.          OCR

**8** The record times for the 100 metres for each age group of the schoolboys' athletic championship in the country of Ocravia are shown in the table.

| Age (years) | 9 | 10 | 11 | 12 | 13 | 14 | 15 | 16 | 17 | 18 |
|-------------|---|----|----|----|----|----|----|----|----|----|
| Time (seconds) | 13.7 | 13.4 | 13 | 12.6 | 12.5 | 12.1 | 11.8 | 11.3 | 11.1 | 10.6 |

(a) Draw a scatter graph to show this information.

(b) Describe the correlation between the ages and the times.

(c) Add a line of best fit to the diagram.

(d) A 100 metres championship for 20-year-old youths is held.
(i) Use your line of best fit to estimate the record for this age.
(ii) Explain why your estimate may be unreliable.          OCR

## Time series

The money spent on shopping **each day**, the gas used **each quarter** and the rainfall **each month** are all examples of **time series**. A time series is a set of readings taken at time intervals.

A time series is often used to monitor progress and to show the **trend** (increases and decreases) so that future performance can be predicted. The type of graph used in this situation is called a **line graph**.

### EXAMPLE

The graph shows the temperature of a patient taken every half-hour.

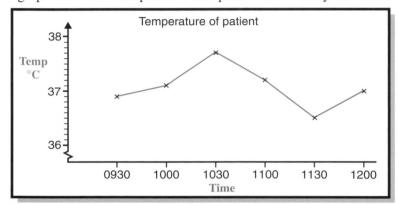

Only the plotted points show **known values**. Lines are drawn to show the **trend**.

*What is the highest temperature recorded?*

*Explain why the graph can only be used to give an **estimate** of the patient's temperature at 1115.*

## Seasonal variation

The graph below shows the amount of gas used by a householder each quarter over a period of 3 years.

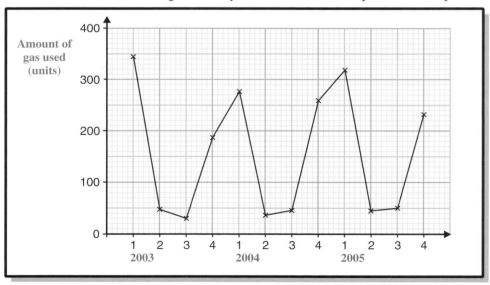

The graph shows high points for winter months and low points for summer months.

These ups and downs occur because more (or less) gas is used at certain times of the year.

As these ups and downs vary with the seasons of the year they are called **seasonal variations**.

To get a better idea of the average number of units of gas used each quarter we need to smooth out these seasonal variations.

## Moving averages

To smooth out seasonal variations we need to find the average for every four quarters moving forward one quarter at a time. These are called **moving averages**.

The first moving average is found by calculating the mean for the four quarters of 2003.

$$\frac{345 + 49 + 30 + 188}{4} = \frac{612}{4} = 153$$

The second moving average is found by calculating the mean of the last three quarters in 2003 and the first quarter in 2004.

$$\frac{49 + 30 + 188 + 277}{4} = \frac{544}{4} = 136$$

This process is repeated moving forward one quarter at a time.

Because these averages are calculated for four consecutive quarters at a time they are called **4-point moving averages**.

The table opposite shows a useful way of setting out the calculations.

*Copy and complete the table.*

The number of points chosen for the moving average depends on the pattern in the data.

In the example given a 4-point moving average was chosen because the pattern was repeated every 4 quarters.

| | Gas used | | Moving average calculations | | | |
|---|---|---|---|---|---|---|
| Year | Quarter | Units | | | | |
| 2003 | 1 | 345 | 345 | | | |
| | 2 | 49 | 49 | 49 | | |
| | 3 | 30 | 30 | 30 | 30 | |
| | 4 | 188 | 188 | 188 | 188 | |
| 2004 | 1 | 277 | | 277 | 277 | |
| | 2 | 37 | | | 37 | |
| | 3 | 46 | | | | |
| | 4 | 260 | | | | |
| 2005 | 1 | 319 | | | | |
| | 2 | 45 | | | | |
| | 3 | 50 | | | | |
| | 4 | 232 | | | | |
| 4-point moving sum | | | 612 | 544 | 532 | |
| 4-point moving average | | | 153 | 136 | | |

## Exercise 38.1

**1** Each year, on his birthday, a teenager records his height. The table shows the results.

| Age (yrs) | 13 | 14 | 15 | 16 | 17 | 18 | 19 |
|---|---|---|---|---|---|---|---|
| Height (cm) | 145 | 151 | 157 | 165 | 174 | 179 | 180 |

(a) Draw a line graph to represent this information.
(b) Use your graph to estimate:
  (i) the height of the teenager when he was $14\frac{1}{2}$ years of age,
  (ii) the age of the teenager when he reached 160 cm in height.

**2** These values have been taken at equal time intervals.
(a) Calculate the 3-point moving averages for: 17  58  30  14  61  33  23  55  42
(b) Calculate the 5-point moving averages for: 27  26  15  34  42  26  24  17  44  54

**3** The number of new cars sold each quarter by a garage for the last three years is shown.

| Year | 2003 | | | | 2004 | | | | 2005 | | | |
|---|---|---|---|---|---|---|---|---|---|---|---|---|
| Quarter | 1 | 2 | 3 | 4 | 1 | 2 | 3 | 4 | 1 | 2 | 3 | 4 |
| Number of cars sold | 20 | 15 | 25 | 12 | 18 | 13 | 21 | 8 | 14 | 9 | 17 | 5 |

Calculate the 4-quarterly moving averages.

**4** Calculate the value of the third average in a 5-point moving average for these values.

   5   7   10   4   1   7   11   13   6   7

**5** These values have been taken at equal time intervals.

   160   640   310   145   670   355   175   640   385

Calculate an appropriate moving average.

## Moving average graphs

Moving averages are calculated in order to investigate the general **trend** in a time series.

To investigate the trend the moving averages are plotted on the same diagram as the original graph.

Each moving average is plotted at the midpoint of the period to which it refers, so, in the case of the gas used, the first moving average is plotted midway between the 2nd and 3rd quarters of 2003, the second is plotted midway between the 3rd and 4th quarters of 2003 and so on.

When all the points have been plotted a line of best fit is drawn for the moving averages to show the general **trend**.

The graph below shows the moving average values and trend line for the amount of gas used over a three-year period.

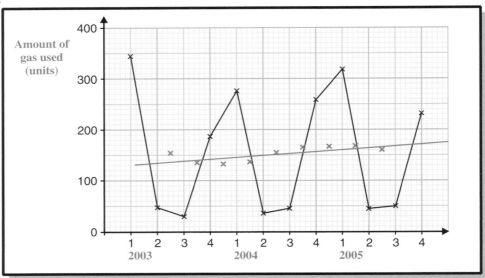

The trend shows a slight increase in the amount of gas used.

## Exercise 38.2

**1** The table shows the amount of water used every 6 months by a householder over a period of 5 years.

| Year | 2001 | | 2002 | | 2003 | | 2004 | | 2005 | |
|---|---|---|---|---|---|---|---|---|---|---|
| Month | Feb | Sept | Feb | Sept | Feb | Sept | Feb | Sept | Feb | Sept |
| Water used (cubic metres) | 46 | 57 | 33 | 55 | 46 | 57 | 72 | 83 | 42 | 57 |

(a) Plot these values on graph paper.
(b) Calculate a 2-point moving average.
(c) Plot the moving averages on your graph.
(d) Comment on the trend in the amount of water used.

**2** The table shows the quarterly electricity bills for a householder.

**Quarterly electricity bills**

| | | Feb | May | Aug | Nov |
|---|---|---|---|---|---|
| | 2003 | £64.75 | £72.16 | £57.71 | £67.80 |
| Year | 2004 | £60.51 | £74.43 | £46.33 | £67.39 |
| | 2005 | £81.39 | £75.69 | £48.24 | £61.65 |

(a) Use the data to draw a graph.
(b) Calculate a 4-point moving average.
(c) Plot the moving averages on your graph.
(d) Comment on the trend in the cost of electricity.

**3** The table shows the termly absences from school for a class over a four-year period.

**Termly absences**

| Year | | Autumn | Spring | Summer |
|---|---|---|---|---|
| | Year 8 | 19 | 54 | 32 |
| | Year 9 | 22 | 132 | 35 |
| | Year 10 | 28 | 57 | 47 |
| | Year 11 | 25 | 51 | 62 |

(a) Use the data to draw a graph.
(b) Calculate the values of a suitable moving average.
(c) Plot the moving averages on your graph.
(d) Comment on the trend in the number of absences for this class.

**4** The table gives the daily sales (in £100's) for a new shop during the first three weeks of trading.

**Daily sales**

| | Mon | Tue | Wed | Thu | Fri | Sat |
|---|---|---|---|---|---|---|
| Week 1 | 57 | 39 | 27 | 34 | 56 | 74 |
| Week 2 | 38 | 34 | 28 | 32 | 61 | 83 |
| Week 3 | 43 | 37 | 31 | 43 | 67 | 92 |

(a) Plot these values on graph paper.
(b) Calculate a 6-point moving average.
(c) Plot the moving averages on the same graph.
(d) Draw a trend line.
(e) Comment on the trend in sales.
(f) Estimate the daily sales for Monday in Week 4.

**5** The number of new homes completed each quarter by a builder for the last three years is shown.

| Year | | 2003 | | | | 2004 | | | | 2005 | | | |
|---|---|---|---|---|---|---|---|---|---|---|---|---|---|
| Quarter | | 1 | 2 | 3 | 4 | 1 | 2 | 3 | 4 | 1 | 2 | 3 | 4 |
| Number of new homes | | 21 | 35 | 36 | 18 | 19 | 23 | 28 | 14 | 15 | 19 | 22 | 9 |

(a) Plot these values on graph paper.
(b) Calculate the values of a suitable moving average.
(c) Plot the moving averages on the same graph.
(d) Draw a trend line by eye.
(e) Comment on the trend.
(f) Estimate the number of new homes completed by the builder in the first quarter of 2006.

## Frequency diagrams

We use **bar charts** when data can be counted and there are only a few different items of data.
If there is a lot of data, or the data is continuous, we draw a **histogram** or **frequency polygon**.

## Histograms with equal class width intervals

**Histograms** are used to present information contained in **grouped frequency distributions**.
Histograms can have equal or unequal class width intervals.
In a histogram with equal class intervals, **frequency** is proportional to the **heights** of the bars.

A histogram with equal class width intervals
looks like a bar chart with no gaps.

*Presentation of Data 2*

## Frequency polygons

**Frequency polygons** are often used instead of histograms when we need to compare two, or more, groups of data.

To draw a frequency polygon:

- plot the frequencies at the midpoint of each class interval,
- join successive points with straight lines.

To compare data, frequency polygons for different groups of data can be drawn on the same diagram.

### EXAMPLE

The frequency distribution of the heights of some boys is shown.

| Height (cm) | 130 - | 140 - | 150 - | 160 - | 170 - | 180 - |
|-------------|-------|-------|-------|-------|-------|-------|
| Frequency   | 1     | 7     | 12    | 9     | 3     | 0     |

**Note:**
130 - means 130 or more but less than 140.

Draw a histogram and a frequency polygon to illustrate the data.

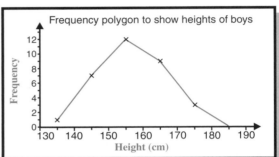

Individual bars are not labelled because the horizontal axis represents a **continuous** variable.

## Exercise 38.3

**1** A supermarket opens at 0800.
The frequency diagram shows the distribution of the times employees arrive for work.

(a) How many employees arrive before 0730?
(b) How many employees arrive between 0730 and 0800?
(c) How many employees arrive after 0800?
(d) What is the modal class?

**2** The frequency polygon shows the distribution of the distances travelled to work by the employees at a supermarket.

When drawing frequency polygons, frequencies are plotted at the midpoints of the class intervals.

(a) How many employees travel between 2 km and 3 km to work?
(b) How many employees travel more than 4 km to work?

**3** The distances, in metres, recorded in a long jump competition are shown.

5.46   5.80   5.97   5.43   6.72   5.93   6.26   6.64   5.13   6.05   6.36   6.88
6.11   5.50   6.38   5.71   6.55   6.10   5.84   5.49   6.20   5.67   6.34   6.00

(a) Copy and complete the following frequency distribution table.

| Distance ($m$ metres) | Frequency |
|---|---|
| $5.00 \leqslant m < 5.50$ | |
| $5.50 \leqslant m < 6.00$ | |
| $6.00 \leqslant m < 6.50$ | |
| $6.50 \leqslant m < 7.00$ | |

(b) Draw a histogram to illustrate the data.
(c) Which is the modal class?

**4** The table shows the grouped frequency distribution of the marks of 200 students.

| Mark (%) | 1 - 10 | 11 - 20 | 21 - 30 | 31 - 40 | 41 - 50 | 51 - 60 | 61 - 70 | 71 - 80 | 81 - 90 | 91 - 100 |
|---|---|---|---|---|---|---|---|---|---|---|
| Number of Students | 0 | 2 | 16 | 24 | 44 | 50 | 35 | 20 | 8 | 1 |

Draw a frequency diagram to show these results.

**5** The frequency polygon shows the distribution of the ages of pupils who attend a village school.

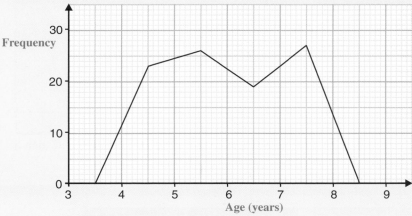

(a) How many pupils are under 4 years of age?
(b) How many pupils are between 5 and 6 years of age?
(c) How many pupils are over 7 years of age?
(d) How many pupils attend the school?

**6** A frequency distribution of the heights of some girls is shown.
Draw a histogram to illustrate the data.

| Height ($h$ cm) | Frequency |
|---|---|
| $130 \leqslant h < 140$ | 3 |
| $140 \leqslant h < 150$ | 5 |
| $150 \leqslant h < 160$ | 12 |
| $160 \leqslant h < 170$ | 4 |
| $170 \leqslant h < 180$ | 1 |

**7** The table shows the distances travelled to school by 100 children.

| Distance ($k$ km) | $0 \leqslant k < 2$ | $2 \leqslant k < 4$ | $4 \leqslant k < 6$ | $6 \leqslant k < 8$ | $8 \leqslant k < 10$ |
|---|---|---|---|---|---|
| Frequency | 27 | 35 | 22 | 10 | 6 |

Draw a frequency polygon to illustrate this information.

**8** The frequency distribution of the weights of some students is shown.

| Weight (kg) | 40 - | 50 - | 60 - | 70 - | 80 - | 90 - 100 |
|---|---|---|---|---|---|---|
| Number of males | 0 | 6 | 11 | 5 | 2 | 1 |
| Number of females | 3 | 14 | 8 | 0 | 0 | 0 |

(a) On the same diagram draw a frequency polygon for the males and a frequency polygon for the females.
(b) Compare and comment on the weights of male and female students.

**9** The table shows the results of students in tests in English and Mathematics.

| Marks | 0 and less than 10 | 10 and less than 20 | 20 and less than 30 | 30 and less than 40 | 40 and less than 50 |
|---|---|---|---|---|---|
| English | 0 | 4 | 9 | 12 | 0 |
| Mathematics | 1 | 4 | 9 | 7 | 4 |

(a) Draw a frequency polygon for the English marks.
(b) On the same diagram draw a frequency polygon for the Mathematics marks.
(c) Compare and comment on the marks of the students in these two tests.

**10** The table shows the results for competitors in the 2004 and 2005 Schools' Javelin Championship. Only the best distance thrown by each competitor is shown.

| Distance thrown ($m$ metres) | Number of competitors 2004 | Number of competitors 2005 |
|---|---|---|
| $10 \leqslant m < 20$ | 0 | 1 |
| $20 \leqslant m < 30$ | 3 | 4 |
| $30 \leqslant m < 40$ | 14 | 19 |
| $40 \leqslant m < 50$ | 21 | 13 |
| $50 \leqslant m < 60$ | 7 | 11 |
| $60 \leqslant m < 70$ | 0 | 2 |

(a) On the same diagram draw a frequency polygon for the 2004 results and then a frequency polygon for the 2005 results.
(b) Compare and comment on the results.

## Histograms with unequal class width intervals

Data is sometimes grouped using **unequal** class width intervals.
In a histogram with unequal class intervals the vertical axis is labelled **frequency density**.
**Frequency** is proportional to the **areas** of the bars.

frequency = frequency density × class width interval

## EXAMPLES

**1** The table shows the frequency distribution of the heights of some women.

| Height | 150 - | 165 - | 175 - | 180 - | 185 - 195 |
|---|---|---|---|---|---|
| Frequency | 15 | 20 | 20 | 10 | 4 |

Draw a histogram for the data.

The data has unequal class intervals.
Before a histogram can be drawn, the height of each bar must be calculated.
The height of each bar is given by the frequency density for each group, where:

$$\text{Frequency density} = \frac{\text{frequency}}{\text{class width interval}}$$

| Frequency | 15 | 20 | 20 | 10 | 4 |
|---|---|---|---|---|---|
| Class width interval | 15 | 10 | 5 | 5 | 10 |
| Frequency density | 1 | 2 | 4 | 2 | 0.4 |

The histogram is shown below.

When drawing histograms mark a **continuous scale** on the horizontal axis. Draw bars, between the lower and upper class boundaries, for each class interval.

**Remember:**
The **area** of each bar is proportional to the **frequency**.

**2** The histogram represents the heights of some plants.

Five plants are less than 20 cm high.
(a) How many plants are at least 30 cm high?
(b) How many plants are there altogether?

Find the frequency density for the plants $10 \leqslant h < 20$.

Frequency density is given by:
$$\frac{\text{frequency}}{\text{class width interval}} = \frac{5}{10} = 0.5$$

The frequency density axis can now be labelled.

(a) Plants at least 30 cm high are in the interval $30 \leqslant h < 45$.
  Frequency　　　　　 = frequency density × class width interval
  Frequency density　 = 0.2　(from vertical axis)
  Class width interval = 45 − 30 = 15　(from horizontal axis)
  Frequency　　　　　 = 0.2 × 15 = 3
  3 plants are at least 30 cm high.

(b) Total frequency = 5 + 1.6 × 5 + 2 × 5 + 3
  　　　　　　　　 = 5 + 8 + 10 + 3 = 26
  There are 26 plants altogether.

**1** The ages of people in a coach party is shown.

| Age (*y* years) | $10 \leq y < 20$ | $20 \leq y < 40$ | $40 \leq y < 45$ | $45 \leq y < 50$ | $50 \leq y < 60$ |
|---|---|---|---|---|---|
| Frequency | 4 | 16 | 13 | 9 | 6 |

Draw a histogram for the data.

**2** The frequency distribution of the weights of some children is shown in the table.

| Weight (*w* kg) | Frequency |
|---|---|
| $40 \leq w < 50$ | 9 |
| $50 \leq w < 55$ | 10 |
| $55 \leq w < 60$ | 17 |
| $60 \leq w < 65$ | 32 |
| $65 \leq w < 75$ | 28 |
| $75 \leq w < 85$ | 4 |

Draw a histogram for the data.

**3** The frequency distribution of the annual wages of all the employees of a small firm is shown in the table.

| Annual Wage (£1000's) | 6 - | 10 - | 15 - | 20 - | 30 - 45 |
|---|---|---|---|---|---|
| Frequency | 6 | 8 | 13 | 17 | 3 |

Represent this information as a histogram.

**4** The histogram shows the age distribution of students delivering newspapers in a town in 2005.

How many students delivered newspapers in the town in 2005?

**5** The histogram shows the distribution of distances thrown by competitors in a throwing competition.

Nine competitors threw 60 metres or more.
(a) How many competitors threw less than 20 metres?
(b) How many competitors took part in the competition?

**6** The histogram represents the age distribution of the employees in a small company.

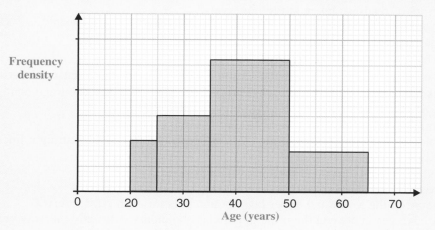

There are 5 employees in the 20 to 25 age range.
(a)  How many employees are in the 50 to 65 age range?
(b)  How many employees has the company?

**7** The table shows the distribution of the heights of all the sixth formers in a school.

| Height ($h$ cm) | Number of students |
|---|---|
| $150 \leqslant h < 165$ | 75 |
| $165 \leqslant h < 175$ | 100 |
| $175 \leqslant h < 180$ | 100 |
| $180 \leqslant h < 185$ | 50 |
| $185 \leqslant h < 195$ | 20 |

(a)  Represent this information as a histogram.
(b)  Francis is 178 cm tall.
      Estimate how many of these sixth formers are taller than him.

**8** The table shows the distribution of the heights of some plants.
The heights were measured to the nearest centimetre.

| Height (cm) | 1 - 5 | 6 - 10 | 11 - 15 |
|---|---|---|---|
| Frequency | 0 | 15 | 10 |

(a)  (i)   What is the height of the smallest plant
            that could be placed in the 6 - 10 class?
      (ii)  What is the width of the 6 - 10 class?
(b)  Draw a histogram of the distribution.

**Note:**
When the classes have gaps between them the upper class boundary is usually halfway between the end of one class and the beginning of the next.

**9** The table below shows the amount of milk, measured to the nearest litre, produced by some cows on a given day.

| Milk (litres) | 5 - 14 | 15 - 19 | 20 - 24 | 25 - 34 |
|---|---|---|---|---|
| Number of cows | 5 | 10 | 7 | 3 |

(a)  Draw a histogram to represent these data.
(b)  Estimate the percentage of these cows which produced less than $17\frac{1}{2}$ litres of milk.

# What you need to know

- A **time series** is a set of readings taken at time intervals.
- A **line graph** is used to show a time series.
  Only the plotted points represent actual values.
  Points are joined by lines to show the **trend**.
- Variations in a time series which recur with the seasons of the year are called **seasonal variations**.
- **Moving averages** are used to smooth out variations in a time series so that the trend can be seen.
- **Frequency polygon.** Used to illustrate grouped frequency distributions.
  Often used to compare two or more distributions on the same diagram.
  Frequencies are plotted at the midpoints of the class intervals and joined with straight lines.
  The horizontal axis is a continuous scale.
- **Histograms.** Used to illustrate grouped frequency distributions.
  The horizontal axis is a continuous scale.
  Bars are drawn between the lower and upper class boundaries for each class interval.
  When the classes have gaps between them the upper class boundary is usually halfway between
  the end of one class and the beginning of the next.
- Histograms can have equal or unequal class width intervals.
  With **equal** class width intervals:
  > **frequency** is proportional to the **heights** of the bars.
  With **unequal** class width intervals:
  > **frequency** is proportional to the **areas** of the bars.
  > $$\text{frequency} = \text{frequency density} \times \text{class width interval}$$
- Before a histogram can be drawn, the height of each bar must be calculated.
  The height of each bar is given by the **frequency density** for each group, where:
  $$\text{frequency density} = \frac{\text{frequency}}{\text{class width interval}}$$

## Review Exercise 38

 **1**
Jim bought his house in 1990.
The table shows the value of Jim's house on January 1st at 5-yearly intervals.

| Year | 1990 | 1995 | 2000 | 2005 |
|---|---|---|---|---|
| Value of house (£) | 95 000 | 68 000 | 84 000 | 136 000 |

(a) Draw a line graph to show this information.
(b) Estimate the value of Jim's house on July 1st, 2003.
(c) Jim uses the graph to estimate the value of his house on January 1st, 2010.
Give a reason why his estimate may not be very accurate.

**2**

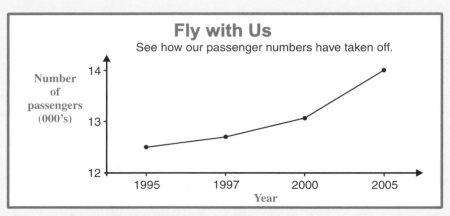

Write down **two** ways in which the graph is misleading.

428

**3** My quarterly gas bills for 2004 and part of 2005 are shown in the table.

| | 2004 | | | 2005 | |
|---|---|---|---|---|---|
| 1st quarter | 2nd quarter | 3rd quarter | 4th quarter | 1st quarter | 2nd quarter |
| £43 | £26 | £18 | £37 | £59 | £24 |

Use this information to calculate the four-quarter moving averages.

OCR

**4** Mrs Mathers marks the French essays of a large number of boys and girls.
The table shows the distribution of marks given.

| Marks | 1 to 5 | 6 to 10 | 11 to 15 | 16 to 20 | 21 to 25 |
|---|---|---|---|---|---|
| Frequency | 2 | 18 | 46 | 35 | 6 |

The frequency polygon shows the distribution of marks for the boys.

Copy the graph.
(a) On the same axes draw a frequency polygon for the girls.
(b) Use the frequency polygons to compare the distribution of marks given to boys and girls.

**5** The ages of 1000 people at a concert are given in the table.

| Age ($t$ years) | $10 \leqslant t < 15$ | $15 \leqslant t < 20$ | $20 \leqslant t < 30$ | $30 \leqslant t < 40$ | $40 \leqslant t < 60$ |
|---|---|---|---|---|---|
| Frequency | 350 | 200 | 250 | 100 | 100 |

(a) In which age group is the median age?
Show how you decide.
(b) Draw a histogram to show the data in the table.

OCR

**6** The histogram shows the time, in seconds, it took for 60 girls to swim one length of a pool.

How many of the girls took 30 seconds or longer to swim one length?

OCR

# Cumulative Frequency

## Cumulative frequency tables

This **frequency table** shows the masses of some stones recorded in an experiment.

| Mass (kg) | 20 - | 30 - | 40 - | 50 - | 60 - 70 |
|-----------|------|------|------|------|---------|
| Frequency | 3 | 5 | 10 | 8 | 4 |

The first class is 20 - 30 kg. The **upper class boundary** of this class is 30 kg.

*What are the upper class boundaries of the other classes?*

**Note:** If the question does not give the upper class boundaries, then the upper class boundary of each class is equal to the lower class boundary of the next class.

The information given in a frequency table can be used to make a **cumulative frequency table**.

To find the cumulative frequencies we must add together the frequencies which are '**less than**' each of the upper class boundaries.

For example, using the data in the experiment above.

| Mass of stone (less than) | Number of stones |
|---------------------------|------------------|
| 20 kg | 0 |
| 30 kg | 0 + 3 = 3 |
| 40 kg | 0 + 3 + 5 = 8 |

This gives the **cumulative frequency table**:

| Mass (kg), less than | 20 | 30 | 40 | 50 | 60 | 70 |
|----------------------|----|----|----|----|----|----|
| Cumulative frequency | 0 | 3 | 8 | 18 | 26 | 30 |

The cumulative frequency table can be used to draw a cumulative frequency graph.

## Cumulative frequency graph

Here is a cumulative frequency graph for the masses of stones in the experiment.

To draw a **cumulative frequency graph**:
1. Draw and label:   the **variable** on the horizontal axis,
   **cumulative frequency** on the vertical axis.
2. Plot the cumulative frequency against the upper class boundary of each class.
3. Join the points with a smooth curve.

### Median

The median of 13 numbers is the 7th number.

The median of 14 numbers is between the 7th and 8th numbers.

We could call this the "$7\frac{1}{2}$th" number.

For $n$ numbers, the rule for finding the median is:

  Median $= \frac{1}{2}(n + 1)$th number

> The median of a frequency distribution is the value of the middle number.
> On a cumulative frequency graph this value is read from the horizontal axis.

### Interquartile range

The **range** of a set of data was covered in Chapter 36.

It measures how spread out the data is.

Range = highest value − lowest value.

The range is influenced by extreme high or low values of data and can be misleading.

A better way to measure spread is to find the range of the **middle 50%** of the data.

This is called the **interquartile range**.

Interquartile range IQR = Upper Quartile − Lower Quartile

For $n$ numbers the rules for finding the quartiles are:

  Lower Quartile $= \frac{1}{4}(n + 1)$th number

  Upper Quartile $= \frac{3}{4}(n + 1)$th number

> On a cumulative frequency graph the values of the Upper Quartile and the Lower Quartile are read from the horizontal axis.

---

### EXAMPLE

Using the cumulative frequency graph from the previous page, estimate:

(a)  the median mass of the stones,

(b)  the interquartile range of the masses of the stones.

(a)  There are 30 stones.

$\frac{1}{2}(30 + 1) = 15.5$,

so, the median is the mass of the 15.5th stone.

Read along from 15.5 on the vertical axis and down to the horizontal axis.

This is shown on the graph.

Median = 48 kg.

(b)  $\frac{1}{4}(30 + 1) = 7.75$,   so, the lower quartile is the mass of the 7.75th stone.

$\frac{3}{4}(30 + 1) = 23.25$,   so, the upper quartile is the mass of the 23.25th stone.

Read these values from the graph.

IQR = Upper Quartile − Lower Quartile

 $= 55 - 39$

 $= 16$ kg

The interquartile range is 16 kg.

> **When $n$ is large:**
> When the total frequency, $n$, is 'large' you need not bother with '+1' in the rules for the median, lower quartile and upper quartile.
> Instead use:   median $= \frac{1}{2}n$th number
>                lower quartile $= \frac{1}{4}n$th number
>                upper quartile $= \frac{3}{4}n$th number
> 'Large' means greater than 50.

① Silvia made a record of the times students took to walk to school in the morning.

| Time (minutes) | 0 - | 5 - | 10 - | 15 - | 20 - | 25 - 30 |
|---|---|---|---|---|---|---|
| Number of students | 4 | 12 | 18 | 15 | 8 | 3 |

(a) Copy and complete this cumulative frequency table.

| Time (minutes), less than | 0 | 5 | 10 | 15 | 20 | 25 | 30 |
|---|---|---|---|---|---|---|---|
| Cumulative frequency | | | | | | | |

(b) Draw a cumulative frequency graph for the data.
(c) Use your graph to find:
    (i) the median time,
    (ii) the upper quartile time,
    (iii) the lower quartile time.
(d) Calculate the interquartile range of the times.

② A secretary weighed a sample of letters to be posted.

| Weight (g) | 20 - | 30 - | 40 - | 50 - | 60 - | 70 - | 80 - 90 |
|---|---|---|---|---|---|---|---|
| Number of letters | 2 | 4 | 12 | 7 | 8 | 16 | 3 |

(a) How many letters were in the sample?
(b) Draw a cumulative frequency graph for the data.
(c) Use your graph to find:
    (i) the median weight of a letter,     (ii) the interquartile range of the weights.

③ The times spent by students on mobile phones one day is shown.

| Time ($t$ minutes) | Number of students |
|---|---|
| $0 \leqslant t < 5$ | 34 |
| $5 \leqslant t < 10$ | 22 |
| $10 \leqslant t < 15$ | 12 |
| $15 \leqslant t < 20$ | 8 |
| $20 \leqslant t < 25$ | 4 |

(a) Draw a cumulative frequency graph for the data.
(b) Use your graph to find:
    (i) the median time,     (ii) the interquartile range of the times.

## Another look at cumulative frequency graphs

Some variables are discrete and can only take certain values.
In many cases these are whole numbers. For these variables there are gaps between the classes.

For example, this frequency distribution table shows the number of spelling mistakes found in some essays.

| Number of mistakes | 0 - 5 | 6 - 10 | 11 - 15 | 16 - 20 |
|---|---|---|---|---|
| Number of essays | 9 | 17 | 8 | 3 |

The first class ends at 5. The highest number of spelling mistakes in the class 0 - 5 is 5.
The second class starts at 6.
We take the upper class boundary for the class 0 - 5 to be halfway between 5 and 6, at 5.5.
*What are the upper class boundaries for the other classes?*

In the following example there are gaps between the classes, because the lengths are measured to the nearest centimetre.

### EXAMPLE

In an experiment Sophie measured and recorded the longest roots of plants.

| Length (to nearest cm) | 0 - 2 | 3 - 5 | 6 - 8 | 9 - 11 | 12 - 14 |
|---|---|---|---|---|---|
| Number of plants | 0 | 14 | 33 | 23 | 10 |

(a) Make a cumulative frequency table for the data Sophie collected.

(b) Draw a cumulative frequency graph for the data.

(c) Use your graph to find:
  (i) the median length,
  (ii) the interquartile range of lengths.

> The class 3 - 5 includes measurements from 2.5 cm to 5.5 cm.
> The upper class boundary is 5.5 cm.

(d) How many plants had roots at least 11.2 cm long?

(a)

| Length (cm) less than | 2.5 | 5.5 | 8.5 | 11.5 | 14.5 |
|---|---|---|---|---|---|
| Cumulative frequency | 0 | 14 | 47 | 70 | 80 |

(b)

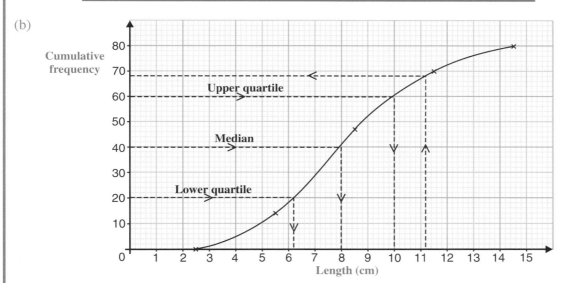

> **Remember:**
> Cumulative frequency is plotted against the upper class boundary for each class.

(c) (i) There are 80 plants.
  $\frac{1}{2}$ of 80 = 40, so, the median is the length of the roots of the 40th plant.
  Median = 8.0 cm

  (ii) For the lower quartile use $\frac{1}{4}$ of 80 = 20.
  Lower quartile = 6.2 cm
  For the upper quartile use $\frac{3}{4}$ of 80 = 60.
  Upper quartile = 10.0 cm
  IQR = Upper Quartile − Lower Quartile = 10.0 − 6.2 = 3.8 cm

(d) From 11.2 cm on the horizontal axis read upwards to the graph and across to the vertical axis.
  There are 68 plants of length less than 11.2 cm.
  So, the number of plants with roots at least 11.2 cm long is   80 − 68 = 12 plants.

**1** The times taken by competitors to complete the crossword in an annual competition were recorded to the nearest minute.

| Time (minutes) | 10 - 14 | 15 - 19 | 20 - 24 | 25 - 29 | 30 - 34 |
|---|---|---|---|---|---|
| Frequency | 7 | 21 | 37 | 12 | 3 |

(a) Copy and complete the cumulative frequency table.

| Time (minutes) | < 9.5 | < 14.5 | < 19.5 | < 24.5 | < 29.5 | < 34.5 |
|---|---|---|---|---|---|---|
| Cumulative frequency | | | | | | |

(b) Draw a cumulative frequency graph for the data.
(c) Use your graph to find:
   (i)   the interquartile range of times,
   (ii)  the number of competitors who took less than last year's winning time of 16 minutes to complete the crossword.

**2** Draw a cumulative frequency graph for the results shown in this table.

| Number of marks | 0 - 20 | 21 - 25 | 26 - 30 | 31 - 40 |
|---|---|---|---|---|
| Number of students | 10 | 17 | 23 | 14 |

(a) Find the median mark.
(b) Find the interquartile range of marks.
(c) The minimum mark for a Grade A is 33.
   What percentage of students gained Grade A?
(d) 10% of students failed.
   What was the minimum mark for a pass?

**3** A survey was made of the heights of plants produced by a batch of seed.

(a) How many plants were measured in the survey?
(b) Draw a cumulative frequency graph for the data.
   Label the horizontal axis from 70 cm to 110 cm.
(c) Use your graph to estimate:
   (i)   the median height,
   (ii)  the interquartile range of heights,
   (iii) the number of plants taller than 97.5 cm.
(d) The shortest 10 plants are used for testing.
   Estimate the height of the tallest of these 10 plants.

| Height ($h$ cm) | Frequency |
|---|---|
| $80 \leqslant h < 85$ | 20 |
| $85 \leqslant h < 90$ | 35 |
| $90 \leqslant h < 95$ | 15 |
| $95 \leqslant h < 100$ | 11 |
| $100 \leqslant h < 105$ | 14 |

**4** The times spent listening to the radio last week by some students is shown.

| Time ($t$ hours) | Number of students |
|---|---|
| $0 \leqslant t < 5$ | 7 |
| $5 \leqslant t < 10$ | 15 |
| $10 \leqslant t < 15$ | 18 |
| $15 \leqslant t < 20$ | 24 |
| $20 \leqslant t < 30$ | 12 |
| $30 \leqslant t < 40$ | 4 |

(a) Draw a cumulative frequency graph for the data.
(b) Use your graph to find the interquartile range of times.
(c) What percentage of the students spent more than 25 hours per week listening to the radio?

**5** The heights of a number of men are shown in the table.

| Height ($h$ cm) | Frequency |
|---|---|
| $140 \leqslant h < 150$ | 1 |
| $150 \leqslant h < 160$ | 6 |
| $160 \leqslant h < 170$ | 8 |
| $170 \leqslant h < 180$ | 21 |
| $180 \leqslant h < 190$ | 14 |

Draw a cumulative frequency graph for the data. Use your graph to find:
(a)   the median and interquartile range of heights,
(b)   the number of men less than 155 cm,
(c)   the number of men at least 163 cm,
(d)   the maximum height of the shortest 20 men,
(e)   the minimum height of the tallest 10% of men.

## Comparing distributions

**EXAMPLE**

A firm tested a sample of electric motors produced by an assembly line.
They kept a running total of the numbers of motors which had failed at any time.
This cumulative frequency graph was plotted using the data collected.

(a)   Find the median lifetime of a motor.
(b)   Find the interquartile range of lifetimes.
(c)   A sample of motors, produced by another assembly line, was tested and found to have:
Median lifetime = 1900 hours,   Upper quartile = 2000 hours,   Lower quartile = 1700 hours.
Compare the two samples of motors.

(a)   Median lifetime = 2100 hours

(b)   IQR = Upper Quartile − Lower Quartile = 2300 − 1700 = 600 hours

(c)   For the second sample:   Median = 1900 hours
                                                IQR = 2000 − 1700 = 300 hours
The first sample has a greater median time.
On average, they lasted 200 hours longer than motors in the second sample.

The spread of the second sample (given by the IQR) is much smaller.
It is 300 hours, compared with 600 hours for the first sample.

**1** The heights of a group of boys and a group of girls were recorded separately.
The results are shown by the cumulative frequency graphs.

(a) How many girls were measured?
(b) Find the interquartile range of heights of the girls.
(c) Find the interquartile range of heights of the boys.
(d) Use your answers to parts (b) and (c) to comment on the heights of the girls compared with the boys.
(e) How many boys are taller than the tallest girl?

**2** The milk yields of a herd of cows is shown in the table below.

| Milk yield (x litres) | $5 \leq x < 10$ | $10 \leq x < 15$ | $15 \leq x < 20$ | $20 \leq x < 25$ | $25 \leq x < 30$ |
|---|---|---|---|---|---|
| Number of cows | 15 | 28 | 37 | 26 | 25 |

(a) Use the data to draw a cumulative frequency graph.
(b) Use your graph to estimate:
  (i) the median milk yield,
  (ii) the interquartile range of milk yields.
(c) A neighbouring farmer calculated the following results for his herd of cows.
  Median yield = 22 litres,  Lower quartile = 9 litres,  Upper quartile = 28 litres.
  Compare and comment on the data for the two herds.

**3** A sample of potatoes of Variety *X* and a sample of potatoes of Variety *Y* are weighed.
The cumulative frequency graphs show information about the weight distribution of each sample.

By finding the median and interquartile range of each sample, compare and comment on the weights of these varieties of potato.

## Box plots

**Box plots** (or **box and whisker diagrams**) provide a useful way of representing the range, the median and the quartiles of a set of data.
They are also useful for comparing two (or more) distributions.

The graph shows the cumulative frequency distribution of the masses of 80 fish.

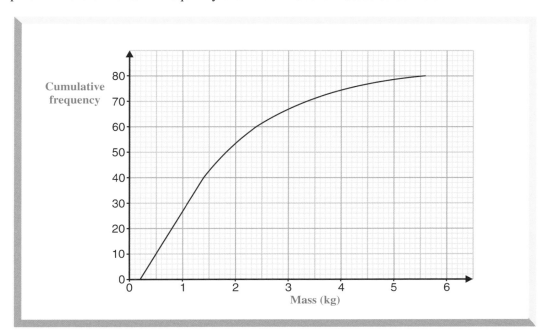

From the graph we can read off the following information:

- the minimum mass is 0.2 kg,
- the maximum mass is 5.6 kg,
- the median mass is 1.4 kg,
- the lower quartile is 0.8 kg,
- the upper quartile is 2.4 kg.

This information can now be represented as a box plot.

Begin by drawing a horizontal line and marking a scale from 0 to 6 kg.
Above your line, draw a box from the lower quartile to the upper quartile and mark in the median with a line across the box.
Draw lines (sometimes called whiskers) from the lower end of the box to 0.2 kg and from the upper end of the box to 5.6 kg to represent the range.

A box plot for the masses of these fish is shown below.

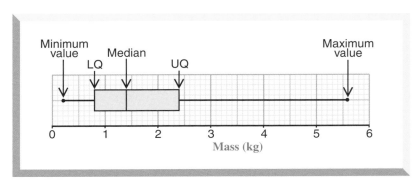

The box plot shows how the masses of these fish are spread out and how the middle 50% are clustered.

The number of points scored by the 11 players in a basketball team during a competition are shown.

13    12    5    34    8    10    11    46    25    23    4

Draw a box plot to illustrate the data.

Begin by putting the data in order and then locate the median, lower quartile and upper quartile.

4    5    8    10    11    12    13    23    25    34    46

LQ          Median          UQ

Then use these values to draw the box plot.

Points

## Exercise 39.4

**1** The midday temperatures, in °C, for 11 cities around the world are:

9    12    20    24    25    28    28    30    31    32    35

Draw a box plot to represent these temperatures.

**2** A group of 15 people were asked to estimate the weight of a large tortoise.
Their estimates, in kilograms, are shown.

| 2.8 | 3.0 | 3.2 | 3.3 | 3.5 | 3.6 | 3.8 | 3.8 |
|-----|-----|-----|-----|-----|-----|-----|-----|
| 4.0 | 4.0 | 4.2 | 4.2 | 4.4 | 4.5 | 4.7 |

Draw a box plot to represent these estimates.

**3** The cumulative frequency graph shows information about the distances travelled by children to get to school.

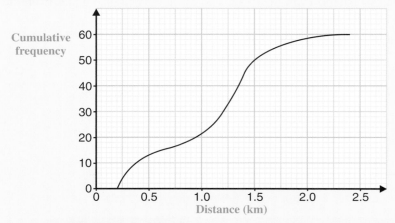

Draw a box plot to illustrate the data.

**4** The table gives information about the heights of players in a rugby team.

| | | | |
|---|---|---|---|
| Median | 188 cm | Tallest | 198 cm |
| Lower quartile | 185 cm | Shortest | 175 cm |
| Upper quartile | 193 cm | | |

Draw a box plot to represent this information.

**5** The box plot illustrates the reaction times of a group of people.

(a) What was the minimum reaction time?
(b) What is the value of the interquartile range?

**6** A group of students took examinations in Mathematics and English.
The box plots illustrate the results.

(a) What was the highest mark scored in English?
(b) What was the lowest mark scored in Mathematics?
(c) Which subject has the higher median mark?
(d) What is the value of the interquartile range for English?
(e) Comment on the results of these examinations.

**7** The cumulative frequency graphs show the times taken by students to run 100 m.

(a) Draw box plots to compare the times for males and females.
(b) Comment on the times for males and females.

Cumulative Frequency

**8** A sample of 23 people were asked to record the amount they spent on food last week.
The amounts, in £s, are shown.

| | | | | | | | |
|---|---|---|---|---|---|---|---|
| 57 | 66 | 75 | 83 | 39 | 83 | 36 | 42 |
| 62 | 67 | 43 | 38 | 71 | 58 | 47 | 53 |
| 62 | 84 | 76 | 68 | 77 | 57 | 42 | |

(a) Find the median and quartiles of this distribution.
(b) Draw a box plot to represent the data.

## What you need to know

- The information given in a frequency table can be used to make a **cumulative frequency table**.
- To draw a **cumulative frequency graph**:

1. Draw and label: the variable on the horizontal axis,
   cumulative frequency on the vertical axis.
2. Plot the cumulative frequency against the upper class boundary of each class.
3. Join the points with a smooth curve.

- If the question does not give the upper class boundaries, then the upper class boundary of each class is equal to the lower class boundary of the next class.
- When the classes have gaps between them then the upper class boundary is halfway between the end of one class and the beginning of the next.
- The **median** is the value of the middle number.

  The **lower quartile** is the value located at $\frac{1}{4}$ of the total frequency.

  The **upper quartile** is the value located at $\frac{3}{4}$ of the total frequency.

  The **interquartile range** measures the spread of the middle 50% of the data.

  Interquartile range = Upper Quartile − Lower Quartile

- A **box plot** is used to represent the range, the median and the quartiles of a distribution.

- The box plot shows how the data is spread out and how the middle 50% of data is clustered.
- Box plots can be used to compare two (or more) distributions.

**1** The 'Heartbeat' keep-fit club has 120 members. There are 64 women and 56 men.
This is the distribution of the men's ages.

| Age ($x$ years) | Frequency |
|---|---|
| $10 \leqslant x < 20$ | 0 |
| $20 \leqslant x < 30$ | 8 |
| $30 \leqslant x < 40$ | 14 |
| $40 \leqslant x < 50$ | 12 |
| $50 \leqslant x < 60$ | 17 |
| $60 \leqslant x < 70$ | 5 |

(a) (i) Work out the cumulative frequencies.  (ii) Draw the cumulative frequency graph.
(b) For the men's ages, find (i) the median, (ii) the interquartile range.

For the women, the median age is 37.8 and the interquartile range is 18.
(c) Make two comparisons between the age distributions of the men and the women.  OCR

**2** A manufacturer investigates how far a car travels before it needs new tyres.
The distances covered by 100 cars before they needed new tyres is shown in the table.

| Distance covered ($x$ thousands of miles) | Number of cars |
|---|---|
| $10 \leqslant x < 15$ | 10 |
| $15 \leqslant x < 20$ | 23 |
| $20 \leqslant x < 25$ | 31 |
| $25 \leqslant x < 30$ | 19 |
| $30 \leqslant x < 35$ | 12 |
| $35 \leqslant x < 40$ | 5 |

(a) Complete a cumulative frequency table for these 100 cars.
(b) Draw a cumulative frequency diagram.
(c) Use your cumulative frequency diagram to estimate:
   (i) the median distance covered,
   (ii) how many cars travelled less than 28 000 miles before needing new tyres.  OCR

**3** Gareth timed how long it took each person in a group to spell their name.
The data he collected are summarised in the table.

| | Quickest | Lower quartile | Median | Upper quartile | Slowest |
|---|---|---|---|---|---|
| Time (seconds) | 3.2 | 5 | 7.6 | 8.5 | 10.4 |

(a) Draw a box plot to represent the data.

Gareth timed how long it took the same people to spell their names backwards.
These data are summarised in the box plot below.

(b) Give one similarity and one difference between the times taken by these people
to spell their names forwards and backwards.  OCR

# Probability

## What is probability?

**Probability**, or **chance**, involves describing how likely something is to happen.

For example:   How likely is it to rain tomorrow?

We often make forecasts, or judgements, about how likely things are to happen.
When trying to forecast tomorrow's weather the following **outcomes** are possible:

In any situation, the possible things that can happen are called **outcomes**.
An outcome of particular interest is called an **event**.

     sun,   cloud,   wind,   rain,   snow,   …

We are interested in the particular **event**, rain tomorrow.

> The chance of an event happening can be described using these words:
> **Impossible**   **Unlikely**   **Evens**   **Likely**   **Certain**

*Use one of the words in the box to describe the chance of rain tomorrow.*

## Probability and the probability scale

Estimates of probabilities can be shown on a **probability scale**.
The scale goes from 0 to 1.
A **probability of 0** means that an event is **impossible**.
A **probability of 1** means that an event is **certain**.
Probabilities are written as a fraction, a decimal or a percentage.

**Less likely**    **More likely**

**Impossible**    **Certain**

0    $\frac{1}{2}$    1

*Describe the likelihood that an event will occur if it has a probability of $\frac{1}{2}$.*

---

### EXAMPLES

Estimate the probability of each of the following events happening.
Show your estimate on a probability scale.

**1** It will snow in London next July.
This is possible but **very unlikely**.
So, the probability is very close to 0.

0    $\frac{1}{2}$    1

**2** You will eat some vegetables today.
This is **very likely**.
So, the probability is close to 1.

0    $\frac{1}{2}$    1

## Exercise **40.1**

**1** Describe each of the following events as:

**Impossible   Unlikely   Evens   Likely   Certain**

(a) You roll a normal dice and get an odd number.
(b) You roll a normal dice and get a 7.
(c) A 6 is scored at least 80 times when a normal dice is rolled 600 times.
(d) It will rain on three days running in August.
(e) Somewhere in the world it is raining today.
(f) A coin is tossed five times and lands heads up on each occasion.

**2** The probability scale shows the probabilities of events **P, Q, R, S** and **T**.

Which of the five events
(a) is certain to happen,
(b) is impossible,
(c) has an evens chance of happening,
(d) is more likely to happen than to not happen, but is not certain to happen?

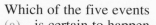

**3** The probabilities of four events have been marked on a probability scale.
Copy the probability scale.

Event V    A coin lands 'heads' up.
Event W    A person is over 3 metres tall.
Event X    Rolling an ordinary dice and getting a score less than 7.
Event Y    There is a 35% chance that it will rain tomorrow.

Label the arrows on your diagram to show which event they represent.

## Calculating probabilities using equally likely outcomes

Probabilities can be **calculated** where all outcomes are **equally likely**.

> The probability of an event X happening is given by:
>
> $$\text{Probability (X)} = \frac{\text{Number of outcomes in the event}}{\text{Total number of possible outcomes}}$$

### Random and Fair

In many probability questions words such as '**random**' and '**fair**' are used.
These are ways of saying that all outcomes are equally likely.
For example:
A card is taken at **random** from a pack of cards.
This means that each card has an equal chance of being taken.
A **fair** dice is rolled.
This means that the outcomes 1, 2, 3, 4, 5 and 6 are equally likely.

---

### EXAMPLE

A fair dice is rolled. What is the probability of getting:
(a)  a 6,          (b)  an odd number,          (c)  a 2 or a 3?

Total number of possible outcomes is 6.   (1, 2, 3, 4, 5 and 6).
The dice is fair, so each of these outcomes is equally likely.

(a)  1 of the possible outcomes is a 6.          $P(6) = \frac{1}{6}$

(b)  3 of the possible outcomes are odd numbers.   $P(\text{an odd number}) = \frac{3}{6} = \frac{1}{2}$

(c)  2 of the possible outcomes are 2 or 3.   $P(2 \text{ or } 3) = \frac{2}{6} = \frac{1}{3}$

**1** A fair dice is rolled. What is the probability of getting a number less than five?

**2** A bag contains a red counter, a blue counter and two green counters.
A counter is taken from the bag at random. What is the probability of taking:
(a)  a red counter,          (b)  a green counter,      (c)  a counter that is not blue?

**3** A bag contains 3 red sweets and 7 black sweets.
A sweet is taken from the bag at random. What is the probability of taking:
(a)  a red sweet,            (b)  a black sweet?

**4** The eleven letters of the word  M I S S I S S I P P I  are written on separate tiles.
The tiles are placed in a bag and mixed up. One tile is selected at random.
What is the probability that the tile selected shows:
(a)  the letter M,            (b)  the letter I,            (c)  the letter P?

**5** A card is taken at random from a full pack of 52 playing cards with no jokers.
What is the probability that the card:
(a)  is red,                  (b)  is a heart,              (c)  is the ace of hearts?

**6** A bag contains 4 red counters, 3 white counters and 3 blue counters.
A counter is taken from the bag at random. What is the probability that the counter is:
(a)  red,                     (b)  white or blue,          (c)  red, white or blue,          (d)  green?

**7** In a hat there are twelve numbered discs.

Nina takes a disc from the hat at random.
What is the probability that Nina takes a disc:
(a)  with at least one 4 on it,
(b)  that has not got a 4 on it,
(c)  that has a 3 or a 4 on it?

43 44 45 46
47 48 49 50
51 52 53 54

**8** This table shows how fifty counters are numbered either 1 or 2 and coloured red or blue.

One of the counters is chosen at random.
What is the probability that the counter is:
(a)  a 1,        (b)  blue,        (c)  blue and a 1?

A blue counter is chosen at random.
(d)  What is the probability that it is a 1?

A counter numbered 1 is chosen at random.
(e)  What is the probability that it is blue?

|   | Red | Blue |
|---|-----|------|
| 1 | 12  | 8    |
| 2 | 8   | 22   |

**9** Tim plays a friend at Noughts and Crosses.
He says: "I can win, draw or lose, so the probability that I will win must be $\frac{1}{3}$."
Explain why Tim is wrong.

**10** The table shows the number of boys and girls in a class of 30 pupils who wear glasses.

|                       | Boy | Girl |
|-----------------------|-----|------|
| Wears glasses         | 3   | 1    |
| Does not wear glasses | 11  | 15   |

A pupil from the class is picked at random.
(a)  What is the probability that it is a boy?
(b)  What is the probability that it is a girl who does not wear glasses?

A girl from the class is picked at random.
(c)  What is the probability that she wears glasses?

A pupil who wears glasses is picked at random.
(d)  What is the probability that it is a boy?

**11** The table shows the way that 120 pupils from Year 7 travel to Linfield School.

A pupil from Year 7 is chosen at random.
What is the probability that the pupil:
(a) walks to school,
(b) is a girl who travels by car,
(c) is a boy who does not travel by bus?

|       | Walk | Bus | Car | Bike |
|-------|------|-----|-----|------|
| Boys  | 23   | 15  | 12  | 20   |
| Girls | 17   | 20  | 8   | 5    |

A girl from Year 7 is chosen at random.
What is the probability that:
(d) she walks to school,
(e) she does not travel by car?

A Year 7 pupil who travels by bike is chosen at random.
(f) What is the probability that the pupil is a boy?

## Estimating probabilities using relative frequency

In question 9 in Exercise 40.2, probabilities **cannot** be calculated using equally likely outcomes.
In such situations probabilities can be estimated using the idea of **relative frequency**.

It is not always necessary to perform an experiment or make observations.
Sometimes the information required can be found in past records.

> The relative frequency of an event is given by:
>
> $$\text{Relative frequency} = \frac{\text{Number of times the event happens in an experiment (or in a survey)}}{\text{Total number of trials in the experiment (or observations in the survey)}}$$

### EXAMPLES

**1** Jamie does the following experiment with a bag containing 2 red and 8 blue counters.

> **Take a counter from the bag at random.**
> **Record the colour then put the counter back in the bag. Repeat this for 100 trials.**

Jamie calculates the relative frequency of getting a red counter every 10 trials and shows his results on a graph. Draw a graph showing the results that Jamie might get.
This is the sort of graph that Jamie might get.

The dotted line shows the **calculated probability**.

$P(\text{Red}) = \frac{2}{10} = 0.2$

As the number of trials increases, relative frequency gives a better estimate of calculated probability.

*Try Jamie's experiment yourself and see what sort of results you get.*

**2** In an experiment a drawing pin is dropped for 100 trials.
The drawing pin lands "point up" 37 times.
What is the relative frequency of the drawing pin landing "point up"?

Relative frequency gives a better estimate of probability the larger the number of trials.

Relative frequency $= \frac{37}{100} = 0.37$

Probability · · · · · Probability · · · ·

**1** 50 cars are observed passing the school gate. 14 red cars are observed.
What is the relative frequency of a red car passing the school gate?

**2** In an experiment a gardener planted 40 daffodil bulbs of which 36 grew to produce flowers.
Use these results to find the relative frequency that a daffodil bulb will produce a flower.

**3** The results from 40 spins of a numbered spinner are:

| | | | | | | | | | |
|---|---|---|---|---|---|---|---|---|---|
| 2 | 1 | 4 | 3 | 2 | 1 | 3 | 4 | 5 | 2 |
| 1 | 2 | 2 | 3 | 2 | 1 | 2 | 4 | 5 | 2 |
| 1 | 5 | 3 | 4 | 2 | 3 | 3 | 3 | 2 | 4 |
| 2 | 3 | 4 | 2 | 1 | 5 | 3 | 3 | 5 | 3 |

Use these results to estimate the probability of getting a 2 with the next spin.

**4** A counter is taken from a bag at random.
Its colour is recorded and the counter is then put back in the bag.
This is repeated 300 times.
The number of red counters taken from the bag after every 100 trials is shown in the table.

| Number of trials | Number of red counters |
|---|---|
| 100 | 52 |
| 200 | 102 |
| 300 | 141 |

(a) Calculate the relative frequency after each 100 trials.
(b) Which is the best estimate of taking a red counter from the bag?

**5** Gemma keeps a record of her chess games with Helen.
Out of the first 10 games, Gemma wins 6. Out of the first 30 games Gemma wins 21.
Based on these results, estimate the probability that Gemma will win her next game of chess with Helen.

**6** Rachel selects 40 holiday brochures at random.
The probability of a brochure being for a holiday in Italy is found to be 0.2.
How many brochures did Rachel select for holidays in Italy?

**7** A counter was taken from a bag of counters and replaced.
The relative frequency of getting a red counter was found to be 0.3.
There are 60 counters in the bag.
Estimate the number of red counters.

**8** 500 tickets are sold for a prize draw.
Greg buys some tickets.
The probability that Greg wins first prize is $\frac{1}{20}$.
How many tickets did he buy?

**9** A bypass is to be built to avoid a town.
There are three possible routes that the road can take.
A survey was carried out in the town.

| Route | A | B | C |
|---|---|---|---|
| Relative frequency | 0.4 | 0.5 | 0.1 |

30 people opted for Route C.
(a) How many people were surveyed altogether?
(b) How many people opted for Route A?
(c) How many people opted for Route B?

## Mutually exclusive events

Events which **cannot happen at the same time** are called **mutually exclusive events**.
For example, the event 'Heads' cannot occur at the same time as the event 'Tails'.

> When A and B are events which cannot happen at the same time:
> $$P(A \text{ or } B) = P(A) + P(B)$$

## The probability of an event not happening

> The events A and not A cannot happen at the same time.
> Because the events A and not A are certain to happen:
> $$P(\text{not } A) = 1 - P(A)$$

### EXAMPLES

**1** A bag contains 3 red (R) counters, 2 blue (B) counters and 5 green (G) counters.
A counter is taken from the bag at random.
What is the probability that the counter is:
(a) red,      (b) green,      (c) red or green?

Find the total number of counters in the bag.
$5 + 2 + 3 = 10$
Total number of possible outcomes = 10.

(a) There are 3 red counters.    $P(R) = \frac{3}{10}$

(b) There are 5 green counters.    $P(G) = \frac{5}{10} = \frac{1}{2}$

(c) Events R and G cannot happen at the same time.
$$P(R \text{ or } G) = P(R) + P(G) = \frac{3}{10} + \frac{5}{10} = \frac{8}{10} = \frac{4}{5}$$

**2** A bag contains 10 counters. 3 of the counters are red (R).
A counter is taken from the bag at random.
What is the probability that the counter is:
(a) red,      (b) not red?

Total number of possible outcomes = 10.

(a) There are 3 red counters.    $P(R) = \frac{3}{10}$

(b) $P(\text{not } R) = 1 - P(R) = 1 - \frac{3}{10} = \frac{7}{10}$

## Exercise 40.4

**1** A fish is taken at random from a tank.
The probability that the fish is black is $\frac{2}{5}$.
What is the probability that the fish is not black?

**2** Tina has a bag of beads.
She takes a bead from the bag at random.
The probability that the bead is white is 0.6.
What is the probability that the bead is not white?

**3** The probability of a switch working is 0.96.
What is the probability of a switch not working?

**4** Six out of every 100 men are taller than 1.85 m.
A man is picked at random.
What is the probability that he is not taller than 1.85 m?

**5** A bag contains red, white and blue balls.
A ball is taken from the bag at random.
The probability of taking a red ball is 0.4.
The probability of taking a white ball is 0.35.
What is the probability of taking a white ball or a blue ball?

**6** Tom and Sam buy some tickets in a raffle.
The probability that Tom wins 1st prize is 0.03.
The probability that Sam wins 1st prize is 0.01.
(a) What is the probability that Tom or Sam win 1st prize?
(b) What is the probability that Tom does not win 1st prize?

**7** A spinner can land on red, white or blue.
The probability of the spinner landing on red is 0.2.
The probability of the spinner landing on red or on blue is 0.7.
The spinner is spun once.
What is the probability that the spinner lands:
(a) on blue,
(b) on white?

**8** A bag contains red, green, blue, yellow and white counters.
The table shows the probabilities of obtaining each colour when a counter is taken from the bag at random.

| Red | Green | Blue | Yellow | White |
|-----|-------|------|--------|-------|
| 30% | 25%   | 20%  | 20%    | 10%   |

(a) (i) How can you tell that there is a mistake in the table?
    (ii) The probability of getting a white counter is wrong.
         What should it be?

A counter is taken from the bag at random.
(b) (i) What is the probability that it is either green or blue?
    (ii) What is the probability that it is red, green or blue?
    (iii) What is the probability that it is not yellow?

**9** Some red, white and blue cubes are numbered 1 or 2.
The table shows the probabilities of obtaining each colour and number when a cube is taken at random.

|   | Red | White | Blue |
|---|-----|-------|------|
| 1 | 0.1 | 0.3   | 0    |
| 2 | 0.3 | 0.1   | 0.2  |

A cube is taken at random.
(a) What is the probability of taking a red cube?
(b) What is the probability of taking a cube numbered 2?
(c) State whether or not the following pairs of events are mutually exclusive.
    Give a reason for each answer.
    (i) Taking a cube numbered 1 and taking a blue cube.
    (ii) Taking a cube numbered 2 and taking a blue cube.
(d) (i) What is the probability of taking a cube which is blue or numbered 1?
    (ii) What is the probability of taking a cube which is blue or numbered 2?
    (iii) What is the probability of taking a cube which is numbered 2 or red?

**EXAMPLES**

**1** A fair coin is thrown twice.
Identify all of the possible outcomes and write down their probabilities.

**Method 1**
**List** the outcomes systematically.

| 1st throw | 2nd throw |
|-----------|-----------|
| Head (H) | Head (H) |
| Head (H) | Tail (T) |
| Tail (T) | Head (H) |
| Tail (T) | Tail (T) |

**Method 2**
Use a **possibility space diagram**.

|  | | |
|--|--|--|
| **T** | H & T | T & T |
| **H** | H & H | T & H |
|  | **H** | **T** |

2nd throw (rows), 1st throw

**Method 3**
Use a **tree diagram**.

| 1st throw | 2nd throw | Outcome |
|-----------|-----------|---------|
| H | H | **H** and **H** |
|   | T | **H** and **T** |
| T | H | **T** and **H** |
|   | T | **T** and **T** |

The lines are called the **branches** of the tree diagram.

When a fair coin is tossed twice, there are four possible outcomes.
Because the coin is fair all the possible outcomes are **equally likely**.
Because all the outcomes are equally likely their probabilities can be worked out.

P(H and H) = P(H and T) = P(T and H) = P(T and T) = $\frac{1}{4}$.

**2** A fair dice is rolled twice.
Use a possibility space diagram to show all the possible outcomes.
What is the probability of getting a 'double six'?
What is the probability of getting any 'double'?
What is the probability that exactly one 'six' is obtained?

|  2nd roll | | | | | | |
|---|---|---|---|---|---|---|
| **6** | 1 and 6 | 2 and 6 | 3 and 6 | 4 and 6 | 5 and 6 | 6 and 6 |
| **5** | 1 and 5 | 2 and 5 | 3 and 5 | 4 and 5 | 5 and 5 | 6 and 5 |
| **4** | 1 and 4 | 2 and 4 | 3 and 4 | 4 and 4 | 5 and 4 | 6 and 4 |
| **3** | 1 and 3 | 2 and 3 | 3 and 3 | 4 and 3 | 5 and 3 | 6 and 3 |
| **2** | 1 and 2 | 2 and 2 | 3 and 2 | 4 and 2 | 5 and 2 | 6 and 2 |
| **1** | 1 and 1 | 2 and 1 | 3 and 1 | 4 and 1 | 5 and 1 | 6 and 1 |
|  | **1** | **2** | **3** | **4** | **5** | **6** |

1st roll

The dice is fair so there are 36 equally likely outcomes.

P(double 6)
There is one outcome in the event (6 and 6).
P(double 6) = $\frac{1}{36}$

P(any double)
The 6 outcomes in the event are shaded blue.
P(any double) = $\frac{6}{36} = \frac{1}{6}$

P(exactly one six)
The 10 outcomes in the event are shaded grey.
P(exactly one six) = $\frac{10}{36} = \frac{5}{18}$

Probability . . . . . Probability . . . . .

**1**  A red car (R), a blue car (B) and a green car (G) are parked on a narrow drive, one behind the other.
(a)   List all the possible orders in which the three cars could be parked.

The cars are parked on the drive at random.
(b)   What is the probability that the blue car is the first on the drive?

**2**  Two fair dice are rolled and the numbers obtained are added.
(a)   Draw a possibility space diagram to show all of the possible outcomes.
(b)   Use your diagram to work out:
    (i)   the probability of obtaining a total of 10,
    (ii)   the probability of obtaining a total greater than 10,
    (iii)  the probability of obtaining a total less than 10.
(c)   Explain why the probabilities you worked out in (b) should add up to 1.

**3**  A fair coin is tossed and a fair dice is rolled.
Copy and complete the table to show all the possible outcomes.

|  |  | Dice |  |  |  |  |  |
|---|---|---|---|---|---|---|---|
|  |  | 1 | 2 | 3 | 4 | 5 | 6 |
| Coin | H |  | H2 |  |  |  |  |
|  | T |  |  |  |  |  |  |

What is the probability of obtaining:
(a)   a head and a 5,
(b)   a tail and an even number,
(c)   a tail and a 6,
(d)   a tail and an odd number,
(e)   a head and a number more than 4,
(f)   an odd number?

**4**  Sanjay has to travel to school in two stages.
Stage 1:   he can go by bus or train or he can get a lift.
Stage 2:   he can go by bus or he can walk.
(a)   List all the different ways that Sanjay can travel to school.

Sanjay decides the way that he travels on each stage at random.
(b)   What is the probability that he goes by bus in both stages?

**5**  The diagram shows a fair spinner.
It is divided into four equal sections numbered as shown.
The spinner is spun twice and the numbers the arrow lands on each time are added to obtain a score.
(a)   Copy and complete this table to show all the possible scores.

|  |  | **2nd spin** |  |  |  |
|---|---|---|---|---|---|
|  |  | **1** | **2** | **3** | **4** |
|  | **1** | 2 | 3 |  |  |
| **1st spin** | **2** | 3 |  |  |  |
|  | **3** |  |  |  |  |
|  | **4** |  |  |  |  |

(b)   Calculate the probability of getting a score of:
    (i)  2,     (ii)  3,     (iii)  6.

**6** Students at a college must choose to study two subjects from the list:

**Maths**      **English**      **Science**      **Art**

(a)   Write down all the possible pairs of subjects that the students can choose.

David chooses both subjects at random.
(b)   What is the probability that one of the subjects he chooses is Maths?

James chooses Maths and one other subject at random.
(c)   What is the probability that he chooses Maths and Science?

**7** Bag A contains 2 red balls and 1 white ball.
Bag B contains 2 white balls and 1 red ball.
A ball is drawn at random from each bag.

Bag A

(a)   Copy and complete the table to show all possible pairs of colours.

(b)   Explain why the probability of each outcome is $\frac{1}{9}$.

(c)   Calculate the probability that the two balls are the same colour.

**8** The diagram shows two sets of cards A and B.

One card is taken at random from set A.
One card is taken at random from set B.
(a)   List all the possible outcomes.

The two numbers are added together.
(b)  (i)   What is the probability of getting a total of 5?
     (ii)   What is the probability of getting a total that is not 5?

All the cards are put together and one of them is taken at random.
(c)   What is the probability that it is labelled A or 2?

**9** A spinner has an equal probability of landing on red, green, blue, yellow or white.
The spinner is spun twice.
(a)   List all the possible outcomes.
(b)  (i)   What is the probability that, on both spins, the spinner lands on white?
     (ii)   What is the probability that, on both spins, the spinner lands on white at least once?
     (iii)   What is the probability that, on both spins, the spinner lands on the same colour?

**10** The diagram shows two fair spinners.
Each spinner is divided into equal sections and numbered as shown.
Each spinner is spun and the numbers that each arrow lands on are added together.

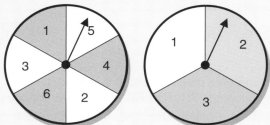

(a)   Draw a possibility space diagram to show all the possible outcomes.
(b)   Calculate the probability of getting a total of 2.
(c)   Calculate the probability of getting a total of 6.

## Independent events

When two coins are tossed, the outcome of the first toss has no effect on the outcome of the second toss.
One person being left-handed does not influence another person being left-handed.
These are examples of events which can happen together but which do not affect each other.
Events like this are called **independent** events.

> When A and B are **independent** events then the probability of A and B occurring is given by:
> $$P(A \text{ and } B) = P(A) \times P(B)$$
>
> This rule can be extended to any number of independent events.
> For example:
> $$P(A \text{ and } B \text{ and } C) = P(A) \times P(B) \times P(C)$$

## Using tree diagrams to work out probabilities

A **tree diagram** can be used to find all the possible outcomes when two or more events are combined.
It can also be used to help calculate probabilities when outcomes are not equally likely.

### EXAMPLE

**1** **Box A** contains 1 red ball (R) and 1 blue ball (B).
**Box B** contains 3 red balls (R) and 2 blue balls (B).

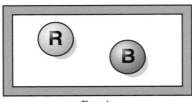

Box A        Box B

A ball is taken at random from Box A.
A ball is then taken at random from Box B.

(a) Draw a tree diagram to show all the possible outcomes.
(b) Calculate the probability that two red balls are taken.

(a)

**Remember:**
When drawing a tree diagram probabilities must be put on the branches.
Using equally likely outcomes:
  **In Box A**
     $P(R) = \frac{1}{2}$       $P(B) = \frac{1}{2}$
  **In Box B**
     $P(R) = \frac{3}{5}$       $P(B) = \frac{2}{5}$

(b) The numbers of red and blue balls are unequal in Box B.
This means that the outcomes RR, RB, BR and BB are not equally likely.

Multiply the probabilities along the branches of the tree diagram.

$$P(RR) = \frac{1}{2} \times \frac{3}{5} = \frac{1 \times 3}{2 \times 5} = \frac{3}{10}$$

The probability that two red balls are taken is $\frac{3}{10}$.

**EXAMPLE**

**2** The probability that Amanda is late for school is 0.4.
Use a tree diagram to find the probability that on two days running:
(a)    she is late twice,
(b)    she is late exactly once.

| Day 1 | Day 2 | Probability |
|---|---|---|
| | 0.4 — late | $0.4 \times 0.4 = \mathbf{0.16}$ |
| 0.4 late | 0.6 — not late | $0.4 \times 0.6 = \mathbf{0.24}$ |
| 0.6 not late | 0.4 — late | $0.6 \times 0.4 = \mathbf{0.24}$ |
| | 0.6 — not late | $0.6 \times 0.6 = \mathbf{0.36}$ |

(a)    The probability that Amanda is late twice.
The outcome included in this event is:    (late **and** late)   P(late twice) = 0.16

(b)    The probability that Amanda is late exactly once.
The outcomes included in this event are:   (late **and** not late)   **or**   (not late **and** late)
These outcomes are mutually exclusive.
P(late exactly once) = 0.24 + 0.24 = 0.48

**Exercise 40.6**

**1**  A bag contains 3 red counters and 2 blue counters.
A counter is taken at random from the bag and then replaced.
Another counter is taken at random from the bag.

(a)    Copy and complete the tree diagram to show all the
possible outcomes. Write the probability of each of the
events on the branches of the tree diagram.

(b)    (i)    Calculate the probability that both counters taken are blue.
(ii)   Calculate the probability that at least one counter taken is blue.

1st counter → 2nd counter. $\frac{3}{5}$ red, blue.

**2**  A manufacturer makes an electrical circuit which contains two switches.
The probability that a switch is faulty is 0.1.

(a)    Copy and complete the tree diagram.

1st switch      2nd switch

0.1 — faulty

not faulty

(b)    (i)    Calculate the probability that both switches are faulty.
(ii)   Calculate the probability that exactly one switch is faulty.

The circuit works if both switches are not faulty.
(c)    The manufacturer makes 1000 circuits.
Estimate the number that work.

**3** Five people in a group of 50 people are left handed.
There are 20 females in the group.
A person is picked at random from the group.

(a) (i) What is the probability that the person is left handed?
  (ii) What is the probability that the person is right handed?
  (iii) What is the probability that the person is female?
  (iv) What is the probability that the person is male?

(b) Copy and complete the tree diagram.

(c) (i) Calculate the probability that the person picked is a left handed female.
  (ii) Calculate the probability that the person picked is a left handed female or is a right handed male.

**4** Bag A contains 3 blue counters, 5 red counters and 2 white counters.
Bag B contains 2 blue counters and 3 red counters.
A ball is taken at random from Bag A.
A ball is taken at random from Bag B.

(a) Copy and complete the tree diagram to show the possible pairs of colours.
Write the probability of each of the events on the branches.

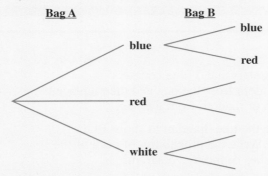

(b) Calculate the probability that a blue counter is taken from Bag A and a red counter is taken from Bag B.

(c) Calculate the probability that both counters are the same colour.

**5** The probability that a car fails an MOT test on lights is $\frac{1}{10}$.

The probability that a car fails an MOT test on brakes is $\frac{1}{5}$.
A car is stopped at random and given an MOT test.
The tree diagram shows the possible outcomes.

(a) Copy and complete the tree diagram.

(b) Calculate the probability that the car will fail the MOT test on lights or brakes.

**6** A fair spinner can land on either black or white.
The probability that it lands on white when it is spun is 0.3.
(a) What is the probability that it lands on black when it is spun?

The spinner is spun twice.
(b) Find the probability of getting two blacks.
(c) Find the probability of getting the same colour on both spinners.

**7** In box A there are 3 red and 5 blue counters.
In box B there are 2 red and 3 blue counters.
A counter is taken at random from each box.
Calculate the probability that:
(a) both counters are red,
(b) at least one of the counters is red.

**8** Colin takes examinations in Maths and in English.
The probability that he passes Maths is 0.7.
The probability that he passes English is 0.8.
The results in each subject are independent of each other.
Calculate the probability that:
(a) he passes Maths and fails English,
(b) he fails both subjects.

**9** Dice A and Dice B are two normal dice. Dice A is a fair dice.
Dice B is biased, so that the probability of getting an even number is $\frac{2}{3}$.
Both of the dice are tossed.
Find the probability that:
(a) an odd number is scored on dice A and an even number on dice B,
(b) an odd number is scored on one dice and an even number on the other.

**10** A box contains cubes which are coloured red (R), white (W) or blue (B) and numbered 1, 2 or 3.
The table shows the probabilities of obtaining each colour and each number when a cube is taken from the box at random.

A single cube is taken from the box at random.
(a) What is the probability that the cube is:
  (i) red and numbered 2,
  (ii) white or numbered 1,
  (iii) white or numbered 3?

Colour of cube

| Number on cube | | R | W | B |
|---|---|---|---|---|
| | 1 | 0.2 | 0 | 0.1 |
| | 2 | 0.1 | 0.3 | 0 |
| | 3 | 0 | 0.1 | 0.2 |

A cube is taken from the box at random and then replaced.
Another cube is then taken from the box at random.
(b) Calculate the probability that:
  (i) both cubes are blue and numbered 1,
  (ii) both cubes are blue.

**11** A bag contains red, white and blue cubes.
The cubes are numbered 1, 2, 3 and 4.
The probabilities of taking cubes from the box at random are shown in the table.

A single cube is taken from the box at random.
(a) What is the probability that:
  (i) the cube is white,
  (ii) the cube is red and numbered 4,
  (iii) the cube is white or numbered 3?

Colour of cube

| Number on cube | | Red | White | Blue |
|---|---|---|---|---|
| | 1 | 0.1 | 0 | 0 |
| | 2 | 0.1 | 0.1 | 0.1 |
| | 3 | 0 | 0.2 | 0.2 |
| | 4 | 0.1 | 0 | 0.1 |

A cube is taken from the box at random and then replaced.
Another cube is then taken from the box at random.
(b) Calculate the probability that both cubes are the same colour.

## Conditional probability

In some situations the probability of a particular event occurring can be affected by other events.
For example:
If it rains, the probability of a particular driver winning a Formula 1 Grand Prix might change.
When probabilities depend on other events they are called **conditional probabilities**.

---

### EXAMPLE

A bag contains six red counters and four blue counters.
Three counters are taken from the bag at random and put in a box.
(a) What is the probability that the **second** counter put in the box is blue:
   (i) if the **first** counter put in the box is red,
   (ii) if the **first** counter put in the box is blue?
(b) What is the probability that the **third** counter put in the box is red:
   (i) if the **first two** counters put in the box are red,
   (ii) if the **first** counter put in the box is blue and the **second** counter put in the box is red?
(c) Show all the possible ways that the counters can be put in the box on a tree diagram.
   Label the branches of the tree diagram with their probabilities.
(d) What is the probability that there are at least two blue counters in the box?

(a) (i) If the first counter put in the box is red,
       then 4 of the 9 counters left in the bag are blue.    So, $P(\text{Blue}) = \frac{4}{9}$
   (ii) If the first counter put in the box is blue,
       then 3 of the 9 counters left in the bag are blue.    So, $P(\text{Blue}) = \frac{3}{9} = \frac{1}{3}$

(b) (i) If the first two counters put in the box are red,
       then 4 of the 8 counters left in the bag are red.    So, $P(\text{Red}) = \frac{4}{8} = \frac{1}{2}$
   (ii) If the first counter put in the box is blue and the
       second counter put in the box is red,
       then 5 of the 8 counters left in the bag are red.    So, $P(\text{Red}) = \frac{5}{8}$

(c)

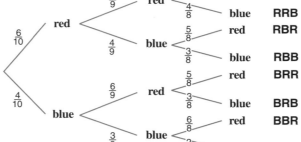

|  | 1st counter | 2nd counter | 3rd counter | Outcome |
|---|---|---|---|---|

(d) The outcomes included in the event at least two blue counters in the box are:

Red (R) and Blue (B) and Blue (B)    $P(\text{R and B and B}) = \frac{6}{10} \times \frac{4}{9} \times \frac{3}{8} = \frac{1}{10}$

Blue (B) and Red (R) and Blue (B)    $P(\text{B and R and B}) = \frac{4}{10} \times \frac{6}{9} \times \frac{3}{8} = \frac{1}{10}$

Blue (B) and Blue (B) and Red (R)    $P(\text{B and B and R}) = \frac{4}{10} \times \frac{3}{9} \times \frac{6}{8} = \frac{1}{10}$

Blue (B) and Blue (B) and Blue (B)    $P(\text{B and B and B}) = \frac{4}{10} \times \frac{3}{9} \times \frac{2}{8} = \frac{1}{30}$

So, $P(\text{at least two blue counters}) = \frac{1}{10} + \frac{1}{10} + \frac{1}{10} + \frac{1}{30}$

$= \frac{1}{3}$

**1** Three female students and two male students are nominated for a school committee.
The committee has two vacancies which are to be filled at random from the nominees.

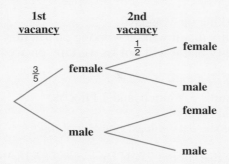

(a) Copy and complete the tree diagram showing all the probabilities.
(b) Calculate the probability that both vacancies are filled by females.
(c) Calculate the probability that the vacancies are filled by one female and one male.
(d) Calculate the probability that at least one vacancy is filled by a male.

**2** Mila has a box of chocolates.
The box contains seven milk chocolates and four plain chocolates.
She takes two chocolates at random from the box.

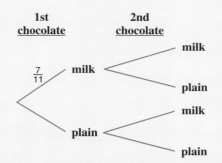

(a) Copy and complete the tree diagram showing all the probabilities.
(b) Calculate the probability that Mila takes one plain chocolate and one milk chocolate.

**3** A pencil case contains 4 red pens and 6 blue pens.
Leo takes two pens at random from the pencil case without looking.
(a) Draw a tree diagram to show all the possible outcomes and probabilities.
(b) Calculate the probability that both pens are the same colour.

**4** Vinnie has a box of flags.
The box contains 3 red flags, 4 blue flags and 5 green flags.
Vinnie takes two flags from the box at random.
(a) Draw a tree diagram to show all the possible outcomes and probabilities.
(b) What is the probability that Vinnie takes two flags of the same colour from the box?

**5** Lydia and Chloe play two games of squash.
The probability of Lydia winning the first game is 0.7.
If Lydia wins the first game the probability of her winning the second game is 0.8.
If Chloe wins the first game the probability of her winning the second game is 0.5.
(a) Draw a tree diagram to show all the possible outcomes and probabilities.
(b) Calculate the probability that Chloe wins both games.
(c) Calculate the probability that they win one game each.

Probability · · · · Probability · · · · Probability · · · ·

**6** Ian has a photocopier in his office.
If the photocopier is working on a certain day then the probability that it will be working the next day is 0.9.
If the photocopier is not working on a certain day then the probability that it will not be working the next day is 0.3.
The photocopier is not working on Monday.
(a) Calculate the probability that it will be working on Tuesday **and** Wednesday.
(b) Calculate the probability that it will **not** be working on Wednesday.

**7** Anne-Marie has a bag of mixed nuts.
The bag contains 8 Brazil nuts, 5 Walnuts and 7 Filberts.
Anne-Marie eats two nuts at random.
What is the probability that she eats at least one Brazil nut?

**8** After a flood, Debbie finds that all the labels have come off the tins in her cupboard.
Debbie knows that she had 5 tins of tomatoes and 7 tins of baked beans.
She opens three tins at random.
What is the probability that she has opened 2 tins of baked beans and one tin of tomatoes?

**9** Ashnil has a security code on his mobile phone.
Each time he switches his phone on he has to enter the code.
The probability that he enters the code correctly on his first attempt is 0.9.
If he enters the code **incorrectly**, the probability that he enters the code correctly on his next attempt is 0.7.
Each time he turns his phone on, Ashnil is allowed 3 attempts to enter the correct code.
Ashnil turns his phone on.
Calculate the probability that Ashnil enters the correct code on either his first attempt, his second attempt or his third attempt.

**10** Bag A contains 2 blue balls and 3 white balls.
Bag B contains 5 blue balls and 3 white balls.

**Bag A**          **Bag B**

Ros takes two balls at random from bag A and places them in bag B.
She then takes two balls at random from bag B and places them in bag A.
Calculate the probability that bag A now contains 5 white balls.

**11** A restaurant offers a choice of a free bottle of red or white wine with lunchtime-special meals of chicken, fish or beef.
Analysis of orders over a month shows that:
    if a customer orders chicken then the probability of choosing white wine is 0.7,
    if a customer orders fish then the probability of choosing white wine is 0.8,
    if a customer orders beef then the probability of choosing red wine is 0.9.

In any one week approximately 800 customers order a lunchtime-special meal.
Of these, the probability that a customer orders chicken is 0.5 and the probability that a customer orders fish is 0.3.
Estimate the number of bottles of white wine that are required.

● You need to know the meaning of these terms: impossible, unlikely, evens, likely, certain.
● **Probability** describes how likely or unlikely it is that an event will occur.
  Probabilities can be shown on a probability scale.
  Probability **must** be written as a fraction, a decimal or a percentage.

**Less likely**   **More likely**

**Impossible**                                        **Certain**

0                 $\frac{1}{2}$              1

● How to work out probabilities using **equally likely outcomes**.
  The probability of an event X happening is given by:

$$\text{Probability (X)} = \frac{\text{Number of outcomes in the event}}{\text{Total number of possible outcomes}}$$

● How to estimate probabilities using **relative frequency**.
  The relative frequency of an event is given by:

$$\text{Relative frequency} = \frac{\text{Number of times the event happens in an experiment (or in a survey)}}{\text{Total number of trials in the experiment (or observations in the survey)}}$$

● How to use probabilities to **estimate** the number of times an event occurs in an **experiment** or **observation**.

  Estimate = total number of trials (or observations) × probability of event

● **Mutually exclusive events** cannot occur at the same time.
  When A and B are mutually exclusive events:

$$P(A \text{ or } B) = P(A) + P(B)$$

● A general rule for working out the probability of an event, A, **not happening** is:

$$P(\text{not } A) = 1 - P(A)$$

● How to find all the possible outcomes when two events are combined.
  By **listing** the outcomes systematically.
  By using a **possibility space diagram**.
  By using a **tree diagram**.
● The outcomes of **independent events** do not influence each other.
  When A and B are independent events:

$$P(A \text{ and } B) = P(A) \times P(B)$$

● **Conditional probabilities** arise when the probabilities of particular events occurring are affected by other events.

**Probability ... Probability ... Probability ...**

## Review Exercise 40

**1**  These are two fair spinners.
  The triangular one is labelled *A*, *B* and *C*
  and the pentagonal one is labelled **1** to **5**.

  (a)  They are spun together.
    Make a list of all the possible outcomes.
    The outcome shown is *A*, **4**.
  (b)  Work out the probability of the following outcomes.
    (i)  The triangular spinner lands on *A*.
    (ii)  The pentagonal spinner lands on an even number.

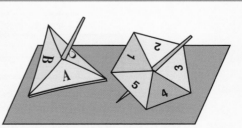

OCR

**2** (a) A bag contains 7 blue, 5 green and 3 yellow balls.
　　　Work out the probability that when one ball is chosen at random it is:
　　　(i)　blue,　　　(ii)　not yellow,　　　(iii)　black.
　　(b) Another bag contains some different sweets.
　　　The probability that a sweet chosen at random is a toffee is 0.7.
　　　Work out the probability that a sweet chosen at random is not a toffee.　　　OCR

**3** (a) In a game, a coin is tossed and a fair dice is rolled.
　　　When the coin shows Heads, the score on the dice is doubled.
　　　When the coin shows Tails, the score on the dice remains the same.
　　　(i)　Copy and complete the table to show the scores for all the possible outcomes.

Dice

| Coin | | 1 | 2 | 3 | 4 | 5 | 6 |
|---|---|---|---|---|---|---|---|
| | H | 2 | | | 8 | | |
| | T | 1 | | 3 | | | 6 |

　　　(ii)　Find the probability that the final score is an even number greater than 3.
　　(b) The probability that a biased dice shows a 6 is 0.35.
　　　The scores of 1, 2, 3, 4 and 5 all have an equal probability of occurring.
　　　The dice is rolled. Find the probability that the dice shows a 2.　　　OCR

**4** Sita puts 5 balls in **Box A** and 4 balls in **Box B**.
The balls in each box are numbered as shown.

**Box A**　　　**Box B**

A ball is taken from each box at random.
(a)　What is the probability that both balls have odd numbers?
(b)　What is the probability that the sum of the numbers on the balls is less than 5?

**5** There are blue, red and yellow discs in a bag.
When a disc is picked out at random, the probability of it being red is 0.4 and the probability of it being blue is 0.3.
(a)　What is the probability of picking a yellow disc?

There are 60 discs in the bag.
(b)　Work out how many of them are red.　　　OCR

**6** The people of a certain tribe of islanders have either blue, brown or green eyes.
The probability that a member of the tribe has blue eyes is 0.3.
In a survey, ten thousand members of the tribe are examined and four thousand two hundred of them have brown eyes.
Estimate the probability that a member of the tribe chosen at random has green eyes.　　　OCR

**7** The Orange Party, the Yellow Party and the Purple Party stand in a school election.
The table shows the voting intentions of a sample of students before the election.

**Voting intentions**

| | Orange Party | Yellow Party | Purple Party |
|---|---|---|---|
| Boys | 4 | 5 | 6 |
| Girls | 5 | 7 | 3 |

(a)　A student in the sample is chosen at random.
　　What is the probability that the person chosen intends to vote for the Orange Party?
(b)　A girl in the sample is chosen at random.
　　What is the probability that she intends to vote for the Purple Party?
(c)　There are 960 students in the school. Use the results of the sample to estimate the number of students in the school who intend to vote for the Yellow Party.

**8** Reshma has a large box of batteries.
The probability that any battery, chosen at random from the box, will work is 0.9.
Reshma chooses two batteries.
(a)    Complete the tree diagram.

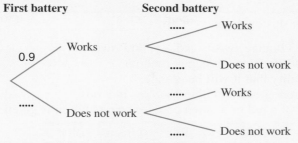

First battery          Second battery

(b)    Calculate the probability that neither battery will work.          OCR

**9** The probability that Jim scores a goal from a penalty shot in hockey is 0.7.
Jim takes two penalty shots.
(a)    Draw a tree diagram to show all the possible outcomes of the two shots.
       Label the diagram carefully.
(b)    Calculate the probability that Jim scores exactly one goal from the two penalty shots.
          OCR

**10** Kate and Sam are coming to a party.
The probability that Kate will wear black clothes to the party is 0.8.
The probability that Sam will wear black clothes to the party is 0.3.
These events are independent.
(a)    Draw a tree diagram to show this information.
(b)    Calculate the probability that both Kate and Sam will wear black to the party.
(c)    Calculate the probability that at least one of them will wear black to the party.          OCR

**11** Saima and Louise play three games.
Each game results in either a win for Saima or a win for Louise.
The probability that Saima wins the first game is 0.6.
For further games the probability that Saima wins is *either* 0.8 if she won the previous game,
*or* 0.3 if she lost the previous game.
Calculate the probability that
(a)    Saima wins all three games,
(b)    Saima wins two games and loses one.          OCR

**12** Thirty students chose their set books for an English examination.
They chose from 'The Colour Purple' and 'Captain Corelli's Mandolin'.
The table below shows the choices that the boys and girls made.

|       | 'The Colour Purple' | 'Captain Corelli's Mandolin' |
|-------|---------------------|------------------------------|
| Boys  | 11                  | 4                            |
| Girls | 5                   | 10                           |

(a)    Two of the 30 students are selected at random.
       What is the probability that they both chose 'The Colour Purple'?
(b)    Two of the 15 boys are selected at random.
       What is the probability that they both chose 'The Colour Purple'?
(c)    Two of the 14 students who chose 'Captain Corelli's Mandolin' are selected at random.
       What is the probability that one is a boy and one is a girl?          OCR

**13** There are 10 cars in a car park. There are 5 red, 3 yellow and 2 white cars.
The order in which they leave the car park is random.
Work out the probability that the first two cars to leave will be of the same colour.          OCR

# Handling Data
# Non-calculator Paper

Do not use a calculator for this exercise.

**1** (a) A bag contains 3 orange sweets and 2 yellow sweets.
One sweet is chosen from the bag at random.
Find the probability that it will be orange.

(b) There are only red, green and blue counters in a box.
The probability of a red or a green counter being chosen is given in the table.

| Colour | Red | Green | Blue |
|---|---|---|---|
| Probability | 0.4 | 0.2 | |

(i) Work out the probability of choosing a blue counter.
(ii) Write down two different things about the number of counters of each colour. OCR

**2** A group of students were each asked how many books they had read last month.
The frequency diagram shows the results.

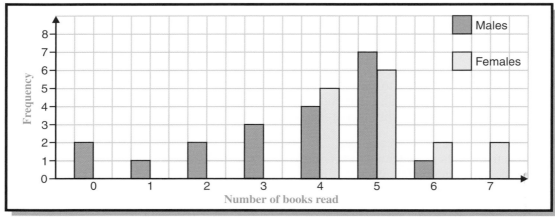

(a) What is the range in the number of books read by females?
(b) Calculate the mean number of books read by females.
(c) Compare and comment on the number of books read by males and the number of books read by females.

**3** A fair six-sided dice and a fair coin are thrown together.
(a) List all the possible outcomes.
(b) What is the probability of getting a tail and a six?

**4** In an opinion poll, 100 women in Manchester are asked how they intend to vote in a General Election.
(a) Give three reasons why this is an unreliable way of predicting the outcome of a General Election.
(b) Give three ways in which the opinion poll could be improved.

**5** The table shows information about a group of children.
(a) One of these children is chosen at random.
What is the probability that the child can swim?
(b) A girl in the group is chosen at random.
What is the probability that she cannot swim?
(c) Tony says, "These results show a higher proportion of girls can swim."
Is he correct? Give reasons for your answer.

| | Can swim | Cannot swim |
|---|---|---|
| Boys | 16 | 4 |
| Girls | 19 | 6 |

**6** Draw scatter graphs to show
(a) moderate negative correlation,
(b) strong positive correlation,
(c) no correlation.

OCR

**7** (a) Jane tests a die to see if it is biased.
She throws it to find the probability of getting a six. She throws it 30 times.
Jane writes down the number of sixes she has obtained after every 10 throws.

| Number of throws | 10 | 20 | 30 |
|---|---|---|---|
| Number of sixes | 3 | 5 | 6 |

Jane decides that the die is biased. Explain why Jane may not be correct.

(b) Sadiq has another die which he tests to see if it is biased.
He carries out a similar experiment. The following table shows Sadiq's results.

| Number of throws | 10 | 20 | 30 | 40 | 50 | 100 | 200 | 500 |
|---|---|---|---|---|---|---|---|---|
| Number of sixes | 3 | 5 | 5 | 7 | 11 | 22 | 39 | 102 |

(i) Does Sadiq's experiment suggest that his die is biased? Explain your answer.
(ii) Estimate the probability of getting two sixes with two throws of Sadiq's die.

OCR

**8** A group of Y11 girls took part in an experiment to test their reaction times.
Their reaction times are summarised in the cumulative frequency diagram drawn below.

(a) What was the median reaction time?

The quickest time for the girls was 20 hundredths of a second and their slowest time was 58 hundredths of a second.

(b) Draw a box plot to summarise the reaction times of the girls.

A group of Y11 boys took part in the same experiment.
Their results are summarised in the box plot drawn below.

**Reaction time of boys**

Reaction time, hundredths of a second

(c) Give one similarity and one difference between the reaction times of the girls and the boys.

OCR

**9** Anne, Babar and Claire are trying to estimate the probability that a student in their school is left-handed.

To do this, they select a number of students at random. Their results are shown in this table.

|  | Anne | Babar | Claire |
|---|---|---|---|
| Number of students selected | 200 | 120 | 20 |
| Number who are left-handed | 40 | 20 | 8 |

(a) Explain why Anne's results are likely to give the most reliable estimate of the probability.

(b) (i) Use Anne's results to estimate the probability that a student, randomly chosen from the school, is left-handed.

    (ii) The school has 1200 students.
Use your answer to part (b)(i) to estimate the number of left-handed students in the school.

(c) Assume your answer to part (b)(i) is representative of the whole population of the United Kingdom.
Find the probability that two randomly chosen people are both left-handed.     OCR

**10** You are doing a survey about kitchen appliances.
You are going to sample the households in a small town.
You decide to take a stratified sample of 10% of the households.

(a) Describe carefully how you would choose your stratified sample.

(b) State one advantage your method has over a simple random sample.

(c) State one advantage your method has over taking every 10th name from the local telephone directory.     OCR

**11** Memoona tosses a fair 6-sided dice *n* times.
Find an expression for the probability that she obtains at least one square number.     OCR

**12** Joshua and Reuben both wear socks all the same style and colour.
Joshua's socks are large size and Reuben's are small size.
There are 10 clean socks in a basket, 6 large and 4 small.
Joshua chooses two socks at random from the basket.

(a) Complete a tree diagram showing how the sizes of socks could be chosen.

(b) What is the probability that Joshua chooses two socks the same size?     OCR

**13**

The histogram shows the lengths of crocodiles found in the River Gambia.
There are 50 crocodiles between 120 cm and 140 cm in length.
How many crocodiles are longer than 140 cm?     OCR

**14** In a class of 20 pupils, 11 have dark hair, 7 have fair hair and 2 have red hair.
Two pupils are chosen at random to collect the homework.
What is the probability that they

(a) both have fair hair,

(b) each have hair of a different colour?     OCR

# Handling Data Calculator Paper

You may use a calculator for this exercise.

**1** Here are the times, in minutes, of some telephone calls.

| 3 | 8 | 13 | 10 | 6 | 35 | 18 | 27 | 22 | 13 |
|---|---|----|----|---|----|----|----|----|----|
| 18 | 20 | 30 | 23 | 38 | 16 | 4 | 18 | 14 | 8 |

(a) Draw a stem and leaf diagram to show these times.
(b) What is the range of these times?

**2** A class survey found the probability of having brown eyes is 0.6.
(a) What is the probability of not having brown eyes?
(b) There are 30 children in the class. Estimate the number with brown eyes.

**3** Georgina picks one letter from **Box X** and then one number from **Box Y**.

List all the pairs she could pick.

Box X (P) (Q) (R)    Box Y (1) (3) (5)

**4** A car was tested to see how far it would travel on one gallon of petrol at different speeds.

| Speed (mph) | 35 | 40 | 45 | 50 | 55 | 60 | 65 | 70 | 75 | 80 |
|-------------|----|----|----|----|----|----|----|----|----|----|
| Distance travelled (miles) | 54 | 57 | 52 | 50 | 47 | 40 | 38 | 31 | 28 | 25 |

(a) Draw a scatter graph for this set of data.
(b) Describe the correlation between the speed and the distance travelled.          OCR

**5** (a) Ian and Alex decide to conduct a survey on the use of computers.
They want to know whether boys and girls use a computer in their coursework for word processing, spreadsheets, or both.
Design an observation sheet to collect information from a group of boys and girls.

(b) Alex used the spell-check on her computer to find spelling mistakes in some coursework.
The table below shows the distribution of spelling mistakes.

| Number of spelling mistakes on the page | 0 | 1 | 2 | 3 | 4 |
|-----------------------------------------|----|---|---|---|---|
| Number of pages | 10 | 6 | 1 | 1 | 2 |

Calculate the mean number of spelling mistakes per page.          OCR

**6** A bag contains counters which are red, white, blue or black.
A counter is taken from the bag at random.
The table shows the probability of getting a red, a white or a blue counter.

| Colour of counter | red | white | blue | black |
|-------------------|-----|-------|------|-------|
| Probability | 0.3 | 0.35 | 0.2 | |

(a) What is the probability of getting:
    (i) a black counter,      (ii) a red or a white counter?
(b) The bag contains 12 red counters.
    How many counters are in the bag altogether?

**7** The probability that a boy is left-handed is 0.2.
The probability that a girl is left-handed is 0.16.
There are 340 boys and 380 girls in a school.
Work out an estimate of the number of students in the school who are left-handed.          OCR

**8** (a) The frequency polygon represents the number of hours spent at work by the employees in one company.
For the employees of another company, the modal class is lower but the range is greater. Copy the diagram and on the same grid draw a frequency polygon which could represent the number of hours spent at work by the employees of the second company.

(b) Some of the workers were asked how long it took them to travel to work that day. The results are summarised in the table.

| Time ($t$ minutes) | $0 < t \leq 20$ | $20 < t \leq 40$ | $40 < t \leq 60$ | $60 < t \leq 80$ |
|---|---|---|---|---|
| Number of workers | 8 | 13 | 14 | 5 |

(i) Calculate an estimate of the mean time.
(ii) Explain why the median is in the class $20 < t \leq 40$.

OCR

**9** David is investigating weekly earnings.
The earnings, in pounds, at one company are listed below.

| 120 | 120 | 120 | 130 | 140 | 140 | 150 |
|---|---|---|---|---|---|---|
| 160 | 160 | 180 | 180 | 200 | 240 | 260 |
| 260 | 290 | 290 | 300 | 600 | 820 | 1300 |

(a) David does not know which one of the mode, mean or median he should use to represent the employees' earnings.
State which you would use, giving your reasons for rejecting the other two.
(b) Find the interquartile range and state why this is a better measurement than the range to represent the spread of earnings at this company.

OCR

**10** The times taken by students to access a website gave the following information.

| | | | |
|---|---|---|---|
| Maximum time | 5.1 minutes | Lower quartile | 2.8 minutes |
| Minimum time | 1.5 minutes | Upper quartile | 4.2 minutes |
| Median time | 3.8 minutes | | |

Draw a box plot to represent this information.

**11** Mike has a fair, ordinary dice, numbered 1 to 6. He throws it twice.
What is the probability that he scores a total of 2?

OCR

**12** Rosie sells goods at car boot sales.
She records her four-monthly profits, in £, over two years.

| | Jan - Apr | May - Aug | Sep - Dec |
|---|---|---|---|
| 2004 | 156 | 678 | 108 |
| 2005 | 147 | 693 | 105 |

(a) Show these data on a graph.
(b) Calculate the 3-point moving averages and plot these values on the graph.
(c) Comment on the trend in Rosie's profits shown by the moving averages.
(d) Use the trend to calculate an estimate of Rosie's profits in January - April 2006.

OCR

**13** Kim and Len travel to school by different routes.
The probability that Kim will arrive late at school is 0.2.
The probability that Len will arrive late is 0.3.
These events are independent.
Calculate the probability that only one of them will be late.                                    OCR

**14** In a competition, a total of 120 fish was caught.
The weights of the 120 fish are summarised in the table below.

| Weight ($w$ grams) | Frequency |
|---|---|
| $0 < w \leq 200$ | 10 |
| $200 < w \leq 400$ | 36 |
| $400 < w \leq 600$ | 46 |
| $600 < w \leq 800$ | 25 |
| $800 < w \leq 1000$ | 3 |

(a) Calculate an estimate of the mean weight of the fish.
(b) Draw the cumulative frequency graph for the weights of the fish.
(c) Find  (i)  the median,         (ii)  the interquartile range.
(d) Estimate the probability that a fish picked at random will weigh
    (i)  less than 500 g,         (ii)  more than 750 g.                    OCR

**15** A teacher knows from experience that if pupils do homework regularly the probability that
they will pass a test is 0.7, otherwise, the probability that they will pass the test is 0.2.
80% of her pupils do their homework regularly.
(a) Show clearly that the probability that a pupil chosen at random will pass the test is 0.6.
(b) The teacher marks the tests of three pupils.
    Calculate the probability that
    (i)  at least one pupil fails,         (ii)  exactly one pupil passes.         OCR

**16** (a) Describe how to obtain a stratified random sample of 50 people from 380 men and
    320 women.
(b) State **one** advantage of stratified random sampling over simple random sampling.

**17** A bag contains 5 white, 2 orange and 3 black beads.
A bead is selected at random and its colour noted. It is not replaced.
A second bead is then selected.
Calculate the probability that the two beads are
(a) both black,         (b) different colours.                                            OCR

**18** The table shows the total time spent in the gym, during one week, by some members of a
fitness club.

| Time ($t$ hours) | $0 < t \leq 2$ | $2 < t \leq 3$ | $3 < t \leq 5$ | $5 < t \leq 8$ |
|---|---|---|---|---|
| Number of people | 32 | 40 | 48 | 45 |

(a) Draw a histogram to represent the information.
(b) One of the members is chosen at random.
    Estimate the probability that this person was in the gym for less than $2\frac{1}{4}$ hours.    OCR

**19** Bag A contains 4 yellow (Y) marbles and 6 red (R) marbles.
Bag B contains 7 yellow and 2 red marbles.
Alex chooses a marble at random from Bag A and places it in Bag B.
Beth then chooses a marble at random from Bag B.
(a) Construct a tree diagram to show this information.
(b) Calculate the probability that Alex and Beth both choose a yellow marble.
(c) Calculate the probability that Beth chooses a yellow marble.                      OCR

Do not use a calculator for this exercise.

**1** In the diagram, *PQR* is an isosceles triangle.
The lines *PQ* and *RS* are parallel.
(a) Work out the size of angle *x*.
(b) (i) What is the size of angle *y*?
(ii) Give a reason for your answer.

**2** (a) What is the value of $2x^2$ when $x = -5$?
(b) Multiply out (i) $2(a - 3)$, (ii) $y(y + 1)$.
(c) Solve (i) $2(x - 3) = 8$, (ii) $3t + 1 = 7 - t$.

**3** Two families, the Mitchells and the Fowlers, decide to go on holiday together.
They share the cost in the ratio: **Mitchells to Fowlers 3 to 1**.
Work out how much each family pays if the total cost is £1200.           OCR

**4** (a) Describe fully the single transformation
which maps Shape *P* onto Shape *Q*.

(b) Describe fully the single transformation
which maps Shape *P* onto Shape *R*.

**5**

The original price of a computer was £800.
It was bought in the sale.
What was the sale price of the computer?

OCR

**6** The weather forecast for Mancunia on any day is always for one of Sun, Cloud, Rain or Snow.
The probability of some of these types of weather is given in the table.

| Weather | Sun | Cloud | Rain | Snow |
|---|---|---|---|---|
| Probability | | 0.35 | 0.3 | 0.15 |

(a) Find the probability that on any day the forecast is for Sun.
(b) Find the probability that the forecast is either Rain or Snow.           OCR

**7** Given that $276 \times 42 = 11\ 592$, work out the following.
(a) $276 \times 0.0042$     (b) $\frac{115.92}{4.2}$           OCR

**8** (a) The rectangular floor of a room measures 37 metres by 28 metres.
A firm charges £4.95 per square metre to repair the floor.
Estimate the charge for repairing the floor. Show all your working.
(b) Is your estimate too big or too small? Give a reason for your answer.           OCR

**9** The number of shots taken by each of 15 golfers to complete 18 holes is given.
72    84    97    103    77    93    86    78    94    99    97    92    81    85    99
Show this information in a stem and leaf diagram.

**10** (a) Write 24 as a product of prime factors.
(b) Find the lowest common multiple (LCM) of 24 and 60.           OCR

**11** A sequence begins  5,  8,  11,  14,  …
Write an expression in terms of $n$ for the $n$th term in the sequence.

**12** The table shows the weights of some of the competitors in 'The World's Strongest Man' competition and the heaviest weight that each can lift.

| Weight of competitor (kg) | 164 | 203 | 238 | 172 | 183 | 225 | 236 | 230 | 248 | 190 | 240 |
|---|---|---|---|---|---|---|---|---|---|---|---|
| Heaviest lift (kg) | 265 | 305 | 355 | 285 | 290 | 360 | 305 | 325 | 330 | 310 | 365 |

(a) Show the information on a scatter graph.
(b) Draw a line of best fit on the graph.
(c)  (i)  Another competitor weighs 180 kg. Estimate the heaviest weight that he could lift.
  (ii)  Another competitor has a best lift of 340 kg. Estimate his weight.
(d) Which of your two answers in part (c) is more reliable? Explain your reasoning.    OCR

**13** A circle has a radius of 4.87 cm.
Use approximation to estimate the area of the circle in terms of $\pi$.

**14** $2n + 1$,  $2n + 3$,  $2n + 5$  are three consecutive odd numbers.
(a) Explain why  (i)  these are odd numbers,    (ii)  these are consecutive odd numbers.
(b) Prove that the sum of these numbers is always divisible by 3.    OCR

**15** A box contains 24 pens and some pencils. The ratio of pens to pencils in the box is 4 : 5.
30% of the pencils need sharpening. How many pencils need sharpening?

**16** (a) Factorise.  (i)  $10x + 5$    (ii)  $x^2 + 7x$
(b) Simplify.  $a^3b^4 \times \dfrac{a^2}{b}$
(c) Rearrange the formula  $v = u + at$  to make $a$ the subject.
(d) Solve.    (i)  $\dfrac{x}{4} = 12$    (ii)  $4(x - 2) = 2x + 5$    OCR

**17** The diagram shows a sketch of triangle $ABC$.
(a) Show that $ABC$ is a right-angled triangle.
(b) Calculate the area of triangle $ABC$.

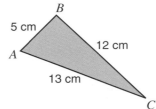

**18** (a) List the values of $n$, where $n$ is a whole number, such that  $3 < 2n + 1 \leqslant 7$.
(b) Solve the simultaneous equations  $x + 2y = -1$  and  $4x - 2y = -9$.

**19** The diagram shows the positions of shapes $T$, $M$ and $N$.
(a) Describe fully the single transformation which maps $T$ onto $N$.
(b) $M$ is mapped onto $P$ by an enlargement, scale factor 2, centre $(-5, 1)$.
Draw a diagram to show the positions of $M$ and $P$.

**20** (a) Write  $\dfrac{5^7 \times 5^2}{5^3}$  as a single power of 5.
(b)  (i)  Write  $1.04 \times 10^5$  as an ordinary number.
  (ii)  Write  0.000 079  in standard form.
  (iii) Work out.  $(8 \times 10^6) \times (5 \times 10^{-3})$
(c) Simplify.  (i)  $6\sqrt{2} + 2\sqrt{2}$    (ii)  $\sqrt{8} \times \sqrt{2}$    (iii)  $\dfrac{\sqrt{8}}{\sqrt{2}}$    OCR

**21** (a) Simplify  $4p^2q \times 3pq$.
(b) Expand and simplify  (i)  $4(5x - 2) - 2(2x - 1)$,    (ii)  $(3x - 1)(2x + 1)$.  OCR

**22** Solve these simultaneous equations algebraically.    $x + 3y = 8$
                                 $2x + 5y = 10$.
                                              OCR

**23** (a) (i) Factorise. $x^2 + 10x + 24$
   (ii) Hence, solve. $x^2 + 10x + 24 = 0$

   (b) Rearrange the formula $P = \sqrt{6T}$ to make $T$ the subject. OCR

**24** In the diagram, $OAX$ and $OBY$ are straight lines.
$AB$ is parallel to $XY$. Angle $AOB = 63°$ and angle $OAB = 39°$.
   (a) Explain why triangle $OAB$ is similar to triangle $OXY$.
   Give a reason for each of your statements.

$AB = 5\,\text{cm}$ and $XY = 12\,\text{cm}$.
   (b) Find the scale factor of the enlargement
   which maps triangle $OAB$ onto triangle $OXY$. OCR

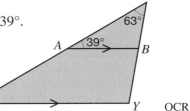

**25** (a) Find the equation of the straight line through $(0, 1)$ and $(3, 7)$.
   (b) Another line has equation $y = 7 - 2x$.
   Without drawing the lines, explain how you can tell whether or not this line is
   perpendicular to the line in part (a). OCR

**26** $TXP$ and $TYQ$ are tangents to a circle, centre $O$.
$Z$ is a point on the circumference.
Angle $XYZ$ is $54°$ and angle $XOT$ is $68°$.

   Find (a) angle $PXZ$, (b) angle $OTY$. OCR

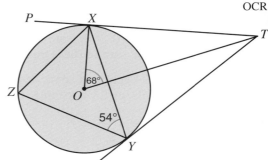

**27** Show clearly that $\dfrac{3}{\sqrt{6}} + \dfrac{\sqrt{6}}{3} = \dfrac{5}{\sqrt{6}}$ OCR

**28** Solve, by factorising, this equation. $2x^2 + 7x - 4 = 0$ OCR

**29** (a) Simplify $(3a)^2 \times 8b^3 \div 4ab$.
   (b) Simplify the following. (i) $9^{\frac{1}{2}} \times 13^{-2}$ (ii) $(\sqrt{3} - \sqrt{2})^2$.
   (c) Write the recurring decimal $0.2\dot{1}\dot{3}$ as a fraction in its lowest terms. OCR

**30** (a) Draw the graph of $y = \dfrac{6}{x}$.
   (b) On the same axes, draw the graph of $y = x$.
   (c) Show why you can use these graphs to solve $x^2 = 6$.
   (d) Use these graphs to solve $x^2 = 6$. OCR

**31** (a) Find the integers $c$ and $d$ such that $x^2 + 6x + c = (x + d)^2$.
   (b) Hence, write down the minimum value of $x^2 + 6x + 13$. OCR

**32** Reuben has 10 bars of chocolate in a tin. They are identical in size and shape.
Three of the bars are coffee flavoured, the others are orange flavoured.
Reuben chooses one bar at random and eats it. He then chooses a second bar at random.
   (a) Construct a tree diagram to show Reuben's choices.
   (b) Calculate the probability that exactly one of the bars that Reuben chooses is
   coffee flavoured. OCR

**33** $ABCD$ is a rectangle with $AB = 20\,\text{cm}$ and $BC = 15\,\text{cm}$.
Rectangle $PQRS$ lies within $ABCD$ such that the sides
of the rectangles are $x\,\text{cm}$ apart, as shown in the diagram.

   (a) Show that the area of $PQRS$ is $4x^2 - 70x + 300$.
   (b) Given that the area of $PQRS$ is half the area of $ABCD$,
   form an equation in $x$ and solve it to find the
   dimensions of rectangle $PQRS$.

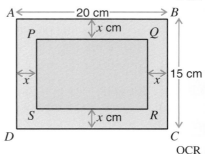

OCR

**34** (a) Evaluate. (i) $16^{0.5} \times 3^{-2}$ (ii) $(7 + \sqrt{3})(7 - \sqrt{3})$

(b) Write $\dfrac{24}{\sqrt{6}}$ in the form $d\sqrt{e}$, where $d$ and $e$ are integers.

(c) Two squares are such that their areas are in the ratio 1 : 2.
The side of the larger square is 6 cm.
What is the side of the smaller square?
Give your answer in the form $a\sqrt{b}$, where $a$ and $b$ are integers. OCR

**35** The diagram shows a sketch of $y = f(x)$.

Sketch the graphs
(a) $y = f(x) + 2$, (b) $y = -f(x)$.

OCR

**36** In the diagram, $A$ and $B$ are the midpoints of $OC$ and $OD$ respectively.

$\overrightarrow{OA} = \mathbf{a}$ and $\overrightarrow{OB} = \mathbf{b}$.

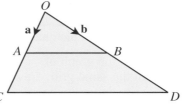

(a) Write down $\overrightarrow{OC}$ in terms of $\mathbf{a}$.

(b) (i) Write down $\overrightarrow{AB}$ in terms of $\mathbf{a}$ and $\mathbf{b}$.
(ii) Use a vector method to prove that $CD$ is parallel to $AB$.
(iii) What other conclusion can you make about $AB$ and $CD$?

$E$ is the midpoint of $CD$.
(c) Use a vector method to prove that $OAEB$ is a parallelogram. OCR

**37** (a) Given that $x^2 + 2x + 5 = (x + a)^2 + b$, find the values of $a$ and $b$.

(b) Prove that $\dfrac{x + 2}{x} - \dfrac{x}{x + 3} = \dfrac{5x + 6}{x(x + 3)}$. OCR

**38** A group of children were given a jigsaw puzzle to complete.
The times taken were recorded in seconds.

| Time taken ($t$ seconds) | $10 \leqslant t < 40$ | $40 \leqslant t < 60$ | $60 \leqslant t < 70$ | $70 \leqslant t < 80$ | $80 \leqslant t < 90$ |
|---|---|---|---|---|---|
| Frequency | 6 | 8 | 15 | 12 | 9 |

(a) Draw a histogram to represent these data.
(b) The same group of children were given a second jigsaw puzzle to complete.
The histogram summarises the times taken to complete this puzzle.

Without doing any calculations, state whether the median time taken to complete this puzzle is greater than, the same as or less than the median time taken to complete the first puzzle. Give a reason for your answer. OCR

**39** The numbers $A$, $B$ and $C$ are such that $B^2 = A \times C$.
(a) Find the number $C$ if $A = \sqrt{3}$ and $B = 1 - \sqrt{3}$.
Give your answer in the form $p + q\sqrt{3}$ where $p$ and $q$ are numbers.
(b) Explain why it would not be possible to find $B$ if $A = \sqrt{5}$ and $C = 1 - \sqrt{5}$. OCR

# Calculator Paper ●●●●●●●●●●●●●●●●●

You may use a calculator for this exercise.

**1** Put the following numbers in order of size, smallest first.
Show how you worked out your answer.

$$\sqrt{70} \qquad 3.1^2 \qquad 9.7\% \text{ of } 58.3$$

OCR

**2** Toni's form have voted on where to go on their end-of-year trip.
The votes are shown in the table.

|  | Doncaster Dome | American Adventure | Alton Towers |
|---|---|---|---|
| Meadowhall | | | |
| 7 votes | 8 votes | 5 votes | 10 votes |

Draw and label a pie chart to illustrate these results.

OCR

**3** (a) Draw the graph of $y = 2x + 5$.
(b) On the same grid, draw the graph of $y = 2$.
(c) Write down the coordinates of the point where the graphs cross.

OCR

**4** A circular pond has radius 8.2 metres.
(a) Calculate the circumference of the pond.
(b) Calculate the area of the pond.

OCR

**5** In the diagram, $QR = RP$ and $QP$ is parallel to $RS$.
Angle $PRS = 37°$.
What is the size of angle $x$?

**6** A two kilogram bar of Chocco costs £5.72.
A one pound bar of Chocco costs £1.45.
Which bar of Chocco gives the better value for money?
You must show your working.

OCR

**7** A garden is a rectangle measuring 26 m by 11.5 m.
Grass covers 67% of the area of the garden.
Calculate the area of grass. Give your answer to a suitable degree of accuracy.

**8** Sachin paid £250 for 36 sweatshirts. He sold them all at £11.99 each.
Calculate his percentage profit.

OCR

**9** A motorist travels 28 miles in 40 minutes.
Calculate the average speed of the motorist in miles per hour.

**10** A candle weighs $x$ grams.
(a) Write an expression, in terms of $x$, for the weight of 20 candles.
(b) A box of 20 candles weighs 3800 g. The box weighs 200 g.
By forming an equation, find the value of $x$.

**11** Belinda buys 200 kites for £300. She sells $\frac{3}{5}$ of them at £3 each.
She then reduces the price of the remaining kites by 40%.
When she has sold 190 kites she gives the last ten away.
Calculate the percentage profit which Belinda made on these kites.

**12** A sequence begins: 5, 3, 1, −1, …
Write an expression, in terms of $n$, for the $n$th term of the sequence.

**13** Alan, Brendan and Chloe shared £768 in the ratio 5 : 4 : 3.
How much did each receive?

OCR

**14** (a) Expand and simplify. $2(5x + 4) - 7x$

(b) Solve the following equations. (i) $\frac{x}{4} = 8$ (ii) $7x - 3 = x - 4$

(c) Simplify. (i) $f^3 \times f^2$ (ii) $\frac{k^8}{k^2}$

OCR

**15** A machine fills bags of sugar.
The weight of each bag of sugar is 515 g, correct to the nearest 5 grams.
Between what limits does the actual weight lie?

OCR

**16** Tatyana invested £5000 at 4.5% simple interest per annum.
Oleg invested £5000 at 4.2% compound interest per annum.
Whose investment was worth more after 5 years and by how much?
You must show how you decided.

OCR

**17** Use trial and improvement to solve the equation $x^3 + 2x = 60$.
Show all your trials and their outcomes. Give your answer correct to 1 decimal place.

OCR

**18** Gary found the playing time of each track in his CD collection.
The table shows the grouped distribution of times.

| Time ($t$ minutes) | $1 < t \leqslant 2$ | $2 < t \leqslant 3$ | $3 < t \leqslant 4$ | $4 < t \leqslant 5$ | $5 < t \leqslant 6$ | $6 < t \leqslant 7$ |
|---|---|---|---|---|---|---|
| Number of tracks | 5 | 25 | 45 | 82 | 33 | 10 |

(a) (i) Write down the modal class.
(ii) Draw a frequency polygon to represent the distribution.
(b) Calculate an estimate of the mean playing time of a CD track.

OCR

**19** (a) Solve the inequality $3m - 5 > 7$.
(b) Write down all the solutions of the inequality $-6 < 3n \leqslant 5$ where $n$ is an integer.
(c) Solve the simultaneous equations $3x - 2y = 15$ and $2x - 4y = 2$.

**20** The diagram shows a trunk in the shape of a
rectangular box with a lid.
The lid is in the shape of a semi-circular prism.
$CD = 0.8$ m, $AD = 0.6$ m and $CF = 2$ m.
Calculate the total volume of the trunk.

OCR

**21**

A rectangular five-bar gate, $ABCD$, is strengthened by a
diagonal strut, $AC$, as shown.
(a) Calculate the length $AC$.
(b) Calculate the angle between $AC$ and $CD$.

For another rectangular gate, $PQRS$, angle $RPS = 53°$
and $PS = 1.7$ m.
(c) Calculate the length $PR$.

OCR

**22** The annual fees at an independent school were increased by 6%.
The fees after this increase are £8957.
Calculate the fees before the increase.

OCR

**23** The mass of a carbon atom is $2 \times 10^{-27}$ g.
How many carbon atoms are there in 6 g of carbon?

OCR

**24** Find the value of $(2.3 \times 10^3) \times (3.4 \times 10^5)$. Give your answer in standard form.

OCR

**25** A circle, centre $O$, has radius 7 cm.
The radius, $RO$, is extended to a point, $P$.
The tangent drawn from $P$
meets the circle at $T$.
$TP = 24$ cm.

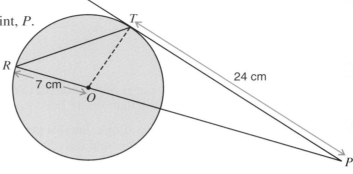

Calculate
(a)   angle $TOP$,
(b)   angle $RTP$.

OCR

**26** The price of a winter coat is reduced in the sales by 35%. The sale price is £94.25.
Calculate the original price of the coat.

OCR

**27** The length of a rectangle is 16 cm, correct to the nearest centimetre.
(a)   Between what limits does the actual length lie?
(b)   The area of this rectangle is known to be 90 cm², correct to the nearest cm².
Calculate the least possible width of the rectangle.
You **must** show full details of your calculations.

OCR

**28** The number of mobile phones sold each quarter by a retailer for the last three years is shown.

| Year | 2003 | | | | 2004 | | | | 2005 | | | |
|---|---|---|---|---|---|---|---|---|---|---|---|---|
| Quarter | 1 | 2 | 3 | 4 | 1 | 2 | 3 | 4 | 1 | 2 | 3 | 4 |
| Number of phones sold | 18 | 28 | 22 | 36 | 20 | 32 | 28 | 42 | 24 | 42 | 40 | 76 |

(a)   Plot these values on graph paper.
(b)   Calculate the 4-quarterly moving averages.
(c)   Plot the moving averages on the same graph and draw a trend line by eye.
(d)   Estimate the number of mobile phones sold by the retailer in the first quarter of 2006.

**29** (a)   Use your calculator to work out these expressions.

   (i)   $\sqrt{24.2 \times 405}$      (ii)   $\dfrac{3.6 \times 5.9}{2.47 - 1.98}$      (iii)   $(3.7 \times 10^5)^2$

(b)   Twenty-three million pounds were promised in donations during a television charity
phone-in. The telephone company reported that approximately $7.8 \times 10^5$ telephone calls,
promising donations, were received.
Calculate the mean amount promised per telephone call.

OCR

**30** A car dealer kept a record of the cars he sold last year.
One-fifth were black. Two-sevenths were made in the UK. Assume that these are independent.
(a)   Construct a tree diagram to show this information.
(b)   One of the cars is chosen at random. What is the probability that
   (i)   it is black and made in the UK,
   (ii)   it is either a black car made abroad or a non-black car made in the UK?

OCR

**31** (a)   Factorise completely.   $3x^2 - 12y^2$      (b)   Simplify.   $\dfrac{x^2 - 3x}{x^2 - 9}$

OCR

**32** Use trial and improvement to solve   $5^x = 7$.
Give your answer correct to 2 decimal places.

OCR

**33** In the diagram   $PQ = 7$ cm,   $QR = 4$ cm   and   angle $PQR = 120°$.
(a)   Show that   $PR = 9.64$ cm,   correct to 3 significant figures.

$PQR$ and $PRS$ are similar triangles.
Angle $PQR$ = angle $PRS$.
Angle $QRP$ = angle $RSP$.
(b)   Calculate the length $PS$.

OCR

**34** Solve. $4y^2 + 5y - 3 = 0$      OCR

**35** Simplify. $\dfrac{2}{x + 2} - \dfrac{1}{x}$      OCR

**36** (a) A coin is biased so that, when it is spun, the probability of it landing heads is 0.6. Calculate the probability that the coin will land tails at least once when the coin is spun twice.

    (b) (i) The probability of another biased coin landing heads is $p$. In a trial this coin is spun twice. Write down an expression in terms of $p$ for the probability of the result one head and one tail.

        (ii) In an experiment, this coin gives the result one head and one tail 39 times out of 100 trials.
Use your answer to (b)(i) to write down an equation in $p$ and show that it simplifies to $200p^2 - 200p + 39 = 0$.

    (c) Solve this equation to find $p$.      OCR

**37** $y$ is inversely proportional to $x^2$ and $y = 0.8$ when $x = 2$.
    (a) Find an equation connecting $y$ and $x$.     (b) Find the value of $y$ when $x = 3$.    OCR

**38** $ABCD$ is a quadrilateral. $BD$ is perpendicular to $DA$.
$AB = BC = 8$ cm. Angle $DAB$ = angle $DBC$ = $54°$.
    (a) Show that $BD = 6.47$ cm, correct to 2 decimal places.
    (b) Calculate the area of triangle $BCD$.
    (c) Calculate $CD$.

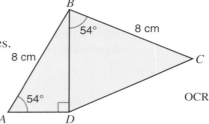

                                         OCR

**39** (a) Simplify $2a^3 \times 4a^2$.
    (b) Solve the equation $x^2 - 8x + 10 = 0$.
    (c) Make $y$ the subject of this formula. $x(2y - 3) = 5(y - 2)$      OCR

**40** A paddling pool has vertical sides. It takes 390 litres of water (to the nearest 10 litres) to fill the pool to a depth of 12 cm (to the nearest cm).
What is the smallest area of cross-section that the paddling pool could have?      OCR

**41** The speeds, $v$ mph, of 100 vehicles travelling along a stretch of road are summarised in the table.

| Speed ($v$ mph) | $0 < v \leqslant 10$ | $10 < v \leqslant 30$ | $30 < v \leqslant 40$ | $40 < v \leqslant 70$ |
|---|---|---|---|---|
| Number of vehicles | 10 | 24 | 54 | 12 |

    (a) Draw a histogram to represent these data.
    (b) Calculate an estimate of the number of cars which exceeded 50 mph.      OCR

**42** The diagram is a sketch of the line $y = 2x - 1$ and the circle $x^2 + y^2 = 13$.
$A$ and $B$ are the points where the line meets the circle.
Use algebra to find the coordinates of $A$ and $B$.      OCR

**43** The curved surface area of a cone is 204.2 cm². The radius of the cone is 5 cm.
    (a) Find the height, $h$ cm, of the cone.
    (b) A cuboid has the same height as the cone and a square base with side length $x$.
The volume of the cuboid is twice the volume of the cone. Find $x$.      OCR

# Answers

## Exercise 1.1 — Page 1

1. (a) 546 (b) 70 209 (c) 1 200 052
2. (a) twenty-three thousand five hundred and ninety
   (b) six thousand and forty-nine
   (c) ninety-three million one hundred and forty-five thousand six hundred and seventy
   (d) nine million eighty thousand and four
3. 7 in 745
4. 3801, 3842, 3874, 4765, 5814
5. 9951, 9653, 9648, 9646, 9434
6. (a) 6512 Digits largest to smallest with the smallest even digit last.
   (b) 1265 Digits smallest to largest with the largest odd digit last.
7. (a) 27 (b) 35 (c) 74 (d) 70
   (e) 112 (f) 17 (g) 49 (h) 105
   (i) 575 (j) 4
8. (a) 952 (b) 2002 (c) 12 203 (d) 1541
   (e) 158 (f) 469 (g) 6268 (h) 3277
9. 40 710
10. 1030 grams
11. 81 030
12. 31 runs
13. 89
14. (a) 17p (b) 6p
15. Car C.
    Car A 8479, Car B 11 643, Car C 13 859

## Exercise 1.2 — Page 3

1. (a) 549
   (b) 252
   (c) 2112
   (d) 15 895
2. (a) 17
   (b) 136
   (c) 206
   (d) 1098
   (e) 20 140
3. 72
4. 29
5. 34 hours
6. (a) 21 480
   (b) 13 000
   (c) 32 960
   (d) 21 510
7. £1450
8. 10 000 m
9. 60 000 staples
10. (a) 253 (b) 79
    (c) 537 (d) 126
11. £35
12. 20 minutes
13. (a) 2432
    (b) 13 338
    (c) 55 311
    (d) 606 375
14. £5191
15. £43 848
16. (a) 43 (b) 504
    (c) 410 (d) 654
17. 23
18. (a) 16 rem 10
    (b) 25 rem 7
    (c) 17 rem 35
    (d) 14 rem 7
19. 14 pints, 10p change
20. (a) 41 (b) 16

## Exercise 1.3 — Page 4

1. 2
2. (a) 37 (b) 3 (c) 9 (d) 58 (e) 6
   (f) 30 (g) 5 (h) 19 (i) 14 (j) 20
   (k) 24 (l) 4 (m) 0 (n) 5 (o) 6
3. (a) $(7 - 2) \times 3 = 15$
   (b) $(3 + 5) \div 2 = 4$
   (c) $(4 + 1) \times (7 - 2) = 25$
4. Many answers, for example:
   $6 - 3 \times 2 + 1 = 1$     $6 - 3 - 2 + 1 = 2$
   $6 \div 3 + 2 - 1 = 3$     $6 \div 3 + 2 \times 1 = 4$
   $6 - 3 + 2 \times 1 = 5$     $6 + 3 - 2 - 1 = 6$
   $6 + 3 - 2 \times 1 = 7$     $6 \times 3 \div 2 - 1 = 8$
   $6 \times 3 \div 2 \times 1 = 9$     $6 + 3 + 2 - 1 = 10$
5. 148 cm     6. 15 g     7. (a) 36 (b) 43

## Exercise 1.4 — Page 5

1. $-28°C, -13°C, -3°C, 19°C, 23°C$
2. $-78, -39, -16, -9, 11, 31, 51$
3. $5°C$
4. 8 kg
5. (a) 2 (b) 1 (c) $-9$ (d) 8
   (e) 4 (f) $-5$ (g) $-7$ (h) 7
   (i) 1 (j) $-15$ (k) $-3$ (l) $-6$
6. (a) 13 (b) 6 (c) 7 (d) 7
   (e) 5 (f) $-12$ (g) $-1$ (h) 13
   (i) $-11$ (j) 11 (k) 9 (l) 0
7. (a) 6 (b) $-8$ (c) $-28$ (d) 0
   (e) $-35$ (f) 19
8. (a) 7 (b) $-1$ (c) 36 (d) $-6$
   (e) 38 (f) 15 (g) $-15$ (h) 25
9. (a) $10°C$ (b) $10°C$ (c) $5°C$ (d) $37°C$
10. $-22°C$
11. (a) $-35$ (b) 35 (c) $-24$ (d) $-45$
    (e) 64 (f) $-42$ (g) $-80$ (h) 32
    (i) $-20$ (j) 60 (k) $-30$ (l) 60
    (m) $-60$ (n) $-100$ (o) $-189$
12. (a) $-4$ (b) 4 (c) 5 (d) $-5$
    (e) $-5$ (f) 5 (g) 6 (h) $-6$
    (i) 4 (j) $-8$ (k) 6 (l) $-5$
    (m) 4 (n) $-4$ (o) $-1$

## Review Exercise 1 — Page 7

1. 4587
2. E.g. 3, 4, 5: $3 + 4 + 5 = 12$, which is even.
3. England, 6 runs
4. 185 miles
5. 184 cm
6. (a) 25 (b) (i) $(1 + 3) \times (5 + 5) = 40$
          (ii) $1 + 3 \times (5 + 5) = 31$
7. 68.4
8. (a) $-1$ (b) 40 (c) $-10$
9. 1488

**10.** 136
**11.** £16 297
**12.** 7500 hours
**13.** −7°C
**14.** 14°F
**15.** Naomi

Tim:  $10 \times 2 + 10 \times (-1) = 10$

Naomi: $8 \times 2 + 5 \times (-1)\ \ = 11$

CHAPTER  2

**1.** (a)  *A*: 5.2,  *B*: 5.6    (b)  *C*: 0.54,  *D*: 0.59
**2.** 3.567, 3.576, 3.652, 3.657, 3.675
**3.** 1.55 m
**4.** (a)  10.9  (b)  1.65  (c)  0.9  (d)  11
  (e)  1.2  (f)  0.6  (g)  0.24  (h)  8.9
**5.** (a)  6.84  (b)  5.22  (c)  5.003
  (d)  3  (e)  1.24  (f)  15.781
**6.** £3.32,   £1.68 change
**7.** 4.88 m

**1.** (a)  £2.50  (b)  £25
**2.** (a)  £7.95  (b)  £0.12  (c)  86.9p
**3.** $12.3 \times 1000$ and $12.3 \div 0.001$
  $12.3 \div 100$ and $12.3 \times 0.01$
  $12.3 \times 0.1$ and $12.3 \div 10$
  $12.3 \div 0.01$ and $12.3 \times 100$
  $12.3 \times 10$ and $12.3 \div 0.1$
  $12.3 \times 0.001$ and $12.3 \div 1000$
**4.** £7.60
**5.** (a)  £14.95  (b)  £5.05
**6.** (a)  8.5  (b)  1.3  (c)  0.48  (d)  0.06
  (e)  15  (f)  4  (g)  50  (h)  24
**7.** £10.35
**8.** £1.35
**9.** (a)  0.075  (b)  8.75  (c)  16.53
  (d)  1.025  (e)  3.888  (f)  9.38
  (g)  0.0432  (h)  0.028
**10.** (a)  21p  (b)  £1.84  (c)  78p
**11.** (a)  1.6  (b)  1.75  (c)  1.125
  (d)  12.3  (e)  2.92  (f)  1430
  (g)  12.5  (h)  37.5
**12.** (a)  (i)  3  (ii)  1.5  (iii) 0.24
  (b)  Each answer is less than the
    original number.
**13.** (a)  (i)  10  (ii)  6  (iii)  0.3
  (b)  Each answer is greater than the
    original number.
**14.** £60.75
**15.** (a)  (i)  £5.32  (ii)  £7.68
    (iii)  £3.60  (iv)  £2.79
  (b)  £1.38
**16.** £1.75
**17.** 67
**18.** 45

**1.** (a)  4.768
**2.** (a)  2.1̇
**3.** (a)  12.2
**4.** (a)  **C**  (b)  **B**  (c)  **D**  (d)  **A**
**5.** (a)  0.077 836 …  (b)  0.355 960 …
  (c)  11.045 …  (d)  3.421 98 …
  (e)  322.528 571 …  (f)  −386
  (g)  0.155

**1.** E.g.  $\frac{15}{24}$, $\frac{30}{48}$, $\frac{45}{72}$, …, $\frac{10}{16}$, $\frac{20}{32}$, …
  simplest form $\frac{5}{8}$
**2.** $\frac{8}{15}$, $\frac{3}{5}$, $\frac{2}{3}$, $\frac{7}{10}$
**3.** $\frac{4}{5}$
**4.** (a)  $\frac{4}{5}$  (b)  $\frac{2}{3}$  (c)  $\frac{2}{3}$  (d)  $\frac{2}{5}$
**5.** (a)  $1\frac{1}{2}$  (b)  $2\frac{1}{8}$  (c)  $3\frac{3}{4}$  (d)  $4\frac{3}{5}$
**6.** (a)  $\frac{27}{10}$  (b)  $\frac{8}{5}$  (c)  $\frac{35}{6}$
**7.** $\frac{3}{5}$
**8.** $\frac{30}{50} = \frac{3}{5}$
**9.** (a)  3  (b)  4  (c)  3  (d)  8  (e)  8
  (f)  9  (g)  12  (h)  20  (i)  40  (j)  12
**10.** (a)  6  (b)  24
**11.** £5
**12.** £148.40
**13.** £3187.50
**14.** (a)  9 squares  (b)  10 squares  (c)  $\frac{5}{24}$

**1.** (a)  $\frac{3}{8}$  (b)  $\frac{7}{12}$  (c)  $\frac{7}{10}$  (d)  $\frac{8}{15}$  (e)  $\frac{9}{14}$
**2.** (a)  $\frac{1}{8}$  (b)  $\frac{1}{12}$  (c)  $\frac{3}{10}$  (d)  $\frac{2}{15}$  (e)  $\frac{5}{14}$
**3.** (a)  $1\frac{1}{4}$  (b)  $1\frac{1}{2}$  (c)  $1\frac{11}{20}$  (d)  $1\frac{8}{21}$  (e)  $1\frac{5}{24}$
**4.** (a)  $\frac{1}{8}$  (b)  $\frac{8}{15}$  (c)  $\frac{5}{8}$  (d)  $\frac{1}{15}$  (e)  $\frac{1}{3}$
**5.** (a)  $4\frac{1}{4}$  (b)  $3\frac{5}{6}$  (c)  $4\frac{3}{8}$  (d)  $5\frac{17}{20}$  (e)  $6\frac{13}{30}$
**6.** (a)  $1\frac{1}{10}$  (b)  $\frac{5}{12}$  (c)  $1\frac{3}{8}$  (d)  $3\frac{3}{10}$  (e)  $2\frac{1}{4}$
**7.** $\frac{4}{15}$    **9.** (a)  $\frac{5}{12}$  (b)  $\frac{11}{12}$
**8.** $\frac{13}{60}$    **10.** (a)  $\frac{1}{4}$  (b)  Billy

**1.** (a)  $3\frac{1}{2}$  (b)  $1\frac{4}{5}$  (c)  $6\frac{1}{4}$  (d)  9  (e)  $10\frac{1}{2}$
**2.** (a)  $\frac{1}{20}$  (b)  $\frac{1}{10}$  (c)  $\frac{3}{8}$  (d)  $\frac{1}{16}$  (e)  $\frac{1}{20}$
**3.** (a)  $7\frac{1}{2}$  (b)  $7\frac{1}{2}$  (c)  $4\frac{4}{5}$  (d)  $7\frac{1}{3}$  (e)  $7\frac{4}{5}$
  (f)  $2\frac{1}{4}$  (g)  $\frac{3}{4}$  (h)  $\frac{4}{5}$  (i)  $\frac{2}{3}$  (j)  $\frac{5}{8}$
**4.** (a)  $\frac{1}{2}$  (b)  $\frac{3}{10}$  (c)  $\frac{1}{3}$  (d)  $\frac{2}{7}$  (e)  $\frac{1}{4}$

**5.** (a) $1\frac{1}{8}$ (b) $2$ (c) $3\frac{3}{4}$ (d) $3\frac{17}{20}$ (e) $4\frac{7}{8}$

(f) $1\frac{13}{15}$ (g) $14$ (h) $13\frac{1}{2}$ (i) $2\frac{7}{10}$ (j) $8\frac{3}{4}$

**6.** (a) $\frac{4}{15}$ (b) $\frac{2}{5}$

**7.** (a) $\frac{4}{15}$ (b) $15$

## Exercise **2.7** — Page 16

**1.** (a) $\frac{1}{10}$ (b) $\frac{3}{8}$ (c) $\frac{1}{3}$ (d) $\frac{1}{10}$ (e) $\frac{2}{7}$

**2.** (a) $\frac{3}{4}$ (b) $\frac{1}{3}$ (c) $\frac{4}{7}$ (d) $\frac{4}{9}$ (e) $\frac{2}{3}$

**3.** (a) $2$ (b) $\frac{2}{5}$ (c) $2\frac{5}{8}$ (d) $3\frac{1}{3}$ (e) $6$

**4.** (a) $\frac{5}{6}$ (b) $\frac{9}{16}$ (c) $\frac{4}{5}$ (d) $1\frac{1}{3}$ (e) $\frac{2}{3}$

(f) $1\frac{1}{2}$ (g) $\frac{2}{3}$ (h) $1\frac{1}{6}$ (i) $1\frac{1}{2}$ (j) $1\frac{4}{5}$

**5.** (a) $14$ (b) $5$ (c) $2$ (d) $6$ (e) $6$

(f) $\frac{4}{5}$ (g) $1\frac{1}{2}$ (h) $1\frac{1}{4}$ (i) $1\frac{1}{7}$ (j) $\frac{21}{25}$

**6.** $\frac{1}{10}$   **7.** $\frac{1}{9}$   **8.** $23$

## Exercise **2.8** — Page 17

**1.** £3.20  **2.** 70 km  **3.** £3.20  **4.** £6  **5.** 96 cm

## Exercise **2.9** — Page 18

**1.** (a) $\frac{3}{25}$ (b) $\frac{3}{5}$ (c) $\frac{8}{25}$ (d) $\frac{7}{40}$ (e) $\frac{9}{20}$

(f) $\frac{13}{20}$ (g) $\frac{11}{50}$ (h) $\frac{101}{500}$ (i) $\frac{7}{25}$ (j) $\frac{111}{200}$

(k) $\frac{5}{8}$ (l) $\frac{21}{25}$

**2.** (a) $0.25$ (b) $0.1$ (c) $0.4$ (d) $0.75$

(e) $0.7$ (f) $0.8$

**3.** (a) $0.15$ (b) $0.16$ (c) $0.07$ (d) $0.95$

(e) $0.36$ (f) $0.53$

**4.** (a) $0.125$ (b) $0.625$

(c) $0.225$ (d) $0.725$

**5.** (a) $0.\dot{7}$ (b) $0.\dot{1}$ (c) $0.\dot{3}\dot{6}$

(d) $0.8\dot{2}$ (e) $0.1\dot{3}\dot{5}$ (f) $0.\dot{2}1\dot{6}$

(g) $0.16$ (h) $0.2857\dot{1}\dot{4}$

**6.** (a) $0.\dot{8}$ (b) $0.\dot{4}$ (c) $0.5\dot{1}$

(d) $0.7\dot{2}$ (e) $0.\dot{1}4285\dot{7}$ (f) $0.\dot{8}5714\dot{2}$

(g) $0.0\dot{3}$ (h) $0.4\dot{6}$ (i) $0.8\dot{3}$

(j) $0.7\dot{7}\dot{2}$

## Review Exercise **2** — Page 19

**1.** (a) $\frac{9}{20}$ (b) (i) $0.28$ (ii) $0.\dot{5}$

**2.** (a) $12.41$ (b) $4.33$ (c) $20$ (d) $0.08$

**3.** (a) $64$ (b) $\frac{7}{16}$

**4.** $\frac{7}{10}$

**5.** (a) $0.375$ (b) $0.0375$

**6.** (a) $\frac{11}{12}$ (b) $\frac{11}{40}$ (c) $\frac{3}{7}$ (d) $\frac{5}{6}$

**7.** $\frac{4}{15}$

**8.** (a) $1.1275$ (b) $27.5$

**9.** (a) $\frac{11}{15}$ (b) $\frac{3}{10}$

**10.** (a) $1\frac{7}{15}$ (b) $2$

---

**11.** £80

**12.** (a) Press $\boxed{=}$ after 1.76.

(b) 3.12 (3 sig. figs.)

**13.** (a) £63.36  (b) 325 km

**14.** (a) 20.8  (b) 18.8125

**15.** Yes

## CHAPTER 3

## Exercise **3.1** — Page 20

**1.** (a) 50 (b) 50 (c) 70

**2.** (a) 7480 (b) 7500 (c) 7000

**3.** (a) 3456 (b) 3500

**4.** (a) 745, 746, 747, 748, 749

(b) 750, 751, 752, 753, 754

(c) Any number from 8450 to 8499

(d) Any number from 8500 to 8549

**5.** (a) £50 (nearest pound)

(b) 24 100 (nearest hundred)

(c) 309 000 km² (nearest thousand km²)

(d) 190 km (nearest ten kilometres)

**6.** Nearest 1000.

**7.** (a) 35 (b) 44

**8.** (a) 1950 (b) 2049

**9.** 42 500

**10.** Smallest: 135,   greatest: 144

**11.** 2749

## Exercise **3.2** — Page 21

**1.** 4   **4.** 24

**2.** 5   **5.** 16

**3.** 9   **6.** 7   **7.** 29

## Exercise **3.3** — Page 22

**1.** (a) 3.962 (b) 3.96 (c) 4.0

**2.** (a) 567.65 (b) 567.7 (c) 568

**3.** 4.86

**4.** 68.8 kg

**5.** Missing entries are:
0.96, 0.97, 15.281, 0.06, 4.99, 5.00

**6.** (a) (i) 46.1 (ii) 59.7

(iii) 569.4 (iv) 17.1 (v) 0.7

(b) (i) 46.14 (ii) 59.70

(iii) 569.43 (iv) 17.06 (v) 0.66

(c) (i) 46.145 (ii) 59.697

(iii) 569.434 (iv) 17.059 (v) 0.662

**7.** (a) 40.9 litres, nearest tenth of a litre

(b) £2.37, nearest penny

(c) 35.7 cm, nearest millimetre

(d) £1.33, nearest penny

(e) £14.26, nearest penny

## Exercise **3.4** — Page 24

**1.** (a) 20 (b) 500 (c) 400

(d) 2000 (e) 20 (f) 0.08

(g) 0.09 (h) 0.009 (i) 0.01

**2.**

| Number | sig. fig. | Answer |
|--------|-----------|--------|
| 456 000 | 2 | 460 000 |
| 454 000 | 2 | 450 000 |
| 7 981 234 | 3 | 7 980 000 |
| 7 981 234 | 2 | 8 000 000 |
| 1290 | 2 | 1300 |
| 19 602 | 1 | 20 000 |

**3.**

| Number | sig. fig. | Answer |
|--------|-----------|--------|
| 0.000567 | 2 | 0.00057 |
| 0.093748 | 2 | 0.094 |
| 0.093748 | 3 | 0.0937 |
| 0.093748 | 4 | 0.09375 |
| 0.010245 | 2 | 0.010 |
| 0.02994 | 2 | 0.030 |

**4.** 490
**5.** (a) (i) 80 000    (ii) 80    (iii) 1000
     (iv) 0.007    (v) 0.002
   (b) (i) 83 000    (ii) 83    (iii) 1000
     (iv) 0.0073    (v) 0.0019
   (c) (i) 82 700    (ii) 82.7    (iii) 1000
     (iv) 0.00728    (v) 0.00190
**6.** 472 $m^2$ (3 s.f.)
**7.** (a) 157 $cm^2$ (3 s.f.)    (b) 6100 $m^2$ (2 s.f.)
   (c) 1.23 m (nearest cm)
   (d) 15.9 $m^2$ (round up 1 d.p.)

## Exercise 3.5     Page 25

**1.** $40 \times 50 = 2000$
**2.** (a) (i) $40 \times 20 = 800$
     (ii) $100 \times 20 = 2000$
     (iii) $800 \times 50 = 40\ 000$
     (iv) $900 \times 60 = 54\ 000$
   (b) (i) $80 \div 20 = 4$
     (ii) $600 \div 30 = 20$
     (iii) $900 \div 60 = 15$
     (iv) $4000 \div 80 = 50$
**3.** $40 \times 50p = £20$
**4.** (a) 30 is bigger than 29 and 50 is bigger than 48. So, $30 \times 50$ is bigger than $29 \times 48$.
   (b) $200 \div 10 = 20$, 14, estimate is bigger.
**5.** (a) $£8000 + £1000 = £9000$    (b) £9312
**6.** $400 \times 0.5 = 200$
Kath's answer is 10 times too small.
**7.** (a) 2.047 009 …
   (b) $(50 + 10) \div (10 \times 3) = 2$
**8.** (a) 6.4, 6.41875    (b) 20, 18.709677…
   (c) 20, 20.45631…    (d) 2000, 2132.9583…
**9.** (a) 410.08316…
   (b) $80 \div (0.04 \times 5) = 400$
**10.** $6\ 000\ 000 \div 0.03 = 200\ 000\ 000$
Niamh's answer is 10 times too big.

## Exercise 3.6     Page 27

**1.** 167.5 cm
**2.** 8.5 m ⩽ height of building < 9.5 m
**3.** Minimum weight: 835 g
Maximum weight: 845 g
**4.** 11.55 seconds
**5.** 9.35 kg
**6.** Least length: 2.65 m,   greatest length: 2.75 m
**7.** 94 ml
**8.** Minimum weight: 7.5 kg
Maximum weight: 8.5 kg
**9.** (a) 38.5 cm     (b) 3.45 kg
**10.** 189 g
**11.** 85.5 km
**12.** (a) 0.525 kg ⩽ weight of book < 0.535 kg
   (b) 5.35 kg

## Exercise 3.7     Page 28

**1.** 1260 cm
**2.** Lower bound: 26.485 km
Upper bound: 26.595 km
**3.** (a) 505 kg     (b) 3.4 kg
**4.** 10
**5.** £1.13
**6.** (a) (i) 7.45    (ii) 3.675
   (b) Lower bound: 3.665, upper bound: 3.775
   (c) 27.01125
   (d) 2.02721…

## Review Exercise 3     Page 29

**1.** 1 500 000
**2.** (a) 102.3    (b) 102.35
**3.** 30
**4.** (a) $90 \times 2 = 180$
   (b) $2000 \div 50 = 40$
**5.** (a) 2.8    (b) $80 \div 30 \approx 3$
**6.** 18.7 is less than 19, but rounds to 19.
0.96 is less than 1, but rounds to 1.
$19 \times 1 = 19$
So, $18.7 \times 0.96$ must be less than 19.
**7.** (a) $800 \times 30 \times 10 = £240\ 000$
   (b) More.   Both 792 and 29 are rounded up.
**8.** 12 packs
**9.** Smallest: 85,   largest: 94
**10.** (a) 2550    (b) 2649
**11.** $£2000 \div 40 = £50$
**12.** $\dfrac{40 \times 5}{20} = 10$
**13.** (a) 9000
   (b) (i) $60 \times £10 = £600$
     (ii) Smaller.
      Both values are rounded down.
**14.** $\dfrac{500 + 100}{30} = 20$.   Answer is wrong.
**15.** 24.5 cm
**16.** (a) 17.5 m
   (b) 17.5 m ⩽ length of bus < 18.5 m

**17.** (a) $S = \dfrac{700 \times 20}{600 + 400} = 14$

    (b) (i) 14.23553… (ii) 14.2

**18.** Greatest: 155.5 Calories, least: 154.5 Calories

**19.** (a) 19 m²

    (b) Round up to the nearest square metre for enough carpet to cover whole floor.

**20.** Lower bound: 1750 kg, upper bound: 1850 kg

**21.** (a) (i) 550 (ii) 55

    (b) (i) 705 (ii) 24 750

    (c) 10

**22.** 39

**23.** 54.5 m²

## CHAPTER 4

### Exercise 4.1      Page 32

**1.** (a) $\frac{1}{10}$ (b) $\frac{1}{4}$ (c) $\frac{1}{20}$

    (d) $\frac{7}{20}$ (e) $\frac{12}{25}$ (f) $\frac{1}{8}$

**2.** (a) 0.2 (b) 0.15 (c) 0.01

    (d) 0.72 (e) 0.875 (f) 1.5

**3.** (a) 34% (b) 48% (c) 15% (d) 80%

    (e) 27% (f) 65% (g) $66\frac{2}{3}\%$ (h) $22\frac{2}{9}\%$

**4.** (a) 15% (b) 32% (c) 12.5%

    (d) 7% (e) 112% (f) 1.5%

**5.** (a) $\frac{2}{5}$, $\frac{1}{2}$, 0.55, 60%

    (b) 0.42, 43%, $\frac{11}{25}$, $\frac{9}{20}$

    (c) 28%, 0.2805, $\frac{57}{200}$, $\frac{23}{80}$

**6.** (a) 60% (b) 21%

**7.** 30%

**8.** (a) 40% (b) 60%

**9.** 12.5%

**10.** 37.5%

**11.** 3%

**12.** Maths. Geog 80%, English 84%, Maths 85%

**13.** Team A

**14.** (a) 10% (b) 60% (c) 15%

**15.** 9.5%

**16.** 25%

### Exercise 4.2      Page 33

**1.** (a) £16 (b) £15 (c) £66

    (d) £52.50 (e) £25 (f) 27 kg

    (g) £11.25 (h) 12 m

**2.** 270

**3.** £20

**4.** £2.70

**5.** £42

**6.** (a) £80 (b) £13

    (c) £16.50 (d) £57.50

**7.** (a) £510 (b) £5.50

    (c) £33.60 (d) £40.95

**8.** 40p per minute

**9.** £215

**10.** 759 g

**11.** £244.64

**12.** £4706

**13.** 40p per pint

**14.** 87.7p per litre

**15.** £10 530

**16.** £109 520

### Exercise 4.3      Page 35

**1.** 20%

**2.** 20%

**3.** 28%

**4.** Becky.

    Hinn's increase = 32%

    Becky's increase = 40%

**5.** (a) $12\frac{1}{2}\%$ (b) 12%

    Rent went up by a greater percentage.

**6.** Car A 13.8%, Car B 18.2%

**7.** 19.5%    **9.** 5.9% decrease    **11.** 19%

**8.** 18.6%    **10.** 8% increase    **12.** 3.5%

### Exercise 4.4      Page 36

**1.** 600 ml    **5.** £312 500    **9.** School A 425

**2.** £600    **6.** 67.5 mg          School B 450

**3.** £220    **7.** £1420    **10.** £400

**4.** 1.89 m    **8.** £8000    **11.** £150

### Exercise 4.5      Page 37

**1.** 36 hours    **5.** (a) £1185

**2.** £694.40          (b) £118.50    **8.** £3837.46

**3.** £347.48    **6.** £3947.90    **9.** £11 911.20

**4.** £10.20    **7.** £432.03    **10.** £704.60

### Exercise 4.6      Page 39

**1.** £5.60    **4.** £67.28

**2.** £40.50    **5.** £537.40    **7.** 678 units

**3.** 700 g    **6.** £198    **8.** £12 400

### Exercise 4.7      Page 40

**1.** £6

**2.** (a) £3.50

    (b) £73.50    **5.** £77.55    **9.** £183.75

**3.** (a) £15.75    **6.** £27 025    **10.** £3.20

    (b) £105.75    **7.** £428.87    **11.** £293.75

**4.** £291.40    **8.** £92.82    **12.** £2928.10

### Exercise 4.8      Page 42

**1.** £10                 **4.** £48

**2.** (a) £30 (b) £15    **5.** £225

**3.** £225             **6.** £242

**7.** (a) earns 78p more interest

**8.** £11 910.16

**9.** (a) £2420 (b) £1938.66

**10.** 81 m

**11.** (a) (i) £8268.73 (ii) 63.6%

    (b) (i) £12 721.12 (ii) 63.6%

    (c) Same percentage reduction.

**12.** 9 years

**1.** (a) 18    (b) 20%
**2.** 68p
**3.** 90%
**4.** 180
**5.** 20%
**6.** £1099.80
**7.** LARGE.
Cost per teabag -
SMALL: **1.7p**
MEDIUM: **1.6p**
LARGE: **1.425p**
**8.** $8000
**9.** £23.50
**10.** 4 hours

**11.** £102.42
**12.** (a) £308.70
     (b) 37%
**13.** £5.76
**14.** £1645
**15.** (a) £80
     (b) 34%
**16.** (a) £4900.17
     (b) 8 years
**17.** (a) £376
     (b) 5 days
**18.** £8470.96
**19.** £704.90
**20.** 35 820

## CHAPTER 5

**1.** (a) 35    (b) 48
**2.** E.g. 2, 3, 4, 5: $2 + 3 + 4 + 5 = 14$
     14 is not a multiple of 4.
**3.** (a) 14, 35   (b) 4, 5, 20   (c) 3, 5
**4.** (a) Second   (b) Second
     (c) Fifth    (d) Third
**5.** (a) 1, 2, 4, 8, 16
     (b) 1, 2, 4, 7, 14, 28
     (c) 1, 2, 3, 4, 6, 9, 12, 18, 36
     (d) 1, 3, 5, 9, 15, 45
     (e) 1, 2, 3, 4, 6, 8, 12, 16, 24, 48
     (f) 1, 2, 5, 10, 25, 50
**6.** (a) 1, 5    (b) 1, 2, 4    (c) 1, 2
     (d) 1, 2, 3, 4, 6, 12    (e) 1, 2, 3, 6
**7.** (a) 31, 37   (b) No. 7 is a factor of 49.

**1.** (a) $2^2 \times 3^2$      (b) $2 \times 3^3 \times 5$
     (c) $2 \times 3 \times 5^2$   (d) $2^3 \times 3 \times 5^2$
     (e) $3^3 \times 5^3$     (f) $7^4$
**2.** (a) 2, 3    (b) 2, 5      (c) 2, 7
     (d) 3, 5    (e) 2, 3, 11   (f) 2, 3
**3.** (a) $2^2 \times 3$   (b) $2^2 \times 5$     (c) $2^2 \times 7$
     (d) $3^2 \times 5$   (e) $2 \times 3 \times 11$   (f) $2^2 \times 3^3$
**4.** $2^7$
**5.** $2^3 \times 5^3$
**6.** (a) 25 000   (b) $2^3 \times 5^6$
**7.** $2^3 \times$ (consecutive prime numbers)
     104, 136, 152
**8.** (a) 24     (b) 160   (c) 20    (d) 90
     (e) 90     (f) 24    (g) 40    (h) 630
**9.** (a) 6      (b) 8     (c) 2     (d) 4
     (e) 11    (f) 4     (g) 3     (h) 15
**10.** (a) $2^3 \times 3$   (b) $2 \times 3^3$   (c) 6    (d) 216
**11.** (a) 3     (b) $2 \times 3^4$   (c) 54   (d) 324
**12.** 9.18 am

**1.** (a) 49      (a) 125     (c) 0.5
**2.** Yes. $7^2 = 49$ and $8^2 = 64$
     55 is between 49 and 64.
     So, $\sqrt{55}$ lies between 7 and 8.
**3.** 64
**4.** No. $2^2 = 4$, $3^2 = 9$ and $5^2 = 25$
     $2^2 + 3^2 = 4 + 9 = 13$
**5.** (a) (i) 9   (ii) $-8$   (iii) 16   (iv) $-125$
     (b) The result of squaring a negative number
     is a positive number. The result of cubing
     a negative number is a negative number.
**6.** (a) 8     (b) 7     (c) 5     (d) 5
**7.** (a) 2     (b) 4     (c) 5
**8.** (a) 6.25     (b) 0.64     (c) 3375
     (d) 13.824   (e) 16 807   (f) 0.0625
     (g) 75 418.89…
**9.** (a) 0.25   (b) 0.05   (c) 0.04   (d) 2
     (e) 4     (f) 2.5    (g) 6.25
**10.** E.g. $5 \times \frac{1}{5} = 1$
**11.** 9.8
**12.** (a) 2.3     (b) 17.3    (c) 4.0
**13.** (a) 27 000   (b) 800     (c) 2.98
     (d) 10.648   (e) 70.56   (f) 31.25
     (g) 25.215   (h) 1.28    (i) 126 216
     (j) 134.4
**14.** (a) E.g. $16 = 4^2$, so, $16^3 = (4^2)^3 = 4^6$
     (b) $x = 12$
**15.** $x = 1.43$

**1.** (a) $2^5$ (b) $3^7$ (c) $5^8$ (d) $7^4$ (e) $9^5$
**2.** (a) 2 (b) $3^3$ (c) $5^4$ (d) $7^2$ (e) $9^5$
**3.** (a) $3^6$ (b) $10^2$    (c) $4^5$ (d) $5^3$
     (e) $2^3$ (f) $5^0 = 1$ (g) $7^{-2}$ (h) $3^3$
**4.** $2^{15}$
**5.** (a) $2^6$ (b) $3^{10}$ (c) $5^6$ (d) $7^9$ (e) $9^0 = 1$
**6.** (a) 8     (b) 7     (c) 11    (d) 3
     (e) 1     (f) 4     (g) 6     (h) 20
     (i) 2     (j) 8     (k) 6     (l) 3

**1.** (a) $9^0$ (b) $2^{-2}$ (c) $5^{-2}$ (d) $8^{-5}$
     (e) $2^{-4}$ (f) $5^{12}$ (g) $11^{-5}$ (h) $7^{-1}$
**2.** (a) $8^2$     (b) $7^{-5}$    (c) $2.5^{-1}$
     (d) $4^0$     (e) $10^{-1}$   (f) $6^{-4}$
     (g) $0.1^{-12}$   (h) $5^{-15}$   (i) $4^5$
     (j) $4^2 \times 8^7$   (k) $4 \times 5^{-2}$   (l) $2^{-2} \times 5^5$
     (m) 3     (n) $5^3$     (o) $2^{-6}$
**3.** (a) $\frac{1}{3^2}$ (b) $\frac{1}{2^3}$ (c) $\frac{1}{3}$ (d) $\frac{1}{5^3}$ (e) $3^2$
     (f) $5^2$ (g) $2^4$ (h) $\frac{1}{3^2}$ (i) $\frac{1}{5^6}$ (j) $3^6$
**4.** (a) 1 (b) $\frac{1}{3}$ (c) $\frac{1}{8}$ (d) $\frac{1}{9}$ (e) 8 (f) 27
**5.** (a) $11\frac{1}{10}$ (b) $2\frac{7}{8}$ (c) $1\frac{6}{25}$ (d) $\frac{5}{6}$
     (e) $\frac{29}{100}$ (f) $\frac{1}{100}$ (g) $\frac{4}{25}$ (h) $1\frac{7}{30}$

**6.** (a) $-4$ (b) $-2$ (c) $-2$ (d) $-3$
(e) $-1$ (f) $-2$ (g) $-3$ (h) $-1$
**7.** $2^{14}$

## Exercise 5.6      Page 53

**1.** (a) 20 (b) 3 (c) 10 (d) 2 (e) 2 (f) 2.5
**2.** (a) 8 (b) 2 (c) 3 (d) 2 (e) 5 (f) 6
**3.** (a) $\frac{1}{10}$ (b) $\frac{1}{7}$ (c) $\frac{1}{2}$ (d) $\frac{1}{5}$ (e) $\frac{1}{4}$ (f) $\frac{1}{3}$
**4.** (a) 100 (b) 27 (c) 8 (d) 4 (e) 32
(f) 243 (g) 25 (h) 32 (i) 81 (j) 216
**5.** (a) $\frac{1}{100}$ (b) $\frac{1}{64}$ (c) $\frac{1}{4}$ (d) $\frac{1}{8}$ (e) $\frac{1}{8}$
(f) $\frac{1}{100\,000}$ (g) $\frac{1}{125}$ (h) $\frac{1}{8}$ (i) $\frac{1}{32}$ (j) $\frac{1}{25}$
**6.** (a) (i) $\frac{1}{2}$ (ii) $\frac{3}{7}$ (b) (i) 25 (ii) 9
**7.** (a) 3 (b) 4 (c) 5 (d) $\frac{1}{2}$ (e) $\frac{2}{3}$
(f) $\frac{1}{4}$ (g) $\frac{3}{4}$ (h) 256 (i) 125 (j) 1.5
**8.** (a) $\frac{3}{4}$ (b) $\frac{1}{2}$ (c) 3 (d) $\frac{15}{56}$ (e) $6\frac{3}{4}$
**10.** (a) 19.300 259 07… (b) 291.866 535 1…
(c) 3.169 674 155… (d) 3.024 773 331…
(e) 8.556 307 844… (f) 6.695 526 189…

## Review Exercise 5      Page 55

**1.** (a) 16 (b) 8 (c) 13
**2.** No. 4 cubed $= 4 \times 4 \times 4 = 64$
**3.** (a) 9 (b) 2, 3, 5
**4.** (a) 2 (b) 108 (c) 0.25
**5.** E.g. 2, 3, 4, 5: $2 + 3 + 4 + 5 = 14$
14 is not a multiple of 4.
**6.** 200
**7.** (a) (i) $2^5$ (ii) $2^2 \times 3^2$ (b) 4 (c) 288
**8.** 60 seconds
**9.** $5^7$
**10.** Positive. $(-) \times (-) = (+)$
**11.** (a) $x = 5$ (b) $x = 1$ (c) $x = 6$
**12.** (a) $\frac{1}{5}$ (b) 1 (c) $\frac{1}{3}$ (d) 4
**13.** (a) 9 (b) $\frac{1}{125}$ (c) $\frac{1}{27}$
**14.** (a) $3\frac{1}{2}$ (b) $-16\,384$
**15.** (a) (i) 15 (ii) 1 (b) $p = -3$
**16.** (a) 7.29 (b) 1.7 (c) 18.4 (d) 729
**17.** (a) 8.04 (b) (i) 7.61 (ii) $\frac{4^2 + 0.5}{4 \times 0.5} = 8.25$
**18.** (a) $-7.16$ (b) $3^2 \times 11^2$
**19.** 46.8
**20.** (a) 343 (b) 0.232 (c) 2.82 (d) 0.0346

## CHAPTER 6

## Exercise 6.1      Page 57

**1.** (a) $6 \times 10^5$ (b) 9 000 000
**2.** Missing entries are:
(a) $7.5 \times 10^4$ (b) 800 000 000, $8 \times 10^8$
(c) 35 000 000 000 000,
$3.5 \times 10\,000\,000\,000\,000$
(d) $6.23 \times 10\,000\,000\,000\,000$, $6.23 \times 10^{13}$

**3.** (a) $3 \times 10^{11}$ (b) $8 \times 10^7$
(c) $7 \times 10^8$ (d) $2 \times 10^9$
(e) $4.2 \times 10^7$ (f) $2.1 \times 10^{10}$
(g) $3.7 \times 10^9$ (h) $6.3 \times 10^2$
**4.** (a) 600 000 (b) 2000
(c) 50 000 000 (d) 900 000 000
(e) 3 700 000 000 (f) 28
(g) 99 000 000 000 (h) 71 000
**5.** (a) (i) $4.5 \times 10^3$ (ii) $7.8 \times 10^7$
(iii) $5.3 \times 10^5$ (iv) $3.25 \times 10^4$
(b) (i) 4500 (ii) 78 000 000
(iii) 530 000 (iv) 32 500
**6.** (a) (i) Brazil (ii) 250 000 000
(b) $1.288 \times 10^9$

## Exercise 6.2      Page 58

**1.** (a) $3.5 \times 10^{-4}$ (b) 0.0025
**2.** Missing entries are:
(a) $7.5 \times 10^{-3}$
(b) $8.75 \times 0.000\,001$, $8.75 \times 10^{-6}$
(c) $0.000\,000\,003\,5$, $3.5 \times 0.000\,000\,001$
(d) $6.23 \times 0.000\,000\,000\,001$, $6.23 \times 10^{-12}$
**3.** (a) $7 \times 10^{-3}$ (b) $4 \times 10^{-2}$
(c) $5 \times 10^{-9}$ (d) $8 \times 10^{-4}$
(e) $2.3 \times 10^{-9}$ (f) $4.5 \times 10^{-8}$
(g) $2.34 \times 10^{-2}$ (h) $2.34 \times 10^{-9}$
(i) $6.7 \times 10^{-3}$
**4.** (a) 0.35 (b) 0.0005
(c) 0.000 072 (d) 0.0061
(e) 0.000 000 000 117
(f) 0.000 000 813 5
(g) 0.064 62
(h) 0.000 000 004 001
**5.** (a) (i) $3.4 \times 10^{-3}$ (ii) $5.65 \times 10^{-5}$
(iii) $7.2 \times 10^{-4}$ (iv) $9.13 \times 10^{-1}$
(b) (i) 0.0034 (ii) 0.000 056 5
(iii) 0.000 72 (iv) 0.913

## Exercise 6.3      Page 59

**1.** (a) 6 E 13, $6 \times 10^{13}$, 60 000 000 000 000
(b) 9.6 E 12, $9.6 \times 10^{12}$, 9 600 000 000 000
(c) 1.05 E 13, $1.05 \times 10^{13}$,
10 500 000 000 000
(d) 1.3 E 14, $1.3 \times 10^{14}$,
130 000 000 000 000
(e) 2.4 E 14, $2.4 \times 10^{14}$,
240 000 000 000 000
(f) 2.5 E 12, $2.5 \times 10^{12}$, 2 500 000 000 000
**2.** (a) 6 E $-12$, $6 \times 10^{-12}$, 0.000 000 000 006
(b) 1.35 E $-10$, $1.35 \times 10^{-10}$,
0.000 000 000 135
(c) 3 E $-11$, $3 \times 10^{-11}$, 0.000 000 000 03
(d) 1.15 E $-10$, $1.15 \times 10^{-10}$,
0.000 000 000 115
(e) 4.24 E $-09$, $4.24 \times 10^{-9}$,
0.000 000 004 24
(f) 9.728 E $-11$, $9.728 \times 10^{-11}$,

## Exercise **6.4** — Page 60

1. (a) 262 500
   (b) 105 000 000 000 000
   (c) 72 250 000 000 000
   (d) 0.000 000 125
   (e) 30 000 000 000
   (f) 263 160 000 000 000 000 000

2. (a) $9.38 \times 10^{19}$
   (b) $1.6 \times 10^{1}$
   (c) $2.25 \times 10^{26}$
   (d) $1.25 \times 10^{-37}$
   (e) $2.4 \times 10^{20}$
   (f) $5 \times 10^{-2}$

3. (a) $2.088 \times 10^{9}$
   (b) $1.525\ 965 \times 10^{16}\,\text{km}$

4. (a) Pluto, Saturn, Jupiter
   (b) $1.397 \times 10^{5}\,\text{km}$, $139\ 700\,\text{km}$

5. (a) $9.273 \times 10^{6}\,\text{km}^2$
   (b) $4.93 \times 10^{5}\,\text{km}^2$

6. $2.52 \times 10^{12}$

7. $2.2 \times 10^{-5}$

8. $1.49 \times 10^{9}$ square miles

9. 30%

10. $9 \times 10^{-28}$ grams

11. (a) $4.55 \times 10^{9}$ years
    (b) About $6.6 \times 10^{3}$ times

## Exercise **6.5** — Page 61

1. (a) $5.2 \times 10^{3}$  (b) $8.4 \times 10^{6}$
   (c) $4 \times 10^{4}$  (d) $5 \times 10^{4}$

2. (a) $2.8 \times 10^{3}$  (b) $9 \times 10^{5}$
   (c) $3 \times 10^{7}$  (d) $9.5 \times 10^{8}$

3. (a) $8 \times 10^{7}$  (b) $6 \times 10^{7}$
   (c) $2.4 \times 10^{8}$  (d) $2.7 \times 10^{15}$

4. (a) $3 \times 10^{3}$  (b) $3 \times 10^{3}$
   (c) $5 \times 10^{1}$  (d) $2 \times 10^{11}$
   (e) $4 \times 10^{5}$  (f) $3 \times 10^{-3}$

5. (a) $1.5 \times 10^{0}$  (b) $2.7 \times 10^{13}$
   (c) $4.5 \times 10^{4}$  (d) $1.25 \times 10^{-13}$
   (e) $6 \times 10^{8}$

6. (a) $1.5 \times 10^{11}$  (b) $2.4 \times 10^{3}$
   (c) $4.2 \times 10^{-8}$  (d) $6.4 \times 10^{7}$
   (e) $5 \times 10^{1}$  (f) $3 \times 10^{9}$
   (g) $6.25 \times 10^{-6}$  (h) $2.5 \times 10^{4}$

## Review Exercise **6** — Page 62

1. (a) (i) $7.8 \times 10^{6}$  (ii) $5 \times 10^{-6}$
   (b) (i) 170 000  (ii) 0.0032

2. (a) (i) $6 \times 10^{4}$  (ii) $3.6 \times 10^{9}$
   (b) $3.13 \times 10^{-2}$

3. (a) $9.317 \times 10^{7}$  (b) $9.292 \times 10^{7}$

4. (a) (i) $8 \times 10^{4}$  (ii) $1.25 \times 10^{-5}$
   (b) $2.1 \times 10^{5}$

5. (a) $4 \times 10^{-4}$  (b) $9.8 \times 10^{11}$

6. (a) $1 \times 10^{-24}$  (b) E.g. $1 \times 10^{-25}$

7. $1.35 \times 10^{9}\,\text{km}^3$

## CHAPTER 7

## Exercise **7.1** — Page 63

1. (a) $1 : 2$  (b) $1 : 3$  (c) $3 : 4$  (d) $2 : 5$
   (e) $3 : 4$  (f) $2 : 5$  (g) $3 : 7$  (h) $9 : 4$
   (i) $4 : 9$  (j) $7 : 3$

2. (a) 12  (b) 28  (c) 100  (d) 20

3. 198 cm

4. 400 g

5. 64

6. 18 years old

7. $2 : 3$

8. $5 : 2$

9. $1 : 250$

10. $1 : 1500$

11. (a) $4 : 1$  (b) $2 : 25$
    (c) $11 : 2$  (d) $5 : 2$
    (e) $4 : 1$  (f) $40 : 17$
    (g) $9 : 20$  (h) $25 : 1$

12. $40 : 9$

13. $2 : 3$

14. $1 : 2$

15. $3 : 2$

## Exercise **7.2** — Page 65

1. (a) 6, 3
   (b) 15, 5
   (c) 7, 28
   (d) 90, 10

2. 8

3. 18

4. Sunny £36, Chandni £12

5. (a) £14, £21
   (b) £32, £24
   (c) £3.50, £2
   (d) £1.80, £3

6. 45

7. £192

8. $\frac{1}{4}$

9. 80%

10. $\frac{5}{8}$

11. 60%

12. 48%

13. $170\ 000\,\text{km}^2$

14. (a) Jenny 50, Tim 30
    (b) 10

15. (a) $5 : 2$
    (b) 6
    (c) 55
    (d) 32 is not a multiple of $5 + 2 = 7$

16. 8 cm, 12 cm, 18 cm

17. 200 kg

18. 40°, 60°, 80°

19. 45%

## Exercise **7.3** — Page 66

1. (a) 16p
   (b) £1.28

2. £2.85

3. 4

4. (a) 120 cm
   (b) 2 kg

5. £201.60

6. 18 minutes

7. (a) 250 g
   (b) 150 g

8. £2.85

9. 15

10. £89.28

11. £9.10

12. (a) 12 minutes
    (b) 16 miles

13. (a) $12\,\text{m}^2$
    (b) 12 litres

14. 24

15. (a) £3.08
    (b) 12 minutes

16. (a) £260
    (b) 32

17. 50 minutes

18. $17\frac{1}{2}$ minutes

19. £8.35

20. £4 213 100

## Review Exercise **7** — Page 68

1. (a) $2 : 1$  (b) 75 g  (c) 75 g

2. (a) $7 : 5$  (b) 32

3. 720 City fans,  480 United fans

4. £4900

**5.** £29.44
**6.** 25 minutes
**7.** 1 : 250
**8.** 306 075

**9.** $0.5\,\text{m}^3$
**10.** Bag P: 25 silver, 15 gold
     Bag Q: 12 silver, 8 gold
**11.** (a) £24.50    (b) £7.32

## CHAPTER 8

### Exercise **8.1**      Page 70

**1.** 8 miles per hour
**2.** 7 km/h
**3.** 25 metres per minute
**4.** (a) 20 km/h
    (b) 50 km/h
    (c) 4 km/h
**5.** 10 km/h
**6.** 8 km
**7.** 30 miles
**8.** 3 km
**9.** (a) 150 km   (b) 86 km
    (c) 40 km
**10.** $\frac{1}{2}$ hour
**11.** 20 seconds

**12.** $1\frac{1}{2}$ hours
**13.** (a) 3 hours
    (b) 2 hours
    (c) $3\frac{1}{2}$ hours
**14.** $2\frac{1}{4}$ hours
**15.** 6 km
**16.** $1\frac{1}{4}$ hours
**17.** (a) $2\frac{1}{2}$ hours
    (b) $1\frac{1}{4}$ hours
**18.** (a) 60 km/h
    (b) 1 hour
**19.** 11.20 am

### Exercise **8.2**      Page 71

**1.** (a) 300 km
    (b) 5 hours
    (c) 60 km/h
**2.** 5 m/s
**3.** 10 km/h
**4.** 10.30 am
**5.** 11.09 am

**6.** (a) 13.8 km/h   (b) 1.10 pm
**7.** (a) 8 hours
    (b) 111 km/h
**8.** (a) 4.81 m/s
    (b) 17.3 km/h
**9.** 150 m
**10.** 300 000 000 m/s

### Exercise **8.3**      Page 72

**1.** $8\,\text{g/cm}^3$
**2.** $9\,\text{g/cm}^3$
**3.** $2.5\,\text{g/cm}^3$
**4.** $28.6\,\text{g/cm}^3$
**5.** 7200 g
**6.** $800\,\text{cm}^3$
**7.** $2000\,\text{cm}^3$

**8.** $0.8\,\text{g/cm}^3$
**9.** (a) $350\,\text{cm}^3$ (b) $2.57\,\text{g/cm}^3$
**10.** 118.3 people/km²
**11.** (a) 30 530 km²
    (b) 104.2 people/km²
    (c) 57 400 000
**12.** 1150 g

### Review Exercise 8      Page 74

**1.** 94 km/h
**2.** 40 miles per hour
**3.** 45 km/h
**4.** 36 minutes
**5.** (a) 4 hours
    (b) 9.6 km/h
**6.** 1.12 m/s
**7.** 2.5 minutes

**8.** 24 km/h
**9.** 5 hours 42 minutes
**10.** 14.7 km/h
**11.** $4.84 \times 10^8$ miles
**12.** $2.92\,\text{g/cm}^3$
**13.** $4.35\,\text{cm}^3$
**14.** 2 900 000 people

**15.** Population density -
    was: 826.92 people/sq. mile,
    now: 909.09 people/sq. mile.
  Increase of 82.17 people/sq. mile.

## CHAPTER 9

### Exercise **9.1**      Page 76

**1.** (a) $\frac{7}{9}$   (b) $\frac{1}{9}$   (c) $\frac{8}{9}$   (d) $\frac{4}{11}$   (e) $\frac{82}{99}$
    (f) $\frac{5}{37}$   (g) $\frac{8}{37}$   (h) $\frac{425}{999}$   (i) $\frac{6}{37}$   (j) $\frac{2}{7}$
**2.** (a) $\frac{1}{6}$   (b) $\frac{1}{30}$   (c) $\frac{11}{18}$   (d) $\frac{7}{15}$   (e) $\frac{7}{30}$
    (f) $\frac{5}{6}$   (g) $\frac{181}{990}$   (h) $\frac{3}{22}$   (i) $\frac{31}{36}$   (j) $\frac{17}{22}$
**3.** $\frac{2}{17}$
**4.** 2, 4, 5, 8, 10, 16, 20

### Exercise **9.2**      Page 77

**1.** (a) $\frac{1}{2}$   (b) $\frac{9}{20}$   (c) $\frac{3}{10}$   (d) $\frac{5}{8}$   (e) $\frac{9}{4}$
    (f) $-\frac{1}{4}$   (g) $\frac{3}{11}$   (h) 7   (i) $\frac{7}{20}$   (j) $\frac{25}{111}$
    (k) 2   (l) $-\frac{1}{5}$   (m) 4   (n) $\frac{3}{4}$   (o) $\frac{11}{90}$
**2.** (a) Rational, $\frac{1}{4}$     (b) Rational, $\frac{5}{9}$
    (c) Irrational         (d) Rational, 5
    (e) Rational, $\frac{3}{5}$     (f) Rational, $-\frac{1}{2}$
    (g) Irrational         (h) Rational, $\frac{19}{9}$
    (i) Rational, 2      (j) Rational, $\frac{4}{3}$

### Exercise **9.3**      Page 78

**1.** (a), (d)
**2.** (a) $2\sqrt{3}$    (b) $3\sqrt{3}$    (c) $3\sqrt{5}$
    (d) $4\sqrt{3}$    (e) $4\sqrt{2}$    (f) $5\sqrt{2}$
    (g) $3\sqrt{6}$    (h) $2\sqrt{6}$    (i) $7\sqrt{2}$
    (j) $4\sqrt{5}$    (k) $3\sqrt{7}$    (l) $10\sqrt{2}$
    (m) $8\sqrt{2}$    (n) $4\sqrt{7}$    (o) $5\sqrt{7}$
**3.** (a) $2\sqrt{2}$    (b) $\sqrt{5}$    (c) $7\sqrt{3}$
    (d) $5\sqrt{2}$    (e) $\sqrt{2}$    (f) $7\sqrt{5}$
    (g) $3\sqrt{3}$    (h) $6\sqrt{3}$    (i) $6\sqrt{2}$
    (j) $12\sqrt{5}$   (k) $14\sqrt{3}$   (l) $5\sqrt{5}$
**4.** (a) $10\sqrt{2}$   (b) $5\sqrt{3}$    (c) $6\sqrt{2}$
**5.** (a) $\frac{3}{2}$      (b) $\frac{5}{4}$      (c) $\frac{3}{2}$
    (d) $\frac{2\sqrt{6}}{3}$    (e) $\frac{\sqrt{6}}{2}$    (f) $\frac{2\sqrt{5}}{5}$
**6.** (a) 3       (b) 6       (c) 30
    (d) 4       (e) 6       (f) $5\sqrt{2}$
    (g) $6\sqrt{2}$    (h) $10\sqrt{2}$   (i) 12
    (j) $6\sqrt{6}$    (k) $8\sqrt{6}$    (l) $12\sqrt{6}$
**7.** (a) $2 + \sqrt{2}$ (b) $3\sqrt{2} - 3$ (c) $5\sqrt{2} - 5$

### Exercise **9.4**      Page 79

**1.** (a) $\frac{\sqrt{3}}{3}$   (b) $\frac{\sqrt{5}}{5}$   (c) $\frac{\sqrt{7}}{7}$   (d) $\sqrt{2}$
    (e) $\sqrt{5}$   (f) $2\sqrt{2}$   (g) $2\sqrt{3}$   (h) $2\sqrt{7}$
    (i) $\frac{\sqrt{6}}{2}$   (j) $3\sqrt{5}$   (k) $3\sqrt{3}$   (l) $\frac{\sqrt{15}}{3}$
    (m) $3\sqrt{6}$   (n) $7\sqrt{5}$

**2.** (a) $\dfrac{3\sqrt{2}}{2}$    (b) $\dfrac{\sqrt{6}}{2}$    (c) $\sqrt{2}$

   (d) $\dfrac{3\sqrt{2}}{2}$    (e) $\dfrac{\sqrt{2}}{2}$    (f) $2$

   (g) $3$    (h) $\dfrac{1}{2}$    (i) $\sqrt{3}$

   (j) $2\sqrt{2}$    (k) $1$    (l) $\sqrt{5}$

   (m) $\dfrac{\sqrt{2}}{2}$    (n) $\dfrac{\sqrt{3}}{3}$    (o) $\dfrac{5\sqrt{3}}{6}$

   (p) $\dfrac{\sqrt{10}}{5}$    (q) $\dfrac{3\sqrt{10}}{10}$    (r) $\dfrac{2\sqrt{3}}{3}$

## Review Exercise 9     Page 80

**1.** (a) $0.\dot{5}$    (b) $\dfrac{23}{90}$

**2.** $\dfrac{35}{99}$

**3.** (a) $2\sqrt{5}$    (b) $\dfrac{6}{5}$    (c) $6$

**4.** (a) $2\sqrt{3}$    (b) $5\sqrt{3}$    (c) $\dfrac{\sqrt{5}}{2}$

**5.** (a) (i) $\dfrac{1}{10}$   (ii) Not possible   (iii) $\dfrac{41}{333}$

     (b) $9\sqrt{2}$

**6.** (a) $6\sqrt{2}$    (b) $10\sqrt{3}$    (c) $5\sqrt{3}$

**7.** (a) $2\sqrt{5}-10$    (b) $k=3$    (c) $4\sqrt{5}$

**8.** $2\sqrt{2}$

**9.** (a) $5\sqrt{3}$    (b) $15$

**10.** (a) (i) $4\sqrt{3}$   (ii) $5\sqrt{2}$   (b) $\dfrac{\sqrt{3}}{6}$

## Number  

## Non-calculator Paper    Page 81

**1.** (a) **1500**   (b) **0.06**   (c) **375**   (d) **10**

**2.** 162

**3.** 1.5 pints

**4.** £340

**5.** (a) $\dfrac{1}{4}$, $\dfrac{1}{3}$, $\dfrac{2}{5}$, $\dfrac{1}{2}$, $\dfrac{2}{3}$, $\dfrac{3}{4}$    (b) E.g. $\dfrac{3}{4}$

   (c) (i) $1\dfrac{7}{15}$   (ii) $30$   (iii) $\dfrac{1}{10}$   (iv) $\dfrac{8}{15}$

**6.** £97.50

**7.** (a) £25    (b) £84

**8.** (a) 4.9224    (b) 0.1758

**9.** £10

**10.** Minimum: 395, maximum: 404

**11.** (a) 18

   (b) $5^3$ is smaller. $3^5=243$, $5^3=125$

**12.** 76p

**13.** (a) $\dfrac{1}{12}$    (b) 36

**14.** 15

**15.** $\sqrt{6^2-3^2}\approx 5$

**16.** (a) $24\times\dfrac{1}{24}=1$   (b) No. E.g. $\sqrt{0.25}=0.5$

**17.** 7 g/cm³

**18.** $2\times3^2\times5$

**19.** Andi is correct.

Increase of 10% $=110\%$ of original speed

$=1.1\times$ original speed

Decrease of 10% $=90\%\times1.1=0.99$

$=99\%$ of original speed

**20.** 84 km/h

**21.** (a) 24      (b) 144

**22.** **A**: False. The prime numbers will be factors of the product.

   **B**: True. Even number + Odd number = Odd number + Even number = Odd number.

**23.** (a) $9^4$   (b) 650 000   (c) $2.5\times10^{-5}$

**24.** (a) $3:7$

   (b) Appleby £24 000, Bunbury £56 000

   (c) Greatest: 35.5 km, least: 34.5 km

**25.** $1\dfrac{1}{6}$

**26.** (a) $4\dfrac{1}{4}$    (b) 2.5

**27.** (a) (i) 0.0012   (ii) 1000

   (b) $1.8\times10^8$   (c) $1.2\times10^{-4}$ terawatts

**28.** £40

**29.** Alex £2500, Brenda £900, Christine £1200, David £800, Ellie £600

**30.** (a) $\sqrt{\dfrac{300^2}{900}}=\sqrt{100}=10$

   (b) No. Maximum weight of one crate: 6.5 tonnes.

     Maximum weight of 7 crates: $6.5\times7=45.5$ tonnes, which is greater than maximum legal load.

**31.** (a) $1.5\times10^3$    (b) $6\times10^5$

**32.** (a) $\dfrac{8}{11}$    (b) $0.\dot{5}$    (c) $0.\dot{1}4\dot{8}$

**33.** (a) $4\sqrt{2}$    (b) $1\dfrac{1}{2}$    (c) $5\sqrt{3}$

**34.** (a) (i) 1   (ii) 3    (b) $2.4\times10^5$

**35.** (a) 18 km/h    (b) 14.4 km/h

**36.** 2.5 m

**37.** $\dfrac{90\times10^6}{2\times10^5}=450$ seconds $\approx 8$ minutes

**38.** (a) $\dfrac{7}{9}$    (b) $\dfrac{43}{90}$

**39.** (a) 2    (b) $\dfrac{1}{9}$

**40.** (a) (i) $10\sqrt{3}$   (ii) $11\sqrt{3}$   (iii) $6\sqrt{6}$

   (b) $\dfrac{\sqrt{10}}{15}$

**41.** (a) $\dfrac{1}{16}$    (b) $\dfrac{1}{12}$    (c) $\dfrac{9}{16}$

**42.** (a) $3\sqrt{11}$

   (b) $\left(\sqrt{2}+\dfrac{1}{\sqrt{2}}\right)\left(\sqrt{2}+\dfrac{1}{\sqrt{2}}\right)$

     $=2+1+1+\dfrac{1}{2}=4.5$

   (c) (i) $\dfrac{1}{x}$, $x^\circ$, $x^2$   (ii) $x^2$, $\sqrt{x}$, $x^\circ$, $\dfrac{1}{x}$

**43.** $\dfrac{8}{37}$

## Number  

## Calculator Paper    Page 84

**1.** (a) £8.60

   (b) 250 g pot.

     **145 g pot**: 3.71 g/p,   **250 g pot**: 3.79 g/p

**2.** (a) 29    (b) 62.8    (c) 9.2

**3.** (a) 55%     (b) 9 : 11     (c) 210

**4.** (a) 800     (b) 4 days

**5.** (a) (i) The numerator is less than double the denominator.
   (ii) Put brackets around $3 + 5$ and $2.5 + 4$.
   (b) 11.46

**6.** £20.68

**7.** 805 euros

**8.** (a) 39.520…     (b) $\frac{20^2}{7+3} = \frac{400}{10} = 40$

**9.** £37 800

**10.** (a) 64 miles per hour     (b) 63 miles

**11.** 95.8%

**12.** (a) £540     (b) (i) £450     (ii) 9.75%

**13.** (a) $6.25 \times 10^7$     (b) $\frac{3}{8}$     (c) 72     (d) 12

**14.** £535.96

**15.** 51.8 cm³

**16.** (a) (i) 14.3     (ii) $5 \times 10^{-10}$
   (b) E.g. reciprocal of 0.5, $\frac{1}{0.5} = 2$

**17.** (a) 100 km/h     (b) 50 miles per hour

**18.** £7.36

**19.** 7.2%

**20.** (a) (i) $\frac{2}{3}$     (ii) 0.025     (b) $8.75 \times 10^{-3}$

**21.** (a) 18     (b) 7560

**22.** $4.78 \times 10^{-1}$

**23.** (a) $6.43 \times 10^{10}$     (b) 1 : 9.2

**24.** (a) 3071     (b) 2008

**25.** (a) 6.5     (b) 1.27 seconds

**26.** 15 tins

**27.** Upper bound: 63.1 miles per hour
   Lower bound: 52 miles per hour

**28.** (a) 17 540     (b) 197.8 million

**29.** (a) $\frac{3}{11}$     (b) E.g. $m = 8$ (or 18, or 32,…)
   (c) $\frac{\sqrt{10}}{2}$

**30.** $a = \frac{30.53 - 17.35}{2.55} = 5.098…$

## CHAPTER 10

### Exercise 10.1     Page 87

**1.** $m + 6$
**2.** $m - 12$
**3.** $8m$
**4.** $p - 1$
**5.** $p + 5$
**6.** $25p$
**7.** $6k$
**8.** $5b$ pence
**9.** $\frac{c}{3}$ pence
**10.** $\frac{a}{5}$ pence
**11.** $\frac{36}{g}$

### Exercise 10.2     Page 88

**1.** (a) $3n$     (b) $5y$     (c) $10g$     (d) $4y$
   (e) $8m$     (f) $-4x$     (g) $-14a$

**2.** (a) Can be simplified, $2v$.
   (b) Cannot be simplified, different terms.
   (c) Can be simplified to $3v + 4$.
   (d) Cannot be simplified, different terms.

**3.** (a) $8x + y$     (b) $w + 2v$     (c) $2a - 2b$
   (d) $a + b$     (e) $5 - 5k$     (f) $a + 3$
   (g) $3b - 2a$     (h) $2x + 3y$     (i) $a + 2b$
   (j) $-2f$     (k) $v - 4w$     (l) $-2 - 5t$

**4.** (a) $2xy$     (b) $2pq$
   (c) $3ab - a + b$     (d) $2x^2$
   (e) $9y^2 - y$     (f) $4a^2 + a$
   (g) $2d^2 - 3g^2$     (h) $5t^2 - t$
   (i) $6m - m^2$

**5.** (a) $4x + 2$     (b) $4a + 6b$
   (c) $3x$     (d) $6y + 9$

### Exercise 10.3     Page 89

**1.** (a) $3a$     (b) $8c$     (c) $9d$
   (d) $8f$     (e) $6p$     (f) $15q$
   (g) $r^2$     (h) $2g^2$     (i) $6g^2$
   (j) $12t^2$     (k) $15u^2$     (l) $9d^2$

**2.** (a) $-3y$     (b) $-5y$     (c) $2y$
   (d) $-6y$     (e) $-t^2$     (f) $-2t^2$
   (g) $-10t^2$     (h) $10t^2$

**3.** (a) $5a$     (b) 12     (c) 20
   (d) 2     (e) 18     (f) $3p$
   (g) 3     (h) 9     (i) 4
   (j) 5     (k) 4     (l) 9

**4.** (a) $-2y$     (b) $-3y$     (c) $-5$
   (d) $m$     (e) $-3$     (f) $-2$
   (g) $-3$     (h) 1

**5.** (a) $ab$     (b) $y^2$     (c) $2pq$
   (d) $2a^2$     (e) $12gh$     (f) $abc$
   (g) $m^3$     (h) $2d^3$     (i) $6x^3$
   (j) $10m^2n$     (k) $3abc$     (l) $18pqr$

**6.** (a) $y^3$     (b) $t^5$     (c) $g^{10}$
   (d) $m^6$     (e) $6d^5$     (f) $8x^5$
   (g) $6t^5$     (h) $24r^6$     (i) $m^3n^2$
   (j) $a^4b^2$     (k) $6r^3s^4$     (l) $10x^5y^3$

**7.** (a) $t^6$     (b) $y^6$     (c) $g^9$
   (d) $x^8$     (e) $9a^2$     (f) $8h^3$
   (g) $2m^6$     (h) $4m^6$     (i) $3d^6$
   (j) $9d^6$     (k) $27a^6$     (l) $8k^9$
   (m) $x^2y^2$     (n) $m^3n^6$     (o) $8s^3t^3$
   (p) $9p^4q^2$

**8.** (a) $y^2$     (b) a     (c) 1
   (d) $g^{-1}$     (e) $6b^2$     (f) $5m$
   (g) $4t$     (h) $3h^{-1}$     (i) $y$
   (j) $m^2n^{-1}$     (k) $\frac{2}{3}p^2q^{-1}$     (l) $3rs^2$

**9.** (a) $t^2$     (b) $x^2$     (c) $\frac{12}{b^3}$
   (d) $15pq^2$     (e) $x^{10}$     (f) $\frac{1}{a}$
   (g) $3x^4$     (h) $\frac{2w^4}{t^5}$     (i) $\frac{1}{a^6}$
   (j) $y^4$     (k) $\frac{5}{m^9}$     (l) $\frac{n^4}{9}$

**10.** (a) $t$     (b) $g^{-1}$     (c) $m^2$
   (d) $y$     (e) $y^2$     (f) $m^{-1}$
   (g) $2t^2$     (h) 3

**11.** (a) $2v$    (b) $4p$    (c) $\dfrac{ac^3}{2}$    (d) $\dfrac{4}{m}$

    (e) $\dfrac{16}{w^2}$    (f) $1$    (g) $4$    (h) $4ac^{-3}$

## Exercise 10.4 — Page 91

**1.** (a) $2x + 10$    (b) $3a + 18$
    (c) $4y + 12$

**2.** (a) $3x + 6$    (b) $2y + 10$
    (c) $4x + 2$    (d) $3p + 3q$

**3.** (a) $a^2 + a$    (b) $2d + d^2$
    (c) $2x^2 + x$

**4.** (a) $2x + 8$    (b) $3t - 6$
    (c) $6a + 2b$    (d) $15 - 10d$
    (e) $x^2 + 3x$    (f) $t^2 - 3t$
    (g) $2g^2 + 3g$    (h) $2m - 3m^2$

**5.** (a) $2p^2 + 6p$    (b) $6d - 9d^2$
    (c) $m^2 - mn$    (d) $5x^2 + 10xy$

**6.** (a) $2x + 5$    (b) $3a + 11$
    (c) $6w - 17$    (d) $10 + 2p$
    (e) $3q$    (f) $7 - 3t$
    (g) $5z + 8$    (h) $8t + 15$
    (i) $2c - 6$    (j) $5a - 9$
    (k) $3y - 10$    (l) $2x + 6$
    (m) $8a + 23$    (n) $10x - 12$
    (o) $2p - 11$    (p) $5a + 2b$
    (q) $3x + y$    (r) $2p - 5q$
    (s) $5x - x^2$    (t) $a^2 - 2a$
    (u) $2y$

**7.** (a) $5x + 8$    (b) $5a + 13$
    (c) $9y + 23$    (d) $9a + 5$
    (e) $26t + 30$    (f) $5z + 13$
    (g) $12q + 16$    (h) $11x - 3$
    (i) $20e - 16$    (j) $6d^2 + 3d$
    (k) $3m^2 - 3m$    (l) $5a^2 - 4a$

**8.** (a) $-3x + 6$    (b) $-3x + 6$
    (c) $-2y + 10$    (d) $-6 + 2x$
    (e) $-15 + 3y$    (f) $-4 - 4a$
    (g) $3 - 2a$    (h) $2d + 6$
    (i) $2b - 6$    (j) $-6p - 9$
    (k) $m - 6$    (l) $5d + 1$
    (m) $-a^2 + 2a$    (n) $d - d^2$
    (o) $2x^2$    (p) $-6g^2 - 9g$
    (q) $7t^2 - 6t$    (r) $8m - 2m^2$

**9.** (a) $3a - 1$    (b) $y - 5$
    (c) $5m - 1$    (d) $3x - 4$
    (e) $1 - d$    (f) $t - 10$
    (g) $4m + 9$    (h) $-x - 18$
    (i) $23 - 6a$

## Exercise 10.5 — Page 93

**1.** (a) $2(x + y)$    (b) $3(a - 2b)$
    (c) $2(3m + 4n)$    (d) $x(x - 2)$
    (e) $a(b + 1)$    (f) $x(2 - y)$
    (g) $2a(b - 2)$    (h) $2x(2x + 3)$
    (i) $dg(1 - g)$

**2.** (a) $2(a + b)$    (b) $5(x - y)$
    (c) $3(d + 2e)$    (d) $2(2m - n)$
    (e) $3(2a + 3b)$    (f) $2(3a - 4b)$
    (g) $4(2t + 3)$    (h) $5(a - 2)$
    (i) $2(2d - 1)$    (j) $3(1 - 3g)$
    (k) $5(1 - 4m)$    (l) $4(k + 1)$

**3.** (a) $x(y - z)$    (b) $g(f + h)$
    (c) $b(a - 2)$    (d) $q(3 + p)$
    (e) $a(1 + b)$    (f) $g(h - 1)$
    (g) $a(a + 3)$    (h) $t(5 - t)$
    (i) $d(1 - d)$    (j) $m(m + 1)$
    (k) $r(5r - 3)$    (l) $x(3x + 2)$

**4.** (a) $3(y + 2 - 3x)$    (b) $t(t^2 - t + 1)$
    (c) $2d(d + 2)$    (d) $3m(1 - 2n)$
    (e) $2g(f + 2g)$    (f) $4q(p - 2)$
    (g) $3y(2 - 5y)$    (h) $2x(3x + 2y)$
    (i) $2n(3n - 1)$    (j) $2b(2a + 3)$
    (k) $\frac{1}{2}a(1 - a)$    (l) $4x(5 + y)$
    (m) $a^2(a + a^3 + 1)$    (n) $\pi r(2 + r)$
    (o) $4ab(5a + 3b)$    (p) $3pq(1 - 3p)$

## Review Exercise 10 — Page 94

**1.** (a) $5n$ pence    (b) $(n - 15)$ pence

**2.** (a) (i) $9b$    (ii) $6y$    (iii) $t^3$
    (b) $12x + 20$

**3.** $(3b + 5g)$ pence

**4.** (a) $2x$ cm    (b) $(x + 3)$ cm
    (c) $(4x + 3)$ cm

**5.** (a) $3ab$    (b) $a^2 + 2a$
    (c) $2x - 6$    (d) $5x + 2$

**6.** (a) $9x + 3y$    (b) $3(x + 6)$

**7.** (a) $3n - 5$    (b) $5a + 1$
    (c) $x(2x + y)$

**8.** (a) $a^5$    (b) $22x - 14$

**9.** (a) $3(2x - 5)$    (b) $y(y + 7)$

**10.** (a) $6a^3$    (b) $24a^2b$
    (c) $2a^2b$

**11.** (a) $13 - 2x$
    (b) (i) $2y(3x - 1)$
       (ii) $7y(y + 2)$
    (c) $5m^2$

**12.** (a) $2x^2 - x$    (b) $1 - 3x$

**13.** $2x + 14$

**14.** (a) $a^9$    (b) $b^3$
    (c) $c^2$    (d) $d^6$

**15.** (a) $p^7$    (b) $4t^3$

**16.** (a) (i) $3y(2x - y)$
       (ii) $2m(2m + 3)$
    (b) (i) $10y^5$
       (ii) $3x^4$
       (iii) $3a^2b^{-1}$

**17.** (a) $2x - 14$    (b) $2y^4$

**18.** (a) $4 - 4x$    (b) $6a^5$

## Exercise **11.1**  Page 95

**1.** (a) 3 (b) 4
(c) 9 (d) 16
**2.** (a) $x = 4$ (b) $a = 3$ (c) $y = 8$
(d) $t = 6$ (e) $h = 22$ (f) $d = 1$
(g) $z = 30$ (h) $p = 0$ (i) $c = 99$
**3.** (a) 5 (b) 5
(c) 18 (d) 21
**4.** (a) $a = 4$ (b) $e = 6$ (c) $p = 4$
(d) $y = \frac{1}{2}$ (e) $d = 10$ (f) $t = 9$
(g) $m = 28$ (h) $x = 100$
**5.** (a) 1 (b) 4 (c) 4
(d) 2 (e) 3 (f) 5

## Exercise **11.2**  Page 96

**1.** 5 **3.** 6 **5.** 4 **7.** 4
**2.** 14 **4.** 11 **6.** 3 **8.** 7
**9.** (a) 2 (b) $2(x + 3) = 2x + 6$
**10.** (a) 9 (b) $3(x - 2) = 3x - 6$

## Exercise **11.3**  Page 98

**1.** (a) $y = 3$ (b) $n = 16$ (c) $x = 2$
(d) $y = 19$ (e) $b = 7$ (f) $x = 29$
(g) $m = 4$ (h) $k = 5$ (i) $y = 7$
**2.** (a) $c = 4$ (b) $a = 4$ (c) $f = 3$
(d) $d = 30$ (e) $e = 14$ (f) $m = 20$
**3.** (a) $p = 4$ (b) $t = 3$ (c) $h = 7$
(d) $b = 2$ (e) $d = 10$ (f) $x = 6$
(g) $c = 5$ (h) $n = 3$ (i) $x = 2$

## Exercise **11.4**  Page 98

**1.** (a) $k = \frac{1}{2}$ (b) $a = -3$ (c) $d = -4$
(d) $n = -\frac{1}{2}$ (e) $t = -5$ (f) $n = 1$
(g) $m = 1\frac{1}{2}$ (h) $x = 2\frac{1}{3}$ (i) $y = -\frac{1}{2}$
**2.** (a) $x = -2$ (b) $y = -3$ (c) $t = -2$
(d) $a = -2$ (e) $d = -3$ (f) $g = -3$
(g) $t = \frac{1}{2}$ (h) $x = 7\frac{1}{2}$ (i) $d = 1\frac{2}{5}$
(j) $a = 1\frac{1}{2}$ (k) $g = \frac{1}{5}$ (l) $b = 4\frac{1}{2}$
**3.** (a) $x = -2$ (b) $n = -\frac{1}{2}$ (c) $a = -1$
(d) $y = -3$ (e) $x = -1$ (f) $d = -3$
(g) $x = -1\frac{1}{2}$ (h) $x = -4$ (i) $x = -1\frac{1}{2}$
(j) $n = 1\frac{1}{2}$ (k) $z = 10$ (l) $m = -3$
(m) $n = 4$ (n) $p = -1\frac{1}{2}$ (o) $v = 9$

## Exercise **11.5**  Page 99

**1.** (a) $x = 3$ (b) $a = 2$ (c) $t = 2$
(d) $p = 5$ (e) $c = 6$ (f) $x = 3$
(g) $d = 9$ (h) $e = 5$ (i) $f = 4$

**2.** (a) $w = 2$ (b) $s = 3$ (c) $t = 3$
(d) $y = 1$ (e) $x = 3$ (f) $y = 5$
**3.** (a) $p = -1$ (b) $d = -2$ (c) $g = -2$
(d) $x = 8\frac{1}{2}$ (e) $y = \frac{2}{5}$ (f) $t = \frac{1}{2}$
(g) $t = 1\frac{3}{4}$ (h) $a = 2\frac{1}{2}$ (i) $m = 2\frac{3}{5}$
**4.** (a) $x = 4$ (b) $a = 2$ (c) $m = -\frac{1}{2}$
(d) $y = 2\frac{1}{2}$ (e) $w = -3$ (f) $e = 2$
(g) $a = 1\frac{1}{2}$ (h) $t = -11$ (i) $x = 1$

## Exercise **11.6**  Page 100

**1.** (a) $x = 5$ (b) $q = 2$ (c) $t = 3$
(d) $e = 3$ (e) $g = 4$ (f) $y = 1$
(g) $x = 2$ (h) $k = 1$ (i) $a = 4$
(j) $p = 6$ (k) $m = 2$ (l) $d = 5$
(m) $y = 5$ (n) $u = 3$ (o) $q = 0$
**2.** (a) $d = 8$ (b) $q = 3$ (c) $c = 2$
(d) $t = 3$ (e) $w = 2$ (f) $e = 3$
(g) $g = 5$ (h) $z = 4$ (i) $m = 6$
(j) $a = 5$ (k) $x = 4$ (l) $y = 3$
**3.** (a) $m = -4$ (b) $t = -2$ (c) $p = -2$
(d) $x = 3\frac{1}{2}$ (e) $a = \frac{1}{2}$ (f) $b = \frac{4}{5}$
(g) $y = \frac{4}{5}$ (h) $d = \frac{3}{4}$ (i) $f = -3\frac{1}{2}$
**4.** (a) $x = 4$ (b) $a = 1\frac{2}{3}$ (c) $m = \frac{1}{2}$
(d) $a = -5$ (e) $y = 5\frac{1}{2}$ (f) $n = -1\frac{1}{2}$
(g) $d = -4\frac{1}{2}$ (h) $k = -11$ (i) $t = -4$
(j) $q = 2$ (k) $x = \frac{2}{3}$ (l) $a = 2\frac{1}{2}$
**5.** (a) $h = 2$ (b) $x = -3$ (c) $w = 3$
(d) $y = 1\frac{1}{2}$ (e) $v = -8$ (f) $c = -1\frac{1}{2}$
(g) $x = -18$ (h) $x = -7$

## Exercise **11.7**  Page 101

**1.** (a) $x = 6$ (b) $d = -10$ (c) $a = 6$
(d) $m = -2$ (e) $t = \frac{4}{9}$
**2.** (a) $h = 11$ (b) $x = 8$ (c) $a = -3$
(d) $d = -3$ (e) $a = \frac{1}{10}$ (f) $h = 1\frac{1}{2}$
(g) $x = \frac{7}{9}$ (h) $a = 5$ (i) $x = 1\frac{1}{4}$
**3.** (a) $x = 1\frac{1}{3}$ (b) $x = 12$ (c) $x = -1\frac{3}{5}$
(d) $x = -4$ (e) $x = 1$ (f) $x = 19$
(g) $x = -1$ (h) $x = -1$ (i) $x = 3\frac{1}{2}$

## Exercise **11.8**  Page 102

**1.** (a) $6k$ kg (b) $2\frac{1}{2}$ kg
**2.** (a) $6x + 3$ (b) 7
**3.** (a) $(n - 7)$ years old
(b) Dominic is 25 years old
Marcie is 18 years old
**4.** (a) $(4y - 2)$ cm (b) 19 cm
**5.** (a) (i) £$(p + 4)$ (ii) £$(p - 3)$
(iii) £$(3p + 1)$
(b) Aimee £12, Grace £8, Lydia £5

**6.** (a) $(x + 10)$ pence    (b) $(3x + 20)$ pence
    (c) 15 pence
**7.** $3x + 2(x - 4) = 77, \ x = 17$
    Cream biscuit 13 pence.
**8.** (a) $(7x - 4)\,$cm    (b) $7x - 4 = 59, \ x = 9$
    (c) 13 cm, 17 cm, 29 cm
**9.** (a) $(x - 4)\,$cm    (b) $(4x - 8)\,$cm
    (c) $x = 7$
**10.** (a) $18x = 540°$    (b) largest angle $= 150°$
**11.** Cake costs 37 pence
**12.** $105\,$cm$^2$
**13.** (a) $(6x + 16)\,$cm   (b) $x = 2$   (c) 28 cm
**14.** (a) $5x + 12$
    (b) $5x + 12 = 2(x + 12)$   so, $x = 4$.
     Sarah has 32 CDs now.

## Review Exercise 11     Page 104

**1.** (a) 3           (b) 23
    (c) Answer should always be a
      whole number.
**2.** (a) $x = 12$     (b) $y = 4$
    (c) $y = 3$      (d) $y = -1$
**3.** (a) $p = 2\frac{1}{2}$      (b) $k = 12$
**4.** (a) $m = 7$     (b) $t = 5$     (c) $x = 13$
**5.** (a) $x = -3$    (b) $y = 4$
**6.** (a) $x = 2$     (b) $x = 1.4$
**7.** (a) $x = 5$     (b) $x = -1$
**8.** (a) $x = 4.5$    (b) $x = 8$
**9.** (a) $a = -5$    (b) $x = 0.8$
    (c) $x = -0.5$
**10.** $x = -1$
**11.** (a) $q = -2$    (b) $t = 1\frac{1}{2}$
    (c) $x = 10\frac{1}{2}$
**12.** (a) 34 years old      (b) 19 years old
**13.** $2\frac{1}{2}$ litres
**14.** (a) $(x - 15)$ pence    (b) 42 pence
**15.** $(2x - 10) + (22 + x) + x = 180$
    $x = 42.$    Angles: $74°, 64°, 42°$
**16.** (a) $x = 6$     (b) $x = 12$
**17.** $x = 4\frac{1}{3}$
**18.** (a) $x = 3$     (b) $x = 3.5$
**19.** $x = 5$
**20.** (a) $x = -1$    (b) $x = 6\frac{1}{3}$

## CHAPTER   12

## Exercise 12.1     Page 105

**1.** (a) $-2$   (b) 10   (c) 11   (d) 25
**2.** (a) $-1$   (b) $-4$   (c) $-12$   (d) 3
**3.** (a) 24     (b) $-3$    (c) 2
    (d) 18     (e) 18
**4.** (a) 27     (b) $-3$    (c) $2\frac{1}{2}$
    (d) 90     (e) 54

**5.** (a) $-5$    (b) $-20$    (c) $-2$
    (d) $-100$   (e) 3
**6.** (a) 3      (b) $-21$    (c) $-2\frac{1}{2}$
    (d) $-9$    (e) 54
**7.** (a) $-24$    (b) 3      (c) 2
    (d) 33     (e) $-2$
**8.** $-17$

## Exercise 12.2     Page 106

**1.** (a) $(a + 1)$ years old
    (b) $(a - 4)$ years old
    (c) $(a + n)$ years old
**2.** $12e$
**3.** $b - 3$
**4.** $(h + 12)\,$cm
**5.** (a) $P = 4g$       (b) $P = 4y + 4$
    (c) $P = 3x - 1$    (d) $P = 2a + 2b$
**6.** $C = 25d$
**7.** (a) $P = y - 2$    (b) $P = 2y$
**8.** (a) £80        (b) $C = 12x + 8$
**9.** (a) 115    (b) 175
    (c) 45     (d)

| $n$ | $n + 1$ | $n + 2$ |
|---|---|---|
| | $n + 11$ | |
| | $n + 21$ | |

    (e) $S_n = 5n + 35$

## Exercise 12.3     Page 108

**1.** 17 points         **12.** $K = 13$
**2.** 26 cm          **13.** $L = 5$
**3.** $T = 97$         **14.** 33
**4.** (a) $M = -7$   (b) $n = 4\frac{1}{2}$   **15.** 96 m
**5.** (a) $H = 2.5$   (b) $g = 6$    **16.** 86°F
**6.** $F = 75$         **17.** 138 minutes
**7.** $V = 2$          **18.** 25°C
**8.** $P = 12$         **19.** 240 volts
**9.** $C = -40$        **20.** $F = 4100$
**10.** $S = 6$          **21.** £45.14
**11.** $T = -13\frac{1}{2}$       **22.** 0.3

## Exercise 12.4     Page 109

**1.** $S = 4$
**2.** (a) $R = 15$       (b) $R = 3$
**3.** $K = 36$
**4.** (a) $S = 18$       (b) $S = 18$
**5.** (a) $S = 36$       (b) $S = 36$
**6.** $T = 39$
**7.** (a) $S = 32$       (b) $S = 32$
**8.** (a) $S = 16$       (b) $S = 16$
**9.** (a) $A = 8$        (b) $A = -27$
**10.** $\frac{3}{4}$
**11.** (a) 4        (b) 1.5      (c) $-3$
**12.** (a) $L = 10$      (b) $L = 0.5$
**13.** $F = 144$
**14.** $R = 2.25$
**15.** (a) $v = 6.3$      (b) $v = 7.4$

**1.** (a) £13
(b) $C = 2k + 3$
(c) 2 km

**2.** (a) 140 minutes
(b) $C = 40k + 20$
(c) 2 kg

**3.** (a) $F = 42$
(b) $F = 2C + 30$
(c) $C = 14$

**4.** (a) 410
(b) $b = 3n + 50$
(c) 140

**1.** (a) $m = a - 5$ (b) $m = a - x$
(c) $m = a + 2$ (d) $m = a + b$

**2.** (a) $x = \dfrac{y}{4}$ (b) $x = \dfrac{y}{a}$ (c) $x = 2y$

(d) $x = ay$ (e) $x = \dfrac{5y}{3}$

**3.** (a) $p = \frac{1}{2}y - 3$ (b) $p = \dfrac{t - q}{5}$

(c) $p = \dfrac{m + 2}{3}$ (d) $p = \dfrac{q + r}{4}$

**4.** $n = \dfrac{C - 35}{24}$

**5.** $R = \dfrac{V}{I}$

**6.** (a) $c = \pm \sqrt{y}$ (b) $c = y^2$ (c) $c = \pm \sqrt{\dfrac{y}{d}}$
(d) $c = 9y^2$ (e) $c = \pm \sqrt{y - x}$
(f) $c = (y - x)^2$ (g) $c = \pm \sqrt{dy - dx}$
(h) $c = (ax + ay)^2$

**7.** (a) $a = b - c^2$ (b) $a = \pm \sqrt{b}$

(c) $a = \dfrac{p - d}{m}$ (d) $a = \pm \sqrt{\dfrac{F}{m}}$

**8.** (a) $x = \dfrac{3a}{2}$ (b) $x = \dfrac{3b - 2a}{5}$

**9.** (a) $a = \dfrac{3x}{2}$ (b) $a = \dfrac{b}{1 - x}$

(c) $a = \dfrac{b + 2}{1 - x}$

**10.** $t = \pm s\sqrt{R}$

**11.** $q = \dfrac{p}{2}$

**12.** (a) $a = \dfrac{3x - 2}{1 - x}$ (b) $a = \dfrac{5y + 3}{1 + y}$

(c) $a = \dfrac{2b + x}{x - b}$ (d) $a = \dfrac{6 + y}{y + 3}$

(e) $a = \dfrac{5x}{3}$ (f) $a = \dfrac{4x^3}{1 + 4x^2}$

**1.** (a) $d = \dfrac{P}{4}$ (b) $d = 0.7\,\text{cm}$

**2.** (a) $l = \dfrac{A}{b}$ (b) $l = 6\,\text{cm}$

**3.** (a) (i) $D = ST$ (ii) $D = 96\,\text{km}$
(b) (i) $T = \dfrac{D}{S}$ (ii) $T = 2.5$ hours

**4.** (a) $b = \frac{1}{2}P - l$ (b) $b = 4.2\,\text{cm}$

**5.** (a) $x = \dfrac{y - c}{m}$ (b) $x = 3$

**6.** (a) $b = \dfrac{2A}{h}$ (b) $b = 6.4$

**7.** (a) $q = \pm \sqrt{p^2 - r^2}$ (b) $q = \pm 6.8$

**8.** (a) $r = \sqrt[3]{\dfrac{3V}{4\pi}}$ (b) $r = 33.7$

**9.** (a) $x = \pm \sqrt{ab}$ (b) $x = \pm 4.0 \times 10^4$

**10.** (a) $n = \dfrac{1 - m}{1 + m}$ (b) $n = 8.4 \times 10^{-1}$

**1.** $V = 7$
**2.** $S = -14$
**3.** $P = 7.5$
**4.** (a) (i) $P = 28$
(ii) $P = 8$
(b) $k = 13$
**5.** (a) $H = 11$
(b) $H = 19$
**6.** 108
**7.** (a) $P = 15$
(b) $P = 5$
**8.** (a) £90
(b) $C = 15d + 45$
**9.** (a) £255
(b) 64
**10.** $1\frac{1}{6}$
**11.** (a) £17
(b) $C = 0.15n + 5$
(c) 480

**12.** $x = \dfrac{P - 13}{2}$

**13.** $x = \dfrac{6y + 5}{8}$

**14.** (a) $a = -2.5$
(b) $d = \dfrac{3a}{b + c}$

**15.** $T = \dfrac{P^2}{6}$

**16.** $s = -8$

**17.** $v = \pm \sqrt{\dfrac{t - u}{s}}$

**18.** (a) $a = \dfrac{4y - 3x}{4x}$
(b) $x = \dfrac{4y}{4a + 3}$

**19.** $y = \dfrac{b - d}{a - c}$

**20.** $m = \dfrac{np}{p - n}$

## CHAPTER 13

**1.** (a) 17, 21, 25 (b) 14, 16, 18
(c) 16, 13, 10 (d) 28, 33, 38
(e) 48, 96, 192 (f) $1\frac{1}{2}$, $1\frac{3}{4}$, 2
(g) 2, 1, $\frac{1}{2}$ (h) 0.9, 1.0, 1.1
(i) 2, 0, $-2$ (j) 5, 2.5, 1.25
(k) 21, 28, 36 (l) 29, 47, 76

**2.** (a) 8, 14 (b) 10, 22 (c) 8, 32
(d) 16, $-2$ (e) 16, 36
(f) 8, 21 (g) 2, 20, 26

**3.** (a) Add 7; 37, 44
(b) Add 2; 13, 15
(c) Add 4; 21, 25
(d) Subtract 5; 11, 6
(e) Divide by 2; 2, 1
(f) Multiply by 3; 81, 243
(g) Subtract 2; $-10$, $-12$
(h) Subtract 3; $-5$, $-8$

**4.** (a) 28
(b) Keep on adding 3 to the last term until you get to the 10th term, 28.

**5.** (a) David multiplies the last term by 2, $4 \times 2 = 8$.
Tony adds the next counting number, $4 + 3 = 7$.
(b) 512 (c) 46
**6.** No. To find the next number, add 6 to the last term. All numbers in the sequence will be odd.

## Exercise **13.2** Page 116

**1.** (a) (i) 21 (ii) 3 (b) 37
**2.** (a) (i) 36 (ii) 123 (b) 10
**3.** (a) 37, 60 (b) 1, 4
**4.** $-6, -27$
**5.** (a) 49, 97 (b) 1537

## Exercise **13.3** Page 118

**1.** (a) 3 (b) 3 (c) 6
(d) 8 (e) $-2$ (f) $-4$
**2.** (a) $3n$ (b) $8n$
**3.** (a) 3 (c) $3n + 1$ (d) 25
**4.** (a) 2 (c) $2n + 7$ (d) 47
**5.** (a) $-4$ (c) $24 - 4n$
**6.** (a) $3n - 2$ (b) $22 - 3n$ (c) $4n + 1$
(d) $4n$ (e) $2n - 1$ (f) $4n + 3$
(g) $8 - 2n$ (h) $3n + 2$ (i) $5n - 2$
(j) $45 - 5n$ (k) $n - 1$ (l) $2n - 3$
**7.** 4, 7, 12.
Substitute $n = 1$, $n = 2$, etc., into $n^2 + 3$.

## Exercise **13.4** Page 120

**1.** (a) (i) 15 (ii) 30 (iii) 300 (b) $3n$
**2.** (a) $22 \text{ cm}^2$ (b) $42 \text{ cm}^2$ (c) $4n + 2 \text{ cm}^2$
**3.** (a) 27 (b) $T = 5n + 2$
(c) 52 (d) 15
**4.** (a) 11 (b) Pattern 18
(c) $m = 2p + 1$
**5.** (a) 25 (b) $4^2 = 16, 5^2 = 25$
(c) $n^2$ (d) 225
**6.** (a) (i) 37, add 2 more than last time.
(ii) 35, add 2 more than last time.
(iii) 39, add 2 more than last time.
(iv) 72, add 4 more than last time.
(v) 42, add 2 more than last time.
(b) (i) $n^2 + 1$ (ii) $n^2 - 1$ (iii) $n^2 + 3$
(iv) $2n^2$ (v) $n^2 + n$
**7.** (a) $T = n^2 + n = n(n + 1)$ (b) 110
**8.** (a) 15 (b) $\dfrac{4 \times 5}{2} = 10$, $\dfrac{5 \times 6}{2} = 15$
(c) $\dfrac{n(n + 1)}{2}$ (d) 55
**9.** (a) 32 (b) $2^4 = 16$, $2^5 = 32$
(c) $2^n$ (d) 1024 (e) 8th
**10.** (a) 10, 100, 1000, 10 000, 100 000
(b) $10^n$ (c) $10^6$
**11.** (a) $3^n$ (b) 59 049

## Review Exercise **13** Page 122

**1.** (a) (i) 16 (ii) 32 (iii) $-6$
(b) (ii) Double the last number.
(iii) Subtract 4 from the last number.
**2.** (a) 25
(b) No. $81 + 5$ is not a multiple of 6.
(c) 103
**3.** (a) 9 (b) 12 (c) 10
**4.** (a) 14, 7, 12
(b) Repeats 6, 3, 8, 4, 2, 1
**5.** (a) **61**
(b) $2x + 3$
(c) Add double the difference between terms.
**6.** (a) 3455 (b) 1024 (c) 2, 5, 10
**7.** (a) 13 (b) 3 (c) $3n + 1$
**8.** (a) 19, 22 (b) Add 3 to last term.
(c) 61 (d) $3n + 1$
**9.** (a) $3n$ (b) $4n + 1$

## CHAPTER (14)

## Exercise **14.1** Page 124

**1.** $P(-2, -3)$, $Q(3, -2)$, $R(-3, 1)$
**2.** (b) $(-1, 1)$
**3.** (c) $D(-1, 2)$
**4.** (a) (1) $y = 4$
(2) $x = -3$
(3) $x = 1$
(4) $y = -1$
(5) $y = x$
(b) $(1, 4)$
(c) $(-3, -1)$

**5.**

**6.** (a)

| $x$ | 0 | 1 | 2 | 3 |
|---|---|---|---|---|
| (i) $y$ | 2 | 3 | 4 | 5 |
| (ii) $y$ | 0 | 2 | 4 | 6 |
| (iii) $y$ | 0 | $-1$ | $-2$ | $-3$ |
| (iv) $y$ | 2 | 1 | 0 | $-1$ |

**7.**

| $x$ | $-1$ | 0 | 1 | 2 | 3 |
|---|---|---|---|---|---|
| (a) $y$ | $-2$ | $-1$ | 0 | 1 | 2 |
| (b) $y$ | $-1$ | 1 | 3 | 5 | 7 |
| (c) $y$ | 4 | 3 | 2 | 1 | 0 |
| (d) $y$ | 8 | 6 | 4 | 2 | 0 |

**8.** (a) Missing entries are: 6, 4, 3
(b) (i) $y = 2.5$ (ii) $y = 4.5$
**9.** (b) (i) $y = -5$ (ii) $x = 0.5$
**10.** (b) $x = 0.5$
**11.** (b) $x = -1.5$
**12.** (b) $(2, 1)$

1. (b) Same slope, parallel.
   $y$-intercept is different.
2. (a) gradient 3, $y$-intercept $-1$
3. $y = 3x$, $y = 3x + 2$
4. gradients: 3, 2, $-2$, $\frac{1}{2}$, 2, 0
   $y$-intercepts: 5, $-3$, 4, 3, 0, 3
5. (a) $y = 5x - 4$ (b) $y = -\frac{1}{2}x + 6$
6. **(1) C, (2) D, (3) B, (4) A**
7. (a) $y = x - 2$ (b) $y = 2x - 2$
   (c) $y = -2x - 2$
8. (c) 1 (d) $(0, -4)$ (e) $y = x - 4$
9. (c) $y = -2x - 1$
10. (a) Line slopes up from left to right.
    (b) Line slopes down from left to right.
    (c) Line is horizontal.
11. $y = 3x$
12. (a) £25 (b) £15 per hour
    (c) $y = 15x + 25$ (d) £145
13. (a) £3 (b) £2
    (c) $f = 2d + 3$ (d) £13

1. (a) $(0, 7)$ 2. (a)
   (b) $(7, 0)$
   (c)

   (b) Parallel lines,
       same gradient.

3. (a) $(0, 6)$ (c)
   (b) $(2, 0)$

4. (a) (b)

   (c)

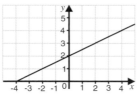

5. (a) $(0, 5)$ (c)
   (b) $(3, 0)$

6. (a) (b)

   (c)

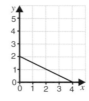

1. (a)

| $x$ | 1 | 2 | 3 |
|---|---|---|---|
| $y = x + 2$ | 3 | 4 | 5 |
| $y = 5 - x$ | 4 | 3 | 2 |

   (c) $(1.5, 3.5)$ (d) $x = 1.5$
2. (b) $(2.5, 8.5)$ (c) $x = 2.5$
3. (b) $x = 0.5$
4. $x = 1$
5. (b) $y = 9$ (c) $x = 3$

1. **B, C**
2. (a) $-\frac{1}{3}$ (b) $-4$ (c) $\frac{1}{2}$
3. (a) (i) $y = -x$ (ii) $y = 2 - x$
   (b) (i) $y = 1 - 2x$ (ii) $y = 2 - 2x$
   (c) $y = 3 - \frac{1}{2}x$
4. Gradient $PR = 2$, gradient $QS = -\frac{1}{2}$
   $2 \times \left(-\frac{1}{2}\right) = -1$,
   so, $PR$ is perpendicular to $QS$.
5. (a) $y = 3x - 14$ (b) $y = -\frac{1}{3}x - \frac{2}{3}$
6. $AB : y = -\frac{1}{2}x - \frac{1}{2}$ $BC : y = 2x - 3$

1. $y = \frac{3x}{2} + 3$
2. (a) $y = -\frac{1}{2}x + 2$ (b) $y = -\frac{4}{5}x + 4$
   (c) $y = -\frac{2}{3}x + \frac{4}{3}$ (d) $y = \frac{2}{7}x - 2$
3. (a) $\frac{1}{2}$ (b) 1 (c) 2
   (d) $-\frac{1}{3}$ (e) $\frac{3}{4}$ (f) $-\frac{2}{5}$
4. (a) $a = 0$ (b) $a = \frac{1}{2}$ (c) $a = -2$
   (d) $a = 2\frac{1}{2}$ (e) $a = 2$ (f) $a = \frac{2}{5}$

**5.** (a)  $y = x + $ (any number)

(b)  $y = 2x + $ (any number)

(c)  $y = \frac{1}{2}x + $ (any number)

**6.**  $y = -\frac{3}{2}x + $ (any number)

**7.** (b)  $3y = x - 6$  and  $y = 1 - 3x$

**8.** (a)  $A(0, 2), B(-4, 0)$      (b)  $\frac{1}{2}$

(c)  (ii)  $y = \frac{1}{2}x + $ (any number)

**9.** (a)  $P(0, 3), Q(6, 0)$      (b)  $-\frac{1}{2}$

(c)  (ii)  $y = -\frac{1}{2}x + $ (any number)

**10.** (a)  (i)  $y = x + 2$      (ii)  $y = 2x + 1$

(iii)  $3y = x + 16$      (iv)  $4y + x = -8$

(b)  (i)  $y = 2 - x$      (ii)  $2y = 7 - x$

(iii)  $y = 2 - 3x$      (iv)  $y = 4x + 15$

**11.**  $P(0, 6), Q(-7, 0)$

**Review Exercise 14**      **Page 134**

**1.** (a)  (1)  $y = 2$      (2)  $x = -4$      (3)  $y = x$

(b)  $(-4, 2)$

**2.** (a)  Missing entries are:  $-1, 1, 5$

(c)  (i)  $y = -2$      (ii)  $x = 1.3$

**3.** (b)  $(2, 4)$

**5.** (a)  3      (b)  $(0, -2)$

**6.**  $m = 0.5, \ c = -2$

**7.** (a)  $y = 6$      (b)  $y = -3x + 6$

**8.** (a)  8 mm      (b)  0.06

(c)  $l = 0.06w + 8$      (d)  26 mm

**9.**  $a = 3, \ b = -1$

**10.** (a)  $y = 3x + 5$      (b)  (i)  $\frac{2}{3}$      (ii)  $(0, -2)$

**11.**  $y = -6x + 2$

**12.**  $\frac{3}{5}$

**13.**  $2y = x + 2$ has gradient $\frac{1}{2}$.

$y = 6 - 2x$ has gradient $-2$.

$\frac{1}{2} \times (-2) = -1$, so, lines are perpendicular.

**14.**  $y = -\frac{1}{4}x + 3\frac{1}{2}$

**15.** (a)  $y = -\frac{2}{3}x + 4$

(b)  $y = -\frac{2}{3}x + 2$

(c)  $y = 1\frac{1}{2}x - 2\frac{1}{2}$

**CHAPTER**      **15**

**Exercise 15.1**      **Page 136**

**1.**  B

**2.**  1: C,  2: B,  3: E,  4: A

**3.**

**4.** (d)  B      (e)  A      (f)  6 days

**5.** (a)      (b)

(c)      (d)

**Exercise 15.2**      **Page 138**

**1.** (a)  1042      (b)  28 km

(c)  (i)  1115      (ii)  8 km

(d)  16 km/h

**2.** (a)  50 km/h      (b)  20 m/s

(c)  9 miles/hour

**3.** (a)  10 km/h      (b)  6.7 km/h

(c)  8 km/h

**4.** (a)  48 miles/hour    (b)  30 miles/hour

**5.** (a)      (b)  (i)

(b)  (ii)  1110

**6.** (a)  1118      (b)  1230

(c)  Twice      (d)  42 minutes

(e)  Between 1200 and 1230

(f)  4 km/h

**7.** (a)  9 miles/hour

(b)  (i)

(ii)  1415

**8.** (a)

(b)  15 km/h

**9.** (a)

(b)  (i)  1220    (ii)  1102    (iii)  14 km/hour

**Exercise 15.3**      **Page 142**

**1.**  $0.8\,\text{m/s}^2$

**2.** (a)  (i)  $B$ and $C$, $D$ and $E$    (ii)  $A$ and $B$

(iii)  $B$ and $C$, $D$ and $E$    (iv)  $F$ and $G$

(b)  (i)  $0.53\,\text{m/s}^2$      (ii)  $-0.5\,\text{m/s}^2$

**3.** (a)  8 m/s      (b)  $0.8\,\text{m/s}^2$

(c)  $1.6\,\text{m/s}^2$      (d)  260 m

**4.** (a) 2 minutes    (b) $1\frac{1}{2}$ minutes

(c) $5\,\text{km/min} = 5000\,\text{m/min} = \frac{5000}{60}\,\text{m/s}$
$1.5\,\text{min} = 1.5 \times 60$ seconds
$\frac{5000}{60} \div (1.5 \times 60) \simeq 0.925\ldots \simeq 0.9\,\text{m/s}^2$

**5.** (a)

(b) 960 m

**6.** (a) $0.8\,\text{m/s}^2$    (b) 27.25 seconds

## Review Exercise 15    Page 144

**1.** (a) Brian (b) Afzal (c) 600 m (d) Afzal

**2.** **A**: **Graph R**,   **B**: **Graph S**

**3.**

**4.** (a) 0945 (b) 38 miles
(c) 2 (d) 23 miles/hour

**5.** (a)         (b)

**6.** (a)

(b) 12.5 litres per minute

**7.** (a) $3\,\text{m/s}^2$    (b) acceleration

## CHAPTER 16

### Exercise 16.1    Page 147

**1.** (a) True (b) True (c) True (d) False
(e) True (f) False (g) False (h) True

**2.** (a) E.g. 5, 4, 3, … (b) E.g. −2, −1, 0 …
(c) E.g. 5, 4, 3, … (d) E.g. 7, 6, 5, …
(e) E.g. 11, 12, 13, …
(f) −1 (g) 5
(h) One of: −6, −5, −4, −3, −2

**3.** (a) 2, 3, 4    (b) −1, 0, 1, 2, 3
(c) −4, −3, −2, −1 (d) −1, 0, 1, 2

**4.** (a) $x \geqslant 2$ (b) $x < 1$
(c) $-1 \leqslant x \leqslant 5$ (d) $-6 \leqslant x < -2$
(e) $-2 < x < 1$ (f) $x < 5$ and $x \geqslant 8$

**5.** (a)
(b)
(c)
(d)
(e)
(f)
(g)
(h)

### Exercise 16.2    Page 148

**1.** (a) $n > 2$ (b) $x < -2$ (c) $a < 4$
(d) $a < 4$ (e) $d \leqslant 3$ (f) $t < -3$
(g) $g > -2$ (h) $y \geqslant 0$

**2.** (a) $a < 4$ (b) $x \geqslant -2$ (c) $y < -3$
(d) $c > 5$ (e) $d < -3$ (f) $b \geqslant 1$
(g) $b \leqslant 1$ (h) $c \leqslant 3$ (i) $d > 4$
(j) $f < -2$ (k) $g \leqslant \frac{1}{2}$ (l) $h < 2$
(m) $x < -3$ (n) $j \geqslant 2\frac{1}{2}$ (o) $k > -4$
(p) $m \leqslant 1\frac{2}{5}$

**3.** (a) (i) $x \geqslant -1$ (ii) $x < 3$
(b) −1, 0, 1, 2

**4.** (a) $a \geqslant 6$ (b) $b < 15$ (c) $m > -6\frac{1}{2}$
(d) $n \leqslant 2$ (e) $p > 8$ (f) $q > 1$
(g) $r \geqslant -1\frac{1}{2}$ (h) $t > 13$ (i) $u \leqslant 9$
(j) $v < -1\frac{1}{2}$ (k) $w > 8$ (l) $x < 1\frac{2}{5}$

### Exercise 16.3    Page 149

**1.** $a < -2$    **6.** $f < 1$    **11.** $m < -3$
**2.** $b \geqslant 3$    **7.** $g > -4$    **12.** $n > -4$
**3.** $c \leqslant -4$    **8.** $h \geqslant 2$    **13.** $p \geqslant \frac{5}{9}$
**4.** $d > -1$    **9.** $j \leqslant 1$    **14.** $q > -2\frac{1}{5}$
**5.** $e \geqslant 2$    **10.** $k > -\frac{1}{3}$    **15.** $n < 9$

### Exercise 16.4    Page 150

**1.** (a) $1 < x \leqslant 5$ (b) $-1 \leqslant x < 9$
(c) $-7 < x \leqslant 4$

**2.** (a) $1 < x \leqslant 3$ (b) $-2 \leqslant x < 4$
(c) $3 < x < 4\frac{1}{2}$ (d) $-\frac{1}{3} \leqslant x \leqslant 4$
(e) $2 < x \leqslant 5$ (f) $-3 \leqslant x < 6$
(g) $-2 < x < 2$ (h) $3 \leqslant x < 6$
(i) $-4\frac{1}{2} \leqslant x \leqslant -1$

**3.** (a) 6, 7, 8     (b) $-2, -1, 0, 1, 2, 3, 4$
    (c) 0, 1, 2     (d) 4, 5, 6, 7
    (e) 5     (f) 2, 3
    (g) $-2, -1, 0$     (h) $-1, 0, 1, 2, 3$
    (i) $-4, -3, -2, -1, 0, 1, 2, 3, 4, 5, 6$
    (j) 8, 9, 10, 11, 12, 13, 14, 15, 16
    (k) $-4, -3, -2, -1, 0, 1, 2, 3$
    (l) $-6$

## Exercise **16.6**      Page 152

**3.** A : ③,   B : ①,   C : ④,   D : ②.
**4.** $y \geqslant 1, \quad y \leqslant x$
**5.** (a)

    (b) (2, 2), (3, 2)

**6.** (a) $x \geqslant 1, \quad y < 5$ and $y > x + 2$
    (b) $y < 4, \quad x \leqslant 3, \quad y \leqslant 2x$ and $y > x$
    (c) $x \leqslant 2, \quad x + y > 3, \quad y \leqslant x + 3$
    (d) $y > 1, \quad 1 \leqslant x < 3, \quad x + y \leqslant 5$
**7.** (b) (2, 3)

## Review Exercise **16**     Page 154

**1.** (a)
    (b)
    (c)
    (d)

**2.** (a) $x \leqslant 2$     (b) $x > -2$
**3.** (a) $x < 3$     (b) $x \geqslant -5$
    (c) $x \geqslant 4$     (d) $x \leqslant 3$
**4.** $x \geqslant 4.5$
**5.** (a) $x < 4$     (b) $-1 < x \leqslant 2$
    (c) $-1 \leqslant x < 1$     (d) $-3 < x < -1$
**6.** (a) $-1, 0, 1, 2, 3, 4$
    (b) $-3, -2, -1, 0, 1$
    (c) $-2, -1$
**7.** (a) $-1, 0, 1, 2, 3$     (b) $x \geqslant 5$
**8.** $x > -3$
**9.** (a) $-2, -1, 0, 1, 2, 3$
    (b) (i) $x > -3$     (ii) $x \geqslant 6$
**10.** $x > 4\frac{1}{3}$
**11.** (a)     (b)     (c)

**12.**

**13.** $x \leqslant 2, \quad y \leqslant 4$ and $x + y \leqslant 4$
**14.** $x \geqslant -2, \quad x + y \leqslant 3$ and $y \geqslant x$
**15.**        **16.** (a)

    (b) (1, 1), (2, 1)

## CHAPTER    17

## Exercise **17.1**     Page 156

**1.** (a)

| $x$ | $-3$ | $-2$ | $-1$ | 0 | 1 | 2 | 3 |
|---|---|---|---|---|---|---|---|
| $y$ | 7 | 2 | $-1$ | $-2$ | $-1$ | 2 | 7 |

    (c) $y = 0.25$
**2.** (b) $y = 7.25$     (c) $x = -1.7$ and $x = 1.7$
    (d) (0, 1)
**3.** (a)

| $x$ | $-3$ | $-2$ | $-1$ | 0 | 1 | 2 | 3 |
|---|---|---|---|---|---|---|---|
| $y$ | $-3$ | 2 | 5 | 6 | 5 | 2 | $-3$ |

    (c) $(-2.4, 0), (2.4, 0)$     (d) (0, 6)
**4.**

| $x$ | $-2$ | $-1$ | 0 | 1 | 2 |
|---|---|---|---|---|---|
| $y$ | 8 | 2 | 0 | 2 | 8 |

**5.**

| $x$ | $-2$ | $-1$ | 0 | 1 | 2 | 3 |
|---|---|---|---|---|---|---|
| $y$ | 8 | 4 | 2 | 2 | 4 | 8 |

## Exercise **17.2**     Page 157

**1.** $x = -3.6$ or $x = 0.6$
**2.** (b) $x = -1$ or $x = 0$
    (c) $(-0.5, -0.25)$
**3.** (a) Entries are: 9, 4, 1, 0, 1, 4
    (c) $x = 1$
**4.** (b) $x = \pm 3.2$     (c) (0, 10)
**5.** (a) $x = \pm 3.2$     (b) $x = \pm 2.2$
    (c) $x = 1$ or $x = 2$     (d) $x = \pm 2.4$
**6.** (a) Missing entries are: 6, 0, 3
    (c) $x = 0.5$ or $x = 1$
    (d) (i) $y = 3$     (ii) $x = -0.5$ or $x = 2$
**7.** (b) $x = 0$ or 1
    (c) (i) $x = -2.6$ or $-1.6$
       (ii) $x = 0$ or 3
**8.** (b) $x = -0.6$ or 1.6
**9.** (b) (i) $x = -2.7$ or 0.7
       (ii) $x = -4.3$ or 2.3
**10.** (b) $x = 0.3$ or 3.7
    (c) (i) $y = 3 - x$     (ii) $x = 0$ or 3
**11.** (b) Draw $y = 3x + 2, \quad x = -1$ or 3
**12.** (b) $x = 0.3$ or 3.7
    (c) Draw $y = x - 3, \quad x = 1$ or 4

**1.**

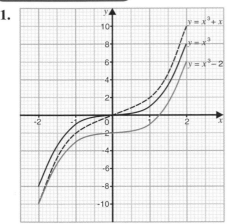

**2.** (a)  Entries are: $-9, 4, 5, 0, -5, -4, 9$
   (c)  (i)   $x = -2.8$
        (ii)  $x = -2.3, \ -0.3$  or  $2.6$

**1.** (c)  $x = 0.27$  or  $3.73$
**2.**

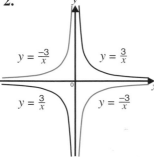

$y = \dfrac{-3}{x}$     $y = \dfrac{3}{x}$

$y = \dfrac{3}{x}$     $y = \dfrac{-3}{x}$

**3.**

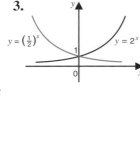

$y = \left(\frac{1}{2}\right)^x$          $y = 2^x$

**4.** (a)  Entries are: $0.04, 0.11, 0.33, 1, 3, 9, 27$
   (c)  (i)   $y = 5.2$          (ii)  $x = 2.7$

**1.** (a)  3     (b)  $(3, 0), (0, 3), (-3, 0), (0, -3)$
**2.** (b)  $x^2 + y^2 = 25$          (d)  $(-3, 4), (3, 4)$
**3.** (c)  $(-2.2, -3.3), (1.4, 3.7)$
**4.** (c)  $(0.6, 0.8), (1, 0)$
**5.** (c)  $x = -1.2$

**1. (1) F,   (2) E,   (3) C,   (4) B,   (5) A,   (6) D**
**2.** (a)          (b)

   (c)          (d)

**3.** (a)  $y = x + 2$          (b)  $y = 2 - x$
   (c)  $y = 2x$          (d)  $y = \frac{1}{2} x$

**1.** (a)  $x = 0$  or  $x = 4$    (b)  $(2, -4)$
**2.** (a)  Missing entries are: $5, -3, -4, 0$
   (c)  $(0, -4)$          (d)  $x = \pm 2.6$
**3.** (a)  Missing entries are: $-3, -3$
   (c)  $x = -0.3$  or  $x = 3.3$
**4.** (a)  Missing entries are: $8, -4, 0$
   (c)  $x = 3.7$
**5. A : R,   B : S,   C : Q,   D : P**
**6.** (b)  $x = 2.6$
**7.** (b)  (i)  $x = 0.4$  or  $2.6$    (ii)  $x = 0$  or  $3$
**8.** (c)  $x = -2$  or  $1$
**9.** (b)  $x = 1.4$  or  $-2.9$
**10.** (b)  $x = 1.4$
**11.** (a)  Missing entries are: $3, 1, -0.125$
   (c)  $x = 1.7$  or  $0.3$  or  $1.6$
   (d)  $y = 2 - 4x$
**12.** $(-4, 3), (-3, 4)$

**CHAPTER**          **18**

**1.** (a)  True,   $a : b = 2 : 3$
   (b)  True,   $c : d = 20 : 1$
   (c)  False,   $e : f$ not the same
   (d)  True,   $h : g = 200 : 7$
**2.** (a)  (i)   $1 : 2$     (ii)  $1 : 5$
   (b)  $a = 2, \ \ b = 60, \ \ c = 8, \ \ d = 350$
**3.** (a)  $k = 6, \ \ y = 6x$     (b)  $y = 48$
**4.** (a)  $y = \frac{1}{5} x$          (b)  $y = 9$
**5.** (a)  $m = 1\frac{1}{2} n$
   (b)  (i)   $m = 9$     (ii)  $n = 10$
**6.** (a)  $q = 0.625p$ (or $p = 1.6q$)
   (b)  $a = 7.5, \ \ b = 32$
**7.** (a)  $y = 0.05x$     (b)  $a = 5, \ \ b = 400$
**8.** (a)  $C = 10.5A$     (b)  £577.50
   (c)  68.75 m
**9.** (a)  $d = 5n$     (b)  1 km
   (c)  600 times
**10.** (a)  (i)  $e = 30w$   (ii)  159 mm   (iii)  3.22 kg
   (b)  $5 : 16$

**1.** (a)  True,   $ab = 10$     (b)  False
**2.** (a)  $pq = 0.5$          (b)  $q = \dfrac{0.5}{p}$
**3.** $k = 20$

| $a$ | 2 | 5 | 10 | 25 | 50 |
|-----|-----|-----|-----|-----|-----|
| $b$ | 10 | 4 | 2 | 0.8 | 0.4 |

**4.** (a) $pq = 30$ or $p = \dfrac{30}{q}$
   (b) $p = 5$

**5.** (a) $y = \dfrac{48}{x}$ or $xy = 48$
   (b) $a = 4$, $b = 96$

**6.** $y = 9$

**7.** $r = 25$

**8.** (a) $LM = 14.4$ or $M = \dfrac{14.4}{L}$
   (b) $a = 1.2$, $b = 16$

**9.** $lw = 200$, $k = 200$,
   $k$ represents the constant area

**10.** (a) $nt = 12$ or $t = \dfrac{12}{n}$
   (b) 2 days
   (c) 3 workers

## Exercise 18.3     Page 168

**1.** (a) $V$ is proportional to the square of $t$.
   (b) $L$ is inversely proportional to $a$.
   (c) $y$ is proportional to the cube of $x$.
   (d) $p$ is inversely proportional to the square of $q$.
   (e) $L$ is proportional to the square root of $m$.
   (f) $b$ is inversely proportional to the cube of $c$.

**2.** $k = 2$, $y = 2x^2$

**3.** (a) $y$ is multiplied by 4.
   (b) $x$ is multiplied by 5.

**4.** $y = \dfrac{64}{x^3}$

**5.** (a) $V = 5t^2$    (b) $R = \dfrac{320}{s^3}$
   (c) $y = 10\sqrt{x}$    (d) $A = \dfrac{100}{b}$
   (e) $L = 3.125p^3$    (f) $Q = 12.5\sqrt{P}$

**6.** (a) 80   (b) $y = 5$   (c) $x = 4$

**7.**

| $a$ | 1 | 2 | 10 |
|---|---|---|---|
| $b$ | 3 | 12 | 300 |

**8.** $A = 250$, $B = 3$

**9.** (a) $k = 1.6$    (b) $y = 0.016$

**10.** (a) $k = 10$    (b) $x = 16$

**11.** (a) $y = 8$    (b) $x = 17.1$

**12.** (a) $q = \dfrac{40}{p^2}$, $a = 0.4$, $b = 20$
   (b) $q = \dfrac{160}{p^3}$, $c = 0.16$, $d = 2$
   (c) $q = 0.15625p^2$, $e = 15.625$, $f = 8$

**13.** (a) $y$ is divided by 4 (is 4 times smaller).
   (b) $x$ is divided by 5 (is 5 times smaller).

**14.** (a) $t = 1.6\sqrt{d}$   (b) $t = 8$ seconds

**15.** (a) $h = 0.05s^2$   (b) 20
   (c) 125

**16.** (a) $h = 16$   (b) $\sqrt{\dfrac{\text{Volume}}{\pi}}$

**17.** (a) $h$ is divided by 4 (is 4 times smaller).
   (b) $r$ is divided by 4 (is 4 times smaller).

## Exercise 18.4     Page 171

**1.** (a) **B**   (b) **A**   (c) **D**   (d) **C**

**2.** (a) (i) 3   (ii) $-1$   (iii) $-\dfrac{1}{2}$
   (b) (i)   (ii)   (iii)

   (c) (i) Less steep, steeper, steeper.
      (ii) Steeper, less steep, less steep.

**3.** $n = -2$

**4.** (a) $n = 2$   (b) 0.25   $k = 10$, $n = -2$

**5.** $q = 0.2p^3$

**6.** $s = \dfrac{20}{\sqrt{t}}$

**7.** (a) $k = 5$, $n = \dfrac{1}{2}$   (b) $x = 9$

## Review Exercise 18     Page 172

**1.** $m = 50$

**2.**

| $p$ | 4 | 64 | 100 |
|---|---|---|---|
| $q$ | 1 | 4 | 5 |

**3.** (a) $d = 5\sqrt{h}$   (b) $h = 49$

**4.** (a) $S = 0.0375L^3$   (b) $S = 8.1\,\text{cm}$
   (c) $L = 2\,\text{m}$

**5.** (a) $F = 5.76$ newtons   (b) $d = 1.71$ metres

**6.** (a) $m = 4$   (b) $n = 25$

## CHAPTER   

## Exercise 19.1     Page 174

**1.** $x^2 + 7x + 12$
**2.** $x^2 + 6x + 5$
**3.** $x^2 - 3x - 10$
**4.** $2x^2 - 3x - 2$
**5.** $3x^2 - 20x + 12$
**6.** $6x^2 + 7x + 2$
**7.** $x^2 + 6x - 16$
**8.** $x^2 + 3x - 10$
**9.** $x^2 + 2x - 3$
**10.** $x^2 - 5x + 6$
**11.** $x^2 - 5x + 4$
**12.** $x^2 - 5x - 14$
**13.** $2x^2 + 7x + 3$
**14.** $3x^2 + 13x - 10$
**15.** $5x^2 - 8x + 3$
**16.** $4x^2 + 4x - 3$
**17.** $6x^2 + 13x - 5$
**18.** $12x^2 + 14x - 10$
**19.** $x^2 - 9$
**20.** $x^2 - 25$
**21.** $x^2 - 49$
**22.** $x^2 + 10x + 25$
**23.** $x^2 - 14x + 49$
**24.** $4x^2 - 12x + 9$

## Exercise 19.2     Page 176

**1.** (a) $x(x + 5)$   (b) $x(x - 7)$   (c) $y(y - 6)$
   (d) $2y(y - 6)$   (e) $t(5 - t)$   (f) $y(8 + y)$
   (g) $x(x - 20)$   (h) $3x(x - 20)$

**2.** (a) $(x - 3)(x + 3)$   (b) $(x - 9)(x + 9)$
   (c) $(y - 5)(y + 5)$   (d) $(y - 1)(y + 1)$
   (e) $(x - 8)(x + 8)$   (f) $(10 - x)(10 + x)$
   (g) $(6 - x)(6 + x)$   (h) $(x - a)(x + a)$

**3.** (a) $(x + 5)(x + 1)$    (b) $(x + 7)(x + 2)$
(c) $(x + 2)(x + 4)$    (d) $(x + 3)(x + 6)$
(e) $(x - 5)(x - 1)$    (f) $(x - 5)(x - 2)$
(g) $(x - 4)(x - 3)$    (h) $(x + 4)(x - 1)$
(i) $(x + 7)(x - 2)$    (j) $(x - 5)(x + 1)$

**4.** (a) $(x + 1)(x + 2)$    (b) $(x + 1)(x + 7)$
(c) $(x + 3)(x + 5)$    (d) $(x + 2)(x + 6)$
(e) $(x + 1)(x + 11)$    (f) $(x + 4)(x + 5)$
(g) $(x + 4)(x + 6)$    (h) $(x + 4)(x + 9)$
(i) $(x + 1)(x + 14)$    (j) $(x + 2)(x + 8)$

**5.** (a) $(x - 3)^2$    (b) $(x - 4)(x - 2)$
(c) $(x - 10)(x - 1)$    (d) $(x - 15)(x - 1)$
(e) $(x - 5)(x - 3)$    (f) $(x - 8)(x - 2)$
(g) $(x - 10)(x - 2)$    (h) $(x - 8)(x - 3)$
(i) $(x - 1)(x - 12)$    (j) $(x - 2)(x - 6)$

**6.** (a) $(x - 3)(x + 2)$    (b) $(x - 6)(x + 1)$
(c) $(x - 4)(x + 6)$    (d) $(x - 3)(x + 8)$
(e) $(x - 5)(x + 3)$    (f) $(x - 3)(x + 6)$
(g) $(x - 8)(x + 5)$    (h) $(x - 6)(x + 2)$
(i) $(x - 2)(x + 5)$    (j) $(x + 4)(x - 5)$

**7.** (a) $(x - 2)^2$    (b) $(x + 5)(x + 6)$
(c) $(x - 2)(x + 4)$    (d) $(x - 7)(x + 3)$
(e) $(x - 4)(x + 5)$    (f) $(x + 3)(x + 4)$
(g) $(x + 4)^2$    (h) $(x - 1)^2$
(i) $(x - 7)(x + 7)$    (j) $t(t + 12)$
(k) $(x - 2)(x - 7)$    (l) $(x - 6)(x - 1)$
(m) $(x + 2)(x + 9)$    (n) $(x + 3)(x + 8)$
(o) $(x + 1)(x + 18)$    (p) $(x - y)(x + y)$
(q) $(x + 3)(x - 2)$    (r) $y(y + 4)$
(s) $(y - 5)^2$    (t) $(x - 6)^2$

## Exercise 19.3     Page 177

**1.** (a) $(2x + 6)(x + 3)$    (b) $(2y + 3)(y - 6)$
(c) $(2a + 9)(a - 2)$    (d) $(2m - 2)(m - 9)$
(e) $(4x - 1)(x - 3)$    (f) $(2d - 1)(2d + 3)$

**2.** (a) $(2x + 1)(x + 3)$    (b) $(2x + 3)(x + 4)$
(c) $(2a + 1)(a + 12)$    (d) $(2x + 1)^2$
(e) $(3y + 2)(2y + 1)$    (f) $(3x + 4)(2x + 3)$
(g) $(11m + 1)(m + 1)$    (h) $(3x + 2)(x + 5)$
(i) $(5k + 2)(k + 2)$

**3.** (a) $(2a - 3)(a + 1)$    (b) $(2y - 7)(y - 1)$
(c) $(2x - 1)^2$    (d) $(3x - 2)(x - 1)$
(e) $(3d - 1)(2d - 3)$    (f) $(2x - 1)(x - 1)$
(g) $(2x - 5)(x - 3)$    (h) $(3y - 2)^2$
(i) $(2t - 3)^2$

**4.** (a) $(2x - 3)(x + 2)$    (b) $(2a - 3)(a + 1)$
(c) $(3x + 1)(x - 5)$    (d) $(3t - 1)(t + 5)$
(e) $(2y - 7)(y + 1)$    (f) $(4y - 1)(y + 2)$
(g) $(3x - 1)(3x + 2)$    (h) $(10x - 3)(x + 3)$
(i) $(5m + 3)(m - 1)$

## Exercise 19.4     Page 178

**1.** (a) $3(x + 4y)$    (b) $(t - 4)(t + 4)$
(c) $(x + 1)(x + 3)$    (d) $y(y - 1)$
(e) $2(d^2 - 3)$    (f) $(p - q)(p + q)$
(g) $a(a - 2)$    (h) $(x - 1)^2$
(i) $2y(y - 4)$    (j) $(a - 3)^2$
(k) $3(m - 2)(m + 2)$    (l) $(v - 3)(v + 2)$
(m) $a(x - y)(x + y)$    (n) $-2(4 + x)$
(o) $(2 - k)^2$    (p) $2(3 - x)(3 + x)$
(q) $2(5 - x)(5 + x)$
(r) $3(2x - 3y)(2x + 3y)$
(s) $3a(2a - 1)$
(t) $(x - 7)(x - 8)$
(u) $(x - 3)(x + 5)$

**2.** (a) $(3a + 4)(a - 2)$    (b) $(3x + 1)(x + 10)$
(c) $(8y + 7)(8y - 7)$    (d) $(3x + 5)(x + 2)$
(e) $(7x - 5)(x - 2)$    (f) $(6x + 5)(x - 5)$
(g) $(5m - 3)(m - 3)$    (h) $(2x + 3)(4x - 5)$
(i) $(5 - 2x)(x - 4)$    (j) $2(y + 4)(2y + 3)$
(k) $3(x + 2)(2x - 3)$    (l) $2(3n - 1)(n + 2)$

## Exercise 19.5     Page 179

**1.** (a) $x = 2$ or $3$    (b) $x = -4$ or $-6$
(c) $x = 3$ or $-1$    (d) $x = 5$ or $-2$
(e) $x = 0$ or $4$    (f) $x = 0$ or $-2$

**2.** (a) $x = 1$ or $2$    (b) $y = -3$ or $-4$
(c) $m = 4$ or $-2$    (d) $a = 3$ or $-4$
(e) $n = 9$ or $-4$    (f) $z = 6$ or $3$
(g) $k = -3$ or $-5$    (h) $c = -7$ or $-8$
(i) $b = 4$ or $-5$    (j) $v = 12$ or $-5$
(k) $w = 4$ or $-12$    (l) $p = 9$ or $-8$

**3.** (a) $x = 0$ or $5$    (b) $y = 0$ or $-1$
(c) $p = 0$ or $-3$    (d) $a = 0$ or $4$
(e) $t = 0$ or $6$    (f) $g = 0$ or $4$

**4.** (a) $x = 2$ or $-2$    (b) $y = 12$ or $-12$
(c) $a = 3$ or $-3$    (d) $d = 4$ or $-4$
(e) $x = 10$ or $-10$    (f) $x = 6$ or $-6$
(g) $x = 7$ or $-7$    (h) $x = 1.5$ or $-1.5$
(i) $x = 3$ or $-3$

**5.** (a) $x = -6$ or $x = 0$
(b) $x = -1$ or $x = -4$
(c) $x = -8$ or $x = 8$
(d) $x = 1$ or $x = 3$
(e) $x = 0$ or $x = 2$
(f) $x = -2$ or $x = 3$
(g) $x = -5$ or $x = 3$
(h) $x = -2$ or $x = 2$
(i) $x = 7$ or $x = 8$

**6.** (a) $x = -2\frac{1}{2}$ or $-1$

(b) $x = \frac{1}{2}$ or $5$

(c) $x = 7$ or $-1\frac{1}{3}$

(d) $y = -\frac{1}{2}$ or $-\frac{2}{3}$

(e) $x = -3$ or $\frac{2}{3}$

(f) $z = -\frac{1}{3}$ or $2$

(g) $m = \frac{3}{5}$ or $1$

(h) $a = -3\frac{1}{2}$ or $3$

(i) $y = 2$ or $-1\frac{1}{4}$

**7.** (a) $y = 5$ or $-1$  (b) $x = 0$ or $1$

(c) $x = 4$  (d) $x = 5$ or $-3$

(e) $n = 12$ or $-2$  (f) $m = 7$ or $1$

(g) $a = 8$ or $-3$  (h) $x = 1$ or $3$

(i) $x = \frac{1}{2}$ or $-\frac{1}{3}$  (j) $m = -5$ or $1\frac{1}{2}$

(k) $a = \frac{1}{2}$ or $-\frac{2}{3}$  (l) $x = \frac{1}{2}$ or $-\frac{3}{4}$

## Exercise **19.6** — Page 180

**1.** (a) $x = -1$ or $x = -3$

(b) $x = 1$ or $x = 2$

(c) $x = -1$ or $x = 3$

**2.** (a) $x = -0.59$ or $-3.41$

(b) $x = -6.19$ or $-0.81$

(c) $x = -1.62$ or $0.62$

(d) $x = -0.56$ or $3.56$

(e) $x = -0.54$ or $5.54$

(f) $x = -4.30$ or $-0.70$

(g) $x = -5.74$ or $1.74$

(h) $x = 0.38$ or $2.62$

(i) $x = -3.56$ or $0.56$

**3.** (a) $x = -1.5$ or $x = 1$

(b) $x = 0.5$ or $x = 1$

(c) $x = -1$ or $x = 0.6$

**4.** (a) $x = 0.23$ or $1.43$

(b) $x = 0.72$ or $2.78$

(c) $x = -7.30$ or $-0.37$

(d) $x = -0.79$ or $2.12$

(e) $z = -2.37$ or $-0.63$

(f) $x = -2.27$ or $2.94$

**5.** (a) $x = 0.55$ or $5.45$

(b) $x = -1.14$ or $2.64$

(c) $x = -0.85$ or $2.35$

(d) $x = -0.74$ or $0.54$

(e) $x = -0.65$ or $4.65$

(f) $x = -3.81$ or $1.31$

(g) $x = 0.15$ or $4.52$

(h) $x = -0.58$ or $2.58$

(i) $x = -1.16$ or $2.16$

**6.** (a) $x = -1.7$ or $-0.3$,
$x = -1$, no solutions

(b) $x = -1.71$ or $-0.293$,
$x = -1$, no solutions

## Exercise **19.7** — Page 182

**1.** (a) $1$  (b) $4$  (c) $9$  (d) $16$

(e) $1$  (f) $2.25$  (g) $25$  (h) $6.25$

**2.** (a) $x^2 + 6x + 9 = (x + 3)^2$

(b) $a^2 - 4a + 4 = (a - 2)^2$

(c) $b^2 + 2b + 1 = (b + 1)^2$

(d) $m^2 - 8m + 16 = (m - 4)^2$

(e) $n^2 - n + \frac{1}{4} = \left(n - \frac{1}{2}\right)^2$

(f) $x^2 + 5x + 6.25 = (x + 2.5)^2$

**3.** (a) $(x + 3)^2 + 11$  (b) $(x + 3)^2 - 4$

(c) $(x + 5)^2 - 29$  (d) $(x - 2)^2 + 1$

(e) $(x - 2)^2 - 2$  (f) $(x - 2)^2 - 8$

(g) $(x - 3)^2 - 5$  (h) $(x - 4)^2 - 16$

(i) $(x + 6)^2 - 36$

**4.** (a) $a = 3,\ b = 6$

(b) $a = 5,\ b = -20$

(c) $a = -3,\ b = -14$

(d) $a = -4,\ b = -12$

(e) $a = 6,\ b = -32$

(f) $a = 3,\ b = 0$

**5.** (a) $(2x + 4)^2 - 11;\ p = 2, q = 4, r = -11$

(b) $(3x + 2)^2 - 1;\ p = 3, q = 2, r = -1$

(c) $(5x - 4)^2 - 19;\ p = 5, q = -4, r = -19$

(d) $(4x + 4)^2 - 21;\ p = 4, q = 4, r = -21$

(e) $(10x + 3)^2 - 6;\ p = 10, q = 3, r = -6$

(f) $(4x - 5)^2 - 16;\ p = 4, q = -5, r = -16$

**6.** (a) $a = -2,\ b = -5$  (b) $-5$

**7.** $a = 8,\ b = -3$

**8.** $1$

## Exercise **19.8** — Page 183

**1.** (a) $x = -1$ or $3$

(b) $t = -3$ or $7$

(c) $x = -9$ or $3$

(d) $y = -2$ or $8$

(e) $m = -2$ or $12$

(f) $e = 6$ or $8$

**2.** (a) $x = -1.3$ or $11.3$

(b) $m = -5.3$ or $1.3$

(c) $x = 0.6$ or $5.4$

(d) $y = -0.6$ or $3.6$

(e) $x = -0.4$ or $12.4$

(f) $a = -5.2$ or $-0.8$

(g) $n = -1.4$ or $0.4$

(h) $x = -1.8$ or $0.8$

(i) $z = 0.3$ or $2.7$

(j) $x = 1.4$ or $2.6$

(k) $x = -4.4$ or $-1.6$

(l) $x = -1.5$ or $-2.5$

**3.** (a) $(x - 2)^2 - 3$  (b) $x = 2 \pm \sqrt{3}$

**4.** $a = 3,\ b = 5$

**5.** $x = 1 \pm \sqrt{\frac{7}{2}}$

**6.** $m = -6,\ n = 7$

**7.** $a = -8,\ b = -3$

## Exercise 19.9 — Page 184

1. (a) $x(x - 4) = 21$
   (b) $x = 7$ ($x$ cannot equal $-3$)
2. $x = 9$ or $-7$
3. (a) $(x + 3)(x + 1) - \frac{1}{2}x^2 = 7.5$
   $$x^2 + 4x + 3 - \frac{1}{2}x^2 = 7.5$$
   $$\frac{1}{2}x^2 + 4x - 4.5 = 0$$
   $$x^2 + 8x - 9 = 0$$
   (b) $x = 1$ ($x$ cannot equal $-9$)
4. (a) $3(8 + 2x)(5 + 2x) =$
   $(15 + 2x)(14.5 + 2x)$
   (b) $2.5$ m
5. $9.3$ cm and $4.3$ cm
6. $24$ cm by $7$ cm
7. $7.24$ m by $2.76$ m
8. (a) $13$ and $18$   (b) $3.55$ and $8.45$
9. $75$ m and $100$ m
10. $9$, $12$ and $15$; $-3$, $0$ and $3$
11. (a) $x^2 - 8x - 20 = 0$
    (b) $10$, $11$, $13$ and $17$; $-2$, $-1$, $1$ and $5$
12. (a) $11$th   (b) $15$th
13. $3$ and $8$

## Review Exercise 19 — Page 186

1. $x^2 + x - 12$
2. (a) $x(x + 5)$   (b) $x^2 + 8xy + 15y^2$
3. (a) $2xy(y + 2)$   (b) $(m - 1)(m - 8)$
4. (a) $5a(2 + 3b - 4a)$
   (b) $(x + 2y)(x - 2y)$
   (c) $(5x - 3)(x + 4)$
5. (a) $(x + 4)(x + 6)$
   (b) $x = -4$ or $x = -6$
6. (a) $t = 0$ or $4$   (b) $y = -1$ or $-2$
7. $x = 1$ or $-10$
8. (a) $x = -1\frac{1}{2}$ or $1$
   (b) Graph crosses $x$ axis at $\left(-1\frac{1}{2}, 0\right)$ and $(1, 0)$
9. (a) $x = 3$ or $-3$   (b) $x = 9$ or $-1$
10. (a) $P = 2x + \dfrac{100}{x}$
    (b) $2x + \dfrac{100}{x} = 33$
    $$2x^2 - 33x + 100 = 0$$
    (c) $12.5$ cm by $4$ cm
11. $x(13 - x) = 36$,   $4$ and $9$
12. (a) $p = 3$,   $q = 2$   (b) $2$
13. $x = 0.78$ or $10.22$
14. (a) Area $= (x + 5)(x - 1) - \left(\frac{1}{2} \times 4 \times 3\right)$
    Area $= x^2 + 4x - 5 - 6$
    Area $= x^2 + 4x - 11$
    (b) (i) $x^2 + 4x - 11 = 59$
    $$x^2 + 4x - 70 = 0$$
    (ii) $x = 6.6$
15. $x = -1.22$ or $0.55$

16. (a) $V = 2(x - 4)^2$
    $$V = 2(x^2 - 8x + 16)$$
    $$V = 2x^2 - 16x + 32$$
    (b) $x = 9.5$
17. (a) $(2x - 3)(x + 4) = 3(x + 1)$
    $$2x^2 + 5x - 12 = 3x + 3$$
    $$2x^2 + 2x - 15 = 0$$
    (b) $x = -3.28$ or $2.28$

## CHAPTER 20

## Exercise 20.1 — Page 189

1. $x = 4$,   $y = 2$
2. $x = 3$,   $y = 5$
3. $x = 2$,   $y = 3$
4. $x = 2$,   $y = 3$
5. $x = 3$,   $y = 1$
6. $x = 4$,   $y = 3$
7. $x = -2$,   $y = 3$
8. $x = 5$,   $y = 0.5$

## Exercise 20.2 — Page 190

1. (a) Both lines have gradient $-1$.
   (b) Both lines have gradient $4$.
   (c) Both lines are the same.
   (d) Both lines have gradient $0.4$.
2. (a) $y = -2x + 6$,   $y = -2x + 3$
   (b) $y = 2x + 3.5$,   $y = 2x + 2$
   (c) $y = 2.5x - 4$,   $y = 2.5x + 1.75$
   (d) $y = -3x + 1.25$,   $y = -3x + 0.5$
3. (b) and (d) have no solution.
   (a) $x = 0.4$,   $y = 4$
   (c) $x = -0.125$,   $y = 1.875$

## Exercise 20.3 — Page 192

1. $x = 1$,   $y = 2$
2. $x = 3$,   $y = 4$
3. $x = 2$,   $y = 1$
4. $x = 1$,   $y = 7$
5. $x = 3$,   $y = 1$
6. $x = 2$,   $y = 3$
7. $x = 5$,   $y = 2$
8. $x = 4$,   $y = 2$
9. $x = 5$,   $y = 4$
10. $x = 3$,   $y = 2$
11. $x = 4$,   $y = 1$
12. $x = 4$,   $y = 2$
13. $x = 2$,   $y = 3$
14. $x = 4$,   $y = -2$
15. $x = 2$,   $y = -1.5$
16. $x = -1$,   $y = 3$
17. $x = -5$,   $y = 6$
18. $x = 2.5$,   $y = -1$
19. $x = -6$,   $y = 2.5$
20. $x = 3$,   $y = -1.5$
21. $x = -1$,   $y = -3$
22. $x = 3.5$,   $y = -1$
23. $x = 1.5$,   $y = -0.5$
24. $x = -0.5$,   $y = -2.5$

## Exercise 20.4 — Page 193

1. $x = 2$,   $y = 1$
2. $x = 2$,   $y = 3$
3. $x = 3$,   $y = 1$
4. $x = 4$,   $y = 2$
5. $x = 2$,   $y = -1$
6. $x = 4$,   $y = -3$
7. $x = 4$,   $y = 0.5$
8. $x = -3$,   $y = 0.5$
9. $x = 4$,   $y = 1$
10. $x = 2.2$,   $y = 5.6$
11. $x = 1.5$,   $y = 2$
12. $x = 1$,   $y = 2$
13. $x = 5$,   $y = 2$
14. $x = 1$,   $y = -2$
15. $x = -1$,   $y = 2$
16. $x = 2$,   $y = 1$

**17.** $x = -1, \quad y = 1$
**18.** $x = -2, \quad y = 3$
**19.** $x = -1, \quad y = 7$
**20.** $x = 4, \quad y = -1$

**21.** $x = 2.5, \quad y = 3$
**22.** $x = 2, \quad y = -1$
**23.** $x = 1, \quad y = -2$
**24.** $x = -2, \quad y = 0.5$

Exercise **20.5**      Page 194

**1.** $x = 2, \quad y = 6$
**2.** $x = 9, \quad y = 18$
**3.** $x = 8, \quad y = 2$
**4.** $x = 3, \quad y = 6$
**5.** $x = 2, \quad y = 13$
**6.** $x = 0, \quad y = 2$

**7.** $x = 2, \quad y = 4$
**8.** $x = 7, \quad y = 6$
**9.** $x = 4, \quad y = 8$
**10.** $x = 10.5, \quad y = 0.5$
**11.** $x = -68, \quad y = -122$
**12.** $x = 8, \quad y = 6$

Exercise **20.6**      Page 195

**1.** (a)   $6x + 3y = 93, \quad 2x + 5y = 91$
   (b)   Pencil 8p, pen 15p
**2.** (a)   $5x + 30y = 900, \quad 10x + 15y = 1260$
   (b)   Apples £1.08 per kg, oranges 12p each
**3.** $x = 95, \quad y = 82$
**4.** 32 children, 4 adults
**5.** $x = 100, \quad y = 70$
**6.** Coffee 90p, Tea 80p
**7.** $x = 160, \quad y = 120$
**8.** $x = 13, \quad y = 9$
**9.** $p = 5, \quad q = -2$
**10.** Ticket £12.50, CD £4.50

Exercise **20.7**      Page 196

**1.** $x = -1, \quad y = 1$   or   $x = 2, \quad y = 4$
**2.** $x = -2, \quad y = 3$   or   $x = 1, \quad y = 0$
**3.** $x = -1, \quad y = -4$   or   $x = 3, \quad y = 0$
**4.** $x = 2, \quad y = 1$   or   $x = 3, \quad y = 3$
**5.** $x = -2, \quad y = -2$   or   $x = 2, \quad y = 2$
**6.** $x = -1, \quad y = -2$   or   $x = 1, \quad y = 2$

Exercise **20.8**      Page 198

**1.** $x = 3, \quad y = -2$   or   $x = 3, \quad y = 2$
**2.** $x = -2, \quad y = 6$   or   $x = 2, \quad y = 6$
**3.** $x = -1, \quad y = 0$   or   $x = 1, \quad y = 2$
**4.** $x = -2, \quad y = 6$   or   $x = -1, \quad y = 3$
**5.** $x = 1, \quad y = 5$   or   $x = 5, \quad y = 25$
**6.** $x = -3, \quad y = 3$   or   $x = 3, \quad y = -3$
**7.** $x = -4, \quad y = -2$   or   $x = 4, \quad y = 2$
**8.** $x = 1, \quad y = 4$   or   $x = 4, \quad y = 1$
**9.** $x = -2.5, \quad y = -2$   or   $x = 1, \quad y = 5$
**10.** $x = -2, \quad y = 3$   or   $x = 1.5, \quad y = -0.5$
**11.** $x = -1, \quad y = 1$   or   $x = 2, \quad y = 7$
**12.** $x = -\frac{1}{3}, \quad y = \frac{1}{3}$   or   $x = 2, \quad y = 12$
**13.** $x = -2, \quad y = -4$   or   $x = \frac{1}{4}, \quad y = \frac{1}{2}$
**14.** $x = \frac{1}{5}, \quad y = \frac{1}{5}$   or   $x = 2, \quad y = 20$
**15.** $x = -1.2, \quad y = 3.4$   or   $x = 2, \quad y = -3$
**16.** $x = 5, \quad y = -0.5$   or   $x = -1, \quad y = 1$
**17.** $x = -2, \quad y = 1\frac{1}{2}$   or   $x = 1\frac{2}{3}, \quad y = -\frac{1}{3}$
**18.** $x = -1, \quad y = -3$   or   $x = 1.5, \quad y = -\frac{1}{2}$

Review Exercise **20**      Page 198

**1.** (a)   (i)

| $x$ | 0 | 1 | 2 |
|---|---|---|---|
| $y$ | $-2$ | 1 | 4 |

   (ii)

| $x$ | 0 | 1 | 3 |
|---|---|---|---|
| $y$ | 3 | 2 | 0 |

   (b)   $x = 1.25, \quad y = 1.75$
**2.** (b)   $x = 1.8, \quad y = 0.8$
**3.** $x = 1.2, \quad y = 1.4$
**4.** $x = 3, \quad y = 2$
**5.** $x = 3, \quad y = 2$
**6.** (a)   $x = 1, \quad y = 3$    (b)   $x = 2, \quad y = -2$
   (c)   $x = -1, \quad y = 2$    (d)   $x = 2, \quad y = 3\frac{1}{2}$
**7.** $x = 6, \quad y = 2$
**8.** $x = 2, \quad y = 3$
**9.** $x = 3, \quad y = -2$
**10.** (a)   Same gradient, 2
     $y = 2x - 2, \quad y = 2x + \frac{3}{2}$
   (b)   Same gradient, $\frac{1}{4}$
     $y = \frac{1}{4}x + \frac{1}{4}, \quad y = \frac{1}{4}x + \frac{3}{8}$
   (c)   $a = 3, \quad b =$ any number, except 2
   (d)   $\frac{q}{p} = -3, \quad \frac{r}{p} \neq 2$
**11.** (b)   $9p + 11q = 5$    (c)   $p = 3, \quad q = -2$
**12.** (a)   $2x + 3y = 185, \quad x + 2y = 105$
   (b)   $x = 55, \quad y = 25$
**13.** (a)   $4x + y = 58, \quad 6x + 2y = 92$
   (b)   $x = 12, \quad y = 10$
**14.** $x = 246, \quad y = 128$
**15.** $x = -2.6, \quad y = 3.3$   or   $x = 1.6, \quad y = 1.2$
**16.** $x = 1\frac{2}{3}, \quad y = 12$   or   $x = 4, \quad y = 5$
**17.** $x = 2, \quad y = 3$   or   $x = 3.6, \quad y = -0.2$
**18.** $x = -3, \quad y = -3$   or   $x = 1.75, \quad y = 2.94$
**19.** $x = -3, \quad y = 5$   or   $x = -5, \quad y = 3$
**20.** $(3, 4), (4, 3)$

## CHAPTER 21

Exercise **21.1**      Page 201

**1.** (a)   $2x^2 - 3x + 34$    (b)   $3x^2 - 2x + 5$
   (c)   1               (d)   $-14x^2 + 66x - 18$
**2.** (a)   $-6x + 29y - 24z$    (b)   0
   (c)   $10x^2 + 12xy + 10y^2$
   (d)   $13x^2 + 24xy + 13y^2$

Exercise **21.2**      Page 202

**1.** (a)   $2d + 3$   (b)   $3x + 2$   (c)   $4a + 5b$
   (d)   $3m - 2n$   (e)   $4x - 2y$   (f)   $a + b$
   (g)   $x - 1$   (h)   $x^2 - 2$
   (i)   $\dfrac{4}{x - 3}$   (j)   $\dfrac{x + 2}{3}$   (k)   $\dfrac{x + 2y + 3z}{2x - 3y + z}$
   (l)   $\dfrac{x + 2}{3x + 2}$   (m)   $\dfrac{x}{3x - 2}$   (n)   $\dfrac{x}{2x^2 - 1}$
   (o)   $\dfrac{1}{2x - 1}$   (p)   $\dfrac{1}{3x}$   (q)   $\dfrac{3}{2}$
   (r)   $\dfrac{m}{3}$   (s)   $\dfrac{x - 3}{x + 2}$   (t)   $-\dfrac{5}{3}$

**2.** (a) **E**   (b) **C**   (c) **B**   (d) **A**   (e) **D**

**3.** (a) $\dfrac{x + 5y}{3 + 4xy}$   (b) $\dfrac{x + y + 2z}{2x - 3y + z}$

  (c) $\dfrac{ab - 3}{b + a}$   (d) $\dfrac{x + b + y}{ab - 2y}$

**4.** (a) $\dfrac{x}{x + 1}$   (b) $\dfrac{x + 2}{x + 3}$   (c) $\dfrac{x}{x + 3}$

  (d) $\dfrac{x - 5}{x + 3}$   (e) $\dfrac{x - 2}{x - 3}$   (f) $\dfrac{x - 5}{x + 4}$

  (g) $x - 1$   (h) $\dfrac{1}{x + 2}$   (i) $\dfrac{x + 1}{2}$

  (j) $\dfrac{x + 2}{x + 3}$   (k) $\dfrac{x - 5}{x - 4}$   (l) $\dfrac{2x - 5}{3x - 1}$

### Exercise 21.3   Page 204

**1.** (a) $\frac{2}{3}$   (b) $-1\frac{1}{4}$   (c) $\frac{y}{2}$

**2.** (a) $\frac{2}{3}$   (b) $-\frac{1}{2}$   (c) $-\frac{2}{x}$

**3.** (a) $\dfrac{7x + 8}{(x + 5)(x - 4)}$   (b) $\dfrac{37x + 3}{(2x + 3)(5x - 3)}$

  (c) $\dfrac{3x^2 + 4x - 14}{(x + 2)(x - 3)}$

**4.** (a) $\dfrac{x - 31}{(x + 5)(x - 4)}$   (b) $\dfrac{13x - 33}{(2x + 3)(5x - 3)}$

  (c) $\dfrac{x^2 + 2x + 10}{(x - 3)(x + 2)}$

**5.** (a) $\dfrac{7x - 12}{x(2x - 6)}$   (b) $\dfrac{7 - x}{2x}$   (c) $\dfrac{x^2 - 3x + 9}{x(2x - 6)}$

  (d) $\dfrac{4}{x - 3}$   (e) $\dfrac{3}{4x}$   (f) $\dfrac{x - 3}{4}$

### Exercise 21.4   Page 205

**1.** $x = -1$  or  $\frac{2}{3}$

**2.** (b) $x = -0.2$  or  6

**3.** (b) $x = -0.5$  or  3

**4.** (a) $x = -1.5$  or  0.25

  (b) $x = -2$  or  0.8

  (c) $x = -0.721$  or  1.39

  (d) $x = -\frac{5}{7}$  or  6

**5.** (a) $\dfrac{75}{v}$

  (b) $\dfrac{75}{v + 5}$

  (c) $\dfrac{75}{v} - \dfrac{75}{v + 5} = \frac{1}{6}.$  45 miles per hour

**6.** (a) $\dfrac{60}{x} + \dfrac{90}{x + 6} = 5\frac{1}{2}$

  (c) 24 km/h

### Exercise 21.5   Page 207

**1.** (b) $x = 4.30$

  (c) $x_{n + 1} = \dfrac{5x_n - 3}{x_n}$  is much faster.

**2.** (b) $x = 1.40$

  (c) $x_{n + 1} = \dfrac{7x_n + 2}{6x_n}$  is quicker.

**3.** $x_2 = 1.7320\ldots,$   $x_3$ does not exist.

**4.** $x_{n + 1} = \sqrt{x_n + 5}$  leads to  $x = 2.79$

**5.** E.g. $x_{n + 1} = \sqrt{100 - 7x_n}$
   with  $x_1 = 7$  leads to  $x = 7.09$

**6.** E.g. $x_{n + 1} = \dfrac{8 - 3x_n}{x_n}$  leads to  $x = -4.70$
   Other root is $x = 1.70$

### Exercise 21.6   Page 208

**1.** $x = 3.8$

**2.** (a)  $w = 4.2$   (b)  $x = 2.3$

**3.** $x = 3.2$

**4.** $x = 9.4$

**5.** (a)  $x = 6.2$   (b)  $x = 6.22$

**6.** (a)  $2x^2(x + 2)$   (b)  $x = 5.3$

**7.** $x = 1.82$

### Review Exercise 21   Page 209

**1.** (a)  (i) $(x + 3)(x - 3)$  (ii) $(2x + 1)(x - 3)$
   (b) $\dfrac{x + 3}{2x + 1}$

**2.** $\dfrac{x}{x - 1}$

**3.** $2(x - 3) + (x + 1) = (x - 3)(x + 1)$
   $2x - 6 + x + 1 = x^2 - 2x - 3$
   $x^2 - 5x + 2 = 0$

**4.** $\dfrac{n(4n - 5)}{(5n - 1)(4n - 1)}$

**5.** LHS $= \dfrac{n + 2}{n} - \dfrac{n}{n - 1} = \dfrac{(n + 2)(n - 1) - n^2}{n(n - 1)}$

   $= \dfrac{n - 2}{n(n - 1)} = $ RHS

**6.** (a) $\dfrac{48}{x} + \dfrac{48}{x - 5} = 8$

   $\dfrac{6}{x} + \dfrac{6}{x - 5} = 1$

   (b)  $x = 2$  or  15

   (c)  10 km/h

**7.** (a) $\dfrac{540}{x} + \dfrac{300}{x + 1} = 90$

   $\dfrac{18}{x} + \dfrac{10}{x + 1} = 3$

   (b)  $x = -\frac{2}{3}$  or  9

   Average production = 9 vans per day.

**8.** $x = 0$  or  7

**9.** (a) $\dfrac{x - 1}{x - 2}$   (b)  $x = 0$  or  $-2$

**10.** $x = 4.1$

**11.** $x = 2.8$

**12.** $x = 4.3$

**13.** $x = 0$  or  1.25

**14.** $x = 0.23$  or  1.43

**15.** $x = -0.14$  or  2.47

**Exercise 22.1**      **Page 212**

**1.** (a)

| $x$ | $-2$ | $-1$ | $0$ | $1$ | $2$ |
|---|---|---|---|---|---|
| $y$ | $-8$ | $-1$ | $0$ | $1$ | $8$ |

(b)

| $x$ | $-2$ | $-1$ | $0$ | $1$ | $2$ |
|---|---|---|---|---|---|
| $y$ | $-6$ | $1$ | $2$ | $3$ | $10$ |

(c)

| $x$ | $1$ | $2$ | $3$ | $4$ | $5$ |
|---|---|---|---|---|---|
| $y$ | $-8$ | $-1$ | $0$ | $1$ | $8$ |

(d)

| $x$ | $-2$ | $-1$ | $0$ | $1$ | $2$ |
|---|---|---|---|---|---|
| $y$ | $-16$ | $-2$ | $0$ | $2$ | $16$ |

(c) (i) Translation, vector $\begin{pmatrix} 0 \\ 2 \end{pmatrix}$

   (ii) Translation, vector $\begin{pmatrix} 3 \\ 0 \end{pmatrix}$

   (iii) Stretch, from $x$ axis, parallel to $y$ axis, scale factor 2

(d) (i) $y = x^3 - 5$   (ii) $y = (x - 2)^3$

**2.** **a**: $y = x^2 + 1$     **b**: $y = x^2 - 4$
   **c**: $y = (x - 1)^2$    **d**: $y = (x + 1)^2$

**3.** **a**: $y = \frac{1}{2} x^2$     **b**: $y = (4x)^2$
   **c**: $y = -2x^2$

**4.** (a) $y = 9 - x^2$
  (b) $y = 2(4 - x^2)$
  (c) $y = 4 - \left(\frac{1}{2} x\right)^2$

**5.** (a) (i) $y = x^2 - x - 5$
     (ii) $y = (x - 3)^2 - (x - 3)$
  (b) $y = \frac{1}{2} (x^2 - x)$
  (c) $y = \left(\frac{1}{2} x\right)^2 - \left(\frac{1}{2} x\right)$

**Exercise 22.2**      **Page 215**

**1.**

(a)

(b)     (c)

(d)     (e)

**2.** (a)

(b) Translation, vector $\begin{pmatrix} 0 \\ 2 \end{pmatrix}$

(c) (i)

Translation, vector $\begin{pmatrix} 0 \\ -1 \end{pmatrix}$

(ii)

Translation, vector $\begin{pmatrix} 3 \\ 0 \end{pmatrix}$

(iii)

Translation, vector $\begin{pmatrix} -2 \\ 0 \end{pmatrix}$

(iv)

Stretch, from $x$ axis, parallel to $y$ axis, scale factor 0.5

(v)

Stretch, from $x$ axis, parallel to $y$ axis, scale factor 2

(vi)

Stretch, from $y$ axis, parallel to $x$ axis, scale factor 2

(vii)

Stretch, from $y$ axis, parallel to $x$ axis, scale factor 0.5

(viii)

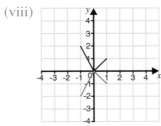

Reflection in $x$ axis

(ix)

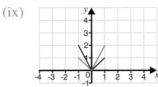

Reflection in $y$ axis

(x)

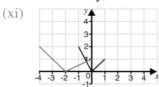

Stretch, from $y$ axis, parallel to $x$ axis, scale factor 0.5, followed by, translation, vector $\begin{pmatrix} 0 \\ 1 \end{pmatrix}$

(xi)

Translation, vector $\begin{pmatrix} -1 \\ 0 \end{pmatrix}$,

followed by, stretch, from $y$ axis, parallel to $x$ axis, scale factor 2

(xii)

Reflection in $x$ axis, followed by, translation, vector $\begin{pmatrix} 0 \\ 1 \end{pmatrix}$

3. (a) (b) (c) (d) (e)

**4.** (a)  (b)

(c)

(d)

(e)

**5.** **a**: $y = 2f(x)$ **b**: $y = f(x - 2)$ **c**: $y = f(-x)$

**6.** (a) (i) Reflection in $x$ axis.
  (ii) Stretch, from $y$ axis, parallel to $x$ axis, scale factor $\frac{1}{2}$.
  (b) Reflection in $x$ axis.
  (c) Reflection in $x$ axis, followed by, stretch, from $y$ axis, parallel to $x$ axis, scale factor $\frac{1}{2}$. (Transformations in either order.)
  (d) **a**: $y = -\sin x$ **b**: $y = \sin 2x$
    **c**: $y = -\sin 2x$

**7.** $g(x) = f(x + 4)$ $h(x) = f(x + 4) + 2$

### Exercise 22.3 Page 218

**1.** (a) $y = 28x + 13$, $q = 40.3 - 12.8p$
  (b) (i) $y = 88.6$ (ii) $p = 2.55$
**2.** (a) $l = 0.0625w + 20$
  (b) (i) $l = 51.25$ (ii) $w = 560$
**3.** $a = 0.1$, $b = 2.4$
**4.** 2.1 m/s²
**5.** (a) Non-linear graph
  (b) Linear graph, $y = 25x^3 + 22.7$,
    $a = 25$, $b = 22.7$
**6.** $a = 0.05$, $b = 2.4$

### Review Exercise 22 Page 220

**1.** (a) (b) (c) (d)

**2.** (a) (i)　　　　(ii)

(b)　**C,** $a = 0.5$

**3.**

**4.** (a)　**P**: $y = -\mathrm{f}(x)$
(b)　**Q**: $y = \mathrm{f}(x - 6)$
(c)　**R**: $y = \frac{1}{2}\mathrm{f}(x)$

**5.** $p = 0.5,\quad q = 1.2$

**6.** $a = 60,\quad b = 3$

---

## Algebra　　　　Section Review

### Non-calculator Paper　　Page 222

**1.** (a)　$3f + 2g$　　(b)　$3ty$　　(c)　$r^2$
**2.** (a)　24　　(b)　$-1$
**3.** (a)　(i)　$a = -2$　　(ii)　$b = 5$
　　(iii)　$c = 5\frac{1}{2}$　　(iv)　$d = \frac{7}{9}$
　(b)　$-4f + 12$
**4.** (a)　1000　　(b)　5 km
　(c)　30 minutes　(d)　20 km/h
**5.** $16x + 1$
**6.** (a)　(i)　25　　(ii)　$-1.2$
　(b)　(i)　$21x + 14y$　(ii)　$a^2 - 3a$
　(c)　(i)　$2(2a + b)$　(ii)　$t(3 - t)$
**7.** (a)　$2x$ pence　　(b)　$3(x + 5)$ pence
　(c)　16 pence
**8.** (b)　$x = 3.5$
**9.** (a)　(i)　$t = 6$　(ii)　$x = 11$　(b)　$n + 2$
**10.** (a)　(i)　$2x - 14$　(ii)　$y^4$　(b)　$z = 8$
**11.** (a)　$x = 6$　　(b)　$x = 36$
**12.** (a)　$x < 4$　　(b)　$x \leq 1$
**13.** $x^2 + 5x + 4$
**14.** (a)　Missing entries are: $-6, -9, -10, 6$
　(c)　$x = \pm 3.2$
**15.** (a)　$-5$　　(b)　$10 - 3n$
**16.** (a)　$x = 3\frac{1}{3}$　　(b)　(i)　1, 2　(ii)　$x \geq \frac{1}{5}$
　(c)　$x = 4,\ y = 1$
**17.** (a)　$y = 5$　　(b)　$x = \dfrac{y - c}{m}$
**18.** (b)　£92　　(c)　£20
　(d)　$C = 20 + 12h$
**19.** (a)　$t^4$　　(b)　(i)　$x = 1.8$　(ii)　$x = 15$
　(c)　$5x(x - 2y)$
　(d)　(i)　$(x - 2)(x - 4)$　(ii)　$x = 2$ or 4
**20.** $x = 3,\ y = -1$
**21.** (a)　$2x$　　(b)　$15a^5$　　(c)　$25t^6$
**22.** (a)　$y = 0$ or $-5$　(b)　$m = 3$ or 4
**23.** (a)　$\dfrac{a}{5}$　　(b)　$2(x - 3)(x + 3)$

**24.** (a)　$y = 3x - 7$　　(b)　$-\frac{1}{3}$
**25.** (a)　$6a^5b^3$　　(b)　$2^{17}$
　(c)　$2x^2 - 12xy - 5y^2$　(d)　$\dfrac{x}{x + 6}$
**27.** (a)　$x = 4,\ y = -2$　　(b)　$n \geq -2$
　(c)　$x = -\frac{1}{2}$ or $-2$
**28.** $(x + 2)(x + 1) = 6$
　　$x^2 + 3x + 2 = 6$
　　$x^2 + 3x - 4 = 0$
**29.** (b)　$x = 0.6$ or $3.4$　(c)　$y = 2 - 2x$
**30.** (a)　$x = 0$ or 7　　(b)　$x = \dfrac{yz - 2y}{1 + 2z}$
**31.** (a)　$y = 3x^2$　　(b)　$y = 48$
**32.** (a)　$m_{AC} = -1,\ m_{BD} = 1$
　(b)　$y = -x + 3$　　(c)　$y = x + 5$
**33.** $x = 1,\ y = 1$ or $x = 0,\ y = 2$
**34.** (a)　(i)　$\dfrac{7}{x - 3}$　(ii)　$\dfrac{81x^8}{y^{12}}$　(iii)　$\dfrac{x}{4 + x}$

　(b)　LHS $= \dfrac{(2n - 1)(2n + 1) + 5n^2}{n(2n + 1)}$

　　　$= \dfrac{9n^2 - 1}{n(2n + 1)}$

　　　$= \dfrac{(3n + 1)(3n - 1)}{n(2n + 1)}$

　　　$= $ RHS

**35.** $m = x + y$
**36.** (a)　$p = 3,\ q = -10$
　(b)　$x = -3 \pm \sqrt{10}$

**37.**

---

## Algebra　　　　Section Review

### Calculator Paper　　Page 225

**1.** (a)　(i)　$n^3$　(ii)　$6ab$　　(b)　$12x - 18$
**2.** (a)

　(b)　$(3, 3)$

**3.** $C = 19$
**4.** (a)　$x + 11y$
　(b)　(i)　$x = 9$　(ii)　$x = 1\frac{1}{2}$
**5.** (a)　$(5a + 3)$ cm　(b)　$5a + 3 = 23,\ a = 4$
**6.** (a)　$10x - 22$　(b)　1, 2, 3, 4
**7.** (a)　31　　(b)　$2n + 6$
**8.** (a)　Missing entries are: $-3, -6, -6$
　(c)　$x = \pm 2.6$
**9.** (a)　(i)　21　　(ii)　$-2$
　(b)　(i)　$14x - 21y$　(ii)　$x^3 - 2x^2$
**10.** (a)　(i)　$4(2x + 3)$　(ii)　$a(b + c)$
　(b)　(i)　$x = 6\frac{1}{2}$　(ii)　$x = 5\frac{1}{2}$

**11.** (a) $3n$      (b) $3n + 1$

**12.** $x = 3.8$

**13.** (a) (i) $t^5$    (ii) $t^{-2}$
     (b) $x^3 + 3x$    (c) $x^2 - x - 12$

**14.** (a) $x > 3$      (b) $-3, -2$
     (c) $x = \dfrac{y - 10}{5}$    (d) (i) $t = 9$   (ii) $x = 8$

**15.** (a) $x = 5$      (b) $x = 0.5, \ y = -2.5$
     (c) (i) $x^5 y^2$    (ii) $p^6$

**16.** (a)

| $x$ | 0 | 1 | 2 | 3 | 4 | 5 | 6 |
|---|---|---|---|---|---|---|---|
| $y$ | 0 | 2 | 6 | 12 | 20 | 30 | 42 |

     (c) $x = 5.4$      (d) $x = 7.4$

**17.** (a) (c)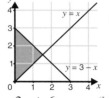
     (b) Where graphs cross.

**18.** (a) $2x^2 - 3x + 6$      (b) $(x + 2)(x - 5)$
     (c) $x < 0.4$

**19.** (a) $c = 1, \ m = \frac{1}{2}$      (b) $A(-2, 0)$

**20.** (a) $V = \pm 0.7$      (b) $P = RV^2$

**21.** (a) $x = 3$      (b) $x = 4, \ y = \frac{1}{2}$
     (c) $x = -0.81$ or $-6.19$

**22.** (a) (i) $p = 4$      (ii) $r = \pm 6$
     (b) $y = \dfrac{36}{x^2}$

**23.** (a) (i) $y = 1 - x^2$    (ii) $2y = 2 + x$
     (iii) $x^2 + y^2 = 3$    (iv) $xy = 1$
     (b)

**24.** (a) $y = -2x + 4$      (b) $\frac{1}{2}$
     (c) Substitute $y = x^2 - 1$ into $y + 2x = 3$
       $x^2 - 1 + 2x = 3$
       $x^2 + 2x - 4 = 0$
     (d) $x = -3.24$ or $1.24$
     (e) $(-3.24, 9.48)$ and $(1.24, 0.52)$

**25.** (a) $x = \dfrac{3}{y - 1}$      (b) $\dfrac{2x^2 - 12x - 6}{(x + 1)(x - 3)}$

**26.** (a) $1.5 \ \text{m/s}^2$      (b) 20 seconds

**27.** (a) $9x^2 y^6$      (b) $x = -0.64$ or $3.14$
     (c) $P = \dfrac{84}{\sqrt{Q}}$

**28.** (a) Area path $= 20 \times 18 - (20 - 2x)(18 - 2x)$
     (b) (i) $360 - (20 - 2x)(18 - 2x) = \frac{1}{4}(360)$
       (ii) $360 - (360 - 76x + 4x^2) = 90$
         $2x^2 - 38x + 45 = 0$
     (c) $x = 1.27$ or $17.73$. Path width $= 1.27 \, \text{m}$

**29.** $x = 0.70$ or $4.30$

**30.** $x = 4.05, \ y = -5.15$ or $x = 0.15, \ y = 6.55$

## Exercise **23.1**      Page 229

**1.** (a) $a = 96°$,   supplementary angles
     (b) $b = 20°$,   complementary angles
     (c) $c = 150°$,   angles at a point

**2.** (a) $a = 130°$,   alt. $\angle$'s
       $b = 130°$,   corres. $\angle$'s
     (b) $c = 60°$,   alt. $\angle$'s
       $d = 120°$,   allied $\angle$'s
     (c) $e = 40°$,   corres. $\angle$'s
       $f = 40°$,   vert. opp. $\angle$'s
     (d) $g = 65°$,   alt. $\angle$'s
       $h = 65°$,   corres. $\angle$'s

**3.** (a) $a = 125°, \ b = 125°$
     (b) $c = 56°, \ d = 116°$
     (c) $e = 61°$

**4.** (a) $\angle ABC = 132°$
     (b) $\angle QRS = 126°$
     (c) $\angle ZYV = 141°$
     (d) $\angle AOB = 153°, \ \angle COD = 37°$
     (e) $\angle QTU = 48°, \ \angle QTS = 132°$
     (f) reflex $\angle TUV = 280°$

## Exercise **23.2**      Page 231

**1.** (a) Yes    (b) Yes    (c) No
     (d) No    (e) Yes    (f) No

**2.** (a) Yes, obtuse-angled   (b) No
     (c) Yes, acute-angled   (d) Yes, right-angled
     (e) Yes, obtuse-angled

**3.** (a) $a = 35°$
     (b) $b = 148°, \ c = 32°$
     (c) $d = 52°, \ e = 64°$
     (d) $f = 63°$

**4.** (a) $a = 18°, \ b = 144°$
     (b) $c = 26.5°, \ d = 153.5°$

**5.** (a) Isosceles    (b) $74°$    (c) $46°$

**6.** (a) $\angle BCD = 120°$
     (b) $\angle PRQ = 80°, \ \angle QRS = 160°$
     (c) $\angle MNX = 50°$

## Exercise **23.3**      Page 233

**1.** $S(3, 1)$      **2.** $Y(6, 4)$      **3.** $A(1, 3)$

**4.** $(3, 1), (3, 5)$

**5.** (a) $a = 62°$      (b) $b = 54°, \ c = 36°$
     (c) $d = 62°$      (d) $e = 116°, \ f = 86°$
     (e) $g = 124°$      (f) $h = 75°$
     (g) $i = 38°, \ j = 42°$
     (h) $k = 55°, \ l = 45°$
     (i) $m = 65°, \ n = 90°, \ o = 25°$
     (j) $p = 117°$      (k) $q = 70°$
     (l) $r = 85°$      (m) $s = 28°, \ t = 80°$
     (n) $u = 70°$

**6.** $\angle SQR = 50°$

**7.** $a = 22\frac{1}{2}°$      $b = 112\frac{1}{2}°$      $c = 22\frac{1}{2}°$

## Exercise 23.4 — Page 235

1. (a) $x + 130° = 180°$ (supp. $\angle$'s)
   $x = 180° - 130° = 50°$
   (b) $y + 130° + 70° + 100° = 300°$
   (sum of $\angle$'s in a quad. $= 360°$)
   $y = 360° - 300° = 60°$
2. (a) $a = 62°$, $b = 55°$   (b) $c = 62°$
   (c) $d = 76°$
3. (a) $900°$   (b) $1080°$   (c) $1260°$
4. (a) $a = 130°$   (b) $b = 250°$   (c) $c = 85°$
5. $720°$

## Exercise 23.5 — Page 237

1. (a) (i) $120°$ (ii) $90°$ (iii) $60°$ (iv) $45°$
   (b) (i) $60°$ (ii) $90°$ (iii) $120°$ (iv) $135°$
2. 20
3. 8
4. (a) $72°$   (b) $108°$   (c) $540°$
5. (a) $a = 90°$, $b = 60°$, $c = 210°$
   (b) $d = 90°$, $e = 120°$, $f = 150°$
   (c) $g = 90°$, $h = 135°$, $i = 135°$
   (d) $j = 105°$
6. $153°$
7. $150°$
8. At any vertex, sum of angles cannot equal $360°$.

## Exercise 23.6 — Page 238

2. (a) $5, 5$   (b) $6, 6$   (c) $8, 8$
3. $1, 1, 3$
4. (a)

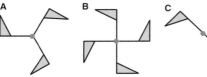

   (b) **A**: 3, **B**: 4, **C**: 2
5.

| A | B | C | D | E | F | G | H | I |
|---|---|---|---|---|---|---|---|---|
| 1 | 0 | 1 | 4 | 2 | 2 | 0 | 0 | 1 |
| 1 | 1 | 1 | 4 | 2 | 2 | 1 | 2 | 1 |

6. (a) 1
   (b) (i) (ii)

7. (a) 1
   (b) (i)

   (ii) 3

## Review Exercise 23 — Page 241

1. (a) (i) $153°$ (ii) $63°$   (b) $\angle BOQ$
2. $a = 50°$
   Sum of angles in a quadrilateral $= 360°$
3. $x = 50°$,   $x + 70° = 120°$,   alt. angles
   $y = 110°$,   $y + 70° = 180°$,   supp. angles
4. (a) (i) $x = 52°$ (ii) $y = 32°$
   (b) Rhombus

---

5. (a) 1   (b) $a = 110°$, $b = 100°$, $c = 95°$
6. $y = 63°$
7. $a = 115°$, $b = 44°$
8. 9 sides
9. (a) 10   (b) 1
   (c) $\angle AED = 54°$   (d) $\angle AEI = 36°$
   (e) $\angle BAJ = 180° - \frac{360°}{10} = 144°$
   $\angle BAE = \frac{1}{2}(540° - 3 \times 144°) = 54°$
   $\angle EAJ = 144° - 54° = 90°$

## CHAPTER 24

## Exercise 24.1 — Page 245

1. (a) $a = 90°$, $b = 50°$   (b) $c = 45°$
   (c) $d = 40°$, $e = 54°$   (d) $f = 20°$
2. (a) $a = 77°$   (b) $b = 72°$
   (c) $c = 38°$   (d) $d = 40°$
   (e) $e = 25°$   (f) $f = 65°$, $g = 65°$
   (g) $h = 130°$, $i = 65°$
   (h) $j = 94°$, $k = 43°$
3. (a) $k = 106°$, $l = 62°$
   (b) $m = 70°$, $n = 140°$
   (c) $p = 108°$, $q = 105°$
   (d) $r = 117°$, $s = 84°$
   (e) $t = 292°$, $u = 56°$
   (f) $v = 140°$
   (g) $w = 110°$, $x = 75°$
   (h) $y = 130°$, $z = 82°$
4. $47°$
5. $\angle BCD = 70°$   $\angle CAD = 76°$
6. $119°$
7. $\angle PQR = 105°$   $\angle QRS = 118°$
8. $\angle PSR = 45°$   $\angle TPQ = 95°$
9. (a) $140°$   (b) $70°$
10. (a) $100°$   (b) $40°$   (c) $25°$
11. $25°$
12. $90°$

## Exercise 24.2 — Page 248

1. (a) $a = 90°$, $b = 50°$
   (b) $c = 35°$, $d = 35°$
   (c) $e = 90°$, $f = 49°$, $g = 49°$
   (d) $h = 63°$
   (e) $j = 67°$
   (f) $k = 50°$
   (g) $l = 65°$, $m = 65°$
   (h) $n = 146°$
2. (a) $a = 78°$, $b = 39°$
   (b) $c = 54°$, $d = 63°$
   (c) $e = 55°$, $f = 38°$, $g = 38°$
   (d) $h = 16°$, $i = 106°$
   (e) $j = 65°$, $k = 65°$
   (f) $l = 57.5°$, $m = 67.5°$, $n = 45°$
3. (a) $67°$   (b) $46°$
4. (a) $100°$   (b) $40°$   (c) $25°$
5. (a) $72°$   (b) $36°$   (c) $54°$

**6.** $x = 120°$,  $y = 36°$,  $z = 60°$

**7.** $p = 42°$,  $q = 55°$,  $r = 13°$,  $s = 55°$

**8.** 90

## Exercise 24.3      Page 250

**1.** (d) $2x + 2y$

**3.** (a) $2x$ ($\angle$ at centre = twice $\angle$ at circum.)

    (b) $x$ (angles in same segment are equal)

**4.** (b) (i) $2x$     (ii) $2y$

      ($\angle$ at centre = twice $\angle$ at circum.)

**5.** (b) Tangent *PTQ* perpendicular to radius *OT*.

    (c) $x$

    (d) Angles in the same segment are equal.

## Review Exercise 24      Page 252

**1.** (a) $a = 59°$     (b) $b = 45°$

    (c) $c = 51°$     (d) $d = 23°$

**2.** $x = 55°$

**3.** (a) $\angle WXY = 90°$ (angle in semi-circle)

    (b) $\angle YZX = 49°$ (angles in same segment)

    (c) $\angle YOX = 98°$ ($\angle YOX = 2 \times \angle YWX$)

**4.** $x = 14°$

**5.** $\angle TBO = 90°$ (tangent perpendicular to radius)

    $\angle TBA = 55°$ (complementary $\angle$'s)

    $\Delta ABT$ is isosceles

    $\angle ATB = 180 - (55 + 55) = 70°$

**6.** $x = 92°$,  $y = 46°$,  $z = 17°$

**7.** $x = 50°$,  $y = 60°$,  $z = 30°$

**8.** (a) $\angle AEC = 70°$

    (b) *E* is the centre of the circle.

**9.** (a) $\angle ABC = \frac{1}{2} \angle AOC = 54°$

      $\angle ABC + \angle ADC = 180°$

      So, $\angle ADC = 180° - 54° = 126°$

    (b) $\angle OAC = \frac{1}{2}(180° - 108°) = 36°$

      $\angle CAE = 90° - 36° = 54°$

## CHAPTER    25

## Exercise 25.1      Page 255

**1.** (a) Perimeter 8 cm, area 3.75 cm².

    (b) Perimeter 9.6 cm, area 5.4 cm².

    (c) Perimeter 28 cm, area 49 cm².

**2.** (a) 9 cm²    (b) 4.16 cm²  (c) 8 cm²

**3.** (a) 13.5 cm²  (b) 20 cm²   (c) 4.35 cm²

**4.** (a) 3 cm     (b) 6 cm    (c) 9 cm

**5.** 14 m²       **7.** 84 cm²

**6.** 25 cm²      **8.** 4 cm      **9.** 60 cm

## Exercise 25.2      Page 256

**1.** (a) 12.6 cm  (b) 15.7 cm

    (c) 22 cm    (d) 28.3 cm

**2.** 75.4 cm     **4.** 30 mm

**3.** 40.8 cm     **5.** 60 cm     **6.** 67 m

## Exercise 25.3      Page 257

**1.** (a) 50.3 cm²  (b) 28.3 cm²

    (c) 176.7 cm² (d) 530.9 cm²

**2.** (a) 28.3 cm²  (b) 59.4 cm²  (c) 128.6 cm²

**3.** 3.99 cm

**4.** 7.14 m

## Exercise 25.4      Page 258

**1.** (a) 27 m         (b) 56.7 m²

**2.** 31 cm

**3.** The circle is bigger.

    Circle: 50.3 cm².   Semi-circle: 47.5 cm².

**4.** (a) $225\pi$ cm²     (b) $30\pi$ cm

**5.** 13.3 cm      **9.** 326 cm²

**6.** 18.2 cm²     **10.** 40.1 cm

**7.** 38.6 cm     **11.** $49\pi$ cm²   **13.** 8 cm

**8.** 18.8 cm     **12.** $24\pi$ cm    **14.** $65\pi$ cm²

## Exercise 25.5      Page 259

**1.** (a) 134 m²   (b) 396 km²

**2.** (a) 129 cm²  (b) 41.1 cm²  (c) 116 m²

**3.** (a) 22.7 cm²  (b) 17.6 cm²  (c) 23.9 cm²

## Exercise 25.6      Page 260

**1.** (a) (i) 3.14 cm     (ii) 2.09 cm

      (iii) 6.28 cm    (iv) 10.5 cm

      (v) 15.6 cm     (vi) 26.4 cm

    (b) (i) 3.14 cm²    (ii) 3.14 cm²

      (iii) 14.1 cm²   (iv) 25.1 cm²

      (v) 43.8 cm²    (vi) 95 cm²

**2.** (a) 170 cm²    (b) 54 cm

**3.** 53.5°

**4.** 6.62 cm

**5.** (a) 9.5 cm      (b) 14.1 cm

**6.** 14.0 cm²

**7.** $a = 19.1°$

**8.** 6.91 cm

## Review Exercise 25      Page 262

**1.** 360 m²

**2.** 20 cm

**3.** (a) 78.5 cm²   (b) 25.1 cm

**4.** 2501

**5.** 1924 m²

**6.** 103 cm²

**7.** $AD = 8.7$ cm

**8.** 140 cm²

**9.** (a) $14\pi$ cm.  Perimeter is equivalent

               to the circumference of

               a circle with diameter 14 cm.

    (b) $35\pi$ cm²

**10.** (a) 3.5 cm     (b) 6.98 cm²

**11.** 3.5 cm

**12.** No.

    Perimeters: $ABO = 25.2$ cm,  $XYO = 15.2$ cm

        Areas: $ABO = 26.2$ cm²,  $XYO = 13.1$ cm²

**13.** 20.3 cm

## CHAPTER 26

### Exercise 26.1 — Page 265

1. (a) North-West    (b) North-East
2. (a) (i) 128°    (ii) 308°
   (b) (i) 4.7 cm    (ii) 47 km
3. (a) 7 m    (b) 30 cm
4. (a) 1 : 20    (b) 5.8 m    (c) 22.5 cm
5. (a) 065°    (b) 282°    (c) 1800 m
7. (a) 8 km    (b) 114°    (c) 294°
8. (a) 6300 km    (b) 248°
9. (a) 50 km    (b) 347°    (c) 167°

### Exercise 26.2 — Page 267

4.

5.

6.

### Exercise 26.3 — Page 269

5. Perpendicular bisectors pass through the centre of the circle.

7.

8.

9.

12.
   (d) Yes

### Review Exercise 26 — Page 274

1. (a) 230°    (b) 140°
   (c) (i) 3.7 cm    (ii) 740 m

2.

3.

4. (a) $BE = 2$ cm

---

5.

6. (a) (b)
   (c) 375 m

## CHAPTER 27

### Exercise 27.1 — Page 275

1. (a) $(2, -1)$   (b) $(-2, 1)$   (c) $(0, 1)$
   (d) $(2, -3)$   (e) $(1, 2)$
3. (a) $(2, -3)$   (b) $(-2, 3)$   (c) $(4, 3)$
   (d) $(-4, 3)$   (e) $(3, 2)$

### Exercise 27.2 — Page 277

3. (a) $(3, -2)$   (b) $(-3, 2)$   (c) $(-2, -3)$
   (d) $(4, 1)$   (e) $(0, 1)$   (f) $(2, -1)$

### Exercise 27.3 — Page 278

3. $T(7, 2)$
4. (a) $\begin{pmatrix} 2 \\ 1 \end{pmatrix}$   (b) $\begin{pmatrix} 1 \\ -2 \end{pmatrix}$   (c) $\begin{pmatrix} -3 \\ 1 \end{pmatrix}$   (d) $\begin{pmatrix} -3 \\ -2 \end{pmatrix}$
5. (b) $\begin{pmatrix} -3 \\ -2 \end{pmatrix}$
6. (a) $A(1, 5)$    (b) $\begin{pmatrix} -1 \\ -5 \end{pmatrix}$

### Exercise 27.4 — Page 280

4. (a) $(4, 6)$   (b) $(6, 9)$   (c) $(4, 4)$
   (d) $(2, 7)$   (e) $(3, 4)$   (f) $(3, 3)$
5. (a) $(3, 2)$   (b) $(3, 4)$

### Exercise 27.5 — Page 281

5. (a) Inverted and smaller
   (b) Inverted and same size
   (c) Inverted and larger
6. (a) $(-6, -6)$    (b) $(-3, 3)$
   (c) $(0, 3)$    (d) $(-1, -1)$

### Exercise 27.6 — Page 284

1. $\mathbf{L_2}$: Reflection in $x$ axis
   $\mathbf{L_3}$: Rotation, 90° anticlockwise, about $(0, 0)$
   $\mathbf{L_4}$: Translation, 3 units right and 2 units up
   $\mathbf{L_5}$: Rotation, 180°, about $(0, 0)$
   $\mathbf{L_6}$: Reflection in $x = 7$
2. (a) Translation $\begin{pmatrix} -7 \\ -4 \end{pmatrix}$
   (b) Reflection in $y = -x$
   (c) Rotation, 90° anticlockwise, about $(1, 0)$
3. (a) Reflection in $x = -1$
   (b) Rotation, 90° clockwise, about $(1, -2)$
   (c) Translation $\begin{pmatrix} 5 \\ 1 \end{pmatrix}$

**4.** (a) Enlargement, scale factor 3, centre (0, 0)
  (b) Enlargement, scale factor 3, centre (5, 0)
  (c) Enlargement, scale factor 2.5, centre (0, 5)
  (d) Enlargement, scale factor $\frac{1}{3}$, centre (5, 7)
  (e) Enlargement, scale factor $\frac{1}{3}$, centre (1, 7)
  (f) Enlargement, scale factor $\frac{2}{5}$, centre (5, 5)

**5.** (a) Enlargement, scale factor $-2$, centre (1, 4)
  (b) Enlargement, scale factor $-\frac{1}{4}$, centre (0, 0)

## Exercise 27.7 — Page 286

**1.** (c) Translation $\begin{pmatrix} 8 \\ 0 \end{pmatrix}$

**2.** (c) Rotation, 90° anticlockwise, about (5, 5)
**3.** (d) Rotation, 90° anticlockwise, about (0, 0)
**4.** (c) Rotation, 180°, about (1, $-1$)

**5.** (c) Translation $\begin{pmatrix} -4 \\ 3 \end{pmatrix}$

**6.** (d) Translation $\begin{pmatrix} 6 \\ 0 \end{pmatrix}$

## Review Exercise 27 — Page 288

**1.** (a) (i) **B** (ii) **C** (iii) **A**
  (b) Reflection in $x = 3$

**2.** (a) Reflection in $x = -1$
  (b) Reflection in $y = -1$
  (c) Translation $\begin{pmatrix} -4 \\ 1 \end{pmatrix}$
  (d) Translation $\begin{pmatrix} 4 \\ -1 \end{pmatrix}$
  (e) Enlargement, scale factor 2, centre (0, 4)
  (f) Enlargement, scale factor $\frac{1}{2}$, centre (0, 4)

**3.** (a) Reflection in the $x$ axis
  (b) (c)

**4.** (a) (i) $P(6, -5)$ (ii) $\begin{pmatrix} 4 \\ -6 \end{pmatrix}$
  (b) (i) $Q(11, -1)$ (ii) $y = 3$

**5.** (a) Translation $\begin{pmatrix} 3 \\ -2 \end{pmatrix}$
  (b) Enlargement, scale factor $\frac{1}{2}$, centre (0, 0)
  (c) Rotation, 180°, about (4, 1)

**6.** (a) Rotation, 90° anticlockwise, about (1, $-1$)
  (b) (i)

  (ii) Translation $\begin{pmatrix} 2 \\ -3 \end{pmatrix}$

**7.** (a) (b)

**8.** (a) (b) (c)

  (d) Rotation, 90° anticlockwise, about (1, 3)

**9.** (b) New triangle has vertices at:
  $(-2, 1), (-6, -1), (-4, -5)$

**10.** (a) Rotation, 90° anticlockwise, about $(-5, 0)$
  (b) (iii) Enlargement, scale factor $-3$,
    centre (0, 0)

## CHAPTER 28

## Exercise 28.1 — Page 292

**1.** (a) 10 cm (b) 25 cm (c) 26 cm
**2.** (a) 7.8 cm (b) 12.8 cm (c) 10.3 cm
**3.** (a) $\sqrt{52}$ cm (b) $\sqrt{20}$ cm
**4.** (a) 5 (b) 9.22 (c) 13 (d) 8.06 (e) 7.21
**5.** (a) $R(9, 7)$ (b) $X(2, 3)$ (c) $Y(4, 2)$ (d) 2.24

## Exercise 28.2 — Page 293

**1.** (a) 8 cm (b) 6 cm (c) 2 cm
**2.** (a) 6.9 cm (b) 10.9 cm (c) 9.5 cm
**3.** 339 m    **4.** 36 cm²    **5.** 3.6 cm

## Exercise 28.3 — Page 295

**1.** (a) 2.9 cm (b) 5.7 cm (c) 2.1 cm (d) 2.0 cm
**2.** 17 cm    **5.** 10.6 cm    **8.** 74.3 cm
**3.** 10 cm    **6.** 15 cm    **9.** 13 cm
**4.** 8.5 cm    **7.** 6.9 cm    **10.** 24 cm
**11.** (a) 11.4 cm (b) 43.5 cm²

## Exercise 28.4 — Page 296

**1.** 10.4 cm  **2.** 20.7 cm  **3.** 11.9 cm  **4.** 19.5 cm
**5.** (a) 11.2 cm (b) 14.1 cm (c) 9.49 cm
**6.** 4.95 cm
**7.** (a) 2 units (b) 4 units (c) 4.5 units
  (d) 3.6 units (e) 5 units (f) 4.5 units

## Review Exercise 28 — Page 298

**1.** $PQ = 15$ cm    **3.** 30 cm
**2.** 8.60 units    **4.** $SP = 12.3$ m
**5.** $25^2 = 24^2 + 7^2$,
  so, $\Delta PQR$ is right-angled at $R$.

**6.** $CD = 3.4\,\text{m}$
**7.** $361\,\text{m}$
**8.** $6.14\,\text{m}$
**9.** $CD = 5.7\,\text{cm}$
**10.** $14.1\,\text{km}$
**11.** $AC = 10$ units,  $AE = \sqrt{80}$ units
   $AF = \sqrt{116}$ units
**12.** $10.7\,\text{cm}$
**13.** $AD = 9.75\,\text{cm}$
**14.** $PX = 5.66\,\text{cm}$
**15.** $MN = 5.4$ units

## CHAPTER 29

### Exercise 29.1 — Page 301

**1.** (a)  $h = 2.27\,\text{m}$   (b)  $h = 4.02\,\text{m}$
   (c)  $h = 8.02\,\text{m}$
**2.** (a)  $x = 1.50\,\text{cm}$   (b)  $x = 2.99\,\text{cm}$
   (c)  $x = 5.78\,\text{cm}$
**3.** (a)  $BC = 3.39\,\text{m}$   (b)  $AC = 11.4\,\text{m}$
   (c)  $BC = 4.74\,\text{cm}$
   (d)  $\angle ABC = 55°$,  $AC = 6.96\,\text{cm}$

### Exercise 29.2 — Page 302

**1.** (a)  $a = 62.1°$  (b)  $a = 25.0°$  (c)  $a = 50.9°$
**2.** (a)  $x = 52.3°$  (b)  $x = 60.5°$  (c)  $x = 61.4°$
**3.** (a)  $\angle QPR = 23.6°$
   (b)  $\angle PRQ = 64.7°$
   (c)  $\angle QPR = 21.8°$
   (d)  $\angle QRP = 24.0°$,  $\angle QPR = 66.0°$

### Exercise 29.3 — Page 303

**1.** (a)  $l = 7.00\,\text{m}$   (b)  $l = 7.49\,\text{m}$
   (c)  $l = 4.93\,\text{m}$
**2.** (a)  $x = 6.49\,\text{cm}$   (b)  $x = 5.31\,\text{cm}$
   (c)  $x = 10.61\,\text{cm}$
**3.** (a)  $AB = 7.62\,\text{m}$   (b)  $AB = 17.5\,\text{cm}$
   (c)  $AB = 66.9\,\text{cm}$
   (d)  $\angle ABC = 17.2°$,  $AB = 25.7\,\text{m}$

### Exercise 29.4 — Page 305

**1.**

|     | $\sin p$ | $\cos p$ | $\tan p$ |
|-----|----------|----------|----------|
| (a) | $\frac{5}{13}$ | $\frac{12}{13}$ | $\frac{5}{12}$ |
| (b) | $\frac{7}{25}$ | $\frac{24}{25}$ | $\frac{7}{24}$ |
| (c) | $\frac{4}{5}$ | $\frac{3}{5}$ | $\frac{4}{3}$ |

**2.** (a)  $p = 40.9°$   (b)  $p = 38.0°$
   (c)  $p = 38.8°$   (d)  $p = 53.3°$
   (e)  $p = 39.7°$   (f)  $p = 35.5°$
**3.** (a)  $a = 5.77\,\text{cm}$   (b)  $a = 6.47\,\text{cm}$
   (c)  $a = 4.18\,\text{cm}$   (d)  $a = 3.78\,\text{cm}$
   (e)  $a = 4.72\,\text{cm}$   (f)  $a = 4.04\,\text{cm}$
**4.** $4.33\,\text{cm}$
**5.** $72.5°, 72.5°, 34.9°$

**6.** (a)  $5.96\,\text{cm}$   (b)  $1.71\,\text{cm}$
**7.** (a)  $2.76\,\text{cm}$   (b)  $19.8°$
**8.** $13.06\,\text{cm}$
**9.** $4.52\,\text{cm}$
**10.** $9.45\,\text{cm}$

### Exercise 29.5 — Page 308

**1.** $21.4\,\text{m}$   **5.** $31.0°$
**2.** $40.1\,\text{m}$   **6.** $51.3°$
**3.** (a)  $135\,\text{m}$   (b)  $53.5°$   **7.** $959\,\text{m}$
**4.** $22.2\,\text{m}$   **8.** $40.5\,\text{m}$

### Exercise 29.6 — Page 309

**1.** (a)  $161\,\text{km}$  (b)  $192\,\text{km}$   **5.** $164°$
**2.** $22.2\,\text{km}$   **6.** $6.40\,\text{km}$
**3.** $145°$   **7.** $174\,\text{km}$
**4.** $41.9\,\text{km}$   **8.** $283°$

### Exercise 29.7 — Page 311

**1.** (a)  $39.8°$   (b)  $36.7°$
**2.** $18.5°$
**3.** (a)  $45°$   (b)  $35.3°$
**4.** (a)  $26.6°$   (b)  $21.8°$
**5.** $48.5°$
**6.** (a)  $7.42\,\text{cm}$   (b)  $69.4°$   (c)  $62.1°$

### Review Exercise 29 — Page 312

**1.** $h = 3.25\,\text{m}$
**2.** $b = 78.2°$
**3.** (a)  $\angle A = 61°$   (b)  $BD = 14.2\,\text{cm}$
**4.** $17.9°$
**5.** (a)  $x = 34°$   (b)  $CB = 14.4\,\text{m}$
**6.** (a)  $6.53\,\text{km}$   (b)  $127°$
**7.** (a)  (i)  $\frac{5}{12}$   (ii)  $\frac{5}{13}$
   (b)  $QR = 6.5\,\text{cm}$,  $PR = 2.5\,\text{cm}$
**8.** (a)  $AB = \sqrt{(9^2 + 4^2) + 5^2}$
      $= \sqrt{122}$
      $= 11.05\,\text{cm}$
   (b)  $26.9°$
**9.** (a)  (i)  $5.29\,\text{cm}$  (ii)  $61.9°$   (b)  $69.3°$

## CHAPTER 30

### Exercise 30.2 — Page 315

**1.** $9$
**2.** (a)  $4$   (b)  $4$   (c)  $2$   (d)  Infinite
**3.** (a)  $2$   (b)  $2$   (c)  $4$
**4.** (a)  $4$   (b)  $1, 4$

### Exercise 30.3 — Page 316

**1.** (a)        (b)        (c)

**2.** (a)

plan    elevation A    elevation B    elevation C

(b)

elevation A

plan    elevation B    elevation C

(c)

plan    elevation A

elevation B    elevation C

**3.**

plan    elevation A

**4.** (a)    (b)

**1.** (b)  52 cm²
**2.** (a)  27 cm³,  54 cm²    (b)  30 cm³,  62 cm²
    (c)  140 cm³,  166 cm²
**3.** (a)  4 cm³,  18 cm²    (b)  5 cm³,  20 cm²
    (c)  8 cm³,  28 cm²    (d)  7 cm³,  24 cm²
    (e)  14 cm³,  42 cm²    (f)  10 cm³,  32 cm²
**4.** 96.8 cm³,  131.5 cm²    **6.** 1155 cm²
**5.** 10 cm    **7.** 343 cm³

**1.** (a)  40 cm³    (b)  140 cm³    (c)  96 cm³
**2.** (a)  11 cm², 15.4 cm³    (b)  6 cm², 15 cm³
    (c)  314 cm², 6280 cm³  (d)  3.14 cm², 15.7 cm³
**3.** (a)  10 cm³    (b)  56 cm³    (c)  330 cm³
    (d)  113 cm³    (e)  393 cm³    (f)  120 cm³
    (g)  848 cm³    (h)  18 cm³
**4.** No.  $\pi \times 5 \times 5 \times 10 = 250\pi$ cm³
           $\pi \times 10 \times 10 \times 5 = 500\pi$ cm³
**5.** 11.5 cm    **6.** 2.7 cm    **7.** 12.0 cm    **8.** 4.5 cm

**1.** (a)  339 cm²    (b)  61.3 cm²    (c)  90.9 cm²
**3.** (a)  1260 cm²    (b)  6280 cm²
**4.** 274 cm²
**5.** (a)  14 100 cm²    (b)  18 800 cm²
**6.** 4 cm

**1.** (a)  101 cm³    (b)  2140 cm³    (c)  37.3 cm³
**2.** (a)  220 cm²    (b)  47.1 cm²    (c)  57.9 cm²
**3.** Hemispherical bowl has greater volume.
    Cone 393 cm³, hemisphere 452 cm³.
**4.** 37.5 cm
**5.** (a)  314 cm²    (b)  188 cm²    (c)  2120 cm²
**6.** (a)  (i)  170 cm³    (ii)  160 cm²
    (b)  (i)  33.5 cm³    (ii)  53.2 cm²
    (c)  (i)  91.6 cm³    (ii)  117 cm²
**7.** 4.73 cm
**8.** 2.40 cm
**9.** 1470 cm³, 837 cm²
**10.** (a)  720 cm³    (b)  564 cm²

**2.** (a)    (b)

**3.** (a)  4    (b)  4
**4.** (a)  Cube.  Cuboid: 120 cm³  Cube: 125 cm³
    (b)  Cube.  Cuboid: 148 cm²  Cube: 150 cm²
**5.** 8 cm          **12.** (a)  (i)  18 000π cm³
**6.** 150π cm²                (ii)  $h = 45$ cm
**7.** 42 m³            (b)  24 cm
**8.** 180 cm³        **13.** 199 cm³
**9.** 7614 cm³       **14.** 3.08 cm
**10.** 31 428 cm²     **15.** (a)  223.8 cm³
**11.** 347 cm³           (b)  123 cm²

## CHAPTER    **31**

**1.** (a)  320 000 ml = 320$l$
    (b)  0.32t = 320 kg = 320 000 g
    (c)  320 mm = 32 cm = 0.32 m
    (d)  32 000 cm² = 3.2 m²
**2.** 9.3 kg           **6.** 8 kg and 8000 g
**3.** 8 m            **7.** 0.5 km
**4.** 30 ml          **8.** 0.3 t
**5.** 2000 m and 2 km    **9.** 2 cm
**10.** (a)  3.123 m    (b)  450 cm    (c)  3240 km
    (d)  1 000 000 g    (e)  0.4 $l$
**11.** 0.5 m² is larger than 500 cm².
    0.5 m² = 5000 cm²
**12.** 800 000 cm³ is larger than 0.08 m³.
    0.08 m³ = 80 000 cm³
**13.** 1.98 $l$    **17.** 50 ml
**14.** 20         **18.** 0.036 m²
**15.** 50 g       **19.** (a)  67 200 cm²  (b)  6.72 m²
**16.** 60         **20.** 600 000 cm³

## Exercise **31.2** — Page 330

1. (a) kilometres (b) metres (c) centimetres
   (d) millimetres (e) kilograms (f) grams
   (g) litres (h) millilitres
2. 250 g
3. 30 cm
4. 200 ml
6. (a) 12 m, nearest metre, 5.9 m, nearest 100 cm
   5 $l$, nearest litre, 500 m², nearest 50 m²
   (b) 1200 cm, nearest 100 cm
   5900 mm, nearest 100 mm
   5000 ml, nearest 1000 ml
   500 000 000 mm², nearest 50 000 000 mm²

## Exercise **31.3** — Page 331

1. (a) 33 pounds (b) 35 pints (c) 200 inches
   (d) 150 mm (e) 20 inches (f) 180 cm
2. 20 miles
3. 7 pints
4. 170 cm
5. 62.7 kg
6. (a) 600 m (b) 4.8 km (c) 5 feet
   (d) 2.75 pounds (e) 45.7 litres
7. 12 gallons
8. 22 pounds
9. Yes. 4 litres is about 7 pints.
   7 pints ÷ 20 = $\frac{7}{20}$ pint,
   which is greater than $\frac{1}{3}$ pint.
10. No. 10 kg is about 22 pounds.
11. No. 6 miles is about 9.6 km.
12. 10 pounds
13. 1500 cm²
14. (a) 48 km/hour (b) 80 km/hour
    (c) 108 km/hour
15. (a) 37.5 miles per hour
    (b) 90 miles per hour
16. 27 metres per second
17. (a) 12.8 km/litre (b) 30 miles per gallon
18. 3.35 kg, nearest 10 g
19. 6.8 m³, 1 d.p.

## Exercise **31.4** — Page 333

1. (a) continuous (b) discrete
   (c) discrete (d) continuous
2. (a) exact (b) 4.5 mins ≤ t < 5.5 mins
   (c) 62.5 kg ≤ w < 63.5 kg
3. (a) 12.5 s ≤ t < 13.5 s
   (b) 82.55 s ≤ t < 82.65 s
4. (a)
   (b)
5. (a) nearest 0.01 m (centimetre)
   (b) 1.525 m ≤ h < 1.535 m
6. (a) 61.5 kg (b) 2.25 m (c) 12.625 s
7. (a) nearest 10 m (b) nearest 50 m
   (c) nearest 100 m

8. (a) 10 499, 9500 (b) 10 049, 9950
   (c) 10 024, 9975 (d) 549, 450
   (e) 504, 495

## Exercise **31.5** — Page 334

1. 98.5°
2. 39.208 cm³ (3 d.p.)
3. (a) 162 minutes (3 s.f.)
   (b) 226 minutes (3 s.f.)
4. 7.428 cm (3 d.p.)
5. 68 330.58 g (2 d.p.)
6. (a) 26.595 km, 26.485 km
   (b) 3.03 km/h (3 s.f.)
7. 5.741 cm² (3 d.p.)

## Exercise **31.6** — Page 336

1. (a) area (b) length (c) length
   (d) length (e) volume (f) area
   (g) volume (h) area
2. (a) perimeter (b) area (c) volume
   (d) none (e) area (f) perimeter
   (g) perimeter (h) none (i) volume
   (j) volume (k) none (l) area
3. (a) (i) $2\pi (x + y)$ (ii) $\pi (x^2 + y^2)$, $\pi xy$
5. $\frac{1}{2} pqs$, volume
   $2\left(p + q + r + \frac{3s}{2}\right)$, edge length
   $s(p + q + r) + pq$, surface area
6. (a) correct (b) correct (c) correct
   (d) wrong (e) correct (f) wrong
7. (a), (b), (c), (e)

## Review Exercise **31** — Page 337

1. (a) 2650 m (b) 175 miles
2. (a) 65 kg (b) 1.55 m
3. 5 gallons
4. 15 000 cm²
5. (a) 0.04 m² (b) 400 cm²
6. (a) 30 mph (b) 13.3 m/s
7. Both same speed
8. 1.3 litres
9. 135 tonnes
10. 76.95 kg
11. $\frac{ar}{2}(4b + \pi r)$ and $2abr + \frac{\pi a r^2}{2}$
12. 0.1 s
13. 35.55 m
14. (a) 0.425 m (b) 32
15. Upper bound: 0.92628…
    Lower bound: 0.87423…
16. Smallest value: 12 cm
    Largest value: 14.7826… cm
17. 26.95%
18. (a) 7.8488… cm
    (b) No. Minimum diameter of holder is
        2 × 3.915 cm = 7.83 cm, which is
        less than maximum diagonal of the
        square cross-section, 7.8488… cm.

## Exercise 32.1  Page 340

1. **D**, **E**
2. (a) $\Delta CED$  (b) $CBFE$
3. $\Delta AXZ$ and $\Delta ZYC$,  $\Delta BXZ$ and $\Delta ZYB$
4. **A**, **D** (SSS)
5. **A**, **D** (ASA)
6. (a) Yes, ASA  (b) No  (c) Yes, SAS
7. (a) Yes, SSS  (b) No  (c) Yes, RHS
   (d) Yes, SAS  (e) No  (f) Yes, ASA
8. (a) No  (b) No  (c) Yes, RHS
   (d) No  (e) Yes, ASA
   (f) Yes, ASA  (g) Yes, SSS
   (h) Yes, SAS  (i) Yes, ASA
9. No lengths given, one triangle is larger than the other.
10. $DE = PQ$ (given)  $DF = PR$ (given)
    $\angle EDF = \angle QPR$ (70°)  Congruent, SAS
11. (a) $\angle BDC = 25°$
    (b) $BD$ is common, $AB = CD$ (7 cm)
       $\angle ABD = \angle BDC$ (alt. $\angle$'s)
       Congruent, SAS
    (c) $\angle ADB$

## Exercise 32.2  Page 342

1. Corresponding lengths not in same ratio.
2. (a) Two circles  (d) Two squares
3. $a = 4$ cm,  $b = 24$ cm
4. (a) Scale factor $= \frac{3}{2} = 1.5$
   (b) $x = 1.8$ cm  (c) $a = 120°$
5. 30 cm
6. (a) $x = 1.5$ cm,  $y = 2.4$ cm,  $a = 70°$
   (b) $x = 5$ cm,  $y = 1.5$ cm,  $a = 53°$
   (c) $x = 30$ cm,  $y = 17.5$ cm,  $z = 10$ cm
7. 15 cm  9. 18°
8. 2.8 cm  10. 5 cm  11. $x = 16$, $y = 48$

## Exercise 32.3  Page 344

1. (a) $x = 10$ cm,  $y = 27$ cm
   (b) $x = 6$ cm,  $y = 10$ cm
   (c) $x = 12$ cm,  $y = 12$ cm
   (d) $x = 12$ cm,  $y = 5$ cm
2. $AB = 8$ cm,  $AE = 5$ cm
3. (a) $AB = 2.96$ cm,  $QR = 3.25$ cm
   (b) $XZ = 14.4$ m,  $BC = 6.25$ m
   (c) $EG = 1.6$ cm,  $MN = 4.0$ cm
   (d) $AC = 4.0$ m,  $XZ = 2.0$ m
4. (a) $PR = 10$ cm
   (b) $QR = 5$ cm,  $PQ = 7.5$ cm,  $QS = 4.5$ cm
5. (a) $AB = 6$ cm
   (b) $BC = 7.5$ cm,  $AC = 6.9$ cm
   (c) $EC = 4.6$ cm
6. $GH = 6$ cm,  $FH = 3$ cm

## Exercise 32.4  Page 346

1. (a) $AC = 2.4$ cm,  $AP = 2.2$ cm
   (b) $AC = 4.5$ cm,  $BP = 1$ cm
   (c) $BC = 4.2$ cm,  $BP = 1.6$ cm
2. (a) $AQ = 2.5$ cm,  $BC = 7$ cm
   (b) $AQ = 4\frac{2}{3}$ cm,  $BQ = 16\frac{2}{3}$ cm
3. (a) $x = 58°$  (b) $x = 56°$
4. (a) (i) 61°  (ii) 29°
   (b) (i) 13 cm,  5.2 cm  (ii) 36 cm,  27 cm
   Same
5. (b) $AB = 1.8$ cm  (c) 12.5 cm
6. 13.5 cm²

## Exercise 32.5  Page 349

1. 30 m
2. (a) 2 : 3  (b) 9 cm
3. (a) 1 : 50
   (b) 2.8 cm
4. Original area multiplied by $2^2 = 4$
5. 40 kg
6. 100 times larger
7. 2.4 cm
8. area is quartered
9. 90 cm²
10. (a) 8 cm  (b) 96 cm²
11. 2.4 m
12. (a) 1.5 km
    (b) 5 km²
13. (a) 14 cm
    (b) 750 000 m²
    (c) 1.92 cm²
14. 8 times original volume
15. 4000 ml
16. (a) 880 cm²
    (b) 55 cm², 25 cm³
17. 540 litres
18. 12 kg
19. $\left(\frac{1}{2}\right)^3 = \frac{1}{8}$ of original volume
20. 25 cm³
21. 405 cm³
22. (a) 10 cm
    (b) 16 : 25
23. 36 cm
24. 391 ml
25. (a) 3.28 m²
    (b) 45 cm³
26. (a) 1 : 300
    (b) 0.741 cm³
    (c) 2880 m²
27. 1.41
28. (a) 33.5 cm³, 524 cm³
    (b) Ratio of surface areas $= 4 : 25$
       As a percentage, $\frac{4}{25} \times 100 = 16\%$
29. (a) 15 cm  (b) $33.75\pi$
30. 0.81 kg

## Review Exercise 32  Page 351

1. **A** and **C**, SAS
2. $BC$ is common  (given diameter)
   $\angle CAB = \angle BDC = 90°$  (angle in semi-circle)
   $\angle ABC = \angle BCD$  (alt $\angle$'s)
   So,  $\angle BCA = \angle CBD$
   $\Delta$s $ABC$ and $DCB$ are congruent, ASA
3. (a) 3  (b) $x = 12.3$ cm  (c) $y = 25°$
4. (a) (i) $x = 7.8$ cm  (ii) $y = 4.3$ cm  (b) $n = 9$
5. (a) $h = 24$ cm  (b) $d = 12$ cm  (c) 3375 grams
6. (a) 6 cm  (b) 8 : 27
7. (a) 3125 cm²  (b) 12 000 m³
8. 1 : 16
9. (a) 6 cm²  (b) 1458 cm³

3. $\mathbf{a} = \begin{pmatrix} 3 \\ 5 \end{pmatrix}$   $\mathbf{b} = \begin{pmatrix} 3 \\ -1 \end{pmatrix}$   $\mathbf{c} = \begin{pmatrix} -2 \\ 4 \end{pmatrix}$

$\mathbf{d} = \begin{pmatrix} -6 \\ -1 \end{pmatrix}$   $\mathbf{e} = \begin{pmatrix} 4 \\ 3 \end{pmatrix}$   $\mathbf{f} = \begin{pmatrix} 2 \\ -5 \end{pmatrix}$

2. (i) $\mathbf{a} = 2\mathbf{p},$   $\mathbf{e} = -\mathbf{p}$
   (ii) $\mathbf{b} = 2\mathbf{q},$   $\mathbf{c} = -\mathbf{q},$   $\mathbf{h} = -3\mathbf{q}$
   (iii) $\mathbf{d} = \frac{1}{2}\mathbf{r},$   $\mathbf{f} = 2\mathbf{r},$   $\mathbf{g} = -\frac{1}{2}\mathbf{r}$

2. (a) $\mathbf{r}$   (b) $\mathbf{s}$   (c) $\mathbf{t}$   (d) $\mathbf{q}$
   (e) $\mathbf{v}$   (f) $\mathbf{u}$   (g) $\mathbf{w}$   (h) $\mathbf{p}$
3. (a)

(b) $\overrightarrow{OB} = \overrightarrow{EH} = \mathbf{y}$.   $OB$ is parallel and equal to $EH$, so, $OBHE$ is a parallelogram.

4. (b) (i) $\frac{1}{2}\mathbf{a} + \mathbf{b}$   (ii) $\frac{1}{2}\mathbf{a} + \mathbf{b}$   (iii) $\mathbf{a} + 2\mathbf{b}$

(c) (i) $\overrightarrow{PC} = \overrightarrow{AR}$, so, $PC$ is parallel and equal in length to $AR$.

(ii) $\overrightarrow{AE} = 2\overrightarrow{PC}$, so, $PC$ is parallel to $AE$ and $AE$ is $2 \times$ length of $PC$.

1. (a) $-\mathbf{a}$   (b) $\mathbf{b} - \mathbf{a}$
   (c) $\frac{1}{2}(\mathbf{b} - \mathbf{a})$   (d) $-\frac{1}{2}(\mathbf{a} + \mathbf{b})$
2. (a) (i) $\mathbf{q} - \mathbf{p}$   (ii) $2\mathbf{p}$
   (iii) $2\mathbf{p} + 2\mathbf{q}$   (iv) $2\mathbf{q} - 2\mathbf{p}$

(b) Parallel, $PQ = \frac{1}{2}XZ$

3. (a) (i) $\frac{1}{2}\mathbf{a}$   (ii) $\frac{1}{2}\mathbf{a} + \mathbf{b}$
   (iii) $\frac{1}{2}\mathbf{a} - \mathbf{b}$   (iv) $\frac{1}{6}\mathbf{a} - \frac{1}{3}\mathbf{b}$
   (v) $\frac{2}{3}\mathbf{a} + \frac{2}{3}\mathbf{b}$   (vi) $\mathbf{a} + \mathbf{b}$

(b) $OYB$ is a straight line.

4. (a) (i) $2\mathbf{q}$   (ii) $2\mathbf{p}$
   (iii) $\mathbf{q} - \mathbf{p}$   (iv) $2\mathbf{p} - 2\mathbf{q}$
   (v) $\mathbf{q}$   (vi) $-\mathbf{p}$

(b) Similar triangles

5. (a) (i) $\mathbf{b} - \mathbf{c}$   (ii) $-\frac{1}{2}\mathbf{b}$
   (iii) $\frac{1}{2}\mathbf{a} + \frac{1}{2}\mathbf{b} - \mathbf{c}$
   (iv) $\frac{1}{2}\mathbf{a} - \frac{1}{2}\mathbf{c}$   (v) $\frac{1}{2}\mathbf{a} - \frac{1}{2}\mathbf{c}$

6. (a) $4\mathbf{a} + 2\mathbf{b}$

(b) $\overrightarrow{OC} = 6\mathbf{a} + (4 + n)\mathbf{b}$   $n = -1$

7. (a) $\overrightarrow{AD} = 3\mathbf{a} - 2\mathbf{b},$    $= 6\mathbf{a} - 4\mathbf{b}$

(b) $ABCD$ is a trapezium.

1. (a) $\mathbf{b} - \mathbf{a}$   (b) $\frac{1}{2}(\mathbf{b} - \mathbf{a})$   (c) $\frac{1}{2}(\mathbf{a} + \mathbf{b})$
2. (a) (i) $B(4, 6)$   (ii) $M(1, 3.5)$
   (iii) $N(0, -0.5)$

(b) (i) $\overrightarrow{BC} = \begin{pmatrix} -2 \\ -8 \end{pmatrix}$   (ii) $\overrightarrow{MN} = \begin{pmatrix} -1 \\ -4 \end{pmatrix}$

(c) Parallel lines.   $BC = 2 \times MN$

3. (a) (i) $2\mathbf{b}$   (ii) $\mathbf{a} - \mathbf{b}$
   (iii) $\frac{1}{2}\mathbf{a} + \mathbf{b} = \frac{1}{2}(\mathbf{a} + 2\mathbf{b})$

(b) $\overrightarrow{OH} = \frac{1}{3}\mathbf{a} + \frac{2}{3}\mathbf{b} = \frac{1}{3}(\mathbf{a} + 2\mathbf{b})$

(c) Colinear

4. (a) (i) $\mathbf{b} - \mathbf{a}$

(ii) $\overrightarrow{BC} = -\mathbf{b} + 4\mathbf{b} - 3\mathbf{a} = 3(\mathbf{b} - \mathbf{a})$
$\overrightarrow{BC} = 3 \times \overrightarrow{AB}$
$B$ is a common point.
So, $A$, $B$ and $C$ lie on a straight line.

(b) $3 : 4$

5. (a) $\mathbf{b} - \mathbf{a}$

(b) $\frac{2}{3}\mathbf{a} + \frac{1}{3}\mathbf{b} = \frac{1}{3}(2\mathbf{a} + \mathbf{b})$

(c) $\frac{1}{2}\mathbf{b}$

(d) Parallel lines.   $AQ = \frac{1}{2}AB$

1. (a) positive   (b) positive   (c) positive
   (d) positive   (e) negative   (f) negative
   (g) negative   (h) negative   (i) positive
   (j) positive   (k) negative   (l) positive
   (m) negative   (n) positive   (o) negative
   (p) positive   (q) positive   (r) negative
   (s) negative   (t) positive   (u) negative
   (v) positive   (w) positive   (x) negative
   (y) negative   (z) positive

2. (a) $-\tan 80°$   (b) $-\cos 30°$   (c) $-\sin 20°$
   (d) $\tan 70°$   (e) $\cos 60°$   (f) $\sin 60°$
   (g) $-\tan 10°$   (h) $-\cos 30°$   (i) $-\sin 70°$
   (j) $-\tan 30°$   (k) $\cos 10°$   (l) $-\sin 80°$
   (m) $\tan 10°$   (n) $\sin 60°$   (o) $-\cos 60°$
   (p) $-\sin 50°$   (q) $-\cos 80°$   (r) $\tan 30°$

3. (a) (i) $\frac{1}{\sqrt{2}}$   (ii) $1$

(b) (i) $-\frac{1}{\sqrt{2}}$   (ii) $1$   (iii) $-\frac{1}{\sqrt{2}}$

(iv) $\frac{1}{\sqrt{2}}$   (v) $-\frac{1}{\sqrt{2}}$   (vi) $-1$

**4.** (a) $\frac{1}{2}$, $\frac{\sqrt{3}}{2}$, $\frac{1}{\sqrt{3}}$

(i) $\frac{1}{2}$ (ii) $-\frac{\sqrt{3}}{2}$ (iii) $-\frac{1}{\sqrt{3}}$ (iv) $\frac{\sqrt{3}}{2}$

(b) $\frac{\sqrt{3}}{2}$, $\frac{1}{2}$, $\sqrt{3}$

(i) $-\frac{1}{2}$ (ii) $\sqrt{3}$ (iii) $-\frac{1}{2}$ (iv) $-\frac{\sqrt{3}}{2}$

## Exercise 34.2 — Page 366

**1.** (a) 0.985 (b) −0.866 (c) 0.364
(d) −0.940 (e) 0.5 (f) −0.176
(g) 0.123 (h) −0.993 (i) −0.799
(j) 0.891 (k) −0.325 (l) 0.438
(m) −0.810 (n) −0.961 (o) −0.616
(p) 0.766 (q) −0.839 (r) 0.643
(s) 0.866 (t) −0.985

**2.** (a) $p = 60°$, $300°$ (b) $p = 210°$, $330°$
(c) $p = 45°$, $225°$ (d) $p = 30°$, $150°$
(e) $p = 135°$, $315°$ (f) $p = 120°$, $240°$
(g) $p = 230°$, $310°$ (h) $p = 40°$, $320°$
(i) $p = 60°$, $120°$ (j) $p = 116°$, $296°$
(k) $p = 10.9°$, $190.9°$ (l) $p = 55.6°$, $304.4°$
(m) $p = 20°$, $160°$ (n) $p = 150°$, $210°$
(o) $p = 35°$, $215°$

**3.** $x = 228.6°$, $311.4°$, $588.6°$, $671.4°$

**4.** $x = -245°$, $-115°$, $245°$

**5.** $x = -307°$, $-233°$, $53°$, $127°$

## Exercise 34.3 — Page 367

**1.** (a) (i) $x = 90°$ (ii) $x = 0°$, $180°$, $360°$
(iii) $x = 270°$
(b) (i) $x = 0°$, $360°$ (ii) $x = 90°$, $270°$
(iii) $x = 180°$

**2.** (a) $x = 45°$, $225°$ (b) $x = 0°$, $180°$, $360°$
(c) $x = 135°$, $315°$

**3.** (a) (i) $x = 30°$, $150°$ (ii) $y = -2.6$

**4.** (b) $x = 78.5°$, $281.5°$

## Exercise 34.4 — Page 370

**1.** (a) $a = 5.79$ cm (b) $a = 13.1$ cm
(c) $a = 4.26$ cm

**2.** (a) $b = 9.92$ cm (b) $c = 8.28$ cm
(c) $b = 10.1$ cm (d) $q = 13.6$ cm
(e) $p = 1.64$ cm (f) $r = 8.48$ cm

**3.** (a) $\angle ACB = 55°$, $AC = 7.41$ cm,
$AB = 6.54$ cm
(b) $\angle MLN = 71.2°$, $LM = 5.84$ cm,
$AB = 5.71$ cm
(c) $\angle RPQ = 69.8°$, $QR = 15.7$ cm,
$PR = 14.9$ cm
(d) $\angle SUT = 31.8°$, $ST = 12.8$ cm,
$UT = 24.1$ cm
(e) $\angle XYZ = 31.2°$, $XY = 7.54$ cm,
$ZY = 9.4$ cm

**4.** (a) $PR = 9.7$ cm (b) $QR = 6.8$ cm

## Exercise 34.5 — Page 372

**1.** (a) 61.7° (b) 53.7° (c) 74.7°
**2.** (a) 137.3° (b) 129.7° (c) 118.5°
**3.** 48.6°, 131.4°
**4.** $\angle QPR = 68.1°$, $\angle PRQ = 51.9°$,
$PQ = 6.36$ cm
$\angle QPR = 111.9°$, $\angle PRQ = 8.1°$,
$PQ = 1.14$ cm
**5.** (a) $\angle ACB = 60.7°$, $\angle BAC = 50°$,
$BC = 7.29$ cm
(b) $\angle DFE = 25.2°$, $\angle EDF = 29.8°$,
$EF = 9.91$ cm

## Exercise 34.6 — Page 373

**1.** (a) $a = 10.8$ cm (b) $a = 8.27$ cm
(c) $a = 15.3$ cm
**2.** (a) $p = 5.98$ cm (b) $q = 3.45$ cm
(c) $r = 15.3$ cm
**3.** 12.7 cm **5.** 13.4 cm
**4.** 11.8 cm **6.** 18 cm **7.** 26.7 km

## Exercise 34.7 — Page 375

**1.** (a) $A = 130.5°$ (b) $A = 32.2°$ (c) $A = 45.8°$
**2.** (a) $B = 64.5°$ (b) $C = 35.4°$ (c) $P = 41.6°$
**3.** 45° **4.** 130.5° **5.** 102.6° **6.** 119.9°

## Exercise 34.8 — Page 376

**1.** (a) 6.83 cm² (b) 14.2 cm²
(c) 6.95 cm² (d) 16.2 cm²
**2.** 84.8 cm²
**3.** (a) 3 cm (b) 5.63 cm²
**4.** 65 cm²
**5.** 8.9 cm **7.** $XY = YZ = 7.37$ cm
**6.** 729 cm² **8.** 56.2°, 123.8°

## Exercise 34.9 — Page 378

**1.** (a) (i) 10.8 cm, 73.9°, 46.1°
(ii) 8.44 cm, 46.4°, 23.6°
(b) (i) 46.8 cm² (ii) 11 cm²
**2.** (a) 118.7°, 35.1°, 26.2°
(b) $XP = 128.5$ m, $\angle XPY = 123°$
**3.** 9.24 km
**4.** 12.7 m
**5.** (a) 7.84 m (b) 29.9° (c) 14.7 m
**6.** (a) 5.17 cm (b) 10.8 cm²
**7.** (a) 28° (b) 38.2° (c) 28 cm²
**8.** 6.63 cm, 15.4 cm

## Review Exercise 34 — Page 380

**1.** (a) $x = -310°$, $50°$, $130°$
**2.** $x = 60°$, $300°$
**3.** (b) $x = 120°$, $240°$
**4.** (a) $BC = 7.53$ m (b) $AD = 15.6$ m
(c) 76.9 m²
**5.** (a) $\angle DBC = 38.8°$ (b) $AD = 8.55$ cm
**6.** (a) 16.7 km (b) 306°

**7.** (a)  *AC* is common.
 *ABCD* is a kite (given), so, *AC* is a line
 of symmetry, so:
 $\angle BAC = \angle DAC$ and $\angle BCA = \angle DCA$
 $\Delta$s *ABC* and *ADC* are congruent, ASA
 (b)  41.6 cm²
**8.** (a)  7 m      (b)  25.1 m
**9.** *BC* = 91 m

## Shape, Space and Measures

### Non-calculator Paper   Page 382

**1.** $p = 28°$   $(p + p + 124° = 180°)$
 $q = 152°$   $(q = p + 124°)$
**2.** 12 cm
**3.** (a)  Reflection in the *y* axis
 (b)  Rotation, 90° clockwise, about (0, 0)
 (c)
**4.** $y = 60°$
**5.** 62 m²
**6.** 25 000 cm²
**7.** (a)  Rotation, through 180°, about the
 midpoint of *BD*.
 (b)  Congruent
**8.** (a)  $100\pi$ cm    (b)  $2500\pi$ cm²
**9.** 165.5 cm ≤ Jean's height < 166.5 cm
**10.** (b)  116 m, 276°
**11.** (a)  (1, 1)    (b)  Translation $\begin{pmatrix} 4 \\ -6 \end{pmatrix}$
**12.** (a)  12 sides    (b)  13 cm
**13.** $y = 8$ m
**14.** (a)  (i)  (ii)  (iii)
 (b)

**15.** (a)  $\angle ACB = 180° - 100° - 52° = 28°$
 $\angle PRQ = 180° - 100° - 28° = 52°$
 So, $\angle A = \angle P, \angle B = \angle R, \angle C = \angle Q$
 $\Delta$s *ABC* and *PRQ* are similar, equal angles
 (b)  *PQ* = 4.8 cm
**16.** (a)  Scale factor $\frac{1}{3}$, centre (2, 1)    (b)  4 cm²
**17.** (b)  $x = 120°, 240°$
**18.** (a)  810 cm³    (b)  248 cm²
**19.** (a)  $r = 6$ cm
 (b)  (i)  $h = 8$ cm    (ii)  $96\pi$ cm³
**20.** (a)  $\angle DBC = 55°$    (b)  $\angle DCO = 35°$
 (c)  $\angle DAB = 80°$
**21.** Surface area sphere = $4\pi r^2$
 Surface area cylinder = $2\pi\frac{d}{2}\left(\frac{d}{2} + 2d\right) = \frac{5\pi d^2}{2}$
 So, $4\pi r^2 = \frac{5\pi d^2}{2}$, $8r^2 = 5d^2$, $r^2 = \frac{5}{8}d^2$

**22.** (a)  $288\pi$ cm³    (b)  $h = 2.88$ cm
**23.** (a)  *CO* is common.
 $PO = OQ$   (radii of circle)
 $\angle OPC = \angle OQC = 90°$
 (tangent 90° to radius)
 $\Delta$s *CPO* and *CQO* are congruent, RHS
 (b)  $\angle POQ = 254°$
**24.** (a)  $3\mathbf{a} - \mathbf{b}$
 (b)  $\frac{3}{4}\mathbf{b} - \frac{1}{4}\mathbf{a} = \frac{1}{4}(3\mathbf{b} - \mathbf{a})$
 (c)  $\frac{9}{4}\mathbf{b} - \frac{3}{4}\mathbf{a} = \frac{3}{4}(3\mathbf{b} - \mathbf{a})$
  $AX : XB = \frac{1}{4} : \frac{3}{4} = 1 : 3$

## Shape, Space and Measures

### Calculator Paper   Page 385

**1.** (a)  123°.  $x + 57° = 180°$
 (b)  (i)  Trapezium    (ii)  $y = 60°$
**2.** (a)  12 000 cm²    (b)  1.2 m²
**3.** (a)  058°    (b)  (ii)  4.5 km
 (c)  1 : 50 000
**4.** (a)  187.5 cm    (b)  172 pounds
**5.** (a)  8 cm³    (b)  30
**6.** 41.25 m²
**7.** (a)  $a = 120°$, $b = 45°$    (b)  540°
**8.**

**9.** (a)  28 cm²    (b)  22.9 cm
**10.** (a)  (i)  Reflection in $y = x$
 (ii)  Rotation, 90° anticlockwise,
 about $(-1, 0)$
 (b)  Enlarged shape has vertices at:
 $(1, 1), (5, 1), (1, -1)$
**11.** 14 800 cm³
**12.** (a)  446 m²    (b)  32.6 m
**13.** 51 bags
**14.** (a)  $\angle ABC = 83.6°$    (b)  $PS = 1.125$ m
**15.** 26.9 mm
**16.** 25.7 m
**17.** (a)  (i)  $\angle ACB = 90°$ (angle in a semi-circle)
 (ii)  $\angle BAC = 53°$ (alt. segment)
 (b)  $\angle ATB = 180° - 2x°$
**18.** 394 cm²
**19.** (a)  $BC = 21.25$ km    (b)  155 km²
**20.** (a)  (ii)  $x = 150°$
 (b)  $x = -156.4°, -23.6°, 203.6°, 336.4°$
**21.** 9.03 cm
**22.** $h = 19.206…$ mm
**23.** 428 cm³

## Exercise **35.1**

1. qualitative
2. quantitative, continuous
3. quantitative, discrete
4. qualitative
5. quantitative, discrete
6. quantitative, continuous
7. quantitative, discrete
8. qualitative
9. quantitative, discrete
10. quantitative, continuous

## Exercise **35.2**

1. 4
2. (a)

| Height $h$ cm | Frequency |
|---|---|
| $145 \leq h < 150$ | 2 |
| $150 \leq h < 155$ | 2 |
| $155 \leq h < 160$ | 7 |
| $160 \leq h < 165$ | 9 |
| $165 \leq h < 170$ | 6 |
| $170 \leq h < 175$ | 8 |
| $175 \leq h < 180$ | 2 |
| Total | 36 |

(b) 5 cm  (c) 7  (d) 11  (e) 32
3. (a) Francis  (b) Louisa  (c) Alistair
4. (a) (i)

| Make | Ford | Nissan | Vauxhall | Total |
|---|---|---|---|---|
| Frequency | 4 | 3 | 5 | 12 |

| Colour | Blue | Green | Grey | Red | White | Total |
|---|---|---|---|---|---|---|
| Frequency | 2 | 1 | 2 | 3 | 4 | 12 |

| Number of doors | 2 | 3 | 4 | 5 | Total |
|---|---|---|---|---|---|
| Frequency | 2 | 5 | 2 | 3 | 12 |

(ii)

| Mileage ($m$) | Frequency |
|---|---|
| $0 \leq m < 5000$ | 0 |
| $5000 \leq m < 10\,000$ | 2 |
| $10\,000 \leq m < 15\,000$ | 0 |
| $15\,000 \leq m < 20\,000$ | 2 |
| $20\,000 \leq m < 25\,000$ | 1 |
| $25\,000 \leq m < 30\,000$ | 2 |
| $30\,000 \leq m < 35\,000$ | 4 |
| $35\,000 \leq m < 40\,000$ | 1 |
| Total | 12 |

(b) (i) Vauxhall  (ii) 2  (iii) 5  (iv) 5

## Exercise **35.3**

1. (a) Too personal  (b) Leading
   (c) (i) Groups overlap
       (ii) ☐ less than 5 ☐ 5 to 9 ☐ 10 or more
2. (a) Too personal  (b) Too open
   (c) Too open  (d) Too open
5. Leading question.

## Exercise **35.4**

1. (a) 8  (b) 16  (c) 20  (d) 40  (e) 50%
2. (a) 14  (b) 20  (c) 70%  (d) 80%
   (e) Disprove.  80% is greater than 70%.
3. (a) (i) 10  (ii) No. Less 8, More 12.
   (b) (i) 37  (ii) No. Girls 37, Boys 37, same.
4. (a)

| | Yes | No |
|---|---|---|
| Men | 47 | 11 |
| Women | 18 | 24 |

(b) Yes.  Taller: $\frac{47}{58} \times 100 = 81\%$

## Exercise **35.5**

1. Small sample.  One data collection time.
2. Women only.  One location.
   One data collection time.
3. Advantage: confidential, wider circulation, etc.
   Disadvantage: slow, non-response, etc.
4. Fewer females than males, no-one under 18.
5. Lower school 23, Upper school 17
6. (a) Pupils from one year group only may be
       chosen.
   (b) 9, 11, 11, 10, 9
7. (a) May not sample all departments.  (b) 49
8. 9, 14, 2
9. 1, 5, 54

## Review Exercise **35**

1. Leading question. Two-part question.
2. How far do you travel to the superstore?
   Less than 5 km ☐  5 km to 10 km ☐
   More than 10 km ☐
   How often do you come to the superstore
   each week?  1 ☐ 2 ☐ 3 ☐ More than 3 ☐
   How much, on average, do you spend per visit?
   Less than £20 ☐  £20 to £50 ☐
   More than £50 ☐
3. (a) E.g. Too personal. Number of hours
       worked will vary.
   (b) How much do you earn per hour?
       Under £6 ☐ £6 to £10 ☐ Over £10 ☐
4. E.g. Only males asked. No-one under 11 years.
   Mainly adults.
5. Do not support.
   Women 75%.  Men 75%.  Same proportion.

6. E.g. Divide pupils into groups by age and gender. Choose at random 1 pupil in 5 from each group.
7. Choose at random: 21 students from Year 9, 17 students from Year 10, 12 students from Year 11.
8. E.g. May result in all same gender, same age, etc., or disproportionate numbers of students from **one** group.
9. (a) E.g. Number all students and place numbers in a hat. Choose 90 numbers at random from hat.
   (b) Stratified.
   (c) All year groups represented in proportion to size.
   (d) Quicker.
10. E.g. Sample consists of 1 in 4 people. This gives: 41, 29.5, 29.5 from the groups, so, one size of group would have to round up and one group round down.

## CHAPTER 36

### Exercise 36.1 — Page 399

1. Mode 1, median 2, mean 3, range 6.
2. (a) 3    (b) 5    (c) 3.5    (d) 3.9
3. (a) 10    (b) 9    (c) 9.3
4. 86.9 kg    **5.** 4    **6.** 129 cm    **7.** 15.4

### Exercise 36.2 — Page 401

1. Mode 2, median 2.5, mean 2.7
2. (a) 5    (b) 4    (c) 5    (d) 5
3. (a) 9    (b) 9    (c) 30    (d) 8.5

### Exercise 36.3 — Page 403

1. (a) £10 000 $\leqslant s <$ £20 000, £20 350
   (b) 30 - 40 hours, 29.4 hours
2. 5.3 kg    **3.** £94 000    **4.** 27.7

### Exercise 36.4 — Page 404

1. (a) (i) 0.5 minutes    (ii) 1.95 minutes
   (b) Girls a little slower on average and more varied.
2. Women: mean 1.6, range 6
   Men: mean 1.5, range 2
   Women made more visits to the cinema, though the number of visits is more spread.
3. Average: Boys 6.2, Girls 7.2
   Range: Boys 4, Girls $4\frac{1}{2}$
   No. Girls' average greater than boys'. Correct about variation.
4. (a) MacQuick 20 - 29, Pizza Pit 30 - 39
   (b) MacQuick - mean 26 years (Pizza Pit 36.5 years)
   (c) Exact ages not known.

5. Before: median 3, range 4
   After: median 3, range 5
   Would have been better to calculate the means.
   Before 2.2, After 3.0

### Exercise 36.5 — Page 405

1. Mode trainers. Cannot calculate others.
2. Mode 15s, median 12s, mean 22.15s
   Median most sensible, not affected by 200 as is mean, mode not much use.
3. Swimmer A.
   Mean is lower (A 30.88s, B 31.38s)
   Range less (A 1.7s, B 15s)
   Median is higher (A 30.9s, B 30.0s)
4. He should use the median mark. The median mark is the middle mark, so, half of the students will get the median mark or higher.
5. (a) Mode.
       Represents the lowest cost for these data.
   (b) Median.
       Mean affected by **one** much higher cost. Mode is equal to the lowest cost.

### Review Exercise 36 — Page 406

1. (a) £27
   (b) At the lower end of the prices. (Mode = £22)
2. (a) 32    (b) 9
   (c) 5    (d) (i) 295    (ii) 9.2
3. 54.6 kg
4. 14
5. (a) No. Only 2 of the 4 cars that had one fault before servicing now have no faults.
   (b) Mode.
   (c) Mean. After servicing mean = 1.2 (1 d.p.)
6. 9.96 hours ≈ 10 hours
7. (a) £14 180
   (b) Mode would not change.
       Mean would increase (£15 075).

## CHAPTER 37

### Exercise 37.1 — Page 409

1. (b) £7    (c) £6.37    (d) 20%
2. (a)

| Cereal | Corn flakes | Muesli | Porridge | Bran flakes |
|---|---|---|---|---|
| Angle | 125° | 100° | 60° | 75° |

   (b) Corn flakes
3. (a) 7 hours
   (b) 5 hours
   (c) 3
   (d) (i) 20    (ii) 20%
   (e) E.g. boys have higher mode and larger range.
4. (a) 288    (b) 174°    (c) 5 : 9

**1.** (a)

| 1 | 0 means 10 litres |

| 1 | 0 2 6 6 7 9 |
| 2 | 3 3 4 5 5 6 7 9 |
| 3 | 1 3 5 5 |
| 4 | 1 2 |

(b) 32 litres

**2.** (a)

| 3 | 2 means 3.2 seconds |

| 1 | 5 |
| 2 | 4 4 5 6 7 8 8 9 |
| 3 | 0 1 2 2 3 5 5 6 7 |
| 4 | 2 2 3 |
| 5 | 6 6 8 |

(b) 3.2 seconds

**3.**

| | 2 | 7 means 2.7 cm |

| 1 | 8 |
| 2 | 0 1 4 5 6 6 7 |
| 3 | 1 4 5 5 6 9 |
| 4 | 0 2 2 5 |
| 5 | 4 |
| 6 | 0 |

**4.** (a) 17    (b) 38 pence    (c) 39 pence

**5.** (a)

| Adults | | Children | 4 | 7 means 4.7 mins |

| | 4 | 7 9 |
| 9 4 | 5 | 1 3 4 9 |
| 7 5 4 1 0 | 6 | 2 3 4 5 5 6 8 |
| 9 8 7 3 3 3 0 | 7 | 1 4 6 7 9 |
| 2 2 0 | 8 | 0 2 |
| 4 2 | 9 | |
| 1 | 10 | |

(b) Adults have larger range.
Fastest time recorded by child,
slowest time recorded by adult.

**1.** (a) Negative   (b) Positive   (c) Zero
    (d) Positive   (e) Negative
**2.** (a) **B**    (b) **C**    (c) **D**
**3.** (a) 2    (b) 164 cm    (c) No.
    (d) Taller girls usually have larger shoe sizes
than shorter girls.
**4.** (b) Positive correlation.
    (c) Different conditions, types of road, etc.
**5.** (b) Negative correlation.
    (c) Points are close to a straight line.

**1.** (b) Positive correlation    (d) 4.8 to 4.9 kg
**2.** (b) Negative correlation    (d) 38 minutes
**3.** (b) Scatter of points suggests correlation is
close to zero.
**4.** (b) Negative correlation.
    (d) (i) 27 to 28    (ii) 91 to 92 kg
**5.** (b) (i) 88 - 89    (ii) 49 - 50
    (c) (ii), as estimated value is within the
range of known values.

**1.**

| | 5 | 4 means 5.4 grams |

| 2 | 8 |
| 3 | 5 9 |
| 4 | 2 4 6 6 7 8 8 |
| 5 | 0 1 4 4 6 6 8 |
| 6 | 0 3 7 |

**2.**

| Fruit | Apple | Orange | Banana | Grapes | Other |
|-------|-------|--------|--------|--------|-------|
| Angle | 58° | 43° | 144° | 65° | 50° |

**3.** ❶ B,    ❷ C,    ❸ A
**4.** (a) 9    (b) 50    (c) 17
    (d) Highest mark scored by a boy.
Lowest mark scored by a girl.
Boys have a greater range of marks.
**5.** (a) 12 : 18 = 2 : 3
    (b) 27%
    (c) Boys: mode 8, range 3.
Girls: mode 10, range 6.
Boys have a lower modal mark but a
smaller range of marks than the girls.
**6.** (b) Positive correlation. Similar scores are
given to competitors by both judges.
    (c) (ii) 5.7
**7.** (b) Positive correlation. Taller pupils tend to
have taller fathers.
    (d) 171 cm
**8.** (b) Negative correlation. The 'record times'
get lower as boys get older.
    (d) (i) 10 seconds
       (ii) Value is beyond known data.

## CHAPTER  38

**1.** (b) (i) 154 cm    (ii) 15 years 4 months
**2.** (a) 35, 34, 35, 36, 39, 37, 40
    (b) 28.8, 28.6, 28.2, 28.6, 30.6, 33
**3.** 18, 17.5, 17, 16, 15, 14, 13, 12, 11.25
**4.** 6.6
**5.** 3-point moving averages are:
370, 365, 375, 390, 400, 390, 400

**1.** (a) (c)

(b) 51.5, 45, 44, 50.5, 51.5, 64.5, 77.5, 62.5, 49.5
(d) There is an upward trend in the amount
of water used.

**2.** (a) (c)

(b) £65.61, £64.55, £65.11, £62.27, £62.17, £67.39, £67.70, £68.18, £66.74

(d) There is an upward trend in the quarterly bills.

**3.** (a) (c)

(b) 3-point moving averages are:
35, 36, 62, 63, 65, 40, 44, 43, 41, 46

(d) Trend shows steady level of absence, greatly affected by Spring figure for Year 9.

**4.** (a) (c) (d)

(b) 47.8, 44.7, 43.8, 44, 43.6, 44.5, 46, 46.8, 47.3, 47.8, 49.7, 50.7, 52.2

(e) The trend shows a general increase in sales.

(f) £4800

**5.** (a) (c) (d)

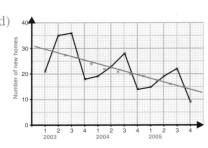

(b) 4-point moving averages are:
27.5, 27, 24, 22, 21, 20, 19, 17.5, 16.25

(e) The trend shows a general decrease in the number of new homes being built.

(f) 11

Exercise **38.3**     **Page 422**

**1.** (a) 3    (b) 17    (c) 3
   (d) 0740 and less than 0750

**2.** (a) 5    (b) 5

**3.** (a) Entries are: 4, 7, 9, 4
   (c) 6.00 and less than 6.50

**5.** (a) 0   (b) 26   (c) 27   (d) 95

**8.** (b) Females have smaller range in weight than males.
Males have higher modal class.

**9.** (c) English results have smaller range.
English modal class is higher.

**10.** (b) 2005 results have a larger range.
2004 results have higher modal class.

Exercise **38.4**     **Page 426**

**4.** 32

**5.** (a) 10    (b) 64

**6.** (a) 12    (b) 71

**7.** (b) 110

**8.** (a) (i) 5.5 cm    (ii) 5

**9.** (b) 44%

Review Exercise **38**     **Page 428**

**1.** (b) £110 000
   (c) Prices of houses rise and fall.
Future prices unpredictable.

**2.** Vertical scale does not begin at zero.
Horizontal scale is not uniform.

**3.** £31, £35, £34.50

**4.** (a) Girls:

| Marks | 1 - 5 | 6 - 10 | 11 - 15 | 16 - 20 | 21 - 25 |
|---|---|---|---|---|---|
| Frequency | 0 | 8 | 19 | 23 | 4 |

(b) Girls have a smaller range of marks.
Boys have a lower modal class.

**5.** (a) 15 years $\leqslant t <$ 20 years

(b)

**6.** 32

**CHAPTER**    **39**

Exercise **39.1**     **Page 432**

**1.** (a) Entries are: 0, 4, 16, 34, 49, 57, 60
   (c) (i) 14 mins    (ii) 18 to 19 mins
     (iii) 9 to 10 mins
   (d) 9 mins

**2.** (a) 52    (c) (i) 61 g    (ii) 28 g

**3.** (b) (i) 6 to 7 mins    (ii) 8 mins

## Exercise **39.2** — Page 434

1. (a) Entries are: 0, 7, 28, 65, 77, 80
   (c) (i) 6 minutes (ii) 12
2. (a) 26 to 27 (b) 7 to 8 marks
   (c) 15 to 16% (d) 17
3. (a) 95
   (c) (i) 89 cm (ii) 10 to 11 cm (iii) 19
   (d) 83 cm
4. (b) 9 to 10 hours (c) 12%
5. (a) 175 cm, 14.5 cm (b) 3 (c) 41
   (d) 172.5 cm (e) 185.5 cm

## Exercise **39.3** — Page 436

1. (a) 40 (b) 13 cm (c) 8.5 cm
   (d) Girls heights are more varied, etc.
   (e) 1
2. (b) (i) 18 litres (ii) 10 litres
   (c) Neighbour's cows have higher average
       yield, but the yield is more varied, etc.
3. Variety $X$, median 350 g, IQR 100 g.
   Variety $Y$, median 350 g, IQR 220 g.
   Same median, but weight of Variety $Y$ is more
   varied, etc.

## Exercise **39.4** — Page 438

1.

Temperature (°C)

2.

Weight (kg)

3.
Distance (km)

4.

Height (cm)

5. (a) 0.06 s (b) 0.08 s
6. (a) 72% (b) 18%
   (c) English (d) 21%
   (e) English mark has a higher median,
       Maths marks more spread.
7. (b) Males have lower median time and not
       spread out. Females have higher median
       time and greater variation.
8. (a) median = £62, lower quartile = £43,
       upper quartile = £75

## Review Exercise **39** — Page 441

1. (a) (i) Cumulative freq.: (0), 8, 22, 34, 51, 56
   (b) (i) 44 to 46 years (ii) 20 to 22 years
   (c) E.g. Men older on average (higher
       median). Age distribution of men
       more spread out.
2. (a) Cumulative freq.: (10), 33, 64, 83, 95, 100
   (c) (i) 22 500 to 23 500 miles (ii) 75 to 77

3. (a)
Time (seconds)

   (b) E.g. Greater spread of times for spelling
       backwards than forwards. Quickest
       time very similar. Similar IQR.

## CHAPTER 40

## Exercise **40.1** — Page 443

1. (a) Evens (b) Impossible (c) Likely
   (d) Unlikely (e) Certain (f) Unlikely
2. (a) **T** (b) **P** (c) **R** (d) **S**
3. W    Y V    X
   0    ½    1

## Exercise **40.2** — Page 444

1. $\frac{2}{3}$
2. (a) $\frac{1}{4}$ (b) $\frac{1}{2}$ (c) $\frac{3}{4}$
3. (a) $\frac{3}{10}$ (b) $\frac{7}{10}$
4. (a) $\frac{1}{11}$ (b) $\frac{4}{11}$ (c) $\frac{2}{11}$
5. (a) $\frac{1}{2}$ (b) $\frac{1}{4}$ (c) $\frac{1}{52}$
6. (a) $\frac{2}{5}$ (b) $\frac{3}{5}$ (c) 1 (d) 0
7. (a) $\frac{2}{3}$ (b) $\frac{1}{3}$ (c) $\frac{3}{4}$
8. (a) $\frac{2}{5}$ (b) $\frac{3}{5}$ (c) $\frac{4}{25}$ (d) $\frac{4}{15}$ (e) $\frac{2}{5}$
9. The events are not equally likely.
10. (a) $\frac{7}{15}$ (b) $\frac{1}{2}$ (c) $\frac{1}{16}$ (d) $\frac{3}{4}$
11. (a) $\frac{1}{3}$ (b) $\frac{1}{15}$ (c) $\frac{11}{24}$ (d) $\frac{17}{50}$ (e) $\frac{21}{25}$ (f) $\frac{4}{5}$

## Exercise **40.3** — Page 446

1. $\frac{7}{25}$   2. $\frac{9}{10}$   3. $\frac{3}{10}$
4. (a) $\frac{52}{100} = 0.52$, $\frac{102}{200} = 0.51$, $\frac{141}{300} = 0.47$
   (b) 0.47
5. $\frac{21}{30} = \frac{7}{10}$   6. 8   7. 18   8. 25
9. (a) 300 (b) 120 (c) 150

## Exercise **40.4** — Page 447

1. $\frac{3}{5}$   2. 0.4   3. 0.04   4. $\frac{47}{50}$
5. 0.6
6. (a) 0.04 (b) 0.97
7. (a) 0.5 (b) 0.3
8. (a) (i) The probabilities add to 105%
       (ii) 5%
   (b) (i) 45% (ii) 75% (iii) 80%
9. (a) 0.4 (b) 0.6
   (c) (i) Yes (ii) No
   (d) (i) 0.6 (ii) 0.6 (iii) 0.7

**1.** (a)  RBG, RGB, GBR, GRB, BGR, BRG

   (b)  $\frac{1}{3}$

**2.** (a)

2nd dice

| | 1 | 2 | 3 | 4 | 5 | 6 |
|---|---|---|---|---|---|---|
| **1** | 2 | 3 | 4 | 5 | 6 | 7 |
| **2** | 3 | 4 | 5 | 6 | 7 | 8 |
| **3** | 4 | 5 | 6 | 7 | 8 | 9 |
| **4** | 5 | 6 | 7 | 8 | 9 | 10 |
| **5** | 6 | 7 | 8 | 9 | 10 | 11 |
| **6** | 7 | 8 | 9 | 10 | 11 | 12 |

1st dice

   (b)  (i)  $\frac{1}{12}$      (ii)  $\frac{1}{12}$      (iii)  $\frac{5}{6}$

   (c)  They cover all possible scores.

**3.**

Dice

| Coin | 1 | 2 | 3 | 4 | 5 | 6 |
|---|---|---|---|---|---|---|
| **H** | H1 | H2 | H3 | H4 | H5 | H6 |
| **T** | T1 | T2 | T3 | T4 | T5 | T6 |

   (a)  $\frac{1}{12}$  (b)  $\frac{1}{4}$  (c)  $\frac{1}{12}$  (d)  $\frac{1}{4}$  (e)  $\frac{1}{6}$  (f)  $\frac{1}{2}$

**4.** (a)  Stage 1: Bus, Bus, Train, Train, Lift, Lift
       Stage 2: Bus, Walk, Bus, Walk, Bus, Walk

   (b)  $\frac{1}{6}$

**5.** (a)

2nd spin

| | 1 | 2 | 3 | 4 |
|---|---|---|---|---|
| **1** | 2 | 3 | 4 | 5 |
| **2** | 3 | 4 | 5 | 6 |
| **3** | 4 | 5 | 6 | 7 |
| **4** | 5 | 6 | 7 | 8 |

1st spin

   (b)  (i)  $\frac{1}{16}$      (ii)  $\frac{1}{8}$      (iii)  $\frac{3}{16}$

**6.** (a)  Maths, English    Maths, Science
       Maths, Art        English, Science
       English, Art      Science, Art

   (b)  $\frac{3}{6} = \frac{1}{2}$      (c)  $\frac{1}{3}$

**7.** (a)

Bag A

| Bag B | R | R | W |
|---|---|---|---|
| **W** | RW | RW | WW |
| **W** | RW | RW | WW |
| **R** | RR | RR | WR |

   (c)  $\frac{4}{9}$

**8.** (a)

| A | 1 | 1 | 2 | 2 | 3 | 3 |
|---|---|---|---|---|---|---|
| B | 2 | 3 | 2 | 3 | 2 | 3 |

   (b)  (i)  $\frac{2}{6} = \frac{1}{3}$   (ii)  $\frac{4}{6} = \frac{2}{3}$   (c)  $\frac{4}{5}$

**9.** (a)

| | R | G | B | Y | W |
|---|---|---|---|---|---|
| **W** | RW | GW | BW | YW | WW |
| **Y** | RY | GY | BY | YY | WY |
| **B** | RB | GB | BB | YB | WB |
| **G** | RG | GG | BG | YG | WG |
| **R** | RR | GR | BR | YR | WR |
| | R | G | B | Y | W |

2nd spin (left label) · 1st spin (bottom label)

   (b)  (i)  $\frac{1}{25}$   (ii)  $\frac{9}{25}$   (iii)  $\frac{5}{25} = \frac{1}{5}$

**10.** (a)

| | 1 | 2 | 3 | 4 | 5 | 6 |
|---|---|---|---|---|---|---|
| **1** | 2 | 3 | 4 | 5 | 6 | 7 |
| **2** | 3 | 4 | 5 | 6 | 7 | 8 |
| **3** | 4 | 5 | 6 | 7 | 8 | 9 |

   (b)  $\frac{1}{18}$

   (c)  $\frac{1}{6}$

**1.** (a)

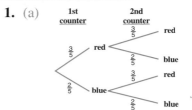

1st counter   2nd counter

$\frac{3}{5}$ red →  $\frac{3}{5}$ red,  $\frac{2}{5}$ blue

$\frac{2}{5}$ blue →  $\frac{3}{5}$ red,  $\frac{2}{5}$ blue

   (b)  (i)  $\frac{4}{25}$
        (ii)  $\frac{16}{25}$

**2.** (a)

1st switch   2nd switch

$0.1$ faulty →  $0.1$ faulty,  $0.9$ not faulty

$0.9$ not faulty →  $0.1$ faulty,  $0.9$ not faulty

   (b)  (i)  0.01
        (ii)  0.18

   (c)  810

**3.** (a)  (i)  $\frac{5}{50} = \frac{1}{10}$      (ii)  $\frac{45}{50} = \frac{9}{10}$

        (iii)  $\frac{20}{50} = \frac{2}{5}$      (iv)  $\frac{30}{50} = \frac{3}{5}$

   (b)  $\frac{1}{10}$ left handed →  $\frac{3}{5}$ male,  $\frac{2}{5}$ female

        $\frac{9}{10}$ right handed →  $\frac{3}{5}$ male,  $\frac{2}{5}$ female

   (c)  (i)  $\frac{2}{50} = \frac{1}{25}$
        (ii)  $\frac{29}{50}$

**4.** (a)  Bag A        Bag B

        $\frac{3}{10}$ blue →  $\frac{2}{5}$ blue,  $\frac{3}{5}$ red

        $\frac{5}{10}$ red →  $\frac{2}{5}$ blue,  $\frac{3}{5}$ red

        $\frac{2}{10}$ white →  $\frac{2}{5}$ blue,  $\frac{3}{5}$ red

   (b)  $\frac{9}{50}$

   (c)  $\frac{21}{50}$

**5.** (a)  Lights        Brakes

        $\frac{9}{10}$ Pass →  $\frac{4}{5}$ Pass,  $\frac{1}{5}$ Fail

        $\frac{1}{10}$ Fail

   (b)  $\frac{7}{25}$

**6.** (a) 0.7    (b) 0.49    (c) 0.58

**7.** (a) $\frac{3}{20}$    (b) $\frac{5}{8}$

**8.** (a) 0.14    (b) 0.06

**9.** (a) $\frac{1}{3}$    (b) $\frac{1}{2}$

**10.** (a) (i) 0.1    (ii) 0.7    (iii) 0.6
     (b) (i) 0.01    (ii) 0.09

**11.** (a) (i) 0.3    (ii) 0.1    (iii) 0.5
     (b) 0.34

## Exercise 40.7      Page 457

**1.** (a)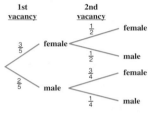
   (b) $\frac{3}{10}$    (c) $\frac{3}{5}$    (d) $\frac{7}{10}$

**2.** (a)
   (b) $\frac{28}{55}$

**3.** (a)
   (b) $\frac{7}{15}$

**4.** (a)
   (b) $\frac{19}{66}$

**5.** (a)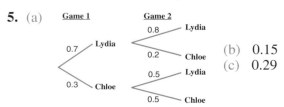
   (b) 0.15    (c) 0.29

**6.** (a) 0.63    (b) 0.16    **8.** $\frac{21}{44}$    **10.** $\frac{1}{150}$

**7.** $\frac{62}{95}$      **9.** 0.991    **11.** 488

## Review Exercise 40      Page 459

**1.** (a) *A*, 1; *A*, 2; *A*, 3; *A*, 4; *A*, 5.
       *B*, 1; *B*, 2; *B*, 3; *B*, 4; *B*, 5.
       *C*, 1; *C*, 2; *C*, 3; *C*, 4; *C*, 5.
   (b) (i) $\frac{1}{3}$    (ii) $\frac{2}{5}$

**2.** (a) (i) $\frac{7}{15}$    (ii) $\frac{12}{15} = \frac{4}{5}$    (iii) 0    (b) 0.3

**3.** (a) (i)
      (ii) $\frac{7}{12}$
   (b) 0.13

**4.** (a) $\frac{3}{10}$    (b) $\frac{3}{10}$

**5.** (a) 0.3    (b) 24

**6.** 0.28

**7.** (a) $\frac{9}{30} = \frac{3}{10}$    (b) $\frac{3}{15} = \frac{1}{5}$    (c) 384

**8.** (a)
   (b) 0.01

**9.** (b) 0.42

**10.** (a) 0.24    (b) 0.86

**11.** (a) 0.384    (b) 0.288

**12.** (a) $\frac{8}{29}$    (b) $\frac{11}{21}$    (c) $\frac{40}{91}$

**13.** (a) $\frac{14}{45}$

## Handling Data

## Non-calculator Paper      Page 462

**1.** (a) $\frac{3}{5}$    (b) (i) 0.4
          (ii) Same number of Red and
             Blue counters. Twice as
             many Red as Green
             counters. Twice as many
             Blue as Green counters.

**2.** (a) 3    (b) 5.1
   (c) Males have greater range, 6 compared
       with 3. Females have greater average,
       5.1 compared with 3.6.

**3.** (a) 1H, 2H, 3H, 4H, 5H, 6H,    (b) $\frac{1}{12}$
       1T, 2T, 3T, 4T, 5T, 6T.

**4.** (a) Only women surveyed.
       Only one location used for survey.
       Sample size too small.
   (b) Survey equal numbers of men and
       women. Survey all over the country.
       Survey a much larger sample.

**5.** (a) $\frac{7}{9}$    (b) $\frac{6}{25}$
   (c) Can swim: girls 0.76, boys 0.8.
       Not true. 0.8 > 0.76

**6.** (a)  (b) (c)

**7.** (a) $\frac{3}{10} = 0.3$, $\frac{5}{20} = 0.25$, $\frac{6}{30} = 0.2$

Experimental probability will get closer to theoretical probability $\left(\frac{1}{6} = 0.17\right)$ if Jane does more trials.

(b) (i) Yes. Even after large number of trials, experimental probability is not getting closer to 0.17.

(ii) 0.04

**8.** (a) 39 hundredths of a second.

(b)

Reaction time of girls

Reaction time, hundredths of a second

(c) Similar median times for both groups. Boys have much greater IQR.

**9.** (a) Much larger sample.

(b) (i) 0.02 (ii) 240 (c) 0.04

**10.** (a) Divide town map into blocks of houses. Sample at random 10% of houses in each block.

(b) All districts of the town will be represented.

(c) All households will have an equal chance of being surveyed.

**11.** $1 - \left(\frac{2}{3}\right)^n$ **13.** 75 crocodiles

**12.** (b) $\frac{7}{15}$ **14.** (a) $\frac{21}{190}$ (b) $\frac{113}{190}$

## Handling Data

Section Review

## Calculator Paper  Page 465

**1.** (a)

| 1 | 3 means 13 minutes |
|---|---|
| 0 | 3 4 6 8 8 |
| 1 | 0 3 3 4 6 8 8 8 |
| 2 | 0 2 3 7 |
| 3 | 0 5 8 |

(b) **35**

**2.** (a) 0.4 (b) 18

**3.** P1, **Q1, R1**, P3, **Q3, R3**, P5, **Q5, R5**

**4.** (b) Negative correlation. As the speed increases the distance travelled decreases.

**5.** (a)

| Gender | Ⓜ/F | M/Ⓕ |
|---|---|---|
| Spreadsheet | Ⓨ/N | Y/Ⓝ |
| Word Processor | Ⓨ/N | Ⓨ/N |
| Both | Ⓨ/N | Y/Ⓝ |

(b) 0.95

**6.** (a) (i) 0.15 (ii) 0.65 (b) 40

**7.** 130 students

**8.** (a) E.g.

Frequency

Time (hours)

(b) (i) 38 minutes

(ii) 40 workers surveyed. Median is the time of the $\frac{20\text{th} + 21\text{st}}{2}$. $8 + 13 = 21$, so, median time in group $20 < t \leqslant 40$.

**9.** (a) Median (£180). Mode (£120) is the lowest earnings. Mean (£293) is distorted by a few very high earnings.

(b) £150. Represents the spread of the middle 50% of earnings and is not affected by very high or very low amounts.

**10.**

Time (minutes)

**11.** $\frac{1}{36}$

**12.** (b) Moving averages: 314, 311, 316, 315

(c) Average profit made is very constant.

(d) £148

**13.** 0.38

**14.** (a) 458 to 460 grams

(b) Cumulative freq.: (10), 46, 92, 117, 119, 120

(c) (i) 450 - 470 grams

(ii) 240 - 290 grams

(d) (i) 0.52 - 0.64 (ii) 0.04 - 0.08

**15.** (a) $(0.8 \times 0.7) + (0.2 \times 0.2) = 0.6$

(b) (i) $1 - 0.6^3 = 0.784$

(ii) $3 \times 0.6 \times 0.4^2 = 0.288$

**16.** (a) Choose at random: $\frac{380}{700} \times 50 \approx 27$ men, and $\frac{320}{700} \times 50 \approx 23$ women

(b) Both men and women are included in proportion to total population.

**17.** (a) $\frac{6}{90} = \frac{1}{15}$ (b) $\frac{62}{90} = \frac{31}{45}$

**18.** (a)

Frequency density

Time (hours)

(b) 0.25

**19.** (a)

Bag A    Bag B

$\frac{8}{10}$ yellow

$\frac{4}{10}$ yellow

$\frac{2}{10}$ red

$\frac{6}{10}$ red

$\frac{7}{10}$ yellow

$\frac{3}{10}$ red

(b) $\frac{8}{25}$

(c) $\frac{37}{50}$

**1.** (a) $x = 54°$
(b) (i) $y = 63°$ (ii) alternate angles

**2.** (a) 50
(b) (i) $2a - 6$ (ii) $y^2 + y$
(c) (i) $x = 7$ (ii) $t = 1\frac{1}{2}$

**3.** Mitchells £900, Fowlers £300

**4.** (a) Translation $\binom{-4}{1}$
(b) Rotation, through 90° anticlockwise, about (0, 0).

**5.** £680

**6.** (a) 0.2 (b) 0.45

**7.** (a) 1.1592 (b) 27.6

**8.** (a) $40 \times 30 \times 5 = £6000$
(b) Too big.
All values have been rounded up.

**9.**

```
                        7 | 2 means 72 shots

        7 | 2   7   8
        8 | 1   4   5   6
        9 | 2   3   4   7   7   9   9
       10 | 3
```

**10.** (a) $2^3 \times 3$ (b) 120

**11.** $3n + 2$

**12.** (c) (i) $285\,\text{kg}$ (ii) $238\,\text{kg}$
(d) Part (i). Heavier competitors have more variation in weights lifted.

**13.** $5 \times 5 \times \pi = 25\pi\,\text{cm}^2$

**14.** (a) (i) $n$ can be any number, therefore, $2n$ is even, and $2n + $ odd number is an odd number.
(ii) The next consecutive odd number is being added to $2n$ each time.
(b) Sum $= 2n + 1 \; + \; 2n + 3 \; + \; 2n + 5$
Sum $= 6n + 9 = 3(2n + 3)$
So, sum is always a multiple of 3.

**15.** 9

**16.** (a) (i) $5(x + 1)$ (ii) $x(x + 7)$
(b) $a^5b^3$
(c) $a = \dfrac{v - u}{t}$
(d) (i) $x = 48$ (ii) $x = 6\frac{1}{2}$

**17.** (a) $13^2 = 12^2 + 5^2$
So, $\Delta ABC$ is right-angled at $B$
(b) $30\,\text{cm}^2$

**18.** (a) 2, 3 (b) $x = -2, \; y = 0.5$

**19.** (a) Reflection in $y = x$.
(b)

**20.** (a) $5^6$
(b) (i) 104 000 (ii) $7.9 \times 10^{-5}$
(iii) 40 000
(c) (i) $8\sqrt{2}$ (ii) 4 (iii) 2

**21.** (a) $12p^3q^2$
(b) (i) $16x - 6$ (ii) $6x^2 + x - 1$

**22.** $x = -10, \; y = 6$

**23.** (a) (i) $(x + 4)(x + 2)$ (ii) $x = -4$ or $-6$
(b) $T = \dfrac{P^2}{6}$

**24.** (a) $\angle AOB = \angle XOY = 63°$ (common)
$\angle OAB = \angle OXY = 39°$ (corres. $\angle$'s)
$\angle OBA = \angle OYX = 71°$ (corres. $\angle$'s)
$\Delta$s $OAB$ and $OXY$ are similar, equal angles.
(b) 2.4

**25.** (a) $y = 2x + 1$
(b) No, as $2 \times (-2) \neq -1$

**26.** (a) $\angle PXZ = 54°$ (b) $\angle OTY = 22°$

**27.** LHS $= \dfrac{3}{\sqrt{6}} + \dfrac{\sqrt{6}}{3} = \dfrac{9}{3\sqrt{6}} + \dfrac{\sqrt{6}\sqrt{6}}{3\sqrt{6}}$
$= \dfrac{3}{\sqrt{6}} + \dfrac{2}{\sqrt{6}} = \dfrac{5}{\sqrt{6}} = $ RHS

**28.** $x = \frac{1}{2}$ or $-4$

**29.** (a) $18ab^2$ (b) (i) $\frac{3}{169}$ (ii) $5 - 2\sqrt{6}$
(c) $\frac{71}{333}$

**30.** (c) Where graphs cross, $x = \dfrac{6}{x^2}$, so, $x^2 = 6$
(d) $x = \pm 2.4$

**31.** (a) $c = 9, \; d = 3$ (b) 4

**32.** (b) $\dfrac{42}{90} = \dfrac{7}{15}$

**33.** (a) Area $PQRS = (20 - 2x)(15 - 2x)$
$\qquad = 4x^2 - 70x + 300$
(b) $4x^2 - 70x + 300 = \frac{1}{2} \times 20 \times 15$
$x = 2.5$ or $15$
So, $PQRS$ is 15 cm by 10 cm

**34.** (a) (i) $\frac{4}{9}$ (ii) 46 (b) $4\sqrt{6}$ (c) $3\sqrt{2}$

**35.** (a) (b)

**36.** (a) $\overrightarrow{OC} = 2\mathbf{a}$
(b) (i) $\overrightarrow{AB} = \mathbf{b} - \mathbf{a}$
(ii) $\overrightarrow{CD} = 2\mathbf{b} - 2\mathbf{a} = 2(\mathbf{b} - \mathbf{a})$
(iii) $CD = 2 \times AB$
(c) $\overrightarrow{AE} = \mathbf{a} + \frac{1}{2} \times 2(\mathbf{b} - \mathbf{a}) = \mathbf{b}$
So, $AE$ and $OB$ are parallel and equal in length.
$\overrightarrow{BE} = \mathbf{b} - \frac{1}{2} \times 2(\mathbf{b} - \mathbf{a}) = \mathbf{a}$
So, $BE$ and $OA$ are parallel and equal in length. Opposite sides of $OAEB$ are parallel and equal in length, so, $OAEB$ is a parallelogram.

**37.** (a) $a = 1$, $b = 4$

(b) LHS $= \dfrac{x + 2}{x} - \dfrac{x}{x + 3}$

$= \dfrac{(x + 2)(x + 3) - x^2}{x(x + 3)}$

$= \dfrac{5x + 6}{x(x + 3)} = $ RHS

**38.** (a)

(b) Greater. More than half of frequency distribution greater than 70 seconds.

**39.** (a) $\frac{4}{3}\sqrt{3} - 2$

(b) $B^2 = \sqrt{5}(1 - \sqrt{5})$

$B^2 = \sqrt{5} - 5$, which is negative.

So, $B$ cannot be found.

## Exam Practice

Exam Practice

## Calculator Paper    Page 472

**1.** **9.7% of 58.3**, **$\sqrt{70}$**, **$3.1^2$**

**2.**

| Trip | Angle |
|------|-------|
| Meadowhall | 84° |
| Doncaster Dome | 96° |
| American Adventure | 60° |
| Alton Towers | 120° |

**3.** (a) (b)

(c) $\left(-1\frac{1}{2}, 2\right)$

**4.** (a) 51.5 m          (b) 211 m²

**5.** $x = 106°$

**6.** 2 kg bar.   2 kg bar = £1.30 per pound

**7.** 200 m²

**8.** 72.7%

**9.** 42 miles per hour

**10.** (a) $20x$ grams      (b) 180 grams

**11.** 62%

**12.** $7 - 2n$

**13.** Alan £320, Brenda £256, Chloe £192

**14.** (a) $3x + 8$

(b) (i) $x = 32$   (ii) $x = -\frac{1}{6}$

(c) (i) $f^5$   (ii) $k^6$

**15.** 512.5 g ⩽ weight of sugar < 517.5 g

**16.** Oleg, by £17

Tatyana: $5000 \times 0.045 \times 5 + 5000 = £6125$

Oleg:          $5000 \times (1.042)^5 = £6142$

**17.** $x = 3.7$

**18.** (a) (i) $4 < t \leqslant 5$

(b) 4.215 minutes

**19.** (a) $m > 4$          (b) $-1, 0, 1$

(c) $x = 7$, $y = 3$

**20.** 1.46 m³

**21.** (a) $AC = 3.7$ m   (b) $\angle ACD = 23.8°$

(c) $PR = 2.8$ m

**22.** £8450

**23.** $3 \times 10^{27}$

**24.** $7.82 \times 10^8$

**25.** (a) $\angle TOP = 73.7°$

(b) $\angle RTP = 126.9°$

**26.** £145

**27.** (a) 15.5 cm ⩽ length < 16.5 cm

(b) $\frac{89.5}{16.5} = 5.424\ldots$ cm

**28.** (b) 26, 26.5, 27.5, 29, 30.5, 31.5, 34, 37, 45.5

(d) 30

**29.** (a) (i) 99   (ii) 43.35   (iii) $1.369 \times 10^{11}$

(b) £29.50

**30.** (a)

UK  $\frac{2}{7}$

Black  $\frac{1}{5}$

Abroad  $\frac{5}{7}$

UK  $\frac{2}{7}$

Not black  $\frac{4}{5}$

Abroad  $\frac{5}{7}$

(b) (i) $\frac{2}{35}$

(ii) $\frac{13}{35}$

**31.** (a) $3(x + 2y)(x - 2y)$

(b) $\frac{x}{x + 3}$

**32.** $x = 1.21$

**33.** (a) $PR^2 = 7^2 + 4^2 - 2 \times 7 \times 4 \times \cos 120°$

$PR = 9.64$ cm

(b) $PS = 13.3$ cm

**34.** $y = -1.69$ or 0.44

**35.** $\frac{x - 2}{x(x + 2)}$

**36.** (a) 0.64

(b) (i) $2p(1 - p)$

(ii) $2p(1 - p) = \frac{39}{100}$

$200p(1 - p) = 39$

$200p^2 - 200p + 39 = 0$

(c) $p = 0.73$ or 0.27

**37.** (a) $y = \frac{3.2}{x^2}$      (b) $0.3\dot{5}$

**38.** (a) $BD = 8 \times \sin 54° = 6.47$ cm

(b) 20.9 cm²      (c) $CD = 6.71$ cm

**39.** (a) $8a^5$          (b) $x = 1.55$ or 6.45

(c) $y = \frac{3x - 10}{2x - 5}$

**40.** $\frac{385\,000}{12.5} = 30\,800$ cm²

**41.** (a) Frequency densities: 1, 1.2, 5.4, 0.4

(b) 8

**42.** $A(2, 3)$, $B(-1.2, -3.4)$

**43.** (a) $h = 12$ cm   (b) $x = 7.236$ cm

527

# Index ●●●●●●●●●●●●●●●●●●●●●●●●●●●●●●●

3-dimensional coordinates . . . . . . . . 273
3-dimensional shapes . . . . . . . . . . . . 314
3-figure bearings . . . . . . . . . . . 264, 308

## a

acceleration . . . . . . . . . . . . . . . . . . . 141
accuracy . . . . . . . . . . . . . . . . . . . 24, 26
accurate drawing . . . . . . . . . . . 268, 271
acute angle . . . . . . . . . . . . . . . . . . . 228
acute-angled triangle . . . . . . . . . . . . 230
addition . . . . . . . . 1, 5, 8, 13, 88, 203
addition of fractions . . . . . . . . . 13, 203
addition of negative numbers . . . . . . . 5
addition of vectors . . . . . . . . . . . . . 356
algebra . . . . . . . 87, 95, 105, 146, 200
algebraic expressions . . . . . . 87, 88, 89,
105, 200
algebraic fractions . . . . . . . 202, 203, 204
algebraic identities . . . . . . . . . . . . . 200
allied angles . . . . . . . . . . . . . . . . . . 228
alternate angles . . . . . . . . . . . . . . . 228
alternate segment theorem . . . . . . . . 248
altitude of a triangle . . . . . . . . . 272, 368
ambiguous case . . . . . . . . . . . . . . . . 371
angle . . . . . . . . . . . 228, 229, 264, 310
angle between a line and a plane . . . . 310
angle bisector . . . . . . . . . . . . . . . . . 268
angle of depression . . . . . . . . . . . . . 307
angle of elevation . . . . . . . . . . . . . . 307
angles at a point . . . . . . . . . . . . . . . 228
anticlockwise . . . . . . . . . . . . . . . . . 276
approximation . . . . . . . . . . . . . . . . . 20
arc . . . . . . . . . . . . . . . . . . . . . . 243, 260
area . . . . . . . . . 254, 257, 258, 259, 260,
317, 320, 322, 335
area of a circle . . . . . . . . . . . . . . 257, 258
area of a trapezium . . . . . . . . . . . . . . 254
area of a triangle . . . . . . . . 254, 375, 377
area of sector . . . . . . . . . . . . . . . . . . 260
areas of similar figures . . . . . . . . . . . 348
average speed . . . . . . . . . . . 69, 71, 138
averages . . . . . . . 399, 400, 401, 402, 405
axes of symmetry . . . . . . . . . . . . . . . 315

## b

back bearings . . . . . . . . . . . . . . . . . 264
back to back stem and leaf diagrams . 410
balance method . . . . . . . . . . . . . . . . . 97
bar charts . . . . . . . . . . . . . . . . 408, 421
bar line graph . . . . . . . . . . . . . . . . . 408
basic hourly rate of pay . . . . . . . . . . 37
bearings . . . . . . . . . . . . . . . . . 264, 308
'best buys' . . . . . . . . . . . . . . . . . . . . 39
bisector of an angle . . . . . . . . . . . . . 268
bounds . . . . . . . . . . . . . 26, 28, 332, 333
box plots . . . . . . . . . . . . . . . . . . . . . 437
brackets . . . . . . . . . . 91, 92, 99, 173, 200
broken lines . . . . . . . . . . . . . . . . . . 151

## c

calculations involving bounds . . . 28, 333
calculations involving continuous
measures . . . . . . . . . . . . . . . . . . . 333
cancelling a fraction . . . . . . . . . 12, 202
capacity . . . . . . . . . . 328, 329, 330, 331
census . . . . . . . . . . . . . . . . . . . . . . . 395

centre of enlargement . . . . . . . . 279, 283
centre of rotation . . . . . . . 238, 276, 283
chance . . . . . . . . . . . . . . . . . . . . . . . 442
changing decimals to fractions . . . 17, 75
changing decimals to percentages . . . . 31
changing fractions to decimals . . . 17, 75
changing fractions to percentages . . . . 31
changing percentages to decimals . . . . 31
changing percentages to fractions . . . . 31
changing recurring decimals to
fractions . . . . . . . . . . . . . . . . . . 75, 77
changing the subject of a
formula . . . . . . . . . . . . . . . . 110, 111
chord . . . . . . . . . . . . . . . . . . . . . 243, 269
circle . . . . . . . . . . 160, 243, 256, 257, 269
circle properties . 243, 244, 247, 248, 250
circumference . . . . . . . . . 243, 256, 258
circumscribed circle of a triangle . . . 269
class intervals . . . . . . . . . . . . . . . . . . 389
classes . . . . . . . . . . . . . . . . . . . . . . . 389
clockwise . . . . . . . . . . . . . . . . . . . . 276
collecting data . . 388, 389, 390, 392, 395
column vector . . . . . . . . . . . . . . . . . 353
combinations of transformations . . . . 286
combining two events . . . . . . . . . . . . 449
common difference . . . . . . . . . . . . . 117
common factors . . . . . . . . . . 45, 92, 174
comparing distributions . . . . . . . 403, 435
comparing quantities . . . . . . . . . . . . . 63
compass points . . . . . . . . . . . . . . . . 264
complementary angles . . . . . . . . . . . 228
completing the square . . . . . . . . 181, 183
Compound Interest . . . . . . . . . . . . . . . 41
compound measures . . . . . . . . . . . 69, 72
compound shapes . . . . . . . . . . . . . . . 259
conditional probability . . . . . . . . . . . 456
cone . . . . . . . . . . . . . . . . . . . . . . 314, 322
congruent shapes . . . . . . . . . . . . . . . 339
congruent triangles . . . . . . . . . . . . . . 339
constant of proportionality . . . . 164, 166
constructions . . . . . . . . . . . . . . 268, 271
continuous data . . . . . . . . . . . . . . . . 388
continuous measures . . . . . . 26, 332, 333
converting units of measurement . 328, 331
coordinates . . . . . . . . . . . . . . . . 123, 273
correlation . . . . . . . . . . . . . . . . . . . . 412
corresponding angles . . . . . . . . . . . . 228
cosine function . . . . . . . . . 363, 364, 367
cosine ratio . . . . . . . . . . . . . . . . 304, 377
Cosine Rule . . . . . . . . 372, 373, 374, 377
cosines of angles between
0° and 360° . . . . . . . . . . . . . . . . . 364
credit . . . . . . . . . . . . . . . . . . . . . . . . 38
cube . . . . . . . . . . . . . . . . . . . . . . 314, 317
cube numbers . . . . . . . . . . . . . . . . . . 48
cube root . . . . . . . . . . . . . . . 48, 77, 78
cubic function . . . . . . . . . . . . . . . . . 158
cuboid . . . . . . . . . . . . . . . . . . . . 314, 317
cumulative frequency . . . . . . . . . . . . 430
cumulative frequency graph . 430, 431, 432
cumulative frequency table . . . . . . . . 430
curved surface area . . . . . . . . . 320, 322
cyclic quadrilateral . . . . . . . . . . . . . . 244
cylinder . . . . . . . . . . . . . . . 314, 319, 320

## d

data . . . . . . . . . . . . . . . . . . . . . . . . . 388
data collection card . . . . . . . . . . . . . 390

data collection sheets . . . . . . . . . . . 389
databases . . . . . . . . . . . . . . . . . . . . 390
decimal places (rounding) . . . . . . . . . 22
decimals . . . . . . . 8, 9, 17, 18, 31, 75, 77
degrees . . . . . . . . . . . . . . . . . . . . . . 228
denominator . . . . . . . . . . . . . . . . . . . 11
density . . . . . . . . . . . . . . . . . . . . . . . 72
describing transformations . . . . . . . . 282
diameter . . . . . . . . . . . . . . . . . . 243, 256
difference of two squares . . . . . . . . . 175
dimensions . . . . . . . . . . . . . . . . . . . 335
direction . . . . . . . . . . . . . . . . . . . . . 264
direct proportion . . . . . . . . . 66, 164, 170
directed line segments . . . . . . . . . . . 353
discrete data . . . . . . . . . . . . . . . . . . 388
discrete measures . . . . . . . . . . . . . . . 332
distance-time graph . . . . . . . . . . . . . 138
division . . . . . . . . . . . 2, 5, 9, 16, 89, 203
division of fractions . . . . . . . . . . . . . . 16
division of negative numbers . . . . . . . . 5
double inequalities . . . . . . . . . . 149, 150
drawing vectors . . . . . . . . . . . . . . . . 353

## e

edges . . . . . . . . . . . . . . . . . . . . . . . . 314
elevations . . . . . . . . . . . . . . . . . . . . 316
enlargement . 275, 279, 280, 281, 282, 342
equal vectors . . . . . . . . . . . . . . . . . . 354
equally likely outcomes . . . . . . . . . . 443
equation of a straight line . . . . . 123, 126,
131, 132
equations . . . . . . . . . 95, 101, 178, 188,
204, 206, 207
equidistant . . . . . . . . . . . . . . . . . . . . 268
equilateral triangle . . . . . . . . . . 230, 236
equivalent fractions . . . . . . . . . . . . . . 11
equivalent ratios . . . . . . . . . . . . . . . . 63
estimated mean . . . . . . . . . . . . . . . . 402
estimating probabilities . . . . . . . . . . 445
estimating quantities . . . . . . . . . . . . 329
estimation . . . . . . . . . . . . . . . . . . . . 25
events . . . . . . . . . . . . . . . . . . . . . . . 442
expanding brackets . . . . 91, 99, 173, 200
exponential function . . . . . . . . . . . . . 159
expressions . . . . . . . 87, 88, 89, 105, 200
exterior angle of a polygon . . . . . . . . 234
exterior angles of a regular polygon . 236
exterior angle of a triangle . . . . . . . . 230

## f

f(x) . . . . . . . . . . . . . . . . . . . . . . . . . 213
faces . . . . . . . . . . . . . . . . . . . . . . . . 314
factor tree . . . . . . . . . . . . . . . . . . . . 46
factorising . . . . . . 92, 174, 175, 176, 177
factors . . . . . . . . . . . . . . . . 45, 46, 174
Fibonacci sequence . . . . . . . . . . . . . 114
forming equations . . . . . . . . . . . . . . 101
formulae . . . . . . 105, 107, 109, 110, 111
formulae (dimensions) . . . . . . . . . . . 335
fractional powers . . . . . . . . . . . . . . . 52
fractions . . . . . . . . 8, 11, 12, 13, 15, 16,
17, 18, 31, 75, 79
frequency . . . . . . . . . . . . . 389, 421, 424
frequency density . . . . . . . . . . . . . . . 424
frequency diagrams . . . . . . . . . . . . . 421
frequency distribution . . . . . . . 389, 400
frequency polygons . . . . . . . . . . 421, 422

frequency table . . . . . . . . . . . . . 389, 400
frustum of a cone . . . . . . . . . . . . . . . 322
function notation . . . . . . . . . . . . . . . 213

**g**

geometric proofs . . . . . . . . . . . . . . . 250
gradient . . . . . . . . . . . 126, 131, 138, 141
graph of a circle . . . . . . . . . . . . . . . 160
graphical solution of equations . 130, 156,
188, 196
graphs . . . . 123, 136, 138, 141, 150, 151,
152, 155, 156, 158, 159, 160,
161, 170, 188, 196, 210
graphs of inequalities . . . . 150, 151, 152
graphs of trigonometric
functions . . . . . . . . . . . . . . . 363, 367
greater than or equal to, ≥ . . . . . . . . 146
greater than, > . . . . . . . . . . . . . . . . 146
gross pay . . . . . . . . . . . . . . . . . . . . . 37
grouped data . . . . . . . . . . . . . . 389, 402
grouped frequency distribution . 389, 402,
421
groups . . . . . . . . . . . . . . . . . . . . . . 389

**h**

hexagon . . . . . . . . . . . . . . . . . . . . . 234
highest common factor . . . . . . . . . . . . 46
histograms . . . . . . . . . . . . . . . 421, 424
household bills . . . . . . . . . . . . . . . . . . 39
hypotenuse . . . . . . . 291, 292, 300, 303
hypothesis . . . . . . . . . . . . . . . . . . . 392

**i**

identities . . . . . . . . . . . . . . . . . . . . 200
image . . . . . . . . . . . . . . . . . . . . . . . 275
imaginary numbers . . . . . . . . . . . . . . . 77
imperial units . . . . . . . . . . . . . . 330, 331
improper fractions . . . . . . . . . . . . . 12, 75
income tax . . . . . . . . . . . . . . . . . . . . 37
independent events . . . . . . . . . . . . . . 452
index notation . . . . . . . . . . . . . . . . . . 46
indices . . . . . . . . . . . 46, 49, 50, 52, 89
inequalities . 146, 148, 149, 150, 151, 152
inscribed circle of a triangle . . . . . . . 269
integer . . . . . . . . . . . . . . . . . . 146, 150
intercept . . . . . . . . . . . . . . . . . . . . . 126
interest . . . . . . . . . . . . . . . . . . . . . . . 41
interior angle of a polygon . . . . . . . . 234
interquartile range . . . . . . . . . . . 431, 437
inverse operations . . . . . . . . . . . 1, 2, 96
inverse proportion . . . . . . . . 66, 166, 170
inverted image . . . . . . . . . . . . . . . . . 281
irrational numbers . . . . . . . . . . . . . 75, 77
isometric drawings . . . . . . . . . . . . . . 314
isosceles trapezium . . . . . . . . . . . . . 241
isosceles triangle . . . . . . . . . . . . . . . 230
iteration . . . . . . . . . . . . . . . . . . . . . 206
iterative formula . . . . . . . . . . . . . . . . 206

**k**

kite . . . . . . . . . . . . . . . . . . . . . . . . 232

**l**

labelling vectors . . . . . . . . . . . . . . . 353
large numbers . . . . . . . . . . . . . . . . . . 56
least common multiple . . . . . . . . . . . . 46
length . . . . . . . . 328, 329, 330, 331, 335
length of arc . . . . . . . . . . . . . . . . . . 260

lengths of similar figures . . . . . . . . . 348
less than or equal to, ≤ . . . . . . . . . . 146
less than, < . . . . . . . . . . . . . . . . . . 146
limits . . . . . . . . . . . . . . . 26, 28, 332
line graph . . . . . . . . . . . . . . . . . . . . 418
line of best fit . . . . . . . . . . . . . . . . . 414
line of symmetry . . . . . . . . . . . . . . . 238
line segment . . . . . . . . . . . . . . 228, 353
linear equation . . . . . . . . 129, 130, 196
linear function . . . . . . . . . . . . . 123, 217
linear sequences . . . . . . . . . . . . . . . 117
listing outcomes . . . . . . . . . . . . . . . 449
loci . . . . . . . . . . . . . . . . . . . . . . . . 266
locus . . . . . . . . . . . . . . . . . . . . . . . 266
long division . . . . . . . . . . . . . . . . . . . 2
long multiplication . . . . . . . . . . . . . . . 2
lower bound . . . . . . . . . . . 26, 28, 332
lower quartile . . . . . . . . . . . . . . 431, 437

**m**

mapping points . . . . . . . . . . . . . . . . 275
maps . . . . . . . . . . . . . . . . . . . . . . . 264
mass . . . . . . . . . . 72, 328, 329, 330, 331
maximum value . . . . . . . . . . . . . . . . 155
mean . . . . . . . . 399, 400, 401, 402, 405
measurement . . . . . . . . . . . . 26, 328, 332
median . . . . . . . . . 399, 400, 401, 402,
405, 431, 437
metric units . . . . . . . . . . . . . . . 328, 331
minimum value . . . . . . . . . . . . . . . . 155
mixed numbers . . . . . . . . . . . . . . . . . 12
modal class . . . . . . . . . . . . . . . . . . . 402
mode . . . . . . . . . . . 399, 400, 401, 405
money . . . . . . . . . . . . 37, 38, 39, 40, 41
moving average graphs . . . . . . . . . . . 420
moving averages . . . . . . . . . . . . . . . 419
multiple-response questions . . . . . . . . 392
multiples . . . . . . . . . . . . . . . . . . 45, 46
multiplication . . . . . 2, 5, 9, 13, 89, 203
multiplication of fractions . . . . . . . . . 15
multiplication of negative numbers . . . . 5
multiplying a vector by a scalar . . . . . 354
mutually exclusive events . . . . . . . . . 447

**n**

*n* th term of a sequence . . . . . . . 117, 119
naming angles . . . . . . . . . . . . . . . . . 229
negative angles . . . . . . . . . . . . . . . . 364
negative correlation . . . . . . . . . . . . . 412
negative numbers . . . . . . . . . . . . . . . . 5
negative powers . . . . . . . . . . . . . . . . 50
negative scale factor . . . . . . . . . . . . 281
net pay . . . . . . . . . . . . . . . . . . . . . . 37
nets . . . . . . . . . . . . . . . . . . . . . . . . 314
non-linear functions . . . . . . . . . . . . . 218
number lines . . . . . . . . . . . . . . . . . . 146
number sequences . . . . . . . . . . . . . . 117
numerator . . . . . . . . . . . . . . . . . . . . 11

**o**

obtuse angle . . . . . . . . . . . . . . . . . . 228
obtuse-angled triangle . . . . . . . . . . . 230
octagon . . . . . . . . . . . . . . . . . . . . . 234
opposite vectors . . . . . . . . . . . . . . . 355
order of operations . . . . . . . . . . . . . . . 4
order of rotational symmetry . . . . . . . 238
outcomes . . . . . . . . . . . . . . . . . . . . 442
overtime rate of pay . . . . . . . . . . . . . . 37

**p**

π . . . . . . . . . . . . . . . . . . . . . . . . . . 256
parabola . . . . . . . . . . . . . . . . . . . . . 155
parallel lines . . . . . . . . . . . . . . 190, 228
parallelogram . . . . . . . . . . . . . 232, 254
pentagon . . . . . . . . . . . . . . . . . . . . 234
per cent . . . . . . . . . . . . . . . . . . . . . . 31
percentage change . . . . . . . . . . . . . . . 33
percentage decrease . . . . . . . . . . . . . . 34
percentage increase . . . . . . . . . . . . . . 34
percentages . . . 31, 32, 33, 34, 36, 40, 41
perfect squares . . . . . . . . . . . . . . . . 181
perimeter . . . . . . . . . . . . . . . . . . . . 254
periodic function . . . . . . . . . . . . . . . 367
perpendicular bisector . . . . . . . . . . . 268
perpendicular bisector of a chord . . . 269
perpendicular from a point on a line . 271
perpendicular from a point to a line . . 271
perpendicular lines . . . . . . . . . 131, 228
pie chart . . . . . . . . . . . . . . . . . . . . . 408
place value . . . . . . . . . . . . . . . . . . . . 1
planes of symmetry . . . . . . . . . . . . . 315
plans . . . . . . . . . . . . . . . . . . . . . . . 316
polygons . . . . . . . . . . . . . 234, 236, 237
population density . . . . . . . . . . . . . . . 72
positive correlation . . . . . . . . . . . . . 412
possibility space diagram . . . . . . . . . 449
powers . . . . . . 46, 48, 49, 50, 52, 89, 121
powers of 2 . . . . . . . . . . . . . . . . . . 121
primary data . . . . . . . . . . . . . . . . . . 388
prime factors . . . . . . . . . . . . . . . . . . 46
prime numbers . . . . . . . . . . . . . . . . . 45
prism . . . . . . . . . . . . . . . . . . . 318, 319
probability . . . . . . . . 442, 443, 445, 447,
448, 452, 456
probability experiments . . . . . . . . . . . 445
probability scale . . . . . . . . . . . . . . . 442
product of prime factors . . . . . . . . . . . 46
proper fractions . . . . . . . . . . . . . . . . . 75
proportion . . . . . . 66, 164, 166, 168, 170
pyramid . . . . . . . . . . . . . . . . . . 314, 322
Pythagoras' Theorem . 291, 294, 296, 377

**q**

quadratic equations . . . . . . 156, 178, 179,
183, 184, 196
quadratic expressions . . . . 174, 175, 176
quadratic formula . . . . . . . . . . . . . . . 179
quadratic function . . . . . . . 155, 175, 176
quadrilaterals . . . . . . . . . . . . . . 232, 234
qualitative data . . . . . . . . . . . . . . . . 388
quantitative data . . . . . . . . . . . . . . . 388
questionnaires . . . . . . . . . . . . . . . . . 392
quota samples . . . . . . . . . . . . . . . . . 395

**r**

radius . . . . . . . . . . . . . . . . . . . 243, 256
random . . . . . . . . . . . . . . . . . . . . . . 443
random sample . . . . . . . . . . . . . . . . 395
range . . . . . . . . . . . . 399, 401, 431, 437
ratio . . . . . . . . . . . . . . . . . 63, 64, 164
rational numbers . . . . . . . . . . . . . . 75, 77
rationalising denominators of
fractions . . . . . . . . . . . . . . . . . . . 79
reading numbers . . . . . . . . . . . . . . . . 1
real numbers . . . . . . . . . . . . . . . . . . 77
rearranging equations . . . . . . . . . . . . 132
rearranging formulae . . . . . . . . . . 110, 111

rearranging quadratics . . . . . . . . . . . 181
reciprocal function . . . . . . . . . . . . . . 159
reciprocals . . . . . . . . . . . . . . . . . . . . 48, 50
rectangle . . . . . . . . . . . . . . . . . . 232, 254
recurring decimals . . . . . . . . 18, 75, 77
reflection . . . . . . . . . . . . 214, 275, 282
reflex angle . . . . . . . . . . . . . . . . . . . . 228
regions . . . . . . . . . . . . . . . . . . . . . . . 151
regular polygons . . . . . . . . . . . 236, 237
regular tessellations . . . . . . . . . . . . . 237
relative frequency . . . . . . . . . . . . . . . 445
removing brackets . . . . . 91, 99, 173, 200
resultant vector . . . . . . . . . . . . . . . . 356
reverse percentage problems . . . . . . . 36
rhombus . . . . . . . . . . . . . . . . . . . . . . 232
right angle . . . . . . . . . . . . . . . . . . . . 228
right-angled triangle . . 230, 291, 300, 377
roots . . . . . . . . . . . . . . . . . . . . 52, 77, 78
rotation . . . . . . . . . . . . . . . 275, 276, 282
rotational symmetry . . . . . . . . . . . . . 238
rounding . . . . . . . . . . . . . . 20, 21, 22, 23
rules for surds . . . . . . . . . . . . . . . . . . 78
rules of indices . . . . . . . . . . . . 50, 52, 89

**s**

sample . . . . . . . . . . . . . . . . . . . . . . . 395
sampling . . . . . . . . . . . . . . . . . . . . . . 395
sampling methods . . . . . . . . . . . . . . . 395
savings . . . . . . . . . . . . . . . . . . . . . . . 41
scalars . . . . . . . . . . . . . . . . . . . . . . . 353
scale drawing . . . . . . . . . . . . . . . . . . 265
scale factor . . . . . . . . . . . . 279, 280, 281,
                              283, 342, 348
scalene triangle . . . . . . . . . . . . . . . . 230
scales on maps and plans . . . . . 264, 265
scatter graphs . . . . . . . . . . . . . 412, 414
scientific notation . . . . . . . 56, 57, 59, 61
seasonal variation . . . . . . . . . . . . . . . 418
secondary data . . . . . . . . . . . . . . . . . 388
sector . . . . . . . . . . . . . . . . . . . . 243, 260
segment . . . . . . . . . . . . . . . . . . 243, 260
semicircle . . . . . . . . . . . . . . . . . . . . . 244
sequences . . . . . . . . . 114, 115, 117, 119
shading regions . . . . . . . . . . . . 151, 152
shape patterns . . . . . . . . . . . . . . . . . 119
sharing in a given ratio . . . . . . . . . . . 64
short division . . . . . . . . . . . . . . . . . . . 2
short multiplication . . . . . . . . . . . . . . . 2
significant figures . . . . . . . . . . . . 23, 25
similar figures . . . . . . . . . . . . . 342, 348
similar triangles . . . . . . . . . . . . 344, 346
Simple Interest . . . . . . . . . . . . . . . . . 41
simple random sample . . . . . . . . . . . . 395
simplifying algebraic expressions . 88, 89,
                                   91, 200
simplifying fractions . . . . . . . . . . . . . 12
simplifying ratios . . . . . . . . . . . . . . . 63
simplifying surds . . . . . . . . . . . . . . . . 78
simultaneous equations . . . 188, 190, 191,
                              192, 194, 196
sine function . . . . . . . . . . . 363, 364, 367
sine ratio . . . . . . . . . . . . . . . . . 300, 377
Sine Rule . . . . . . . . . . . . . 369, 370, 377
sines of angles between
    0° and 360° . . . . . . . . . . . . . . . . 364
sketch diagram . . . . . . . . 200, 294, 309
sketching graphs . . . . . . . . . . . . . . . 161
slope of a line . . . . . . . . . . . . . 126, 138
small numbers . . . . . . . . . . . . . . . . . . 57
solid lines . . . . . . . . . . . . . . . . . . . . . 151
solid shapes . . . . . . . . . . . . . . . . . . . 314

solving equations . . . . 95, 96, 97, 98, 99,
                        100, 101, 204, 206, 207
solving equations: by inspection . . . . . 95
solving equations:
    by trial and improvement . . . . . . . 207
solving equations:
    using the balance method . . . . . . . 97
solving equations:
    by working backwards . . . . . . . . . 96
solving equations graphically . . 130, 156,
                                       188
solving inequalities . . . . . . 148, 149, 150
solving quadratic equations
    by completing the square . . . . . . . 183
solving quadratic equations
    by factorising . . . . . . . . . . . . . . . 178
solving quadratic equations
    graphically. . . . . . . . . . . . . . . . . . 156
solving quadratic equations
    using the formula . . . . . . . . . . . . 179
solving simultaneous equations
    by substitution . . . . . . . . . . 194, 196
solving simultaneous equations
    graphically. . . . . . . . . . . . . . 188, 196
solving simultaneous equations
    using the elimination method . 191, 192
speed . . . . . . . . . . . . . . 69, 71, 138, 141
speed-time graph . . . . . . . . . . . . . . . 141
sphere . . . . . . . . . . . . . . . . . . . 314, 322
spread . . . . . . . . . . . . . . . . . . . . . . . 399
square . . . . . . . . . . . . . . . . . . . 232, 236
square numbers . . . . . . . . . . . . . 48, 119
square root . . . . . . . . . . . . . . . 48, 77, 78
standard form . . . . . . . 56, 57, 58, 59, 61
standard index form . . . 56, 57, 58, 59, 61
statistical bias . . . . . . . . . . . . . . . . . 395
statistical diagrams . . 408, 410, 412, 418,
                        420, 422, 424, 430, 437
stem and leaf diagrams . . . . . . . . . . . 410
straight line graph . . . 123, 126, 129, 130,
                        131, 188, 217
stratified random sample . . . . . . . . . . 395
stretches . . . . . . . . . . . . . . . . . 210, 211
subject of a formula . . . . . . . . . . . . . 110
substituting into formulae . . . . . 107, 109,
                                   111, 206
subtraction . . . . . 1, 5, 8, 13, 88, 89, 203
subtraction of fractions . . . . . . . . . . . 13
subtraction of negative numbers . . . . . 5
sum of angles in a triangle . . . . . . . . 230
sum of the angles of a quadrilateral . . 232
sum of the exterior angles of a
    polygon . . . . . . . . . . . . . . . . . . . . 234
sum of the interior angles of a
    polygon . . . . . . . . . . . . . . . . . . . . 234
supplementary angles . . . . . . . . . . . . 228
surds . . . . . . . . . . . . . . . . . . . . . . . . . 78
surface area . . . . . . . . . . . 317, 320, 322
symmetrical . . . . . . . . . . . . . . . . . . . 238
symmetry . . . . . . . . . . . . . . . . . 238, 315
systematic random sample . . . . . . . . 395

**t**

table of values . . . . . . . . . . . . . . . . . 123
tally marks . . . . . . . . . . . . . . . . . . . . 389
tangent (to a circle) . . . . . . 243, 247, 248
tangent function . . . . . . . . 363, 364, 367
tangent ratio . . . . . . . . . . . . . . . 304, 377
tangents of angles between
    0° and 360° . . . . . . . . . . . . . . . . 364
tax . . . . . . . . . . . . . . . . . . . . . . . . . . 37
tax allowance . . . . . . . . . . . . . . . . . . 37

taxable income . . . . . . . . . . . . . . . . . 37
terminating decimal . . . . . . . . . . . . . 77
terms . . . . . . . . . . . . . . . . . . . . . . 88, 89
terms of a sequence . . . . . . 114, 115, 117
tessellations . . . . . . . . . . . . . . . . . . . 237
Theorem of Pythagoras . . . 291, 294, 296
three-dimensional problems . . . 296, 307,
                                       310
three-figure bearings . . . . . . . . 264, 308
time series . . . . . . . . . . . . . . . . . . . . 418
'top heavy' fractions . . . . . . . . . . . . . 12
transformations . 210, 211, 214, 275, 276,
                   278, 279, 280, 282, 286
transforming graphs . . . . . . 210, 211, 214
translation . . . . . . . . . 210, 275, 278, 282
transversal . . . . . . . . . . . . . . . . . . . . 228
trapezium . . . . . . . . . . . . . . . . . 232, 254
tree diagram . . . . . . . . . . . . . . 449, 452
trend . . . . . . . . . . . . . . . . . . . . 418, 420
trial and improvement . . . . . . . . . . . . 207
trials . . . . . . . . . . . . . . . . . . . . . . . . . 445
triangle . . . . . . . . 230, 234, 254, 269, 291,
                   300, 339, 344, 368, 375
triangular numbers . . . . . . . . . . 119, 121
trigonometric functions . . . 363, 364, 367
trigonometric ratios . . . . . . . . . 300, 304
trigonometry. . . . . . . . 300, 363, 369, 373
two-way tables . . . . . . . . . . . . . . . . . 393
types of angles . . . . . . . . . . . . . . . . . 228

**u**

unequal class width intervals . . . . . . 424
units of measurement . . . . 328, 330, 331
upper bound . . . . . . . . . . . . 26, 28, 332
upper class boundary . . . . . . . . . . . . 430
upper quartile . . . . . . . . . . . . . 431, 437
using a calculator . 11, 17, 48, 56, 57, 58,
                        59, 301, 302, 303

**v**

variables (statistical) . . . . . . . . . . . . 388
VAT . . . . . . . . . . . . . . . . . . . . . . . . . 40
vector . . . . . . . . . . . . 210, 278, 353, 354,
                        355, 356, 358
vector addition . . . . . . . . . . . . . . . . . 356
vector diagrams . . . . . . . . . . . . . . . . 356
vector geometry . . . . . . . . . . . . . . . . 358
vector notation . . . . . . . . . . . . . . . . . 353
vertex . . . . . . . . . . . . . . . . . . . . . . . 314
vertex of a graph . . . . . . . . . . . . . . . 181
vertically opposite angles . . . . . . . . . 228
volume . . . . . . . . 72, 317, 319, 322, 335
volumes of similar figures . . . . . . . . 348

**w**

wages . . . . . . . . . . . . . . . . . . . . . . . . 37
whole numbers . . . . . . . . . . . . . . . 1, 45
writing equations . . . . . . . . . . . . . . . 101
writing expressions . . . . . . . . . . . 87, 105
writing formulae . . . . . . . . . . . . . . . . 105
writing numbers . . . . . . . . . . . . . . . . 1

**y**

$y = mx + c$ . . . . . . . . . . . . . 126, 217
$y$-intercept . . . . . . . . . . . . . . . . . . . 126

**z**

zero correlation . . . . . . . . . . . . . . . . 412